Electrical Grounding

Based on the 1996
NATIONAL ELECTRICAL CODE®

Electrical Grounding

Bringing Grounding Back to Earth

Fourth Edition

Ronald P. O'Riley

Delmar Publishers

I(T)P An International Thomson Publishing Company

Albany • Bonn • Boston • Cincinnati • Detroit • London • Madrid
Melbourne • Mexico City • New York • Pacific Grove • Paris • San Francisco
Singapore • Tokyo • Toronto • Washington

NOTICE TO THE READER

Publisher does not warrant or guarantee any of the products described herein or perform any independent analysis in connection with any of the product information contained herein. Publisher does not assume, and expressly disclaims, any obligation to obtain and include information other than that provided to it by the manufacturer.

The reader is expressly warned to consider and adopt all safety precautions that might be indicated by the activities described herein and to avoid all potential hazards. By following the instructions contained herein, the reader willingly assumes all risks in connection with such instructions.

The publisher makes no representations or warranties of any kind, including but not limited to, the warranties of fitness for particular purpose or merchantability, nor are any such representations implied with respect to the material set forth herein, and the publisher takes no responsibility with respect to such material. The publisher shall not be liable for any special, consequential, or exemplary damages resulting, in whole or part, from the readers' use of, or reliance upon, this material.

Cover Image by Mick Brady

Delmar Staff
Publisher: Susan Simpfenderfer
Acquisitions Editor: Paul Shepardson
Developmental Editor: Jeanne Mesick
Project Editor: Patricia Konczeski

Production Coordinator: Dianne Jensis
Art/Design Coordinator: Cheri Plasse
Marketing Manager: Lisa Reale

Printed in the United States of America

For more information contact:

Delmar Publishers
3 Columbia Circle, Box 15015
Albany, New York 12212-5015

International Thomson Publishing Europe
Berkshire House 168–173
High Holborn
London WC1V 7AA
England

Thomas Nelson Australia
102 Dodds Street
South Melbourne, 3205
Victoria, Australia

Nelson Canada
1120 Birchmount Road
Scarborough, Ontario
Canada M1K 5G4

International Thomson Editores
Campos Eliseos 385, Piso 7
Col Polanco
11560 Mexico D F Mexico

International Thomson Publishing GmbH
Königswinterer Strasse 418
53227 Bonn
Germany

International Thomson Publishing Asia
221 Henderson Road
#05–10 Henderson Building
Singapore 0315

International Thomson Publishing-Japan
Hirakawacho Kyowa Building, 3F
2-2-1 Hirakawacho
Chiyoda-ku, Tokyo 102
Japan

10 9 8 7 6 5 XXX 00 99 98

Library of Congress Cataloging-in-Publication Data

O'Riley, Ronald P., 1914-
Electrical grounding : bringing grounding back to earth / Ronald P. O'Riley.—4th ed.
p. cm.
"Based on the 1996 National Electric Code®."
Includes index.
ISBN 0-8273-6657-4
1. Electric currents—Grounding. I. Title.
TK3227.078 1996
621.317—dc20 95-13272
CIP

CONTENTS

Preface ix
Introduction xiv

Chapter 1 *ARTICLE 250, GROUNDING* 1
Overview of *Article 250, Grounding* 3
Definitions 5

Chapter 2 ELECTRICAL THEORY APPLICABLE TO GROUNDING 14
Current Flow 14
The Electron 15
Ohm's Law 16
Direct Current 17
Series Circuit 17
Alternating Current 19
Impedance 21
Amps and Overcurrent Protective Devices 21
Parallel Circuit 22
Series-Parallel Circuit 23

Chapter 3 GROUNDING FOR SAFETY 24
Electric Shock 24
Potential Difference 26
Grounding and Electric Shock 27

Chapter 4 FAULTS 30
Types of Faults 31
Stresses Caused by Faults 32
Ionization 32
Grounded-System Faults 33
Impedance-Grounded Systems 35
Ungrounded-System Faults 37
Ground-Fault Detectors 39

Chapter 5 GROUNDING ELECTRODE SYSTEM 40
Grounding Theory 40
Responsibility of the Grounding Electrode 41
The Ground Rod 43
Metal Water Pipe Electrode 47
Building Steel as an Electrode 49

	Concrete-Encased Electrode	50
	Ground Ring Electrode	51
	Made Electrodes	51
	Summary	57
Chapter 6	GROUNDING ELECTRODE CONDUCTOR	59
	Definition of *Grounding Electrode Conductor*	60
	Materials	61
	Installation and Protection	62
	Connecting the Grounding Electrode Conductor	66
	Sizing the DC Grounding Electrode Conductor	68
	Sizing the AC Grounding Electrode Conductor	69
	Sizing Grounding Electrode Conductors	72
	Summary	78
Chapter 7	CIRCUIT AND SYSTEM GROUNDING	80
	Why Ground Circuits and Systems?	81
	Definitions	81
	Direct-Current Systems	83
	Alternating-Current Systems	85
Chapter 8	GROUNDED CONDUCTOR	94
	Definition of *Grounded Conductor*	94
	Grounded Conductor Connection in a Direct-Current System	95
	Grounded Conductor Connection in an Alternating-Current System	95
	Bringing the Grounded Conductor to Service	96
	Sizing the Grounded Conductor	98
	Installing the Grounded Conductor	102
	System or Circuit Conductor to be Grounded	103
	Identifying the Grounded Conductor	104
	Grounded-Conductor Overcurrent Protection	107
Chapter 9	MAIN BONDING JUMPER	108
	Definition of *Main Bonding Jumper*	109
	Location of the Main Bonding Jumper	110
	Materials for the Main Bonding Jumper	111
	Connections	112
	Sizing the Main Bonding Jumper	112
Chapter 10	EQUIPMENT GROUNDING CONDUCTOR	120
	Definition of *Equipment Grounding Conductor*	121
	Definition of *System*	121
	Definition of *Circuit*	123
	Effective Ground Path	124
	Types of Equipment Grounding Conductors	125
	Wire Used for Equipment Grounding Conductor	125

	Identification of Equipment Grounding Conductor	126
	Installation of Equipment Grounding Conductor	128
	Raceways as Equipment Grounding Conductors	131
	Earth as an Equipment Grounding Conductor	140
	Equipment Grounding Conductor Connections	140
	Equipment Grounding Conductor Continuity	141
	Sizing Equipment Grounding Conductors	141
	Equipment Grounding Conductor in Boxes	148
	Agricultural Buildings	151
Chapter 11	EQUIPMENT AND ENCLOSURE BONDING	153
	Definitions	154
	Materials	156
	Connections	156
	Bonding at Service Equipment	156
	Sizing Bonding Jumpers on Supply Side of Service	162
	Grounding Electrode Conductor Enclosure Bonding	171
	Flexible Metal Conduit in Service-Entrance Raceway	172
	Bonding Other Than at Service	172
	Structural Bonding Steel	176
	Sizing Load Side of Service Bonding Jumpers	176
	Bonding Grounding Electrode Systems	178
	Bonding Receptacles	181
	Bonding Lightning Rod Conductors and Electrodes	182
	Swimming Pool Bonding Grid	184
	Summary	185
Chapter 12	EQUIPMENT AND ENCLOSURE GROUNDING	187
	Why Ground Metal Enclosures and Equipment?	187
	Enclosure and Raceway Grounding	188
	Equipment Grounding	191
	Methods of Grounding Enclosures and Equipment	197
	Grounding Panelboards	197
	Isolated Equipment Grounding Receptacles	200
	Tower Grounding	202
	Computer Grounding	203
Chapter 13	GROUNDED CIRCUIT CONDUCTOR FOR GROUNDING EQUIPMENT	209
	The Basic Rule	210
	Supply-Side Use	210
	Second Building	211
	Separately Derived System	211
	Load-Side Use	212
	Summary	214
Chapter 14	GROUND-FAULT PROTECTIVE EQUIPMENT	216
	Ground-Fault Protection of Equipment	217

	Ground-Fault Protection Equipment Required at Service	218
	Ground-Fault Protection Equipment Required—Feeder	221
	Definition of *Ground-Fault Circuit Interrupter*	221
	Receptacles Requiring GFCI Protection	223
Chapter 15	SYSTEM AND CIRCUIT GROUNDING 1 kV AND OVER	233
	Neutral Grounded Systems	234
	Neutral Grounded Systems Required and Permitted	234
	Equipment Grounding	238
Chapter 16	SEPARATELY DERIVED SYSTEMS	240
	Definition of *Separately Derived System*	240
	Main Bonding Jumper	243
	Grounding Electrode Conductor	244
	Grounding Electrode	244
	Bonding at Separately Derived Systems	245
	Dedicated Five-Wire System	246
	Portable Generators	246
	Vehicle-Mounted Generators	247
Chapter 17	TWO OR MORE BUILDINGS SUPPLIED BY ONE SERVICE	249
	Grounded and Ungrounded Systems	251
	Grounding Installation at Second Building	252
	Sizing the Grounded Conductor	255
	Sizing the System Grounding Conductor at the Second Building	256
	No Disconnecting Means at Second Building	257
	Agricultural Building Housing Livestock	260
Chapter 18	CALCULATING FAULT CURRENTS AND GROUNDING CONDUCTOR WITHSTAND RATING	262
	Introduction	262
	Purpose of Grounding	263
	Short Circuits and Ground Faults	264
	Protective-Device Terms	264
	Important Code Sections	266
	Available Fault Current	266
	Factors Affecting Amount of Fault Current	268
	Transformer Secondary Current	268
	Transformer Impedance	270
	Other Factors Affecting Fault-Current Values	271
	Point-to-Point Calculations	272
	Fault Current and Parallel Conductors	275
	Combining Fuse and Circuit Breaker for Protection	275
	Summary	276
Appendix		279
Index		286

PREFACE

There seems to be a need to eliminate some of the myths that cloud the subject of electrical grounding. Therefore, the purpose of this book is to give members of the electrical industry a better understanding of grounding, clear up some of the misconceptions, lift some of the veil of mystics, and simplify some of the Code requirements for acceptable field installations of grounding.

In this book, we'll get back to the basic fundamentals of electricity and see how they work in conjunction with grounding. Grounding is no big secret. It obeys the laws of electricity, and when examined piece-by-piece and conductor-by-conductor, all elements fit together very nicely to form an effective grounding system—one that all branches of the electrical industry can use successfully.

The author's wish is for this book to be a learning experience for members of, and those in training for a career in, the electrical industry. It is the author's hope that simplifying, illustrating, reasoning through, and coordinating the grounding requirements, as contained in *Article 250* of the *National Electrical Code (NEC)®*, will promote better understanding and use of the *National Electrical Code®*. This can result in safer, cleaner electrical installation and maintenance. The first rule is to make it safe; the second is to make it work. Both can be done. With this thought in mind, this book is directed at vocational instructors of electricity, electrical engineers, design engineers, construction electricians making installations in the field, maintenance electricians in factories or buildings, electrical inspectors, and many other members of the electrical industry. It is also the author's hope that the apprentice or person preparing for a career in the electrical industry and studying the *National Electrical Code®* will find its detailed explanations and accompanying diagrams to be an interesting learning experience.

This book is based on the author's many years of experience teaching electricity and the *National Electrical Code®*, field experience in the electrical construction industry, and association with the International Association of Electrical Inspectors (IAEI). The big motivator to get this book started was the many questions on grounding that were asked about the *National Electrical Code®* at the First Friday meetings of the Texas Chapter of the IAEI and the journeyman training classes conducted by the Dallas Joint Electrical Apprenticeship and Training Committee (JATC).

ABOUT THE AUTHOR

After serving for four years as an electrician's mate in the U.S. Navy during World War II, and then serving a four-year electrical apprenticeship, Ronald P. O'Riley rose through the ranks on the job to become an electrical superinten-

---

National Electrical Code® and NEC® are Registered Trademarks of the National Fire Protection Association, Inc., Quincy, MA 12269.

dent. In the process, he has accumulated over forty years of experience in the electrical industry. During the past thirty-five years, he has been an instructor of electrical theory and Code classes for electrical apprentices and journeyman training, serving for many of those years as the training director of the Dallas JATC.

Mr. O'Riley holds an honorary degree in electrical construction from North Lake College of the Dallas County Community College District and a master electrician's license. He is a retired member of the International Brotherhood of Electrical Workers and an active associate member of the IAEI, where he has served for several years as an officer of the Texas Chapter.

Among Mr. O'Riley's credits is authorship of the theory and safety lessons of the first national course material for JATCs. Noted for his ability to communicate in the classroom, he has served as a Code panelist and moderator and has conducted many seminars on both the Code and vocational teacher training for instructors of electrical apprentices. These experiences, both on the job and in the classroom, are a live part of ELECTRICAL GROUNDING.

ACKNOWLEDGMENTS

Special acknowledgment is made to the National Fire Protection Association for permission to quote passages and tables from the *National Electrical Code*®. My sincere thanks to Ralph Walters and A. C. McAfee for their encouragement and constructive criticism. This book is dedicated to my wife Lillian, who for so many years has been my inspiration.

The author and Delmar Publishers would like to thank the following reviewers for their contributions:

Robert Blakely
Mississippi Gulf Coast Community College
Gulfport, MS

Les Brinkley
Ashtabula County Joint Vocational School
Jefferson, OH

Michael Callanan
International Brotherhood of Electrical Workers
Philadelphia, PA

David R. Carpenter
University of Alabama
Tuscaloosa, AL
Shoals Community College
Muscle Shoals, AL

Electrical Wiring—Industrial, 9E/Smith & Herman

Learn Industrial wiring essentials based on the 1996 NEC®. Complete with industrial building plans.

Order # 0-8273-6653-1

Cables and Wiring/AVO Multi-Amp

Your comprehensive practical guide to all types of electrical cables.

Order # 0-8273-5460-6

Raceways and Other Wiring Methods/Loyd

This excellent new book provides you with complete information on metallic and nonmetallic raceways and other common wiring methods used by electricians and electrical designers.

Order # 8273-6659-0

Illustrated Electrical Calculations/Sanders

Your quick reference to all of the formulas and calculations electricians use.

Order # 8273-5462-2

Electricians Formula and Reference Book/Holt

A concise and easy-to-use pocket reference that features up-to-date formulas for proper electrical calculations as they apply to any and all electrical installations. This handy pocket reference is a great companion to the NFPA's National Electrical Code® and any other electrical book.

Order # 0-8273-6961-1

Motor Control

Electric Motor Control, 5E/Alerich

The standard for almost thirty years, this best-selling textbook explains how to connect electromagnetic and electric controllers.

Order # 0-8273-5250-6

Industrial Motor Control, 3E/Herman

This excellent third edition combines a solid explanation of theory with practical instructions and information on controlling industrial motors with magnetic and solid-state controllers. Includes coverage of programmable controllers.

Order # 0-8273-5252-2

Electric Motors and Motor Controls/Keljik

This new book focuses on the hows and why behind all types of motors and controls. Special attention is given to why electrical systems work, throughly explaining the function and purpose behind all types of electric motors and controllers.

Order # 0-8273-6174-2

Exam Preparation

Journeyman Electrician's Review, 2E/Loyd

Order #0-8273-6680-9

Master Electrician's Review, 2E/Loyd

Order #0-8273-6678-7

Master Electrician's Preparation Exam/Holt

Order #0-8273-7623-5

Journeyman's Exam Preparation/Holt

Order #0-8273-7621-9

To request examination copies, call or write to:

Delmar Publishers
3 Columbia Circle
P.O. Box 15015
Albany, NY 12212-5015
Phone: 1-800-347-7707 • 1-518-464-3500 • Fax: 1-518-464-0301

INTRODUCTION

In the construction industry, the first step when erecting a building is to prepare the ground for the building to set on. The ground supports the weight of the building. Unless the building is set firmly on the ground, it may have continuing structural and electrical problems and may even experience a disaster. The grounding electrode must be properly installed in the ground, and all grounding paths must be directed to it. The grounding system must be effectively connected to the grounding electrode.

ELECTRICAL GROUNDING starts with a discussion of the ground and the grounding electrode, because the grounding electrode supports the entire grounding system, and all grounding paths lead to the grounding electrode.

Although it is often used as one, the *National Electrical Code®* is not a textbook. It gives no background, reasons, application, or illustrations of rules and regulations set down in the Code. The Code is more a catalogue of rules for an electrical construction installation. ELECTRICAL GROUNDING is a textbook on grounding that contains illustrations, reasons, and job applications.

There is a need to know What, Where, and Why Effective Grounding is needed and How Effective Grounding can be made a part of the overall electrical installation. For ease of communication, one of the first things we'll do here is to set the stage for understanding each other. This is done in Chapter 1 by reviewing *Article 250* and the Code definitions of terms used in conjunction with grounding.

When there is agreement on what a term means, it is easier to communicate. Therefore, we need to accept the same definition of various terms used with grounding. The definitions of terms used in this text agree with the definitions in the *National Electrical Code®*. It should be noted that the Code definition of a term is not the same as a definition for the same word in a standard dictionary. When a term or word is used and not defined in the Code, the Institute of Electrical and Electronic Engineers (IEEE) dictionary definition or the standard dictionary definition will prevail. In addition, the word *Code* used throughout this text means the 1996 edition of the *National Electrical Code®*.

The Code indirectly requires certain things of the individual studying or using it. One of these things is a background in electrical theory. The Code does not say this in so many words, but indirectly indicates it in an early part of the Code. For example, it states very specifically in *Section 90-1(c)* that the book is not intended as a design specification or as an instruction manual for untrained persons.

The term *untrained persons* can be interpreted to mean that anyone who does not have an understanding of electricity and electrical construction is going to have a hard time trying to understand this Code. It can also mean that the Code assumes a person reading or studying it knows and understands voltage, current, resistance, impedance, transformers, motors, electrical circuits, and their properties. Therefore, Chapter 2 of this text is a basic, short review of electrical theory that will bring the basic theory back to mind and show how some of these fundamentals fit into the overall grounding system. This will also help improve understanding of some of the reasoning behind some of the grounding regulations in the Code. After all, remember that grounding is an electrical circuit, and there will be electrons traveling the grounding circuit.

When grounding is improperly installed, the results can range from minor physical harm to even death to an individual, or costly damage to electrical equipment and/or property. The results can range from erratic operation of equipment (a phenomenon often referred to in the field as a "ghost" because the cause is so difficult to track down) to minor physical harm or even death, or costly damage to electrical equipment and/or property. This unwanted harm and damages are caused by electric shock and electrical faults. These faults are often the result of improper grounding and create an electrical hazard. The Code works for the safety of the individual; grounding is a vital part of personal safety. Chapter 3 covers electric shock and how grounding helps to prevent hazardous conditions that may result in an electric shock.

The grounding circuit follows the basic laws of electricity, just as any other electrical circuit does. Therefore, it must be treated and installed just like any other electrical circuit. Chapter 4 illustrates some electrical faults and what happens in the grounding circuit when a fault occurs.

There are things covered in this text that are not in *Article 250* of the *National Electrical Code®*, such as those that are documented in research by manufacturers and others on the subject of grounding. These documented things make grounding more interesting and help one to understand, in a practical way, what *Article 250* is trying to accomplish, especially when looking at a particular regulation.

This book covers almost everything in *Article 250* of the Code, plus grounding information and requirements from other parts of the Code. However, the information is *not* presented in the same sequence as it is in *Article 250*. There is a lot of mixing of the so-called grounding conductors in *Article 250* and grounding regulations for particular installations. This text first looks at each of the grounding conductors as an individual conductor and eliminates as much mixing as possible. After each one has been looked at individually, the mixing starts and some different installations are covered.

Article 250 has sections that apply to more than one of the overall system grounding conductors. In this book, each of these conductors is looked at individually and information concerning the type, use, purpose, installation, and size is gathered into the one chapter devoted to that particular grounding conductor or phase of the grounding system. Information is repeated where necessary to avoid referring to material covered earlier or later in the book.

Code grounding requirements and information located in sources other than *Article 250* have been gathered and are covered when they are applicable. Note in the following chapter outline of this text (figure I–1) how Chapter 5 starts with a discussion of the ground and the grounding electrode and works itself through the grounding system to the end of the branch circuit and the installation of a ground-fault circuit interrupter in Chapter 14.

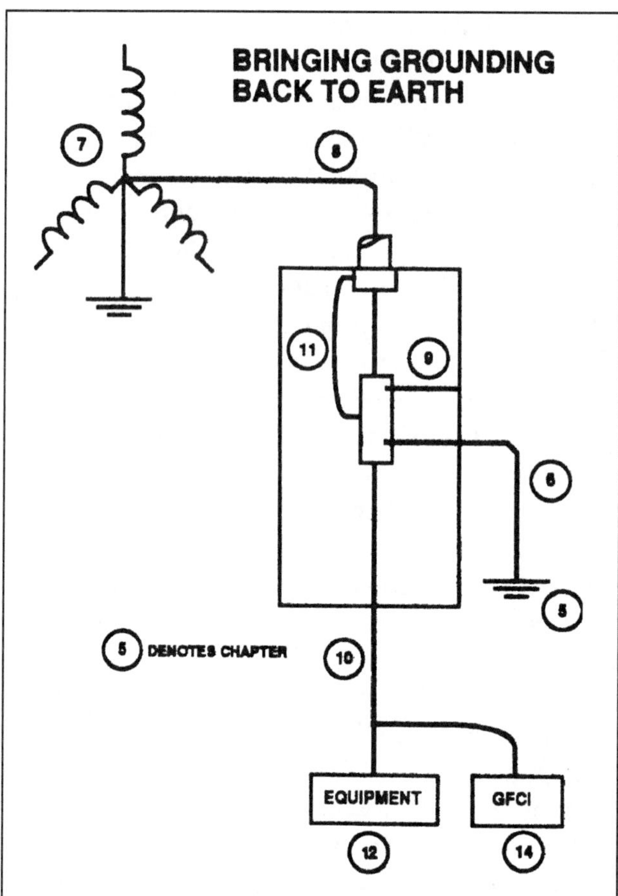

Fig. I–1 Diagram of Chapters 5 through 12, and 14. The circled numbers denote chapters of this book.

Chapter 5 — Grounding Electrode System
Chapter 6 — Grounding Electrode Conductor
Chapter 7 — Circuit and System Grounding
Chapter 8 — Grounded Conductor
Chapter 9 — Main Bonding Jumper
Chapter 10 — Equipment Grounding Conductor
Chapter 11 — Equipment and Enclosure Bonding
Chapter 12 — Equipment and Enclosure Grounding
Chapter 13 — Grounded Circuit Conductor for Grounding Equipment
Chapter 14 — Ground-Fault Protective Equipment

Chapter 5 starts off the discussion of the entire grounding system. It is devoted to the grounding electrode conductor installed in the ground system, the means by which the electrons enter the earth. It covers installation, types, and some related theory applicable to the grounding electrode. The next step is to connect the grounding electrode to the service with the grounding electrode conductor; this is accomplished in Chapter 6. Also covered are the installation, methods of sizing, and reasoning behind some of the Code provisions for the grounding electrode conductor.

Chapter 7 moves to the outer end of the service and is devoted to the installed electrical distribution system. It also covers instances when the Code requires or permits systems and circuits to be intentionally grounded by using a solidly or impedance-grounded system. Chapter 8 covers the grounded conductor and discusses when it is necessary to install one, where it is to be connected at the service equipment, its identification, and methods of sizing it when it does not extend beyond the service equipment.

Chapter 9 is devoted to the main bonding jumper and covers types, materials, purpose, connections, and methods of sizing. Also discussed are the various sites in the service equipment where the main bonding jumper is permitted to be located.

Note how everything so far has revolved around the service equipment, the line side of the service equipment, and the connections at the service equipment. Chapter 10 connects the equipment grounding conductor to the service and extends it to the entire distribution system on the load side of the service. It covers the purpose, types, identification, installation, and sizing of equipment grounding conductors on the line and load side of the service equipment.

The equipment grounding conductor is required to have continuous continuity, and Chapter 11 is devoted to maintaining this continuity by bonding the equipment and enclosures on the line and load side of the service equipment. This chapter also covers where, why, and how bonding is required and accomplished and the methods of sizing.

Chapter 12 is devoted to the specifics for grounding equipment and enclosures by means of the equipment grounding conductor necessary for individual safety. Chapter 13 is devoted to the use of the grounded conductor (neutral) as the equipment grounding conductor. Because of the limitations placed on the use of the neutral as the equipment grounding conductor, a special chapter is devoted to it.

Ground-fault protection is interlaced with grounding and Chapter 14 is devoted to ground-fault protection. Ground-fault protection for personnel and ground-fault protection of equipment are discussed separately. Operation of and requirements for ground-fault circuit interrupters (GFCI) and ground fault protection of equipment are also covered, with specific applications.

The later chapters—15, 16, and 17—take installations presented early by the Code in *Article 250* and look at them individually. Chapter 15 starts looking at some special types of installations that are covered by some special Code provisions. It discusses when systems and circuit grounding over 1 kV is required and permitted, impedance grounding, and the use of the grounded transformer. Chapter 16 covers separately derived systems, such as those that can be derived from a transformer. Chapter 17 covers the supply for a second building when both buildings are supplied from one service. Chapter 18 is devoted to calculating the magnitude the fault can reach and the importance of coordinating the sizing of the grounding conductors with the interrupting capacity of the protective device.

One very practical and current problem connected with faulty grounding installations is the effect they have on microelectronic equipment such as computers. Faulty or improper grounding results in what is called "dirty electricity." Everywhere we turn—at the checkout stand in the supermarket, in hospital diagnostic labs and operating rooms, in the computerization of government records, and in the use of computerized graphics on TV, to name only a few—we see the high-technology branch of the electrical industry. The use of high technology is not decreasing; rather, it will continue to increase. Stable, clean electrical power is now a requirement; anything less is unsatisfactory. Proper, effective electrical grounding is an absolute necessity today in any commercial or industrial installation. As high technology moves into the home and the "smart house" becomes a reality, the residential area will also demand stable, clean electrical power.

The Code is put together in an outline form. There are Articles with Parts, Parts with Sections, Sections with Subsections, and Subsections with Subsections. Take care to apply information given in the Code *only* to the heading under which it is presented.

There are sections in the Code that are very long because they contain a lot of necessary information in as concise a form as possible. There are no unnecessary descriptive adjectives used in the Code. When quoting the Code, this text often lists the Code section in an outline form by phrases or statements, so that all the important parts in a section can be readily seen. Direct quotes from the 1996 *National Electrical Code®* are so marked.

The Code contains the minimum provision considered necessary for safety of persons and equipment. Everyone might not agree with the minimum provisions of the Code. Therefore, when the authority having jurisdiction feels the rule needs to be more stringent then expressed in the Code, that authority can make it more stringent with a City ordinance. This is not an uncommon happening. In addition to the Code and the explanations in this text, an electrical person must also be aware of any specific rules set down by the local authority having jurisdiction.

It is highly recommended that the person using this text keep the Code book close at hand, and that he/she read the Code sections indicated in the referenced sections of this text. This can greatly assist the student's learning experience. To imagine the actual path the electrons will travel in the grounding circuit, the user of this book will need to give all electrons life, watch them move, watch them travel, and watch them make up their minds which way they are going to go. Electrons are very real. Make them real, make them move, and watch what happens. Watch them travel the ground path.

CHAPTER 1

Article 250, Grounding

OBJECTIVES

After completing this chapter, the student should be able to:

- gain an understanding of the sequence in which *Article 250, Grounding* is assembled.
- identify the terms *guarded*, *isolated*, and *insulated.*
- recognize the terminology covered under the umbrella of grounding terms.
- define the specific terms used in conjunction with grounding.
- explain why systems and circuits are grounded.
- explain why conductive materials are grounded.
- explain what is meant by effective grounding.
- discuss what the bull's eye of effective grounding is and where it is located.

This chapter covers *Article 250, Grounding* in a general way. It also looks at some of the more common terms that are used in conjunction with grounding. Note that all quotations in this text are from the 1996 *National Electrical Code®* and are reprinted courtesy of the National Fire Protection Association.

When anyone in the electrical field starts to talk about grounding, it brings to mind *Article 250* of the *National Electrical Code®*. So, let's take an overall look at *Article 250,* with some particular attention given to *Section 250-1, Scope.*

The scope of any article tells what the article is going to cover, and/or what the article is trying to accomplish. In this case, it gives a very good outline of *Article 250.*

Figure 1–1 is a basic outline of what *Section 250-1* covers. This section indicates that both general and specific information will be presented. It also indicates that the article will cover what systems and circuits, and what equipment, are required to be grounded, are permitted to be grounded, and are not permitted to be grounded.

The section also indicates what circuit conductors of different systems are required to be

ARTICLE 250, GROUNDING

SCOPE — GENERAL AND SPECIFIC REQUIREMENTS FOR GROUNDING AND BONDING OF ELECTRICAL INSTALLATIONS

1. SYSTEMS AND CIRCUITS
   - REQUIRED TO BE GROUNDED
   - PERMITTED TO BE GROUNDED
   - NOT PERMITTED TO BE GROUNDED

   EQUIPMENT
   - REQUIRED TO BE GROUNDED
   - PERMITTED TO BE GROUNDED
   - NOT PERMITTED TO BE GROUNDED
2. CIRCUIT CONDUCTORS TO BE GROUNDED
3. TYPES AND SIZES OF
   - GROUNDING CONDUCTORS
   - BONDING CONDUCTORS
   - ELECTRODES
4. METHODS OF GROUNDING AND BONDING
5. SUBSTITUTES FOR GROUNDING
   - GUARDS
   - ISOLATION
   - INSULATION

Fig. 1–1 Scope of *Article 250, Grounding*.

grounded, as well as types and sizes of grounding conductors, bonding conductors, and electrodes. Also covered will be the recognized methods of grounding and bonding.

The Code lists three things that can be substituted for grounding in particular situations. These three things defined in *Article 100* are:

1. Guarded
2. Isolated
3. Insulated

Electrical equipment is identified as *guarded* when persons are protected from likelihood of approach or contact, where an electrical danger exists, by means of covering, shielding, fencing, enclosure, or other suitable means of protection. Fig. 1–2 illustrates one example of the recognized means of enclosure when an enclosure is being used for *guarding*. A fence is built around a premises substation to *guard* against anyone contacting energized equipment.

When electrical equipment is *isolated,* it is so installed that it is not readily accessible to a person unless special means will be needed to reach it, such as a ladder. An example of isolated, figure 1–3, is a lighting fixture mounted high enough on a wooden pole that it makes it necessary to use a ladder, bucket truck, lift, or the like to reach it. There are several height mounting requirements throughout the Code, and they are based on the voltage involved. The higher the voltage is, the greater the clearance required is. A transformer on a pole or a transformer bank mounted on an elevated platform between two poles are examples of *isolation* by elevation.

When *insulated,* the equipment is covered with an insulating material. The material is of sufficient thickness to contain the electrical pressure of the circuit and to protect a person from coming in direct contact with an energized part, or a part that might accidentally become energized. Insulated electrical conductors and bus bars are a common means of protection. The double insulated tool, figure 1–4, is an example of insulation being used for personnel protection.

Article 250 is divided into twelve parts, all of which are very much interlocking. There is a lot of referring back and forth and cross-referencing in the article. The following is an overall look at the twelve parts of *Article 250.*

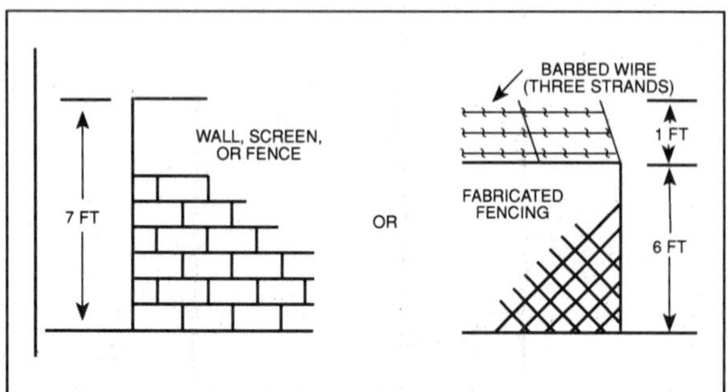

Fig. 1–2 Guarded by Enclosure.

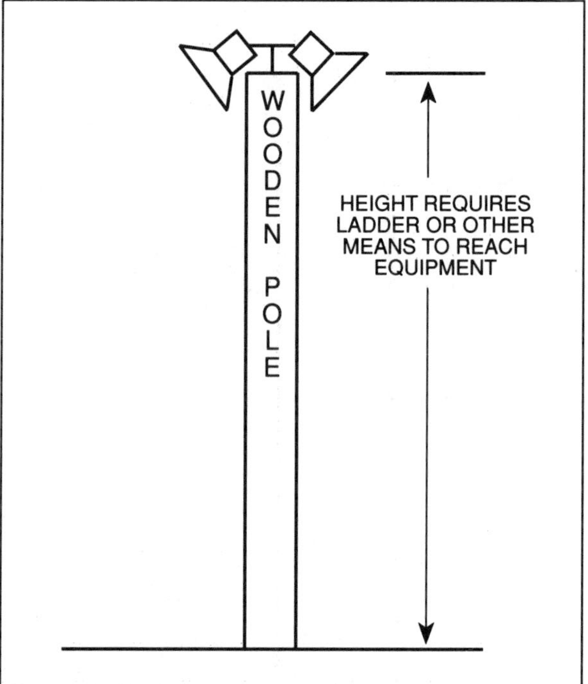

Fig. 1–3 Isolation by elevation.

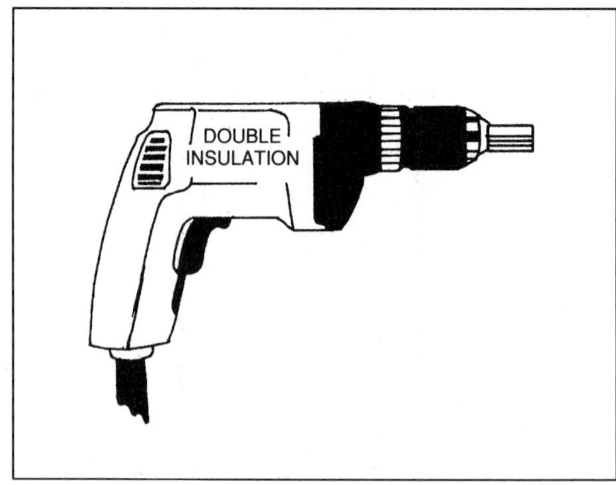

Fig. 1–4 Double insulation protection.

OVERVIEW OF *ARTICLE 250, GROUNDING*

Part

A. General

B. Circuit and System Grounding

C. Location of System Grounding Connections

D. Enclosure Grounding

E. Equipment Grounding

F. Methods of Grounding

G. Bonding

H. Grounding Electrode System

J. Grounding Conductors

K. Grounding Conductor Connections

L. Instrument Transformers, Relays, etc.

M. Grounding of Systems and Circuits of 1 kV and Over

It is interesting to note the number of times the word *grounding* appears in the titles of the different parts (nine times out of twelve). Also notice that the words *ground* and *grounded* are conspicuous by their absence. In each title, the word *grounding* is used in conjunction with another descriptive word, such as enclosure grounding and equipment grounding.

There is no definition in *Article 100* of the word *grounding* by itself. It is usually combined with an identifying word and then the definition specifically points out some part of the entire grounding system or the effective grounding path; for example, "grounding electrode," "grounding conductor," "equipment grounding conductor." It takes all these various parts of the grounding system, working together, to make grounding complete. The following is a quick look at some of the interesting things that can be found in each one of the parts of *Article 250.*

Part A. General

This first part has only two sections, but both are very important. The first section is the scope, which has just been covered. The second section is a table or index of other grounding requirements located elsewhere in the Code. This quick reference, useful for locating information for grounding specific equipment or conditions, gives the article number and section number where the information can be found. One thing to learn from this particular section is that all grounding requirements are neither confined to nor covered in *Article 250*.

Part B. Circuit and System Grounding

The basic regulations are established in this part for solidly grounded systems and impedance grounded systems. This applies to the *electrical supply* and *distribution conductors* of an installation, when one of the circuit conductors is a grounded conductor and is expected to carry current. An example is the neutral of a 120/208-volt, four-wire, grounded wye system or a 120/240-volt, three-wire system, with the center tap grounded.

This part also covers direct-current and alternating-current systems and explains when they shall be grounded, permitted to be grounded, and not permitted to be grounded. It also notes the exceptions. Particular attention is given to separately derived systems, and to portable and vehicle-mounted generators.

Part C. Location of System Grounding Connections

This part is still talking about the *electrical supply* and *distribution conductors,* when one of the circuit conductors is grounded. An example is a system with a neutral. It discusses how the grounded conductor of a direct-current system or an alternating-current system shall be connected to the premises wiring system.

When the utility supply system has a grounded conductor, it must be brought to the service equipment even if it is not utilized. Also covered is the sizing of the grounded conductor when it is not utilized.

This part tells how to make the proper installation when two or more buildings are supplied by one common service, whether it is a grounded system or an ungrounded system. There are several electrical distribution systems that utilize a grounded conductor. This is the part of the Code that specifies which conductor in each different distribution system shall be the grounded conductor. This part also designates which conductor is to be the neutral conductor. Specific attention is also given to the connections for a separately derived system.

Part D. Enclosure and Raceway Grounding

Here the Code shifts and starts talking about the *grounding of metal enclosures* for current-carrying electrical equipment and conductors. Nothing here has to do with circuit conductors used for branch circuits or feeders.

This is a very short part—it has only two sections and each is only a sentence long. But with these two sentences, the entire electrical installation is covered. The first section states: "Metal enclosures and raceways for service conductors and equipment shall be grounded."* That covers everything in conjunction with the service. The second section covers everything else in the installation when it states, "Metal enclosures and raceways for other than service conductors shall be grounded."* Of course, exceptions are listed.

Part E. Equipment Grounding

An electrical circuit is installed so that a piece of electrical equipment can be used. Therefore, the Code is very specific as to how electrical equipment shall be grounded. Part E looks at grounding electrical equipment in three different situations:

- The location and/or environment of the equipment
- The equipment being fastened in place or connected by permanent wiring methods
- Cord- and plug-connected equipment

Attention is given to the grounding of metal parts of nonelectrical equipment.

This part also gives a laundry list of specific electrical equipment located in residential occupancies. This is followed by a list of equipment for other than residential occupancies.

Part F. Methods of Grounding

This part gives the essentials for accomplishing what was required in Part E. Here is where the term *Effective Grounding Path* is introduced and explained. There are three parts to effective grounding: electrical continuity, ampacity, and low impedance of the equipment grounding conductor. All three are necessary for proper operation, just as all three phases are necessary for the proper operation of a three-phase motor.

Considerable attention is given here to maintaining the electrical continuity of the equipment grounding path. Also covered is what the Code considers to be effectively grounded equipment.

Special attention is given to the use of the grounded conductor (the neutral) as a method of grounding equipment. This part also gives some of the necessary information on how to build or install the grounding circuit for equipment grounding, so that the equipment is effectively grounded. The term *grounded effectively* is defined in *Article 100, Definitions.* It is used throughout the Code.

Part G. Bonding

It is interesting to note that the definition of the word *bonding,* as given in *Article 100, Definitions,* follows closely the explanation of effective grounding. The installation and sizing of the *Main Bonding Jumper* and *Equipment Bonding Jumpers* are detailed in this part.

An electrician often takes precautions when installing an electrical circuit to make sure there are no places in the circuit that can come open and interrupt the flow of the current. Bonding is one way of trying to make sure there are no opens in the effective grounding path or the grounding circuit. Bonding makes the grounding circuit complete, so that when there is a fault and a fault

---

*Reprinted with permission from NFPA 70-1996, the National Electrical Code®, Copyright © 1995, National Fire Protection Association, Quincy, Massachusetts 02269. This reprinted material is not the complete and official position of the National Fire Protection Association, on the referenced subject, which is represented only by the standard in its entirety.

current flows, it will not be interrupted. Sufficient current will be allowed to flow until the current flow causes the overcurrent protective device to function.

Part H. Grounding Electrode System

What the Code means by the phrase *Grounding Electrode System* is covered here. Also covered is how to establish a grounding electrode system, and what can and cannot be used as a grounding electrode system.

Two types of electrodes are discussed. One is the made electrode; the other is not specifically identified in the Code, but might be considered as the existing electrode. An example is something that is already on the premises, or is part of the building construction that is effectively grounded. The various types of electrodes are also listed, with specifications for sizing and installing them.

Part J. Grounding Conductors

Note that the word *conductors,* in the title of this part, is plural. There are two grounding conductors listed here and each is identified. Each has its particular function and is so identified by its title.

1. *Grounding Electrode Conductor*
2. *Equipment Grounding Conductor*

The recognized types, materials, installations, and sizing are given for both conductors. Two very important tables are listed here. *Table 250-94* is used for sizing the "grounding electrode conductor." *Table 250-95* is used for sizing the "equipment grounding conductor."

Part K. Grounding Conductor Connections

The grounding conductor connections are specified as "grounding electrode conductor" and "equipment grounding conductor" connections. Various regulations are set down for connecting each conductor. The materials and type of connectors or clamps that are permitted or not permitted to be used, and the protection of the connection, are some of the things covered.

Part L. Instrument Transformers, Relays, etc.

This part is devoted to special instrumentation equipment that might be mounted on or used in conjunction with a switchboard or other electrical equipment. It covers the grounding of instrument transformer circuits and enclosures.

Part M. Grounding of Systems and Circuits of 1 kV and Over

Solid neutral grounding and impedance grounding are recognized here for use with systems operating at 1000 volts or more. Such a system might be a 2400/4160 volt, wye distribution system. The specific requirements for resistance and impedance grounding are listed here.

DEFINITIONS

There are words in the English language that can be called "umbrella" words because they cover a multitude of things that have a lot in common. One such word is *vehicle* (figure 1–5). A vehicle is used for transportation or as a means

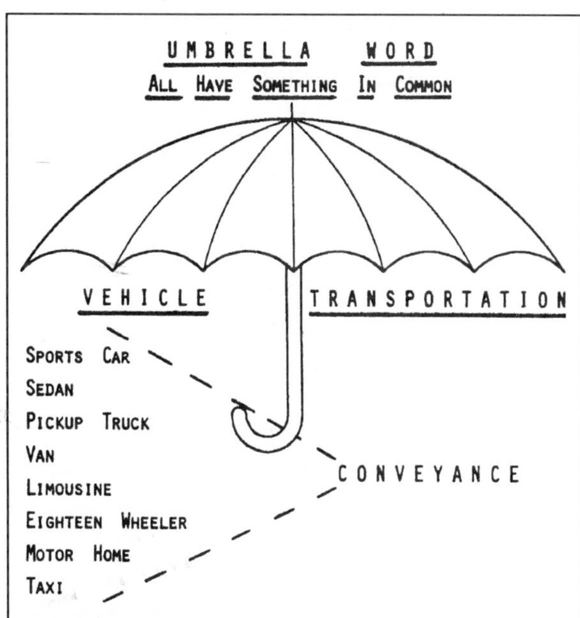

Fig. 1–5 Umbrella word—*vehicle*.

of conveyance. The vehicle might be a sports car, sedan, pickup truck, station wagon, van, limousine, eighteen wheeler, motor home, taxi, bicycle, or horse-drawn wagon, or might be some other type of vehicle.

Sometimes the word *vehicle* is not enough to identify the particular mode of transportation. More information is needed. But even when we get more information, we still are aware of the fact that we are talking about a vehicle. We are able to switch back and forth and talk about a van or a pickup and still not lose the relationship to *vehicle*.

There are a lot of terms and situations covered by the word *grounding*. Therefore, grounding can be considered an umbrella word. The words ground, grounded, and grounding conductor can all be considered part of the umbrella word *grounding*. Figure 1–6 shows how many of the terms used in conjunction with grounding fit under the grounding umbrella. All have one common goal: to protect people and equipment by making a continuous, effective grounding path to earth.

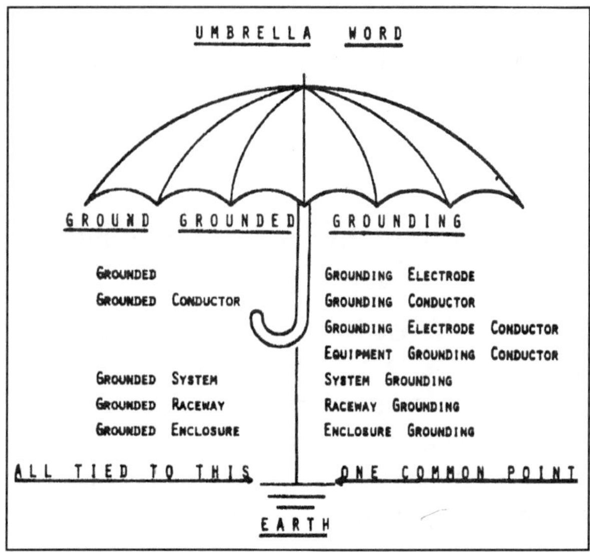

Fig. 1–6 Umbrella word—*grounding*.

Reviewing the Word *Ground*

One of the keys to understanding grounding is to be able to shift fluently from the term *ground* to *grounded* or to *grounding* as the situation demands. Figure 1–7 illustrates the definition of the word *ground*.

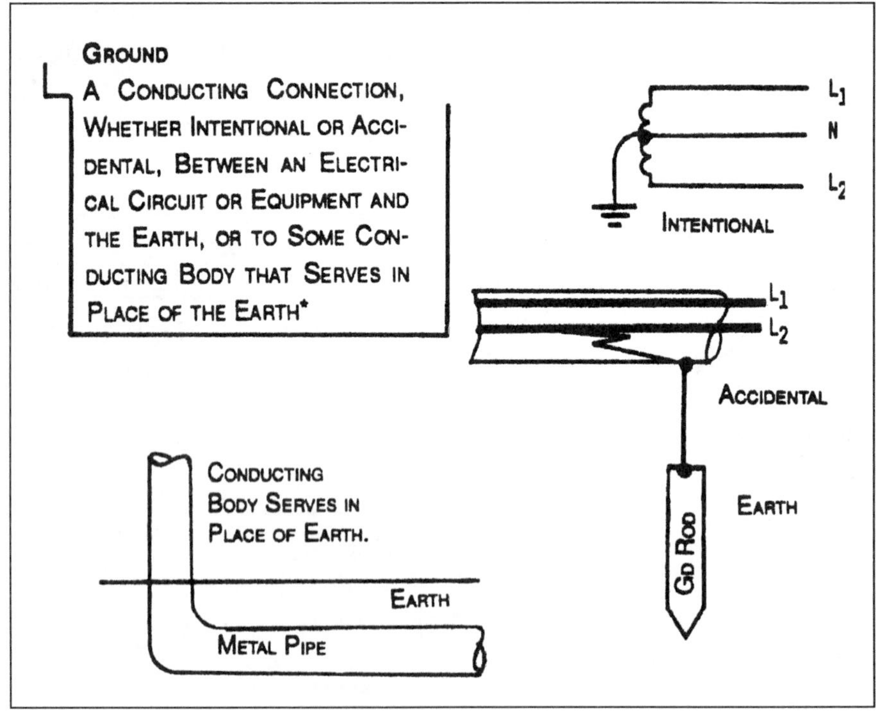

Fig. 1–7 Definition of *ground*.*

* Reprinted with permission from NFPA 70-1996, the National Electrical Code®, Copyright © 1995, National Fire Protection Association, Quincy, Massachusetts 02269. This reprinted material is not the complete and official position of the National Fire Protection Association, on the referenced subject, which is represented only by the standard in its entirety.

Breaking the definition of *ground* into phrases brings out more of the meaning. The following breaks down the definition so the phrases can be looked at individually.

Quote – "Article 100. Ground.

1. A conducting connection,
2. whether intentional or accidental,
3. between an electrical circuit
4. or equipment
5. and the earth,
6. or to some conducting body
7. that serves in place of the earth."*

Phrase 1 indicates the word *ground* is associated with the point of connection. Therefore, when the word *GROUND* is used, think "POINT OF CONNECTION." In order to ground anything, a *connection* must be made, either intentionally or accidentally.

Phrase 2 shows that this point of connection can be either. An *intentional point of ground* would be the ground connection made at the premises supply, such as that for a three-wire system or a three-phase, four-wire, wye connected system. An *accidental ground* occurs when a circuit conductor accidentally touches a grounded surface, better known as a *fault*.

Phrase 3 indicates the ground connection can be intentionally made on an electrical circuit. An example is a three-phase, four-wire, wye-connected system.

Phrase 4 indicates the ground connection could be unintentionally made to a piece of electrical equipment, such as a motor casing, a metal enclosure for electrical equipment, or a metal raceway for conductors. This indicates an accidental ground resulting in a fault condition.

Phrase 5 shows that the connection for the ground is made to earth. The grounding electrode makes the actual connection.

Phrase 6 indicates some other conducting body can be used in place of earth. "Some other conducting body" can be a variety of conductors, such as a piece of wire, a piece of metal conduit, a metal enclosure, or a combination of all of these.

Phrase 7 indicates these other conducting bodies serve in place of earth. For example, *Section 250-6(a)* permits the frame of a portable generator to be the conducting body serving in place of earth.

Reviewing the Word *Grounded*

The word *grounded* is past tense. The action has already taken place. The connection has been made. The phrase "to earth, or to some conducting body that serves in place of the earth" is the same phrase used in the definition of the word *ground*.

Figure 1–8 illustrates how an equipment enclosure can be grounded by using a metal raceway, a metal cabinet, a piece of wire, and a water pipe as the conducting bodies until earth is reached. Note the number of connections that had to be made before the equipment enclosure was actually grounded.

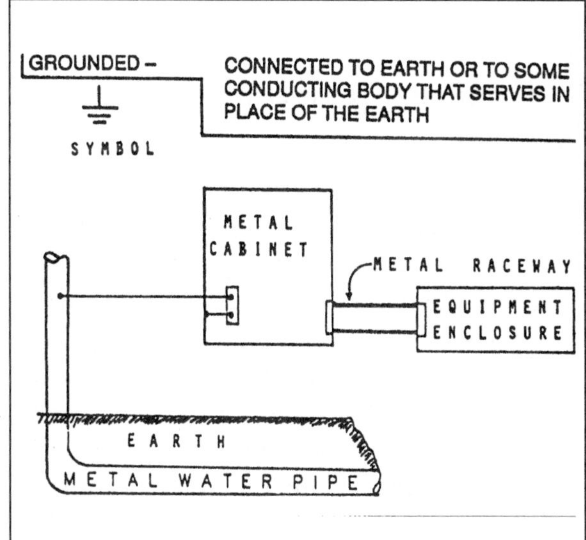

Fig. 1–8 Definition of *grounded*.*

*Reprinted with permission from NFPA 70-1996, the National Electrical Code®, Copyright © 1995, National Fire Protection Association, Quincy, Massachusetts 02269. This reprinted material is not the complete and official position of the National Fire Protection Association, on the referenced subject, which is represented only by the standard in its entirety.

Reviewing the Word *Grounding*

When the "ing" is added to *ground,* it makes the word *grounding*. *Grounding* is a very continuous word. The action is ongoing. It is happening now. Running, working, planning, operating—all indicate ongoing action. Grounding also indicates an ongoing action. The grounding is continuously there, waiting to conduct fault current, should the occasion arise. Part of grounding's job is maintaining all noncurrent-carrying metal parts and enclosures of an electrical system at ground or zero potential. *Grounding* is the umbrella word that results when all the individual parts of the grounding circuit are put together.

Ground is the start, the connection.

Grounded indicates that the connection has been made.

Grounding occurs when everything is in place, ready to perform its protective functions.

As a way of comparison, suppose that an artist is going to "paint" a picture. While working on the picture, the artist is in the process of "painting" the picture. When the picture is completed, it is said to be "painted." Now that it is completed and is hanging on the wall, what is it called? Is it called a "paint," a "painted," or a "painting"? It is called a "painting" and it is continuously there for all to enjoy.

The "grounding" is continuously there for the protection of all to enjoy.

PAINT–GROUND–**Making**
PAINTED–GROUNDED–**Completed**
PAINTING–GROUNDING–**Ongoing**

Reviewing the Term *Grounded Conductor*

The term *grounded conductor* indicates the conductor has been intentionally connected to ground, as in figure 1–9. The grounded conductor is a circuit conductor for the 120/208-volt, three-phase, four-wire system. In this type of grounded system, it is also the neutral conductor and is identified by the color white. This grounded conductor is installed with the full intention of it carrying load current and is sized according to *Article 220, Branch-Circuit, Feeder, and Service Calculations.*

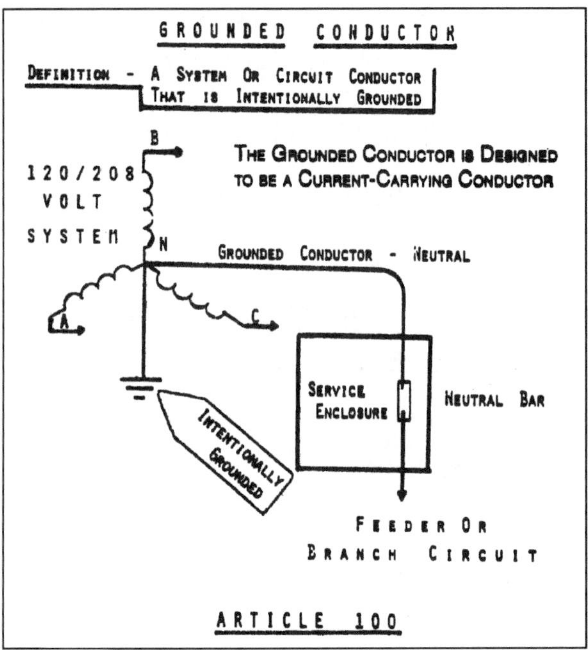

Fig. 1–9 Definition of *grounded conductor*.*

Reviewing the Term *Neutral*

The term *neutral* is not defined in *Article 100* of the Code. The term is used very sparingly in the Code. Theoretically, there should be no potential difference between the neutral conductor and ground. Also, when the load is balanced and there are no harmonic currents present, there is no current flow in the neutral. For all practical purposes the grounded conductor is considered the neutral conductor, except when there is a corner grounded delta. Then the grounded conductor is not a neutral conductor and will have a voltage to ground. The neutral conductor is installed as a current carrying conductor as it will carry current when there is an unbalanced situation.

Reviewing the Term *Grounding Conductor*

Figure 1–10 illustrates where grounding conductors are installed. The Code talks about grounding conductors and identifies them by

*Reprinted with permission from NFPA 70-1996, the National Electrical Code®, Copyright © 1995, National Fire Protection Association, Quincy, Massachusetts 02269. This reprinted material is not the complete and official position of the National Fire Protection Association, on the referenced subject, which is represented only by the standard in its entirety.

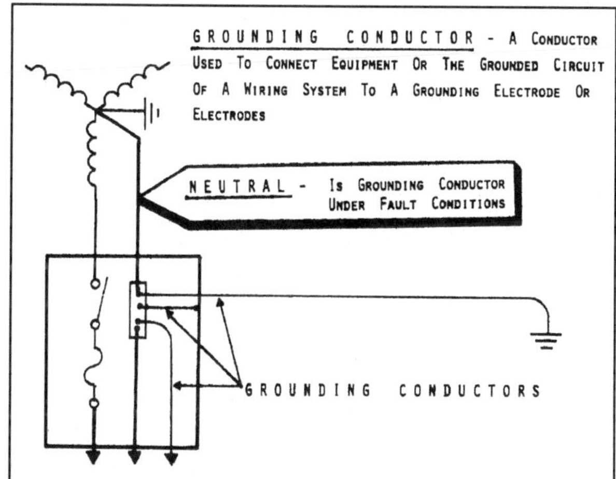

Fig. 1–10 Definition of *grounding conductor.**

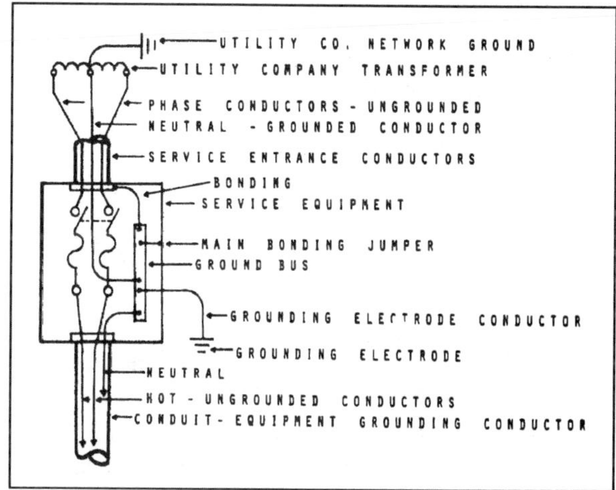

Fig. 1–11 Identification of terms used at service.

their location and function in the overall grounding system. These conductors are:

1. The main bonding jumper
2. The grounding electrode conductor
3. The equipment grounding conductor
4. The equipment bonding jumper

Each of the four grounding conductors will be taken up individually later in this text.

The main bonding jumper is installed at the service only as a bond between the grounding electrode conductor and the service equipment enclosure. The grounding electrode conductor is installed between the service and the grounding electrode. The equipment grounding conductor is neither designed nor intended to carry load current. It is hoped that it will never have to carry current. The equipment grounding conductor will only carry current under fault conditions. The equipment bonding jumper is used to maintain continuity of the equipment grounding conductor path.

Note: In figure 1–10, it is indicated that the neutral is an equipment grounding conductor under fault conditions. How this comes about will be explained in detail in Chapter 4, "Faults," and Chapter 8, "The Grounded Conductor."

*Reprinted with permission from NFPA 70-1996, the National Electrical Code®, Copyright © 1995, National Fire Protection Association, Quincy, Massachusetts 02269. This reprinted material is not the complete and official position of the National Fire Protection Association, on the referenced subject, which is represented only by the standard in its entirety.

Figure 1–11 illustrates various terms that are used in conjunction with installing a service. At the service equipment, a lot of action takes place that applies to the installation of an effectively grounded system.

Future illustrations in this text may show only that portion of the service equipment being discussed. This does not mean the things left off are not really there or are not also very important. Things will be left off the illustrations only to keep the illustrations from being cluttered and to emphasize the particular point under discussion.

Why Ground Systems and Circuits?

The first Fine Print Note (FPN) to *Section 250-1* lists five reasons that systems and circuits are grounded. Figure 1–12 (page 10) illustrates these reasons. Lightning, line surges, unintentional contact with higher-voltage lines, and stabilizing the voltage to ground during normal operations are the responsibility of the grounding electrode and have little or nothing to do with the operation of the overcurrent protection device. The grounded conductor of a grounded system establishes a low-impedance path for fault current through the overcurrent protective device to limit the length of time a fault exists.

The five reasons systems and circuits are grounded add up to two things stated in *Section 90-1, Purpose* (of the Code):

1. Protection of people
2. Protection of equipment

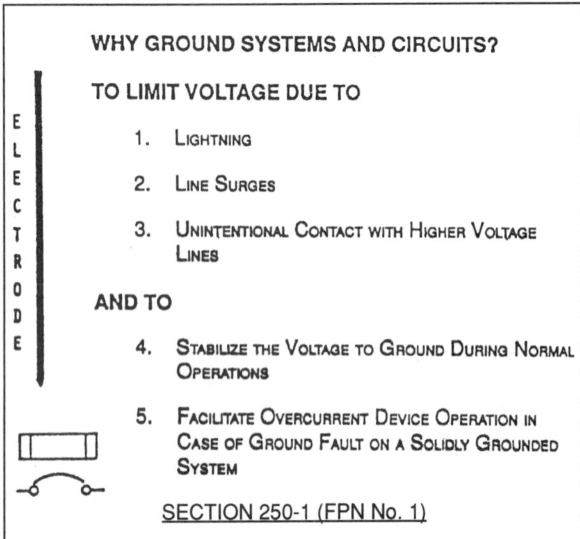

Fig. 1–12 Reasons for grounding systems and circuits.

It is a misconception to think that grounding is only for the purpose of maintaining everything at ground potential to protect people against electric shock. It is just as important to plan to help the overcurrent protection device to operate as soon as possible and keep the electricity as clean as possible. Remember:

THE HAZARD EXISTS ONLY DURING THE PERIOD OF TIME THE FAULT IS THERE.

The ground-fault circuit interrupter (GFCI) is an excellent example of how the length of time a fault exists can be limited. The sooner the fault can be cleared, the sooner the hazard ceases to exist. GFCIs are people protectors.

The sooner the circuit overcurrent protection device, fuses, or circuit breaker can operate, the shorter the period of time that the fault exists. Overcurrent devices are equipment protectors that limit the time an overcurrent condition exists.

The operation of the overcurrent protection device, which opens the circuit and clears the fault, may not eliminate the damage done by the fault. A fault might start a fire, and even after the circuit is cleared, the fire could continue to burn. However, with the overcurrent protection device operating, no more electrons are used to heat the fault and fuel the fire.

Why Ground Conductive Materials Enclosing Electrical Conductors or Equipment?

As illustrated in figure 1–13, there are three reasons for grounding conductive materials enclosing electrical conductors or equipment. The first two reasons are given in the second FPN of *Section 250-1*.

Number one is to "limit the voltage to ground." Number two is to "facilitate overcurrent device operation." Once again, the concern is to limit the voltage and limit the current.

The third reason, although not specifically listed in this FPN, is to drain leakage and/or static electrical currents to ground. An example is grounding the shield of a shielded cable. Special recognition is given in *Article 517, Health Care Facilities* to static and leakage currents. Draining leakage and static currents to ground helps reduce electrical noise. Electrical

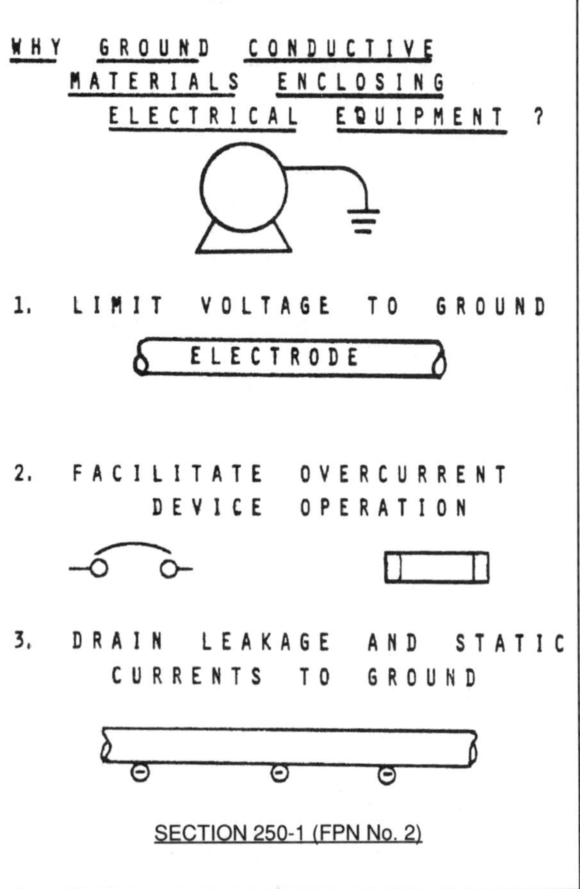

Fig. 1–13 Reasons for grounding conductive materials and enclosures.

noise can cause problems and causes data errors in sophisticated electronic equipment. It is important that these leakage and static currents be quickly drained to ground to ensure optimal operation of the electronic equipment.

The FPNs emphasize the importance of the *bonding* between the equipment grounding conductor and the circuit grounded conductor. This bonding is accomplished by the main bonding jumper, located at the service equipment. It is the key link in completing the fault current path for the operation of the overcurrent protective device. The fine print note also calls attention to the important role the equipment grounding conductor plays in the operation of the overcurrent device under fault conditions.

What Is Effective Grounding?

Figure 1–14 illustrates what must be taken into consideration to have effective grounding. A more detailed look is possible when it is broken down into parts.

The path to ground covers the installation of three things. These are:

1. Circuits
2. Equipment

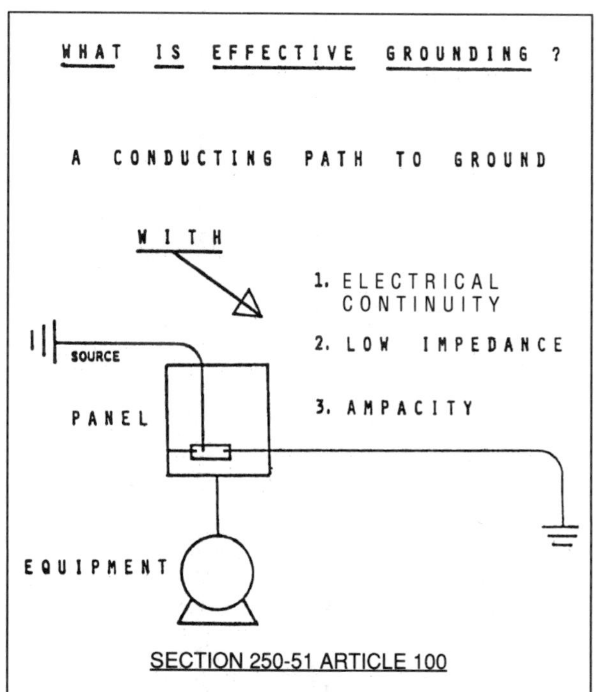

Fig. 1–14 Requirements for effective grounding.

3. Conductor enclosure

The path to ground:

1. is *intentionally* made.
2. must be permanent.
3. must be electrically continuous.
4. must have ampacity to conduct any fault current *safely*.
5. must be a low-impedance path.

The impedance must be kept low for three reasons:

1. To limit the voltage to ground.
2. To facilitate the operation of the circuit protective devices.
3. To drain leakage, static, and unwanted noise-making currents to ground.

Article 100, Definitions, gives a definition of *"Grounded, Effectively,"* which again reemphasizes the same points just discussed for *"effective grounding."*

Comment: Note how effective grounding is required in three different installations: circuits, equipment, and conductor enclosures.

The *path to ground* is something that is built into the electrical circuit at the time it is installed. All connections are made permanent and electrically continuous. The conductor that is installed is large enough to carry potential fault current.

Impedance is the opposition to the flow of current. Everything that can be done must be done to hold that opposition as low as possible. How this is accomplished will be covered later in this text.

When an electrical circuit is installed, continuity of the conductor is maintained. The proper wire size is used to give the conductors the ampacity needed for the load to be served. Also, consideration is given to holding down, as much as possible, the opposition to the flow of current in the feeder or branch circuit conductors, more commonly referred to as "line loss."

Therefore, the definition of effective grounding is telling us that grounding is just another electrical circuit. It is also saying that it

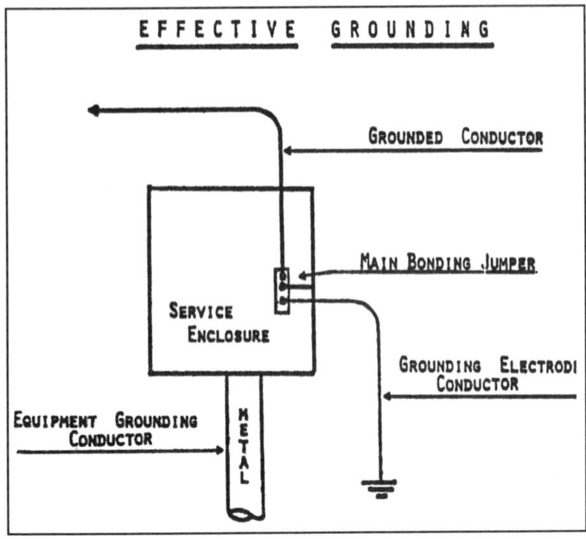

Fig. 1–15 Effective grounding at the service.

Fig. 1–16 The grounding target.

shall be installed with the same consideration and care as any electrical distribution system or branch circuit.

The grounding target. Figure 1–15 illustrates the system grounded conductor, the grounding electrode conductor, the main bonding jumper, and the enclosure used as the equipment grounding conductor all coming together to establish effective grounding.

Figure 1–16 illustrates a target with all four of the grounding conductors zeroed in on the effective grounding bull's eye of the target.

In order to have effective grounding, all four grounding conductors must be on target. To be on target, all four must be properly installed. The ground bar at the service (figure 1–17) is the practical, on-the-job bull's eye of the installation. This is the focal point where all four of the grounding conductors are required by the Code to be connected together.

Article 250 of the Code contains the guidelines for staying on target for an effectively grounded installation. When the effective grounding target is kept in mind, it will be easier to understand why there is so much referencing back and forth in *Article 250*. In this book, each of these four grounding conductors will be given special attention individually, as well as collectively.

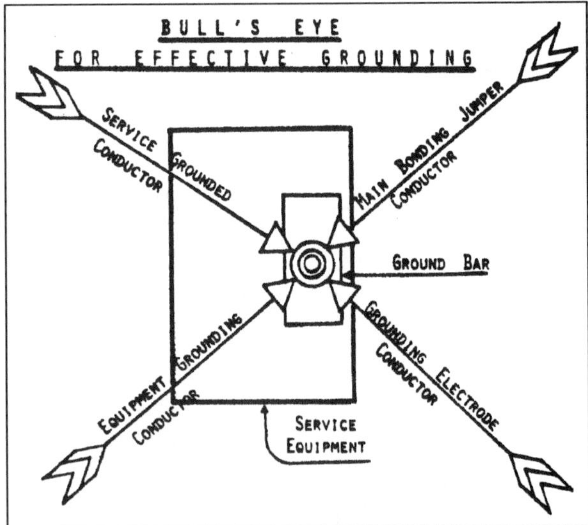

Fig. 1–17 The grounding target at the service.

FOLLOW UP

Topics for self-study, discussion, or questioning.

1. Explain the difference between the terms *guarded* and *isolated.*
2. Discuss what the regulations in Part B of *Article 250* apply to.
3. Discuss what the regulations in Part H of *Article 250* apply to.
4. Which specific grounding conductors are identified in Part J of *Article 250*?
5. Discuss what Part E of *Article 250* is intended to apply to.
6. List some of the grounding terms found under the grounding umbrella.
7. Define the term *grounded.*
8. Define the term *grounded conductor.*
9. Define the term *grounding conductor.*
10. Why are systems and circuits grounded?
11. Why ground conductive materials enclosing electrical conductors and/or equipment?
12. What is "effective grounding?"
13. Discuss where the bull's eye of effective grounding is located and what conductors are connected together at the bull's eye.

CHAPTER 2

Electrical Theory Applicable to Grounding

OBJECTIVES

After completing this chapter, the student should be able to:

- explain what current flow is.
- define an electron.
- discuss some of the habits of the electron.
- apply basic Ohm's law.
- explain why a short circuit does not always trip a circuit breaker.
- explain the various factors that make up the opposition to the flow of current in an alternating current circuit.
- be aware of the term "impedance" as used in conjunction with grounding.
- explain how impedance of the grounding path can affect the operation of the overcurrent protective device.
- be aware of how long the hazard exists when a fault takes place.
- explain how some current will flow in all branches of a parallel circuit.

This chapter is intended as a general review of electrical theory. The points covered actually take place in the grounding circuit as the electrons search out the paths to ground under both normal and fault conditions. There are many good reference books available if more in-depth study of electrical theory is needed.

CURRENT FLOW

When working with electricity, we zero in on the current flow and the path that current will take. That path is called the *circuit*. When working with grounding, we also zero in on the current flow and concentrate on the path the current will take in the circuit to ground. Figure 2–1 zeros in on the *current flow*, which is the movement of electrons.

Chapter 2 looks at some of the ways to zero in on current flow and reviews some of the basic electrical laws and circuits. Especially important here is watching the electrons travel the path

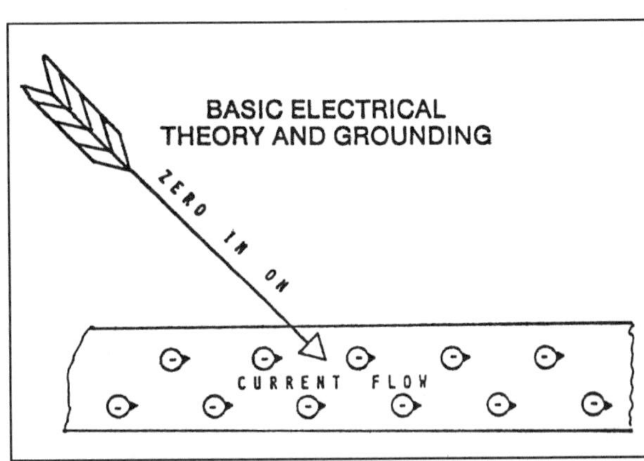

Fig. 2–1 Zeroing in on the current flow.

or paths built for them to get into the earth. There is no better starting place than with the electron itself; that is the fellow we want to keep our eye on.

THE ELECTRON

The *electron* is often defined, very simply, as a negatively charged particle of electricity. I like to think of the electron as a highly motivated, restless, lively little electrical juice bug with tremendous potential to be productive. But, at the same time it has a fiery temper to be just as destructive. It travels from place to place at phenomenal speed. Then when everything is said and done, the electron likes to hole up in the earth. The following is a sort of checkout system on the electron.

The Electron Creed

Do you believe in electrons?
I do.

Do you believe in the molecular theory of matter that all matter is composed of atoms and, therefore, there are electrons in all materials?
I do.

Do you believe electrons can move very fast?
I do.

Do you believe electrons can jump?
I do.

Do you believe electrical current flow is the controlled movement of electrons?
I do.

Do you believe static electricity is the uncontrolled movement of electrons?
I do.

Do you believe electrons can accumulate on a surface?
I do.

Do you believe electrons crowding to a point will cause "pressure piling" at a jumping-off place?
I do.

Do you believe in free electrons?
I do.

Do you believe an electron has a fiery temper?
I do.

Do you believe electrons will travel on special paths built for them?
I do.

Do you believe electrons are always trying to get back into the earth?
I do.

Once you accept and believe the electron creed, you will be able to watch the electrons move about the world. It will also be easier for you to see them travel the grounding path into the ground.

The world is a place that is highly infested with electrons. My closet is full of them, jumping all over my clothes. They are in my pants, socks, shirts, sweaters, and what have you. Sometimes the electrons in my pants legs get to acting up—popping, snapping, grabbing, and just generally making a nuisance of themselves. They get in my hair, especially right after I shampoo and dry it with an electric dryer on a cool, dry day. Some carpets have more electrons in them than a dog has fleas. People are electron carriers. They carry electrons across the room, from the house to the car, and on into the workplace. The odd thing is that these people take about as many back home with them.

Everything in the world is infested with electrons. Everything in the world is matter, which is composed of atoms. Atoms contain electrons. So there are electrons in and around us at all times, even if we cannot see them. Some electrons are held tightly in the material they are a part of and have little chance to escape, while others fit loosely and can be easily dislodged and go off on their own.

Some of the electrons in the world travel controlled highways of conductors; they accomplish work. This is usually referred to as "current electricity." Then there are the free-spirited, mischievous electrons that travel around on their own from point to point, from object to object, jumping from here to there and causing considerable havoc with their electrostatic behavior. These free-spirited electrons are referred to as "static electricity."

Static electricity is often referred to as "electricity at rest." That may be true, but it wakes up with a pretty good jolt. Think of it as a collection of electrons that have migrated to a point and are just waiting to jump and throw a scary little spark at someone or something that gets near.

In the following analogy, visualize droplets of water as individual electrons and watch them collect and move on a surface. For example, when there is a heavy dew or dampness in the air, droplets of water form on a surface. As more droplets form, they start to accumulate. When sufficient droplets have gathered they accumulate weight, which pressures them to move as a group along the surface. Gravity will also cause them to run down the side of the surface.

Electrons collect on surfaces much like the droplets of water forming on a surface. As more electrons accumulate, they tend to move together to a point and build up a pressure at that point. Electrons have it easier than the droplets of water, however, because the pressure causing them to move can be exerted up, down, sideways, or in any direction, since they don't have to wait for gravity to move them. The pressure buildup at a given point is called *pressure piling;* the electrons stand ready to jump to another material as soon as a material with the correct polarity comes close. These free-spirited electrons are much more active in a cool, dry, crisp atmosphere than they are in a warm, moist atmosphere.

Proper grounding drains away surface electrons. It eliminates pressure-piling points on metal surfaces by giving the electrons an easy, direct, but controlled path into the earth.

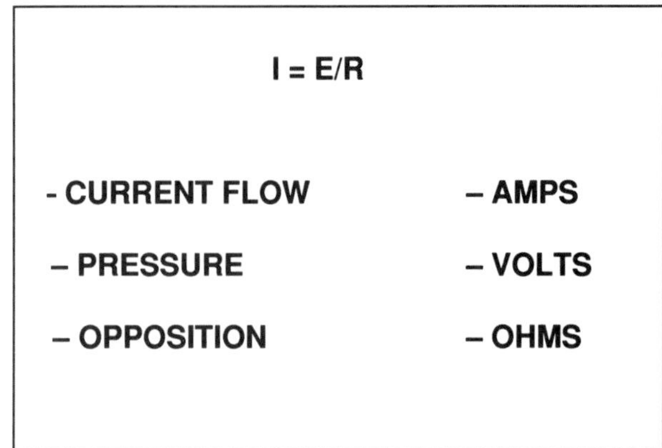

Fig. 2–2 Ohm's law.

OHM'S LAW

Ohm's law (figure 2–2) shows the relationship between the current, voltage, and resistance of an electrical circuit. "I" stands for current flow and is measured in amperes. "E" stands for electrical pressure (voltage) and is measured in volts. "R" stands for the opposition offered to the flow of current and is measured in ohms.

When Ohm's law is set up as an equation, figure 2–3, I = E/R. The figure indicates that when E is constant, I is limited by R (the opposition).

The voltage in an electrical circuit is considered to be constant. Technically, there may be some voltage drop, but for all practical purposes

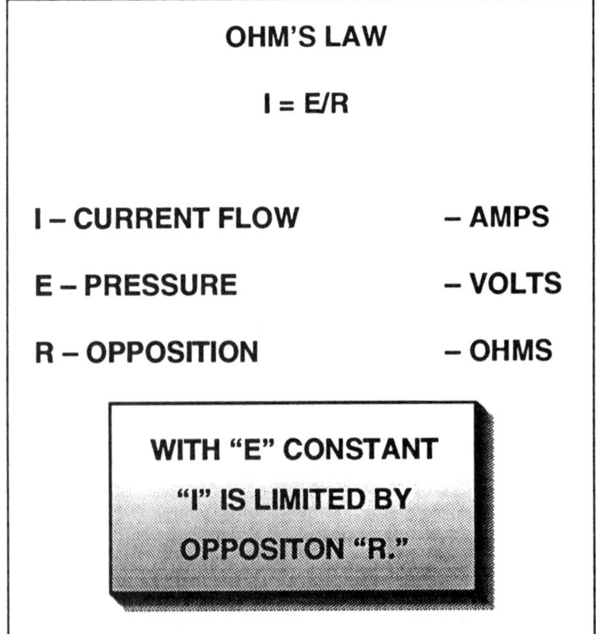

Fig. 2–3 Ohm's law. With E constant, I is limited by R.

it is considered constant. A 120-volt system will be 120 volts across all parts. A 480-volt system will measure 480 volts across all parts. This is because feeders and loads are connected across the line in parallel.

But the current in an electrical circuit varies with the connected load or the opposition to the current flow. Opposition to current flow comes from the various connected loads of the circuit. There is also some resistance in the conductors of the circuit.

When planning electrical circuits, consideration is given to the size of the connected load in amps, which determines the ampacity of the circuit conductors. Use a wire size that will carry a given number of amps adequately. In order to size the wire, we zero in on the amps.

The rating of the branch circuit is determined by the size of the overcurrent device protecting the circuit. In order to size the overcurrent protective device, we zero in on the amps.

DIRECT CURRENT

For a given load, *direct current* (DC) is a steady flow of current in one direction only, while *alternating current* (AC) is continually changing magnitude and direction. Therefore, their characteristics differ. However, basic Ohm's law, E = IR, is applicable to DC circuits. It is also applicable to AC circuits only when the AC circuit contains a pure-resistance load. A resistor or an electric heater are examples of pure-resistance loads. The first use of Ohm's law here will show how it would apply to a DC circuit or an AC circuit containing pure resistance.

SERIES CIRCUIT

We zero in on these same amps in the grounding system to control their travel. The "ground path" is often a "series circuit." Figure 2–4 illustrates a simple *series circuit* and one very important point about such a circuit: it has only one path for the current to travel on.

One of the important laws of a series circuit is that the current flow is the same in all parts of the circuit because there is only one path for current flow. When looking at grounding, keep this law for series circuits in mind because this

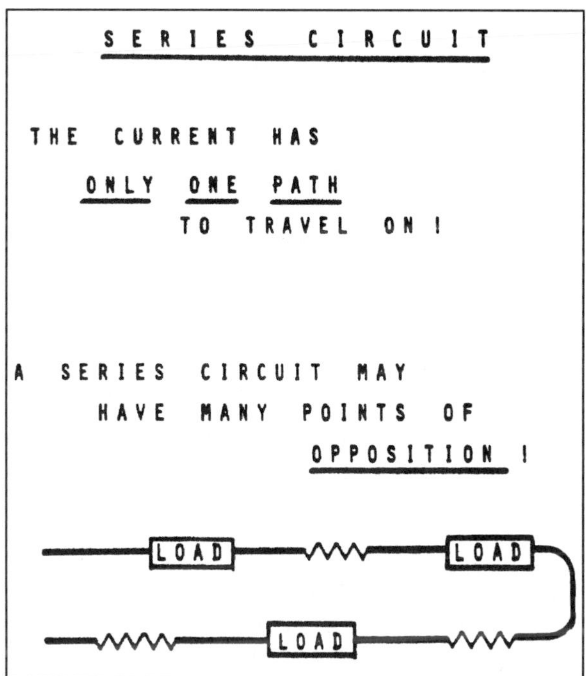

Fig. 2–4 A simple series circuit.

one path for current flow will become very important, regardless of the amount of fault current or electrical pressure.

A series circuit may also have many points of opposition built into it. First, the load is in series with the conductors of the circuit. Also, every connection, both at the load and between the source of supply and the load, could be a possible source of opposition, especially if it is a loose or poorly made joint or connection. The conductors will have some resistance to them that will increase the opposition to the flow of current. Fully loaded or overloaded conductors, and the ambient temperature in which they are installed, can cause an increase in the opposition to the flow of current. There are a lot of things connected in series with a load in an electrical circuit and in a grounding circuit.

Figure 2–5 is a series circuit with two 5-ohm resistors connected in the circuit. There is a

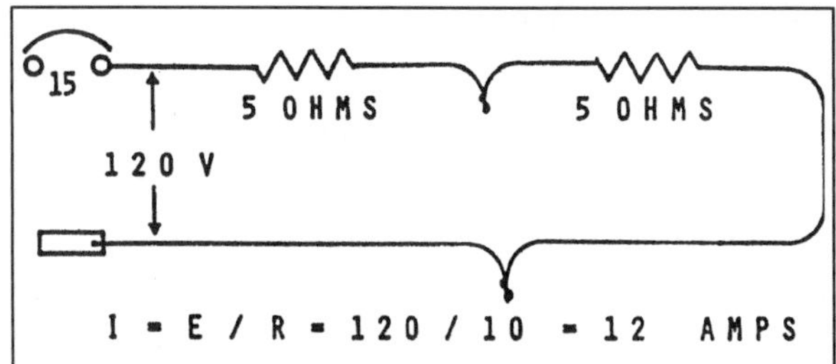

Fig. 2–5 A properly operating series circuit.

connection on the breaker in the distribution panel, a connection on the neutral bus in the panel, and a couple of joints made in the conductors of the circuit. All joints and terminations in this circuit are well made.

When Ohm's law is applied to the circuit, we find that 12 amps flow in the circuit. With everything in order, there is no problem. Everything works very nicely.

Figure 2–6 indicates that one of the joints was not properly made, came apart, and shorted out part of the circuit. Now there is a fault. Now only one of the 5-ohm resistors is connected in the circuit and one is shorted out. The short makes a good connection and does not noticeably increase the opposition to current flow.

Using Ohm's law, we find that 24 amps will now flow in the circuit. This 24 amps can be considered a fault current. It will cause the 15-ampere breaker to operate and clear the fault quickly.

Figure 2–7 shows a third situation. The same circuit and fault are illustrated, but this time it is a high-resistance connection, as indicated by the extra 2 ohms at the point of fault. A second fault point is also introduced at the panel, where the connection to the neutral bus is *not* good and offers some opposition. Now the total opposition to the flow of current is 9 ohms instead of the 5 ohms in the previous circuit. This time the 12-amp circuit breaker will not trip and clear the fault. Instead, it will allow the fault to continue to exist.

At the point of one or both faults, heat is generated. As heat is generated at the point of a fault, it will increase the resistance of the fault. As the opposition to current flow increases, the amount of current flow will de-

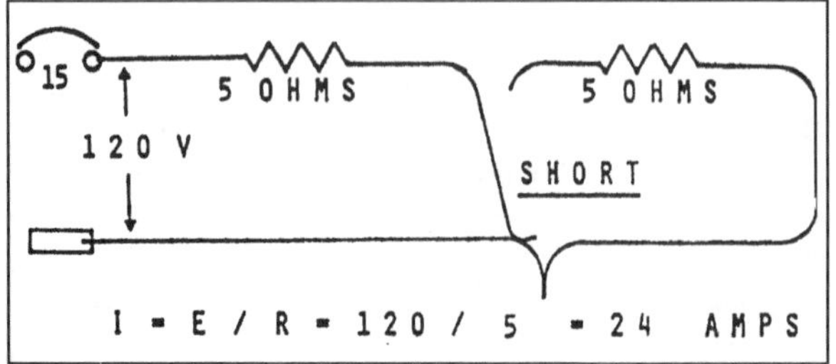

Fig. 2–6 A series circuit with a low-resistance fault.

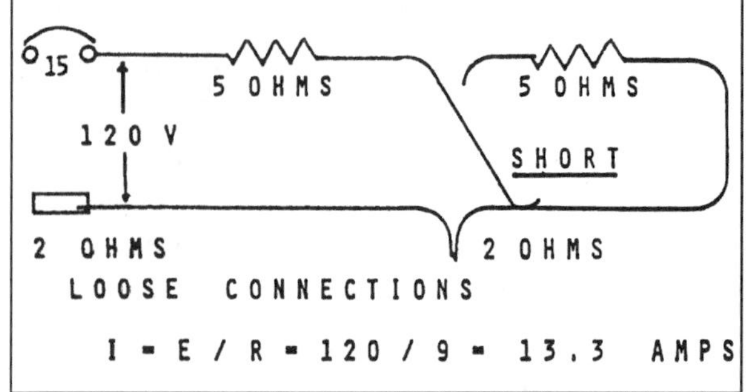

Fig. 2–7 A series circuit with a high-resistance fault.

crease, thereby giving the circuit breaker less chance to operate. This situation will continue until enough damage has been done to cause the insulation to break down almost completely. This will result in a short, with little or no resistance, and sufficient current flow to cause the circuit breaker to open the circuit. This illustration shows how a fault situation can take place and how the overcurrent protective device will not open the circuit, even though it is a good circuit breaker and is functioning properly.

An interesting thing about a circuit breaker, or any other overcurrent protective device, is that when it is built for a specific number of amps, it always remembers that number (unless it is a faulty breaker; that is a different story). If it is a 50-amp breaker, it operates at 50 amps. If it is a 100-amp breaker, it operates at 100 amps.

For example, a 100-ampere breaker counts the number of electrons that travel through it until the number of electrons exceeds the 100-amp value. Then it says "no more" and stops the electron flow by opening the circuit.

But the one thing that overcurrent protective devices have not been programmed to do is to be able to tell what the electrons will do after they pass through the overcurrent protective device. The breaker cannot tell the difference between an electron that is traveling out to the load to accomplish work, or an electron that is traveling out somewhere just to cause trouble. Unfortunately, under certain conditions an overcurrent protection device will allow some trouble-causing electrons continually to get out into the circuit.

Some electrons are good workers and others can be regular terrorists. Once an electron gets out of the controlled path, it can be a holy terror. Grounding tries to work to control these terrorist electrons quickly by causing them to travel through the overcurrent protective device.

ALTERNATING CURRENT

The previous Ohm's law illustration basically showed direct current. Most of the circuits and distribution systems the electrician works with use alternating current. It is necessary to realize that there are some differences and that these differences are taken into consideration when discussing grounding. Sometimes it is mistakenly assumed that some of the properties of an alternating-current circuit are understood. Some electricians may not be aware of the difference alternating current makes. But the "grounding path" knows the difference.

Some of the things that happen in an alternating-current circuit have a special and definite effect on the ground path. Alternating current can introduce more opposition to the flow of current than meets the eye.

A quick mini-review of alternating current might bring back to mind the part alternating current actually plays in the grounding path. Just as in the direct-current circuit, in an alternating-current circuit there is a certain amount of built-in "pure resistance." But there are two other components that increase the opposition to the flow of current. They appear to be resistance, measured in ohms, but are not found in direct-current circuits. These two components are called "inductive reactance" and "capacitive reactance."

Pure Resistance

Now for a quick look at each of the components in an alternating-current circuit. The first, *pure resistance* (figure 2–8), is opposition to the flow of current. It is built into a circuit. The conductors have resistance in them. Conduit offers resistance to the flow of current. When

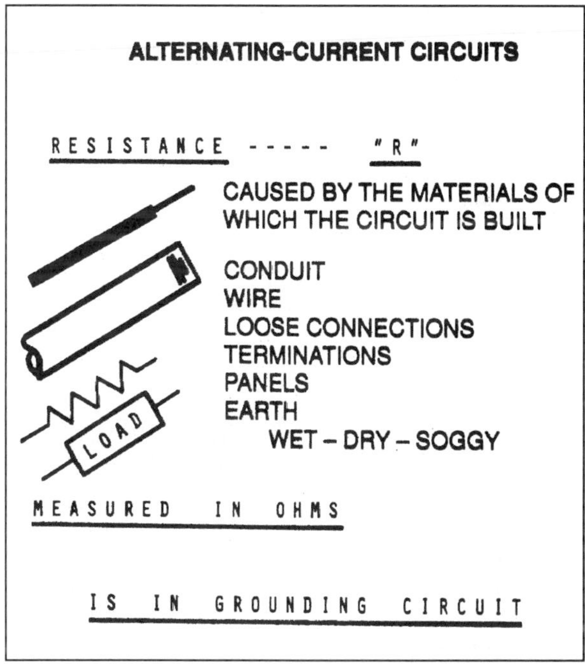

Fig. 2–8 Pure resistance.

improperly or poorly made, terminations, connections, and splices can introduce resistance into the circuit. One of the things that will change the built-in resistance of conductors is heat. The resistance of the earth varies with how dry, wet, or soggy the soil is.

When installing a grounding system, care is required to ensure that resistance is not built into the grounding path by leaving loose connections or an open circuit.

Inductance-Inductive Reactance

Inductive reactance in an alternating-current circuit is caused by the inductance of the circuit (figure 2–9, page 20). The inductance is caused by the alternating current's magnetic field.

When current flows through a conductor, it sets up a magnetic field. The inductance is caused by the alternating current changing direction, which in turn causes the magnetic field's magnetic lines of force to rise and fall. As these magnetic lines of force rise and fall, they cut the conductor, thereby inducing into the conductor an AC voltage directly opposite the applied voltage. This induced voltage is called "counter-electromotive force" (CEMF). When this induc-

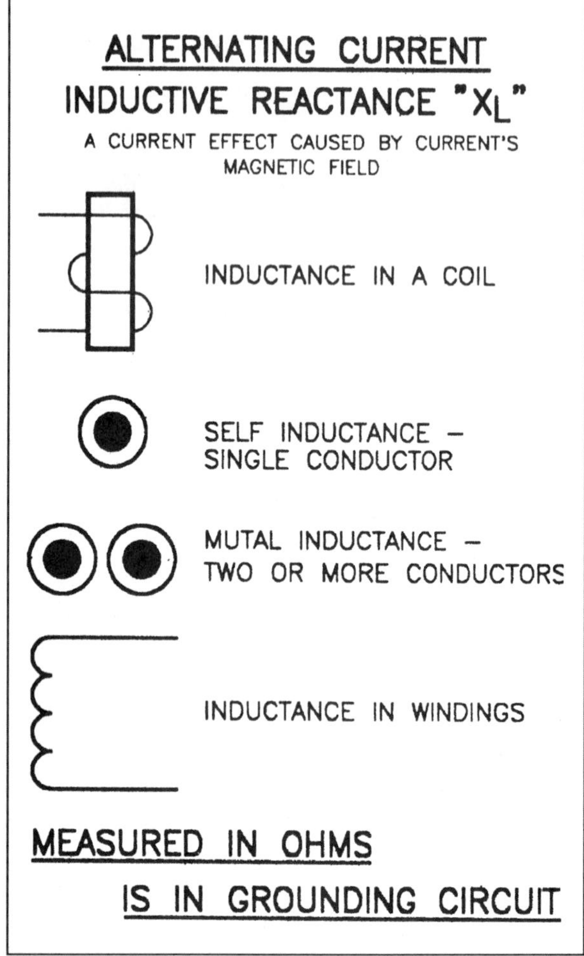

Fig. 2–9 Inductive reactance.

tion takes place in a single conductor, it is called "self-induction." Watch for self-induction to take place when the grounding electrode conductor is discussed in chapter 6 of this book. When this induction occurs between two or more conductors, it is called "mutual induction."

Induction is a current effect of the alternating-current circuit. Where there is an alternating current, there is an alternating magnetic field and there will be induction. This induction will result in inductive reactance, which results in opposition to the flow of current. It is measured in ohms, just as pure resistance is measured in ohms.

The Code pays some special attention to induction in *Section 300-20(a) (Induced Currents in Metal Enclosures or Metal Raceways)* (figure 2–10). Here the Code requires all phase conductors, and the neutral and equipment grounding conductors, to be installed in the same raceway to avoid induction. When there is induction in these situations, it shows up as heat and creates more opposition to the flow of current.

Capacitance-Capacitive Reactance

The third component is *capacitive reactance* (figure 2–11), which is an opposition to the flow of current due to capacitance. It is a voltage effect of the circuit and is also measured in ohms.

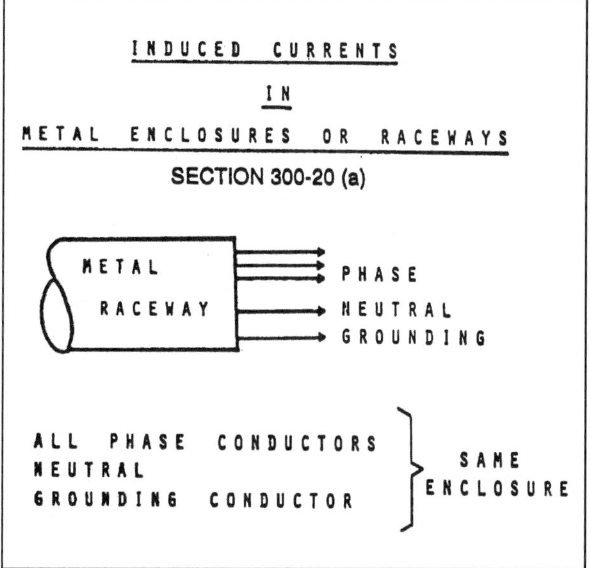

Fig. 2–10 A Code requirement for induced currents.

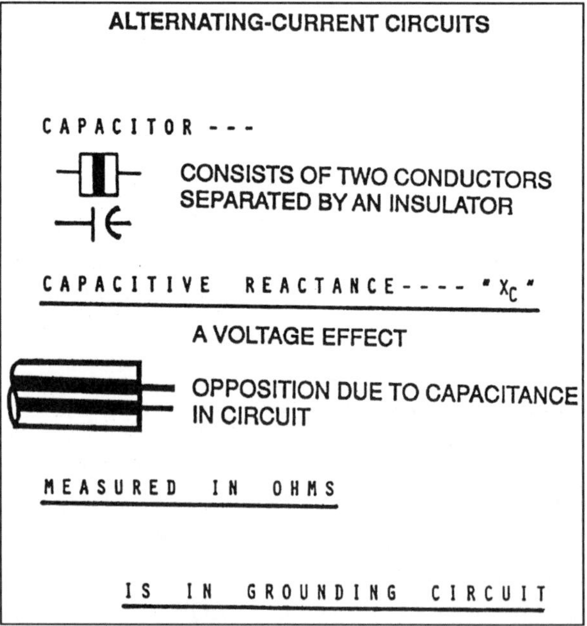

Fig. 2–11 Capacitive reactance.

"Condensers," also called "capacitors," introduce capacitance into the alternating-current circuit. The mechanical definition of a *condenser* or a capacitor is:

> "A condenser consists of two conductors separated by an insulator."

A condenser is often built into an electrical installation when conductors are installed in conduit. For example, when insulated conductors are installed in metal conduit, a condenser is built. A cross-sectional view of the installation will show the metal conduit as a condenser plate, each of the metal conductors as a condenser plate, and the insulation on the conductors as the insulation between the metal plates. Conductors separated by insulators have been installed. A condenser has been built.

The electrical definition of a *capacitor* is:

> "A capacitor stores electrostatic stress."

When the two definitions of a capacitor are considered together, it means that any time there are two metal surfaces (conductors) separated by air (an insulator) or any other insulating material, a condenser has been built. The electrical function then takes place, and electrostatic stress is stored by an accumulation of electrons on the surfaces of each plate of the condenser.

Problems caused by capacitance being built into the circuit are minor for general grounding as it is presented in *Article 250* and applied to general power distribution. Current caused by capacitance built into the circuit is often measured in fractions of amps and volts called microamps and microvolts. However, these microamps and microvolts do become very important and are given consideration when grounding in health care facilities (*Article 517*) and for the operation of microelectronic equipment such as computers.

IMPEDANCE

Resistance, inductive reactance, and capacitive reactance all offer opposition to the flow of current in alternating-current circuits. To find the total opposition to the flow of current in an alternating-current circuit, it is necessary to add the resistance, the capacitive reactance, and the inductive reactance, all of which are measured in ohms.

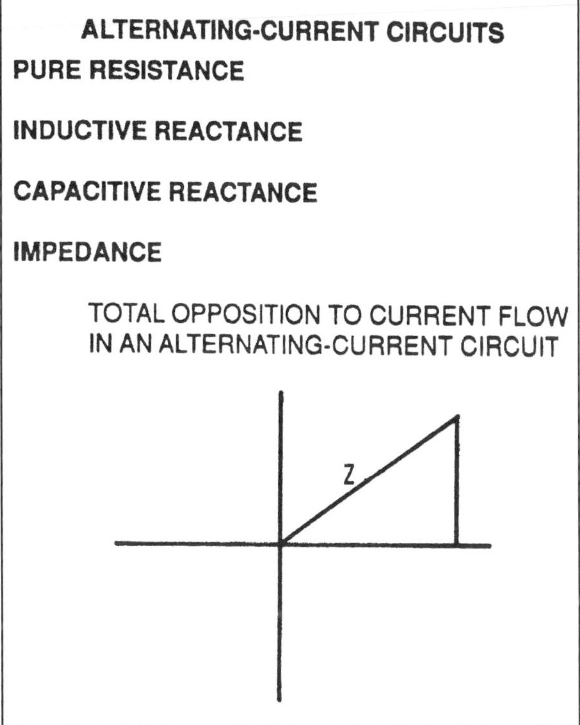

ALTERNATING-CURRENT CIRCUITS
PURE RESISTANCE
INDUCTIVE REACTANCE
CAPACITIVE REACTANCE
IMPEDANCE
TOTAL OPPOSITION TO CURRENT FLOW IN AN ALTERNATING-CURRENT CIRCUIT
Z

Fig. 2–12 Impedance.

These three components are not added directly, as might be thought; they are added vectorially. The result is called the *impedance* of the alternating-current circuit, which is the total opposition to the flow of current in an alternating-current circuit (figure 2–12). It is measured in ohms and the symbol is "Z."

The term *impedance* and its symbol Z are used many times in conjunction with grounding alternating-current circuits. So when the word *impedance* or the symbol Z is used, think "opposition to the current flow." When the Code uses the phrase "low impedance," it is calling for a path of low opposition to the flow of current.

Once again we can look at Ohm's law, but this time as it applies to an alternating-current circuit (figure 2–13, page 22). Amps is the current flow, volts is the pressure, and ohms is the impedance of the total opposition to the flow of current.

AMPS AND OVERCURRENT PROTECTIVE DEVICES

In the illustration, the voltage is maintained constant. The impedance is lowered. The result is that the current is increased.

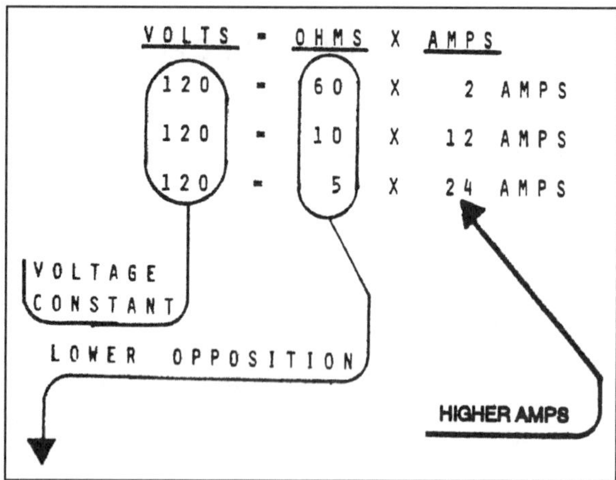

Fig. 2–13 Increasing the current in an alternating-current circuit by lowering the impedance.

Why increase the amps in the grounding circuit?

Note what has been added in figure 2–14; "Amps operate overcurrent protective devices." Think what this means in terms of effective grounding for equipment protection (figure 2–15). The hazard exists only during the period of time the fault is there. The higher the impedance, the longer the fault exists. The lower the impedance, the shorter the time the fault exists.

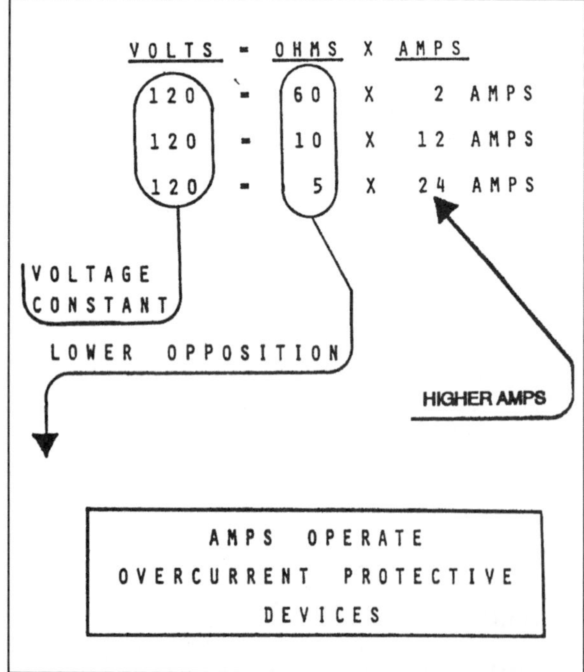

Fig. 2–14 Amps operate overcurrent protective devices.

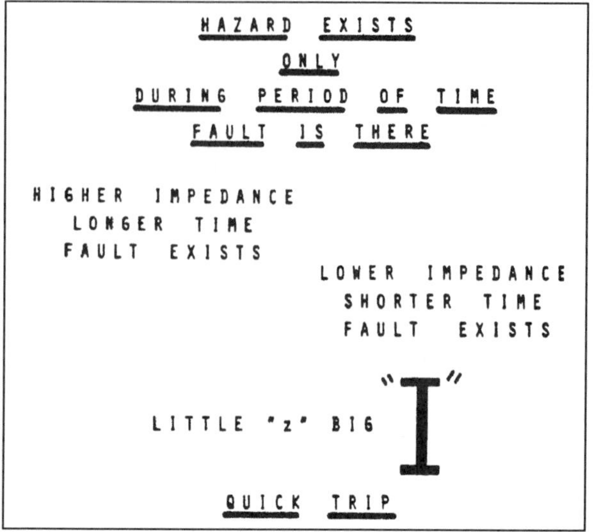

Fig. 2–15 Effective grounding to protect people and equipment.

It all adds up. With a little "z" and a big "I," the grounding circuit will give a quick trip for the protection of equipment.

PARALLEL CIRCUIT

Figure 2–16 illustrates a "parallel circuit" with two loads connected. A *parallel circuit* has more than one path for the current to flow. One of the basic laws of a parallel circuit is that the voltage is the same across all branches of the parallel circuit. The second law is that the current is the sum of the currents through the separate branches.

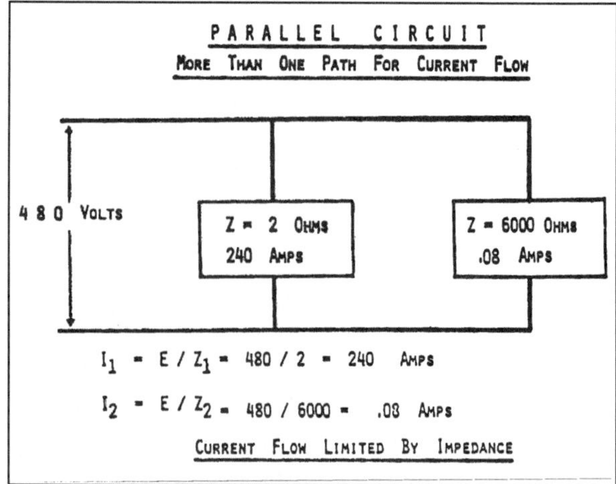

Fig. 2–16 A parallel circuit with two current paths.

One load has a very low impedance of 2 ohms. Ohm's law indicates that 240 amps are flowing through the load.

The second load has a very high impedance. Ohm's law indicates that .08 amp is flowing through the load.

This illustration makes two points. First, the current flow is limited by the impedance. Second, no matter how high the impedance is, there will be some current flow through the high impedance when the loads are connected in parallel. Give the current flow—the electrons—more than one grounding path to travel on and, no matter what the impedance of the grounding path is, some electrons will travel all branches of the parallel circuit. Unintentionally establishing parallel paths can interrupt control of the electron flow and establish unwanted paths for electrons to travel on, resulting in unwanted circulating currents.

SERIES-PARALLEL CIRCUIT

Figure 2–17 combines the basic laws for current flow in a series circuit and a parallel circuit. The current in the series portion of the illustration has only one path to flow on. But when it reaches the point where there are many parallel paths, the current divides. Current will flow on each and every path offered.

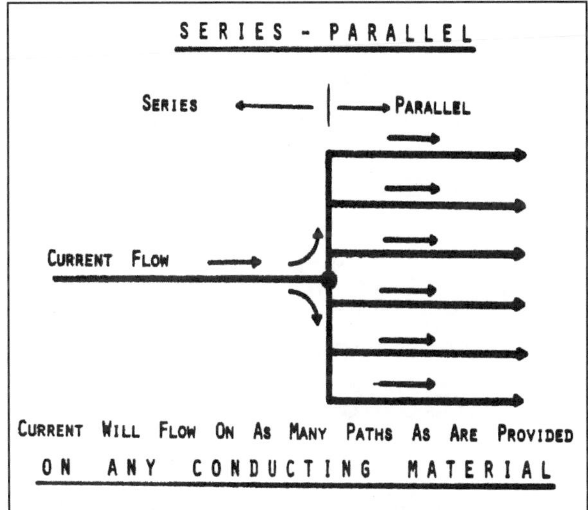

Fig. 2–17 Current flow in a series-parallel circuit.

A thought to keep in mind: "The current will flow on as many paths as are available." The path, of course, must be conducting material and could be a path that is intentionally or accidentally provided. The current has a habit of searching out and finding all possible paths it might take.

FOLLOW UP

Topics for self-study, discussion, or questioning.

1. Define an electron.
2. What is current flow?
3. Discuss some of the characteristics of an electron.
4. Explain and illustrate Ohm's law for a simple electrical circuit.
5. Discuss the relationship between voltage, current, and resistance using Ohm's law.
6. Discuss the current flow in a series circuit.
7. Discuss the three types of opposition—resistance, inductive reactance, and capacitive reactance—encountered in an alternating-current circuit.
8. Define *impedance.*
9. Discuss how the amps operate the overcurrent protective device.
10. What results when a fault occurs in an electrical circuit and the ground path has a "little z and a big I?"
11. Discuss the current flow in a parallel circuit.

CHAPTER 3

Grounding for Safety

OBJECTIVES

After completing this chapter, the student should be able to:

- explain why proper and effective grounding plays a very important part in SAFETY related to electric shock.
- explain the relationship of voltage and current to electric shock.
- explain what factors determine the severity of an electric shock.
- explain the resistance of the human body.
- identify how small an amount of current can be fatal when passed through the body.
- compare the resistance of the human body to the resistance of a conductor.
- explain how bonding the metal parts of current-carrying enclosures to ground can protect against electric shock.
- explain the two main functions of grounding as to control of voltage and current.

This chapter covers the relationship between electric shock and grounding. It shows what happens to an individual who receives an electric shock.

ELECTRIC SHOCK

When signs are put up to warn people about electricity, they usually read

DANGER
HIGH VOLTAGE
KEEP OUT

But what actually happens when an individual receives an electric shock?

Is it the *voltage* that does the damage? Or is it the *current* that does the damage?

With the lower voltages, those in the 120/208-volt range, the current does most of the damage. With the higher voltages, both the current and the voltage do damage.

When an electric baseboard heater is installed, the heater has a pure resistive element in it. As current passes through the resistive element, heat is produced. When an electrical current flows through the body's resistance, heat is produced, just as it is in a heater. This production of heat damages the body.

Voltage is the pressure in an electrical circuit. The pressure causes the current to flow; pressure also causes explosions. Often when an individual receives a shock from high voltage, the voltage will cause an explosion at the point the current leaves the body. The higher the voltage, the more chance there is of forcing more current through a low body resistance.

Determining the Severity of an Electric Shock

When an individual touches a hot wire of a 120-volt circuit with one hand and has one foot grounded, a path for current flow is established through the body. The amount of current passing

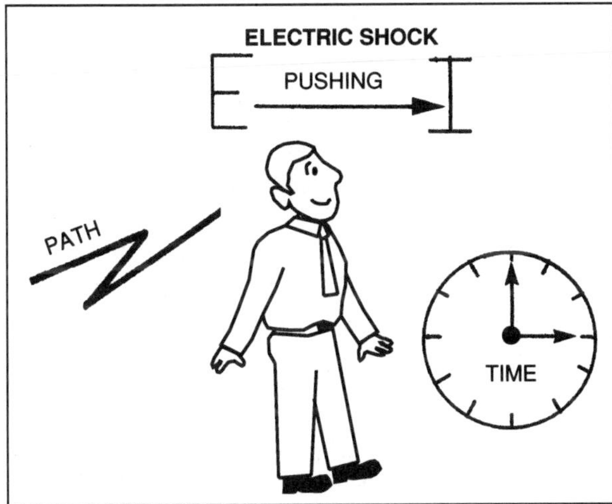

Fig. 3–1 Electric shock—E pushing I.

ELECTRIC SHOCK SEVERITY –

1. PATH OF CURRENT THROUGH BODY
2. LENGTH OF TIME CURRENT FLOWS
3. AMOUNT OF CURRENT THROUGH BODY

UNGROUNDED METAL IS A POTENTIAL SHOCK HAZARD!!

VOLTAGE TO GROUND STANDS READY TO PUSH CURRENT THROUGH BODY!!

Fig. 3–2 Electric shock severity.

through the body is limited by the pressure (voltage) and the resistance of the body (figure 3–1). The severity of the electric shock is determined by three things (see figure 3–2).

Current is mentioned in each of the three things that contribute to the severity of an electric shock. Voltage is conspicuous by its absence, although both voltage and current play a damaging part in an electric shock.

Figure 3–3 illustrates a comparison between the body and an insulated electrical conductor as conductors of electricity. A conductor has an outer covering of insulation. There are many kinds of insulation. Its main function is to contain the pressure (voltage) and also to keep the electrons on track. The insulation works two ways. It keeps the voltage and the electrons within the conductor and also keeps other voltages out of the conductor. The most common voltage rating is the 600-volt building wire. In addition, the insulation on the wire is the mechanical protection for the conductor.

The human body is covered with an insulating material known as the *epidermis*, or outer skin. Like the insulation on the wire it varies a lot, and its main job is to keep the voltage out. There are many different types of skin and skin conditions that affect its function as an insulator. The skin also offers mechanical protection. Its voltage rating, however, is rather low—not nearly as good as that of the 600-volt building wire.

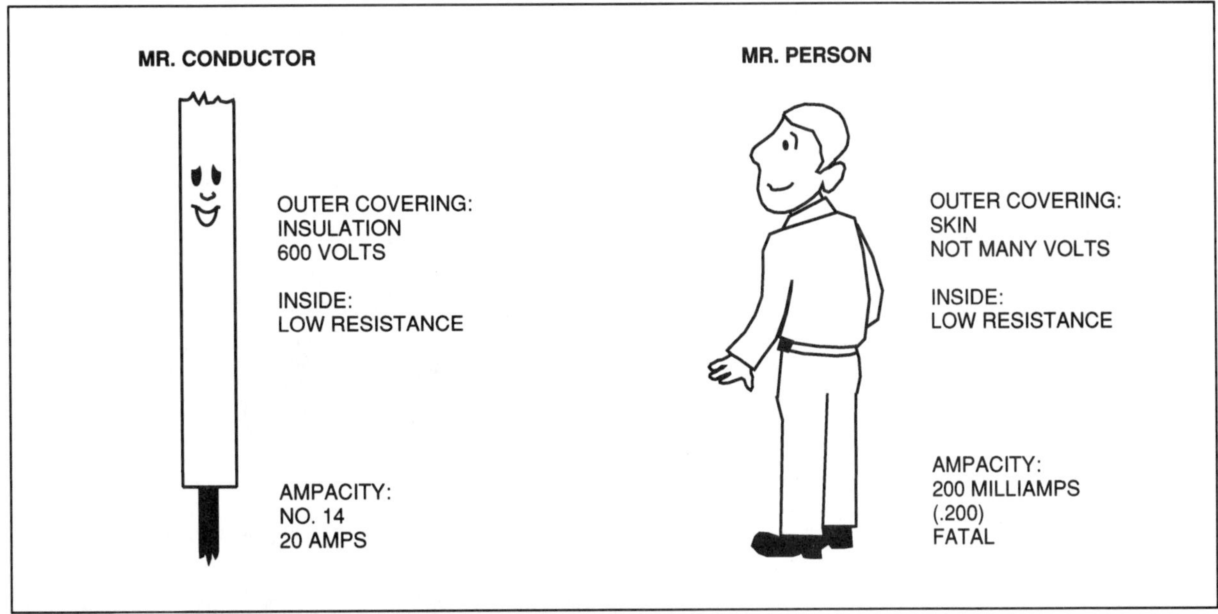

Fig. 3–3 Comparison of an electrical conductor to a person.

Inside the outer covering of a wire's insulation, there is a copper conductor. The copper conductor has a very low resistance. It offers very little opposition to the flow of current.

There is also a conductor inside the human body. Inside the body there is mostly salt water, a good conductor. Once the current has broken through the skin, the inside resistance of the body is very low, and the body becomes a very good conductor.

The ampacity of the conductor is rated according to the metal in the conductor and the insulation on the conductor. But a No. 14 conductor with a rating of 20 amps would not be hard to find in *Table 310-16*.

The ampacity of the body is very low. The body can carry only a very fractional part of an amp before real damage is done. Two hundred milliamps (.200 amps) can be fatal. A milliamp is one thousandth (.001) of an amp.

In hospitals and health care facilities, as covered in *Article 517* of the Code, there is concern for the possibility of microamps doing damage to the body. A microamp is one millionth (.000001) of an amp. Leakage currents can be measured in microamps.

A 100-watt lamp on a 120-volt circuit will draw about .833 amps. A fatal shock can be caused by less current than it takes to light a 100-watt lamp.

Figure 3–4 uses Ohm's law and a constant body resistance of 100 ohms to illustrate how the current will increase as the voltage is increased. There is very little we can do to increase the resistance of the body, except to use protective equipment such as rubber gloves or other insulating materials. It is necessary to work with both the voltage and current when trying to protect against electric shock. Therefore, to protect against electrical shock two very important things need to be taken into consideration.

1. **HOLD THE VOLTAGE DOWN AS MUCH AS POSSIBLE.**

   This will reduce the electrical pressure. By reducing the electrical pressure, less current will flow and less damage will be done.

2. **HOLD THE CURRENT DOWN AS MUCH AS POSSIBLE.**

   As previously seen, the flow of current through the body is what does the real damage. It takes less than one ampere of current flowing to cause the heart to fibrillate.

Properly installed electrical grounding works towards both of these goals.

BODY RESISTANCE (FOR EXAMPLE, 100 OHMS AT ANY VOLTAGE) REMAINS THE SAME. AN INCREASE IN VOLTAGE RESULTS IN AN INCREASE IN CURRENT.

120 VOLTS	**I = E/R**	**= 120/100**	**= 1.2 AMPS**
480 VOLTS	**I = E/R**	**= 480/100**	**= 4.8 AMPS**
4160 VOLTS	**I = E/R**	**= 4160/100**	**= 41.6 AMPS**

Fig. 3–4 Ohm's law and body resistance.

POTENTIAL DIFFERENCE

A term often used in conjunction with grounding is *potential difference*. Actually, potential difference and voltage mean the same thing; they both measure pressure. When you want to know the voltage between two particular points of a circuit, the term *potential difference* is often used.

Figure 3–5 shows that the potential difference between points 1 and 4 is 120 volts. This is also the supply voltage for this circuit. The circuit is a series circuit where loads A, B, and C are resistive loads of equal size, all connected in series.

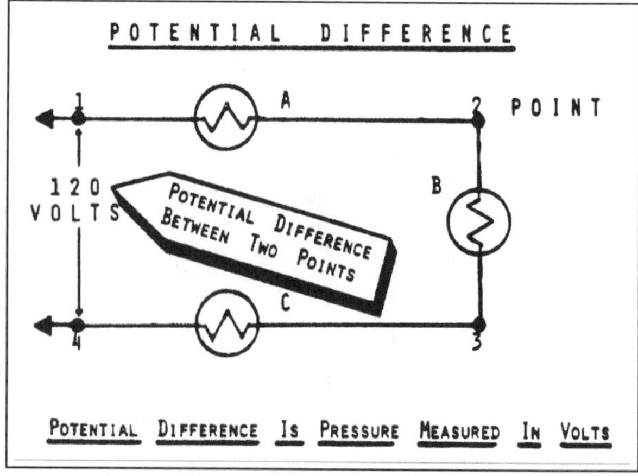

Fig. 3–5 Potential difference is pressure measured in volts.

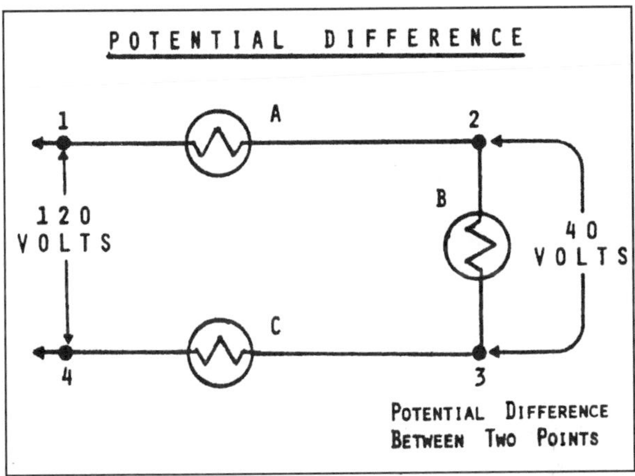

Fig. 3–6 **Potential difference between two points.**

Figure 3–6 illustrates the potential difference across load B or between points 2 and 3. True, because it is a series circuit there will be the same reading when the potential difference between points 1 and 2 or 3 and 4 is measured. But in this illustration, there is a particular interest in the potential difference between points 2 and 3, which is 40 volts.

When a jumper is installed between points 2 and 3, as shown in figure 3–7, the potential difference falls to zero. By installing the jumper, two things were accomplished:

1. The same potential was maintained at both points. (Something was done about the voltage.)
2. The current was given another path of very low opposition to flow on. (Something was done about the current.)

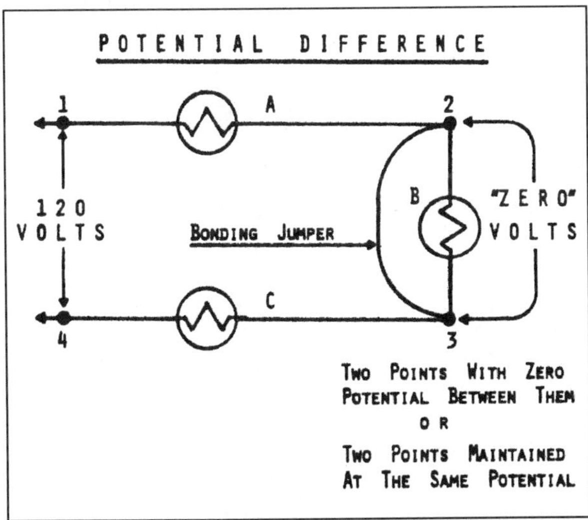

Fig. 3–7 Using a bonding jumper to maintain two points at the same potential (zero).

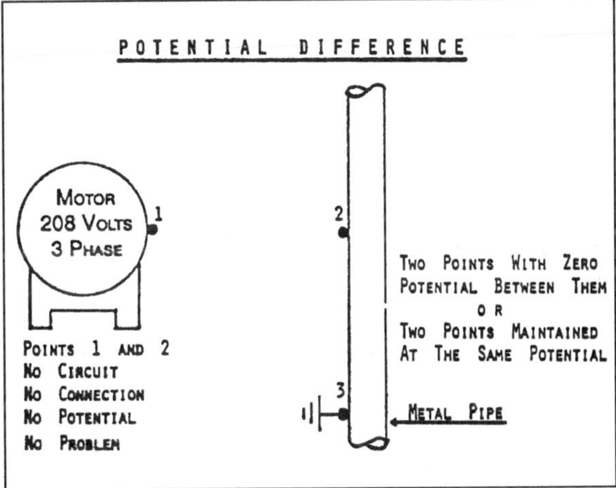

Fig. 3–8 Potential difference between a grounded water pipe and an ungrounded motor.

By the use of a bonding jumper, two points were bonded together and now have the same potential. Bonding jumpers are used in conjunction with grounding to accomplish just such a purpose.

In figure 3–8, points 2 and 3 are located along the same metal water pipe and can be considered to be bonded together. Therefore, they have the same potential. The motor is not bonded or grounded to anything. It is isolated. There is no connection between the frame of the motor and the water pipe. There is no connection between the motor and ground.

GROUNDING AND ELECTRIC SHOCK

Figure 3–9 shows a fault occurring inside the three-phase, 208-volt motor, so that the frame

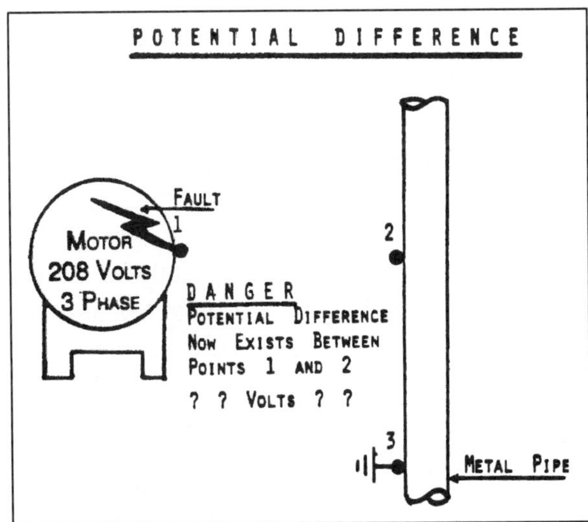

Fig. 3–9 Motor ground fault. A hazard now exists.

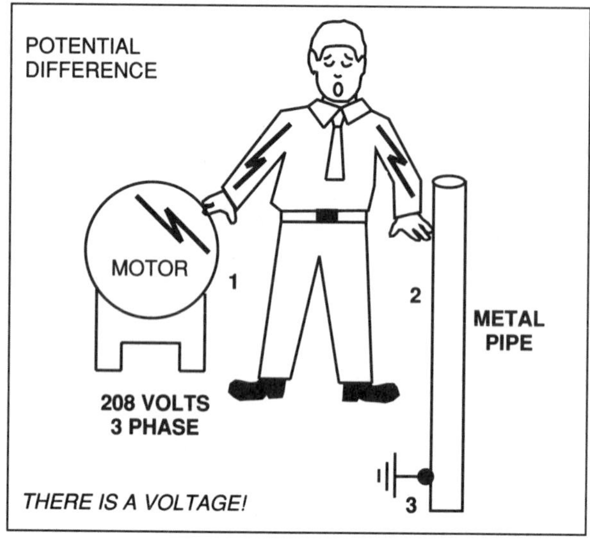

Fig. 3–10 The hazard results in an electric shock.

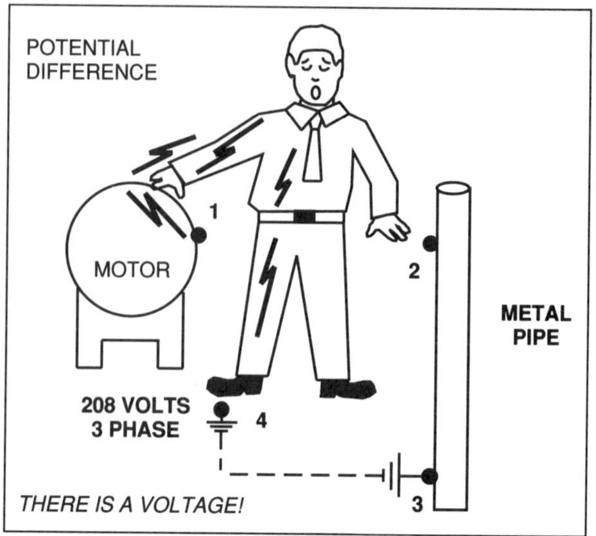

Fig. 3–11 Another shock hazard exists.

of the motor is now referred to as "hot." Once a fault takes place inside the motor, the outside metal of the motor will now be the same potential to ground as a hot conductor. The first phrase that might be used to identify this fault is, "the motor has gone to ground." But it really has not done so because there is no ground connected to the frame of the motor. The motor casing is not bonded to the water piping, so it is not held at ground potential.

There is now an unseen hazard that exists, just waiting for an accident to happen—just waiting for someone to touch the motor frame and a grounded surface at the same time. A potential difference now exists between point 1 and either point 2 or point 3.

How much difference is there? It's hard to say; that depends on how good a connection the fault has made to the motor frame. It could be the full 208 volts or any portion thereof. But there is without a doubt a potential difference between the frame of the motor and any grounded surface.

Figure 3–10 shows the accident happening. Someone touches the frame of the motor and the grounded water pipe. This actually creates a complete electrical circuit through the individual, who now receives an electric shock. Note the path of the current through the body.

What will the voltage across the victim be? That all depends on how good a contact the victim has made to complete the circuit and what the impedance of the arc and the contact within the motor are.

This is not the only hazard that exists. Figure 3–11 illustrates the second hazard. An individual might touch the frame of the motor and another grounded surface at the same potential as the grounded water piping. Once again, notice the path of the current though the body. Note that how the victim is connected into the electrical circuit is going to determine how severe an electric shock the victim receives.

In figure 3–12, an equipment bonding jumper has been installed. Such an installation would be part of a properly grounded system and would eliminate the hazards that existed. However, the bonding jumper would not be run open from the water piping to the motor frame. The equipment grounding conductor would be installed with the regular circuit conductors.

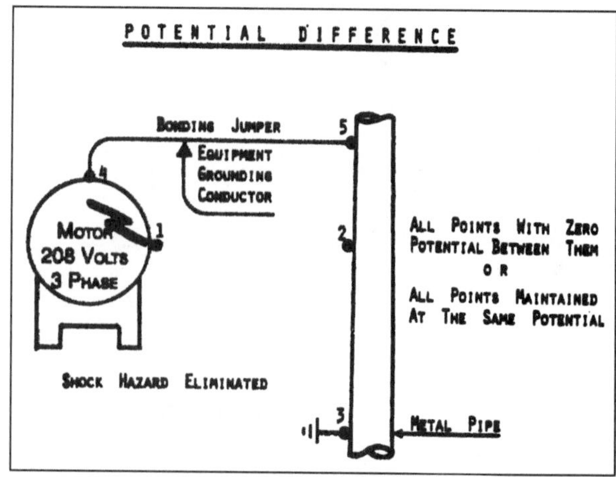

Fig. 3–12 Shock hazard eliminated by installing a bonding jumper.

By adding the bonding jumper, the potential difference between the frame of the motor and the grounded surfaces has been eliminated. By adding the bonding jumper, another path has been given for the current to flow on and very possibly allows the circuit's overcurrent protective device to operate, thereby eliminating the shock hazard and protecting the motor from more costly damage.

Compare figure 3–12 (page 28) with figure 3–7 (page 27). In each case there is a bonding jumper, and in each case the bonding jumper accomplishes the same things.

Figure 3–13 sums it up: eliminate the potential difference. Then there is nothing to push the current through the body, and the low opposition path allows the current to flow through something other than the body. The proper installation of effective grounding works to establish protection for the individual from voltage and current.

GROUNDING ELIMINATES

1. VOLTAGE

   PRESSURE TO GROUND

   NOTHING TO PUSH CURRENT THROUGH BODY

GROUNDING BUILDS

2. LOW OPPOSITION PATH FOR CURRENT FLOW

   GIVES PATH FOR CURRENT FLOW OTHER THAN THROUGH BODY

Fig. 3–13 Grounding eliminates voltage and gives current a low opposition path.

FOLLOW UP

Topics for self-study, discussion, or questioning.

1. What part does voltage play in an electric shock?
2. What part does current play in an electric shock?
3. How does grounding reduce voltage that might cause an electric shock?
4. How does grounding reduce current that might cause a fatal electric shock?
5. Discuss and compare the amount of current flowing through the human body that can cause a fatal electric shock and the current required to operate a 100-watt, 120-volt incandescent lamp.
6. Discuss the paths the current may take through the human body.
7. Discuss the length of time the current passes through the human body.
8. Discuss some potential shock hazards.

CHAPTER 4

Faults

OBJECTIVES

After completing this chapter, the student should be able to:

- explain the difference between a direct short and a ground fault.
- define the term *overload.*
- define the term *overcurrent.*
- discuss the various stresses on electrical equipment caused by electrical faults.
- explain why the grounded conductor is always brought to the service, when the service supply is a grounded system.
- explain how the grounded conductor can lower the impedance of the ground path.
- identify a solidly grounded system.
- identify an impedance grounded system.
- explain how a solidly grounded system is connected.
- explain how an impedance grounded system is connected.
- explain the dangers of using an ungrounded system.
- explain why and where ground fault detectors are used.

The term *fault* is used a lot in conjunction with grounding. Grounding does not prevent a fault, but proper grounding can limit the time the fault exists, and thereby limit the length of time the hazard exists. Faults are characterized as a "line side" or "load side" fault. When a fault takes place on the line side of the service, it is called a line side fault. The line side of the service is any equipment or conductors ahead of the service overcurrent protective devices (figure 4-1).

As a general rule, the line side of the service equipment is backed up only by the utility company's power system and their overcurrent protection, which will not clear a ground fault on the line side of the service without doing damage. About the only overcurrent protection here is what the utility company has on the primary side of the supply transformer.

Therefore, on the line side of the service equipment, planners and installers should think in terms of making the continuity so good that

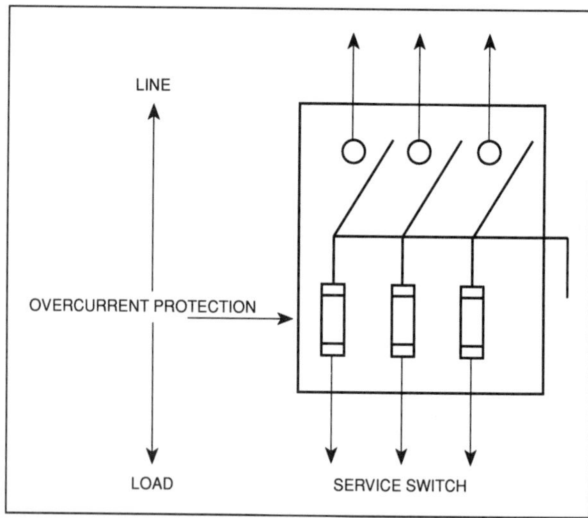

Fig. 4–1 Point of Division for line and load.

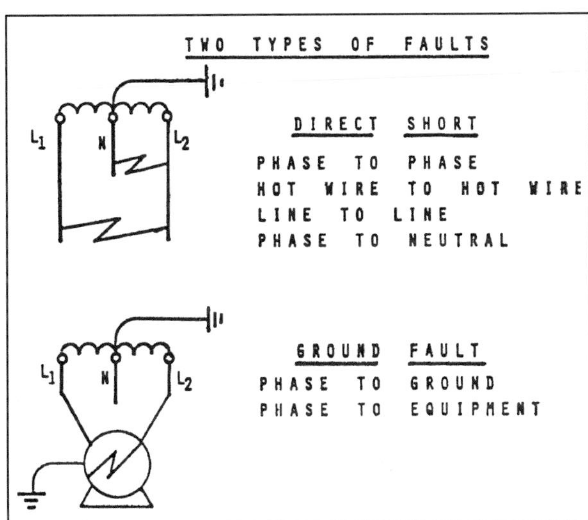

Fig. 4–2 Two types of faults: direct short and ground fault.

when a fault occurs, it will burn itself clear as quickly as possible.

The load-side faults take place on the load side of the service overcurrent protective devices. The load side consists of all equipment and conductors connected after the service overcurrent devices. This chapter is directed more toward what happens on the load side rather than what happens on the line side of the overcurrent protective devices. When a fault happens, the grounding system goes into action to limit the time of the load-side fault.

TYPES OF FAULTS

Faults are generally divided into two types—direct short and ground fault (figure 4–2). The Code calls attention to the possibility of both of these types of faults in *Section 110-10*.

A *direct short* can be caused by a phase-to-phase connection, also referred to as "line to line" or "hot wire to hot wire." A phase-to-neutral connection can also be considered a direct short. These are accidental connections. Direct-short faults cause the largest fault current to flow.

Ground fault occurs when a phase conductor is connected to ground. It can be an accidental connection between a phase conductor and any grounded surface, such as a grounded metal enclosure. A ground fault will cause about 75 percent as much fault current to flow as a direct short. When a ground fault takes place, the equipment grounding conductor serves a very important function. It furnishes a low-impedance path for the fault current to reach and cause the circuit overcurrent protective device to operate, thereby limiting the time the fault exists.

Two terms the Code uses in conjunction with overcurrent protective devices are *Overload* and *Overcurrent*; these are defined in *Article 100, Definitions*. An *Overload* occurs when electrical equipment or a conductor is operated in excess of its rated current. When 22 amps are connected to a 20-ampere circuit, the circuit is overloaded but the 22 amps is not a fault current. If an overload continues to exist for a period of time, however, damage can be done and a fault can result. Basically, the term *Overload* does not include fault currents. *Overcurrent* is an excessive current caused by a short circuit or a ground fault. Electrical faults cause overcurrent conditions.

Some overcurrent devices are so designed that they protect only against overloads. The overcurrent protective device can also be designed to protect against both overloads and overcurrents. The Code recognizes the possibility of either a direct short or a ground fault occurring and requires that both types of faults be considered when selecting the overcurrent protective device to interrupt fault currents.

Section 110-9 requires that equipment intended for use in interrupting fault current be so rated. An FPN references *Section 110-10*, which lists some of the things to be taken into consideration for potential fault currents:

1. Total impedance.
2. Component's short-circuit withstand rating.
3. Other characteristics such as:

   Voltage—amount of current
   Wire size—length of circuit

Sections 250-70 and *250-75* both indicate that equipment grounding bonding jumpers shall be large enough to conduct the fault current they may be exposed to. Chapter 18 will deal with calculating the magnitude of fault currents.

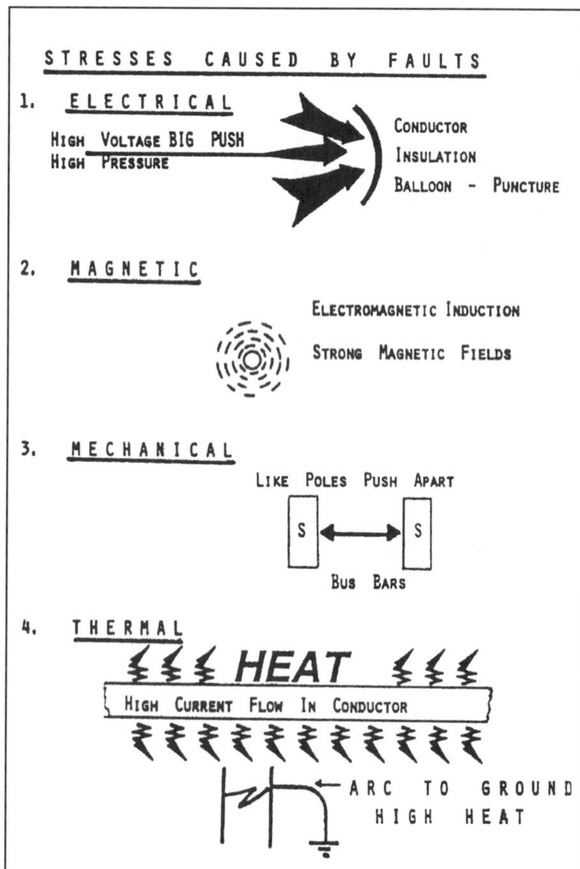

Fig. 4–3 Stresses caused by faults: electrical, magnetic, mechanical, and thermal.

STRESSES CAUSED BY FAULTS

When a fault takes place, the fault current causes certain stresses on equipment. These stresses are electrical, magnetic, mechanical, and thermal (figure 4–3).

An example of electrical stress would be when a high-voltage line falls on a low-voltage service drop and the 600-volt insulation of the building wire is subjected to a much higher voltage than the 600-volt rating. As a result, the high voltage, which is high pressure, causes a ballooning of the 600-volt insulation. Just like anything else that starts to balloon, there is an eventual breaking point.

When there is a direct short or a ground fault, there is a very high current. The strength of the magnetic field set up by the current flow is directly proportional to the amount of current flowing in the circuit. Magnetic fields have north and south polarities and function just like any north and south pole. Unlike poles will attract and like poles will repel each other.

A mechanical fault might be caused in a switchboard if an A phase bus and a B phase bus each had the properties of a north pole and repelled each other. The result would be that the magnetic field could be strong enough to rip the buses loose from their supports. Fault currents can be extremely high, resulting in powerful magnetic fields, because the strength of a magnetic field is directly proportional to the current flowing in the conductor.

When current flows through a conductor it creates heat, thermal heat. The higher the current the higher the heat, and heat starts fires.

High current surges can damage equipment. For example, a utility company fault might result in a higher voltage than the service is rated for. The higher voltage can cause a high current surge.

Surge currents are often caused in electronic equipment by EMI, or *Electromagnetic Induction*. The surges can cause spikes in the sine wave of the voltage, the spike being of high value when compared with normal voltage. Since most microelectronic equipment is very small, it operates on a low voltage and can stand only a low pressure. A small component part of a piece of electronic equipment operates at less than one volt. A voltage spike of well over one volt would completely destroy it.

IONIZATION

Very often when there is a fault, there is an arc. The arc creates a situation that sustains the arc (figure 4–4, page 33). Air is considered a good insulator; often it is used to insulate between buses or where it is necessary to have bare electrical conductors or contacts. Once the air becomes ionized, it becomes a conductor and will sustain both the flow of current and the path of the arc.

When the contacts of electromagnetic switches used to control motor loads open, an arc is formed and the arc will ionize the air around it. Manufacturers use various methods to deionize the air around the arc where electrical equipment must break currents. For example, a magnetic

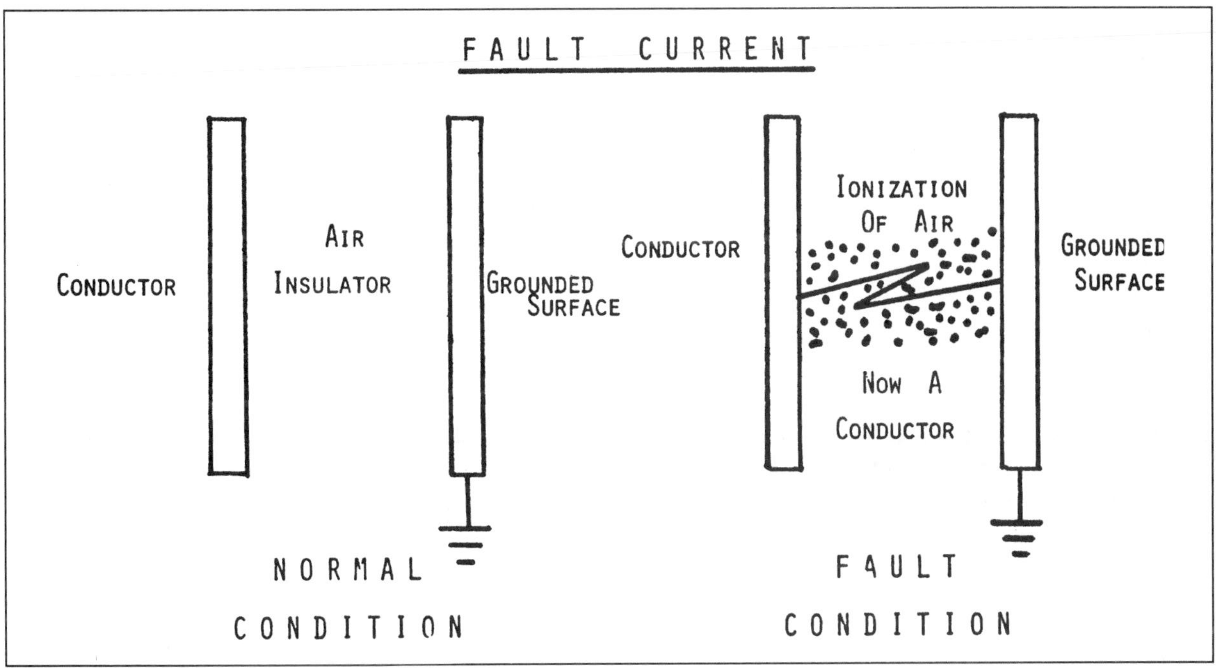

Fig. 4–4 Fault current and ionization.

blowout installed in magnetic switches has a deionizing effect on an electric arc. Deionization equipment is only used with equipment that creates an electric arc under normal operation.

Fault currents cause ionization of the air around the arc and there are no blowout coils or deionization method provided, because there is no telling where a fault will take place in or around electrical equipment.

As some specific fault conditions are illustrated and discussed in this chapter, watch the flow of current in the regular circuit and in the alternate path, the grounding circuit. Most of the figures use two types of diagrams. The wiring diagram shows the point-to-point connections of the circuit and the one-line or schematic diagram shows the scheme of operation. What is happening in each figure can often be seen more quickly, and the current flow followed more easily, on the one-line diagram. In setting up some of these fault situations, we have not taken Code regulations into consideration. However, some of the faults will graphically illustrate why a certain Code regulation exists.

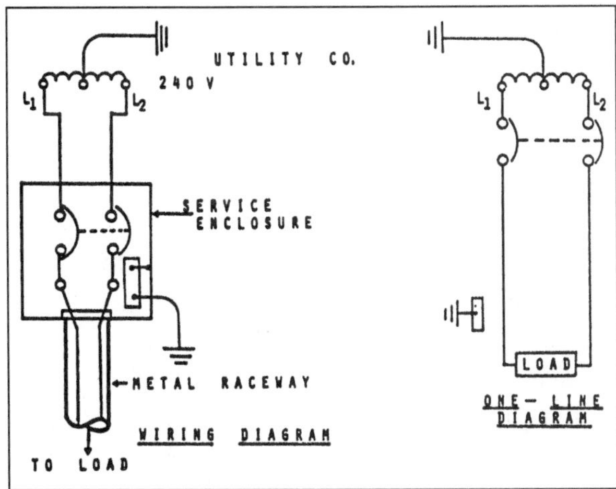

Fig. 4–5 Wiring diagram and a one-line diagram of a two-wire service without grounded conductor brought to service—no-fault situation.

GROUNDED SYSTEM FAULTS

Figure 4–5 illustrates a 240-volt, single-phase service. The utility company has the center tap of the transformer grounded. There is no grounded conductor brought to the service because there is no need for one. The service will serve only 240-volt motor loads. However, note that the grounding electrode conductor and the main bonding jumper are installed to maintain all metal enclosures at ground potential.

When the grounded conductor is not brought to the service, the installation could be made and nothing would show up to indicate anything is

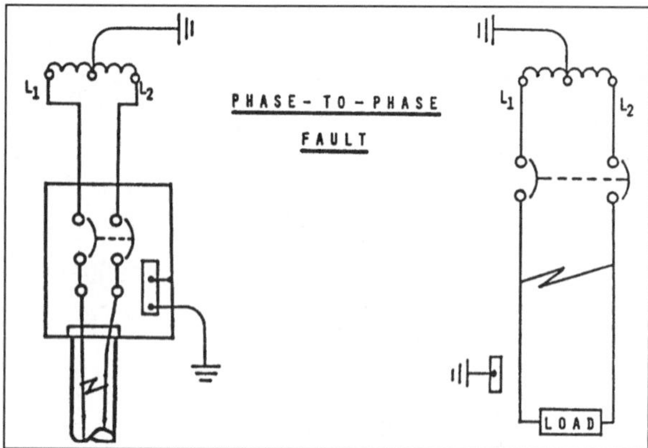

Fig. 4–6 Wiring diagram and one-line diagram of two-wire service without grounded conductor brought to service—direct short—line-to-line fault.

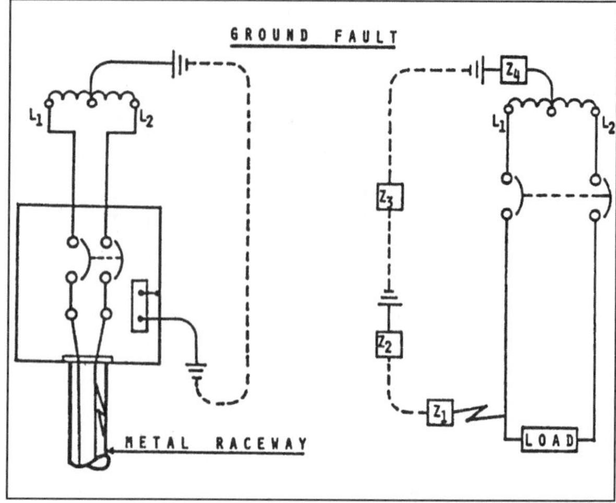

Fig. 4–7 Wiring diagram and one-line diagram—two-wire service—ground fault without grounded conductor brought to service.

wrong. The motors would run fine. The service would perform its function fine. Everything would work great, until a fault occurred.

Figure 4–6 illustrates a direct short, a line-to-line fault. The total fault current has to travel through the circuit breaker, which gives the circuit breaker a chance for quick tripping. In the case of the direct short, the current has only one path to travel, and that includes traveling through the overcurrent protection device. There is a low-impedance path for the current to flow. The low opposition to the flow of current will allow a small circuit breaker, such as a 15- or 20-amp breaker, to trip, eliminating the hazard with little or no damage done. The larger the circuit rating, the greater the current to be interrupted, and the greater the possibility of damage before the overcurrent protective device can operate.

The fault exists only until the overcurrent protective device operates. The aftereffects of the fault may continue, however. For example, a fire would continue to burn once it started.

Figure 4–7 illustrates what happens when there is a phase-to-ground fault. The situation is considerably different here, although the illustration might indicate that there is a fault in the conduit, close to the service. This is for illustration purposes only. In reality, the fault could be in a piece of equipment or any place on the load side of the service equipment.

In this situation, the low-impedance path to the overcurrent protection device is not there. When this type of fault happens, there are a number of oppositions (impedances) to the current flow that must be taken into consideration. Those illustrated in figure 4–7 are:

Z_1 = Impedance of the earth or ground
Z_2 = Impedance of raceway and enclosure path
Z_3 = Impedance of grounding electrode path
Z_4 = Impedance of utility grounding electrode path

Note on the figure how all the impedances are connected in series. The total Z is the total opposition to the flow of current. The higher the Z, the lower the current, the less chance the overcurrent protection device has to clear the fault, and the longer the hazard exists. This fault could exist for a period of time and until enough damage is done to result in a possible phase-to-phase fault.

In this case, the fault current has to travel from the point of the fault, through the metal raceway, then through the metal enclosure of the service to the main bonding jumper, and then to the ground bar. From there it flows on the grounding electrode conductor to the grounding electrode and into the earth, then through the ground to the grounding electrode of the utility company, through the grounding electrode conductor of the utility company, through the transformer to L_2, through the overcurrent protection device, and back to the fault.

Figure 4–8 brings the grounded conductor from the utility transformer to the service equipment, even though it is not needed. This is done according to the Code. Once again everything will work very nicely, until trouble pops up and a fault takes place. Should a line-to-line fault occur, it would be the same as the one illustrated in figure 4–6 (page 34).

Figure 4–9 illustrates a ground fault, with the grounded conductor brought to the service and connected to the ground bus. Now there is another path for the current to flow on, a low-impedance path. It is easy to see in the schematic diagram that two impedances, Z_3 and Z_4, are eliminated. These are the two largest impedances in the previous grounding circuit (figure 4–7). At first it might seem like the impedance is cut in half, but actually it is cut by close to 90 percent.

The question often asked is, "Will there be any current flow through the grounding electrodes and the earth when the grounded conductor is brought to the service?" This is best answered with a question: Is the ground path through the earth a parallel path? The answer is yes. There is current flow in all branches of a parallel circuit; therefore, there will be some current flow through the earth. However, the amount of current that will take the earth ground path is small because of the high impedance.

A very interesting thing takes place here when this ground fault happens. Note how the

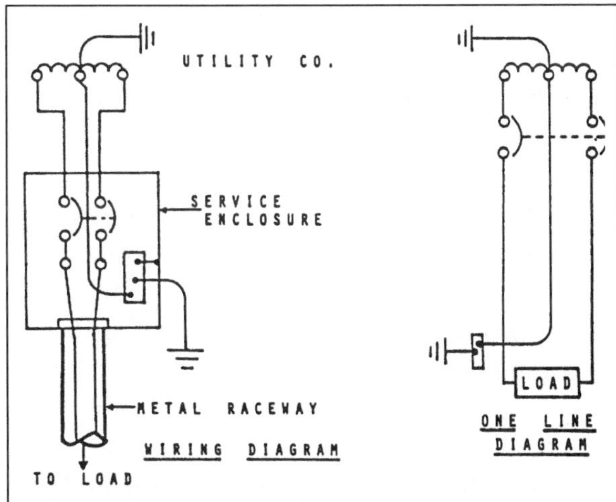

Fig. 4–8 Wiring diagram and one-line diagram—two-wire service—with grounded conductor brought to service with a no-fault situation.

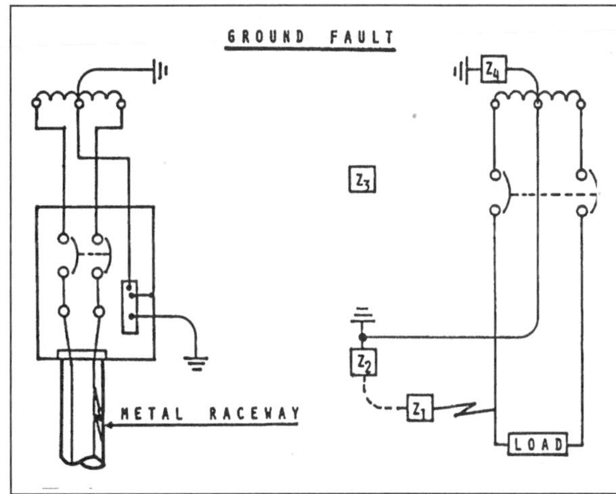

Fig. 4–9 Wiring diagram and one-line diagram—two-wire service with grounded conductor brought to service—ground-fault current flow.

fault current used the grounded conductor to travel back to the transformer. During the fault condition, the "grounded conductor" also became the "equipment grounding conductor." Things can change fast in the grounding circuit.

IMPEDANCE-GROUNDED SYSTEMS

Until now the intention has been to build a circuit that will allow the overcurrent protective device to act automatically by reducing the impedance of the ground fault path to a minimum, thereby limiting the time the fault exists. Now we find that there are situations where the automatic tripping of the device could be more of a disadvantage than an advantage. For example, if a factory is operating on a process control system, and the overcurrent device causes the lines to shut down without notice, the operators could be put in a dangerous situation and/or a considerable amount of damage could occur to equipment and materials.

Impedance grounding is used to solve this problem of automatic tripping. However, the intent is still to get the fault cleared as soon as possible under controlled conditions. Note in figure 4–10 (page 36) how the grounding resistor and its equipment are mounted in an enclosure separate from the service equipment. It could also be mounted within the service enclosure itself.

Impedance grounding is used to limit the fault current and to monitor any ground currents

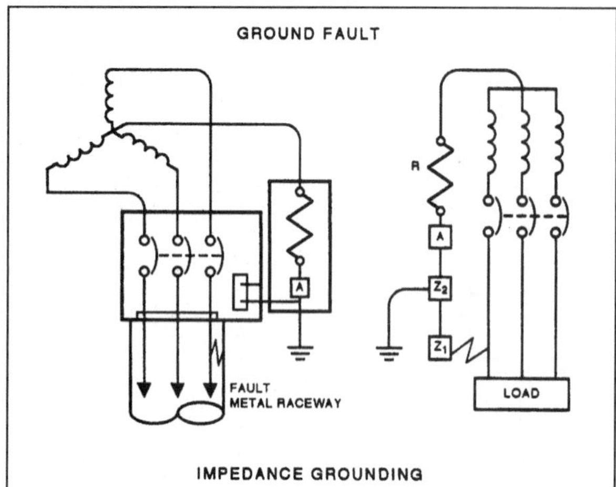

Fig. 4–10 Wiring diagram and one-line diagram—impedance grounding.

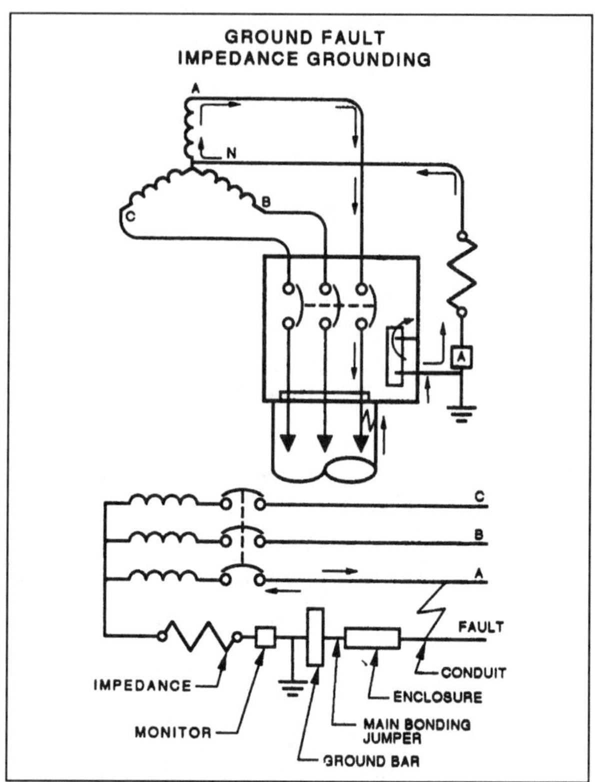

Fig. 4–11 Wiring diagram and one-line diagram—ground-fault impedance grounding.

that might flow. Figure 4–10 illustrates an impedance-grounded system. The illustration uses a resistor, but an impedance coil is also used. The "A" indicates the monitoring equipment used in conjunction with the impedance. The monitoring equipment could be current or voltage-responsive. Current responsive equipment would be connected in series with the impedance. Voltage responsive equipment would be connected in parallel with the impedance. In the illustration, box A is a current-responsive device. Once the current flow through the resistor is greater than the designed current flow, the monitoring equipment will give an audible or visual alarm. When a voltage-responsive device is used, there is a designed voltage drop (I square R) across the impedance. When there is a fault there will be an increase of current flow through the impedance, the I square R drop will increase, and the monitoring equipment operated.

The grounding impedance acts just like any other current-limiting resistor used to limit current flow in a series circuit. The impedance used is a calculated amount of opposition to the flow of current. This is usually limited to a low current, sometimes in the milliamp range. Using a current-limiting resistor limits the fault current. Although an arc is used on the illustration to indicate a fault, there may never be an arc with impedance grounding. The fault may just be an accidental connection to ground that can be corrected before serious damage happens.

Current-limiting resistors are used for starting direct-current or alternating-current motors, for signal or indicating lights, and for other uses. Impedance grounding acts very much in the same way by limiting current flow.

The impedance resistor is connected in series with the grounding electrode conductor, the neutral, the system overcurrent protective device, and the fault. Figure 4–11 illustrates the fault current flow for an impedance-grounded system. A wiring diagram and a simplified one-line diagram are used to illustrate the impedance controlling the current flow in a series circuit.

The flow of current starts at phase A of the transformer, continues to the line side of the overcurrent protective device, goes through the overcurrent protective device, and travels on the feeder to the fault. After traveling through the fault, it goes to the steel raceway, through the steel raceway to the metal enclosure, through the main bonding jumper to the ground bar, and then through the equipment grounding conductor to the grounding resistor and monitoring equipment. From there, the current goes through the grounding

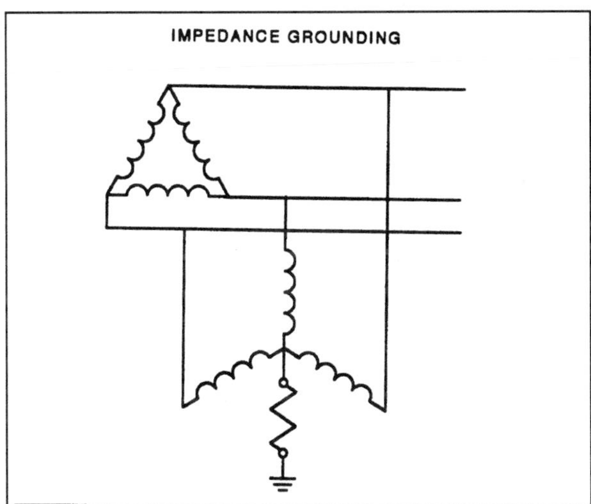

Fig. 4–12 Delta connected system with a wye-connected transformer for impedance grounding.

impedance, through the neutral to the wye point of the transformer, and through the transformer to phase A, which completes the series circuit.

Section 250-5, Exception No. 5, permits high-impedance grounding where continuity of service is required for three-phase 480- to 1000-volt systems with some other specific requirements. *Section 250-154(a)* requires the use of impedance grounding as one method of grounding systems supplying equipment operating at more than 600 volts. Detailed rules for the installation of impedance grounding are covered in Chapter 7, Circuit and System Grounding.

Figure 4–12 illustrates the use of a wye-connected transformer to accomplish the impedance grounding for a delta connected system. The connection could be used on a 480-volt delta system or a high-voltage system.

UNGROUNDED SYSTEM FAULTS

Figure 4–13 illustrates what might be considered a three-phase, 480-volt or three-phase, 240-volt, three-wire system. There is no established ground at the utility transformer. There is a grounding electrode conductor and a grounding electrode system installed with the service, basically to maintain all metal enclosures at zero or ground potential.

This is a popular installation where only power is needed. Even though there is no grounded conductor, the Code still requires establishing a grounding electrode system and installing an equipment grounding system.

When there is a phase-to-phase fault, the overcurrent protective device reacts very quickly, because there is a low impedance path for the current to flow on. When a ground fault happens, the result is completely different. When this type of fault occurs, for example on phase A as shown in figure 4–14, nothing that can be readily seen happens. There is no current flow path directing the current back through the overcurrent protective device, which would activate the device. There is no complete circuit for the fault current to flow on, so nothing happens and a hazard is created. There must be a second ground, on a different phase, before there is a complete circuit for the current to flow on and cause the overcurrent protection device to operate.

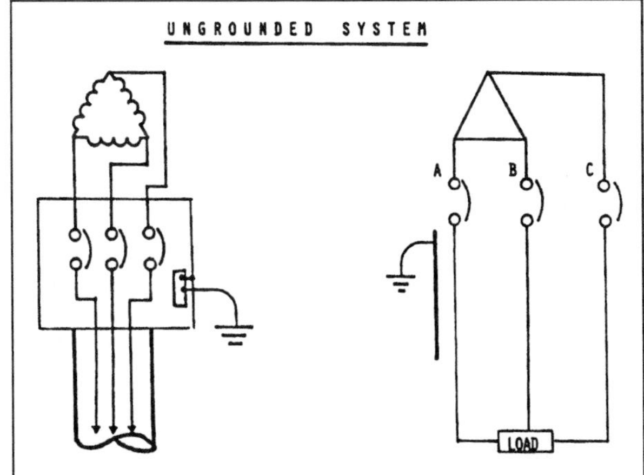

Fig. 4–13 Ungrounded system—Three-phase, three-wire delta—no-fault situation.

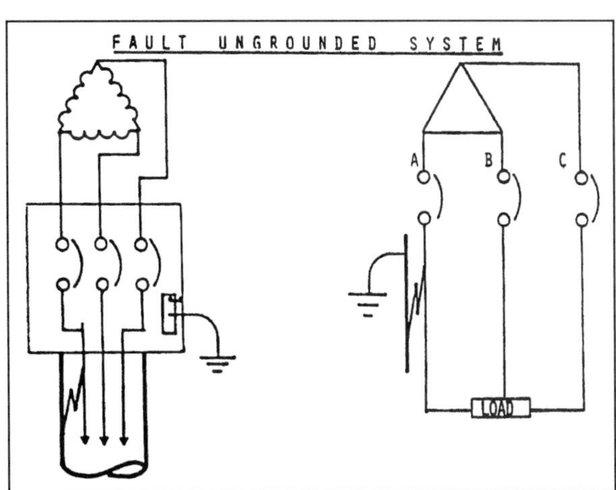

Fig. 4-14 Ungrounded system—three-phase, three-wire delta with first ground fault.

There are some unseen and dangerous things that have taken place. Remember, the enclosure has been grounded to keep it at ground potential. The enclosures are now at the same potential as phase A, and phase A is now at ground potential. This means that a voltage now exists between phase B and any enclosure and phase C and any enclosure. Because a grounding electrode system has been established and an equipment grounding system has been installed, voltage to ground and the voltage between phases are the same.

For example, consider the system to be a three-phase, 480-volt, three-wire delta system, with a ground fault on phase A, as illustrated in figure 4–14. The following voltages would then exist. All phase-to-phase voltages will still be 480 volts.

Phase A to ground	zero volts
Phase B to ground	480 volts
Phase C to ground	480 volts

Figure 4–15 illustrates what happens when a second ground fault appears on phase C. Now there is a complete path for the current to flow on. Starting at the source of supply through phase A, the current flows through the overcurrent protective device to the fault, from the fault to ground, through the ground to the ground of phase C, through phase C, through the overcurrent protective device, and back to the source of supply. Now that the second fault has taken place, the overcurrent protective device has a chance to operate.

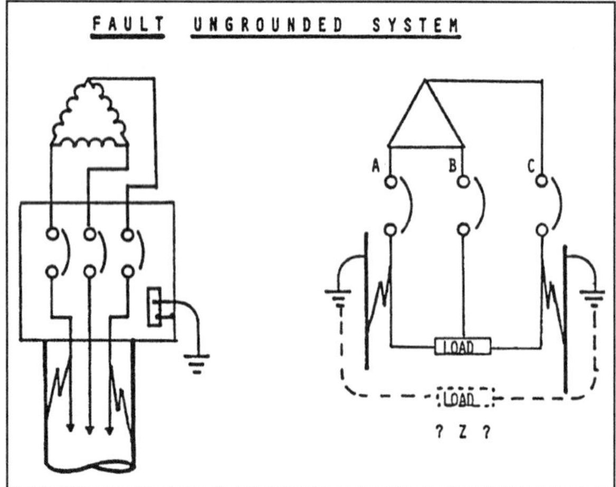

Fig. 4–15 Ungrounded system—three-wire delta with second ground fault.

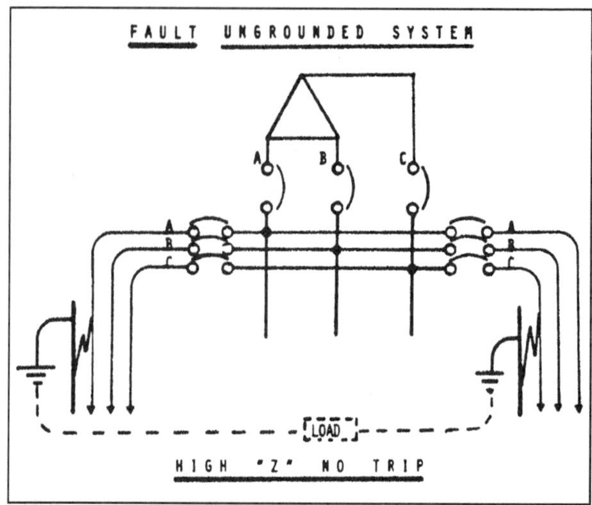

Fig. 4–16 Ungrounded system—high-impedance fault, no trip.

Whether or not it will operate depends on the impedance of the circuit through the ground path. If the impedance is low, the device will operate nearly as quickly as it would in a direct-short situation. If the impedance is high, the overcurrent protective device will look at it; treat it as if it were just a single-phase, phantom load in the overall circuit; and not operate. It is called a phantom load because there is really no load connected. It appears as a load because the ground path is a completed circuit with high impedance; a small current will flow, but not enough to cause the protective device to operate. Depending on the size of the regular connected load, the overcurrent protective device will read the phantom load as just more load and furnish current to it accordingly until the current that is demanded exceeds the rating of the overcurrent device. More often than not, the impedance of the second ground is low enough to cause the overcurrent protective device to operate.

Figure 4–16 illustrates a three-phase, three-wire system with a ground fault on both phase A and phase C. There is a lot of distance in the ground path from the fault on phase A to the fault on phase C, and under these conditions it is likely that the overcurrent protective device will not operate.

GROUND FAULT DETECTORS

The Code does not make recommendations, but gives information in FPN that is often taken as recommendations or suggestions. The FPN following *Section 250-5(b)(4)* recommends that ground detectors be used with ungrounded systems because they provide additional protection.

Figure 4–17 illustrates the use of lights as ground fault detectors. Each phase conductor is connected through a lamp to a wye connection and then grounded. This really establishes a ground so that when a phase goes to ground, creating a ground fault, it completes a circuit to the grounded part of the wye at the lamps. This provides a circuit through the lamp and the lamp lights up, which indicates there is a ground fault and something should be done to clear it. Ground detector systems are often used in conjunction with any three-phase, three-wire ungrounded system.

Another alternative to the ground detector lights is to ground one of the three phases at the source of supply, so that the first ground is established. When the second ground takes place, it is hoped that the overcurrent protective devices will operate.

Another system being used with ungrounded systems is the zig-zag transformation connection. This system adds protection against arching ground faults. The zig-zag connection is illustrated in Chapter 15 of this text.

Grounding does not keep faults from happening. Proper grounding, however, works to create a low-impedance path for current flow and to limit the time that the hazard caused by the fault will exist.

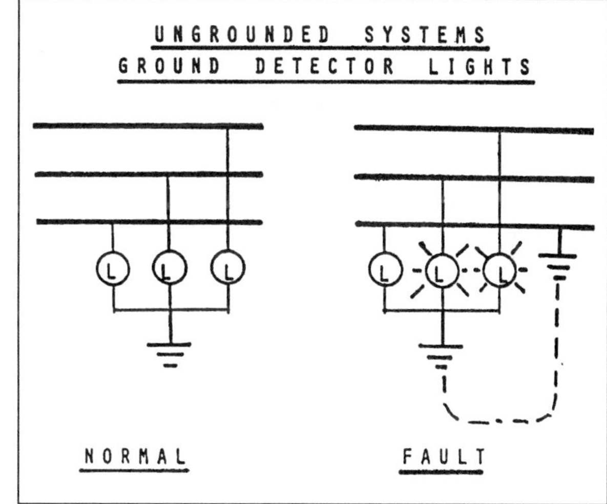

Fig. 4–17 Ungrounded system—ground detector lights.

FOLLOW UP

Topics for self-study, discussion, or questioning.

1. Discuss the difference between a direct short and a ground fault.
2. What is meant by the term *ionization*?
3. Discuss the various stresses caused by electrical faults.
4. Discuss the impedance of the ground path with and without the installation of a grounded conductor.
5. Draw a diagram of a solidly grounded single-phase system.
6. Draw a diagram of a solidly grounded three-phase, wye connected system.
7. Draw a diagram of an impedance grounded three-phase, wye connected system.
8. Explain the hazard that will exist when a ground fault takes place on one phase of a three-phase, ungrounded system.
9. Explain what is recommended for safety when an ungrounded, three-phase, delta connected system is installed.
10. Discuss how ground fault detectors are used.
11. Discuss the advantage of interrupting the fault current as soon as possible.

CHAPTER 5

Grounding Electrode System

OBJECTIVES

After completing this chapter, the student should be able to:

- define an electrode.
- explain what a grounding electrode system is.
- explain the purpose of the grounding electrode system.
- explain how electrons are conducted into the earth via the grounding electrode system.
- explain the requirements and use of a metal water pipe when used as the grounding electrode.
- identify what can and cannot be used as a made electrode.
- locate the requirements for the various types of ground rods in Part H of *Article 250*.
- locate the requirements for the concrete-encased electrode in Part H of *Article 250*.
- explain what an electrolytic ground rod is.
- discuss how the resistance to ground of a ground rod is measured.
- explain the necessity of bonding all grounding electrodes together, when more than one is installed for a single building.
- explain the connections to the grounding electrode, when more than one service is installed to the same building.

This chapter focuses on the grounding electrode system (figure 5–1, page 41). We will look at some grounding theory, types, and specifications for installing grounding electrodes and grounding electrode systems.

GROUNDING THEORY

The term *electrode* means "a way in or a way out for electricity." This term is used to identify the terminals of a battery that indicate the path for electricity to travel in and out of the battery. That electricity is made up of the electrons moving in and out of the battery.

The grounding electrode of an electrical installation is the way into the earth for the electrons. Therefore, installing a grounding electrode in the earth means installing an electrical terminal to help the electrons travel into the earth.

The 1978 Code changed the title of Part H of *Article 250* from "*Grounding Electrode*" to "*Grounding Electrode System,*" a major change that resulted in many changes to Part H. Prior to

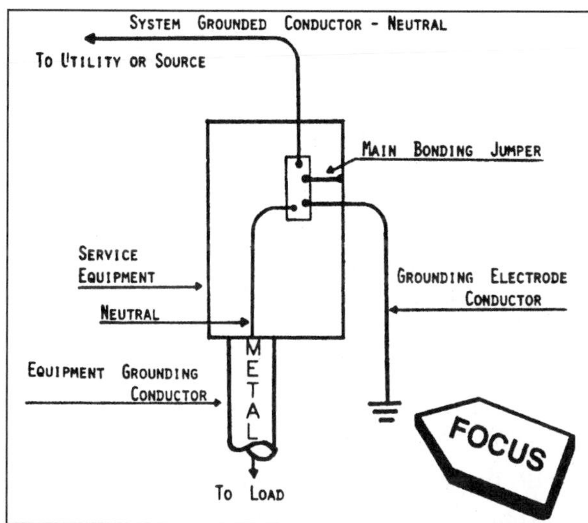

Fig. 5–1 Focusing on the grounding electrode system.

that time it was known as the "grounding electrode," and one grounding electrode was sufficient. The change from a single grounding electrode to a grounding electrode system has been accepted in some localities, and in some areas it's still just a grounding electrode.

The reason for the change to the grounding system was the increased use of plastic piping. Before plastic water pipe came along, the steel or copper water pipe that was used was always looked upon as a very good grounding electrode, because there was a lot of metal in direct contact with the earth for good dissipation of electrons.

RESPONSIBILITY OF THE GROUNDING ELECTRODE

Just the term *grounding electrode* seems to trigger thoughts of either a driven ground rod or a water pipe buried in the ground. That might be good enough to start out with, but later in this chapter we will look at various other grounding electrodes.

A grounding electrode system can consist of one or more grounding electrodes with specific purposes or responsibilities as part of that system. The grounding electrode's responsibilities are:

1. To maintain good contact with the earth so that all noncurrent-carrying metal parts of the electrical installation, connected to the grounding system, are maintained at ground or zero potential.
2. To provide many paths into the earth for a large number of electrons in a very high current flow caused by lightning or line surges to be dissipated into the earth as quickly as possible.
3. To drain leakage and/or static currents, which can be generated or accumulated in or on the system equipment enclosures, into the ground.

One responsibility that is often wrongfully assigned to the grounding electrode is to carry the current to operate the overcurrent protection device. That is not a responsibility of the grounding electrode.

Reason: The ground path through the grounding electrode to the circuit overcurrent device is a very high impedance path. It will not allow nearly enough current flow for the operation of the overcurrent protective device.

Responsibility number one of the grounding electrode is to maintain zero potential between ground and the noncurrent-carrying metal parts of electrical equipment and enclosures. This can be accomplished by having an effectively grounded system, with special care given to maintaining continuity of the system's equipment grounding conductors. Bonding all grounding electrodes together is an important step in maintaining a zero potential.

How does the grounding electrode system accomplish its second and third responsibilities?

It does so by giving the electrons as many "low"-opposition paths into the earth as possible. How well the grounding electrode carries out these responsibilities might well depend on the earth surrounding it.

Old Mother Earth

Lots of variables come into play here, including the type of earth and the surface-to-surface contact between the grounding electrode and the earth. Figure 5–2 (page 42) lists some interesting facts concerning "Old Mother Earth."

Earth is considered to be zero potential; therefore, the Code requires all noncurrent-

SOME DOWN-TO-EARTH
FACTS ABOUT OLD MOTHER
EARTH

EARTH IS ZERO POTENTIAL.

EARTH IS A CONDUCTOR.
NOT THE BEST, BUT NEVERTHELESS A GOOD ONE.

EARTH IS A VERY LARGE CONDUCTOR.
CONDUCTOR LENGTH – VERY LONG
CONDUCTOR CROSS-SECTIONAL AREA – VERY WIDE

EARTH'S CONDUCTIVITY VARIES WITH
TYPE OF SOIL
TEMPERATURE AND TIME OF YEAR
MOISTURE CONTENT
BURIED TRASH
INSULATING OR CONDUCTING MATERIALS

EARTH IS GROUND – GROUND IS EARTH.

Fig. 5–2 Some facts about Old Mother Earth.

carrying metal parts of electrical equipment to be maintained at zero or ground potential. Earth is a conductor of electricity, although not the best by any means. The larger the cross-sectional area of a conductor, the more current it can carry. As a conductor, the earth offers a very large cross-sectional area for current flow.

The *conductivity* (the ease with which a material conducts electrons) of the earth varies with the type of soil or chemical makeup of the soil. Sandy soil is not as good a conductor as black dirt. The higher the moisture content of the soil, the better conductor it is; the lower the moisture, the poorer conductor the soil is. Areas that are very arid may be required by local ordinance to supply moisture or to provide some means of making the ground area more conductive at the point the electrons are trying to get into the earth. The conductivity of the earth around a grounding electrode can vary with both the season of the year and the temperature.

The opposite of conductivity is *resistivity* or the resistance offered by the earth. Salt water decreases resistivity and increases conductivity. When the term *resistance to earth* is used, it has the same meaning as resistivity.

Just as with electrical conductors, the greater the diameter, the greater the cross-sectional area and the less the resistivity will be. The larger the diameter of a ground rod of the same material, the less resistivity.

With the amount of fill work being done today to reclaim land for more buildings, there is growing concern for the content of the material used to fill the ground. Glass, plastic, and similar items are not good conducting materials.

The earth can be looked at as one gigantic storage tank for electrons, just as the ocean can be looked at as one gigantic storage tank for little drops of water. The accumulation of a large number of little drops of rain can become a very powerful current of water. This current of water will do its best to work its way to the ocean and into that gigantic storage tank for droplets of water. People may divert, control, and make use of the water, for example, by building dams and dikes to control the flow of water to the ocean. But whenever given the opportunity, the water will try to get to the ocean.

Electrons are very small, but as they accumulate they can become a very powerful current as they do their best to work their way into the earth. Man may divert, control, and make use of the electron flow by installing conductors and insulators. But give the electrons the opportunity and they will get into the earth.

Helping Electrons into the Earth

Grounding can be looked at as a system of conductors furnishing a controlled path for the electrons into the earth. The electrons taking this path could come from static electricity, leakage currents, lightning, surge currents, or fault currents.

Normally when the word *ground* is used, it means earth. When the word *earth* is used, it means ground. The terms are interchangeable. Some foreign countries, such as England, today use the word *earth* and not the word *ground*. However, occasionally something other than earth is used to serve in the place of earth, such as the frame of a portable generator, as indicated in *Section 250-6(a)*.

When lightning strikes or there is a line surge of current, there are a tremendous number of electrons looking for a way into the earth. The lower the impedance or opposition paths given to the electrons to get into the earth, the quicker they will be dissipated and the less damage will be done elsewhere.

A bolt of lightning is ionized air carrying electrons toward the earth. Dry air is an insulator, but ionized air is an electrical conductor. The electrons are being pressured to travel toward earth by a very high voltage of thousands of volts and a current flow in the thousands-of-amps range. This means that a tremendous number of electrons are trying to get into the earth, almost all at the same time. This could be compared to a wall of water coming down a raging river as it races to the ocean.

The grounding electrode will try its best to give these electrons as many paths into the earth as possible. There are many suggestions on how to help the electrode accomplish its job, as well as several analogies as to how the electrode conducts the electrons into the earth.

Lightning does not have to make a direct hit on a service drop or on utility company conductors to cause problems. Lightning striking near transmission lines will cause a tremendous magnetic field and will induce a very high current in nearby conductors, resulting in large line-current surges. An improperly installed grounding electrode system may appear to be operating satisfactorily until lightning strikes or there is a heavy line surge of electrons.

THE GROUND ROD

Section 250-83(c) sets the minimum length of a copper ground rod at 8 feet, with a minimum diameter of 1/2 inch. This gives about 150 square inches of surface area for contact with the earth.

Rod electrodes of iron or steel are required to be a minimum of 5/8 inch in diameter. Iron and steel are ferrous metals. A ferrous metal contains iron and is a magnetic material. A nonferrous material does not contain iron and is nonmagnetic. Copper is a nonferrous material. A nonferrous rod electrode is permitted to be as small as 1/2 inch in diameter. Nonferrous materials are better electrical conductors than ferrous materials.

Are there any advantages to be gained by increasing either of these measurements? The answer is yes.

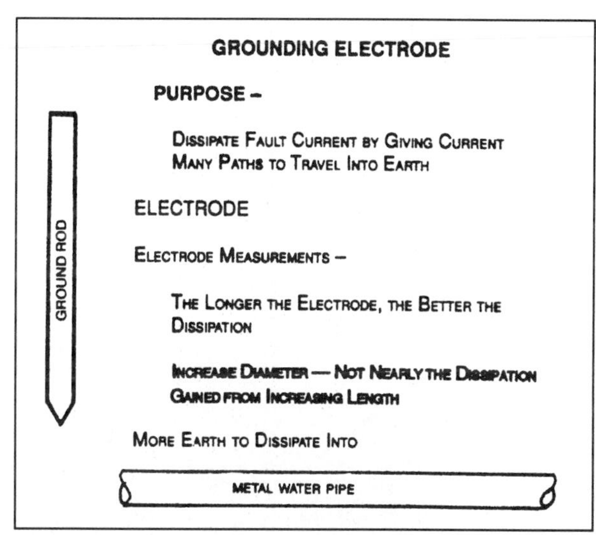

Fig. 5–3 Purpose and length of the grounding electrode.

Experimentation has proven that an increase in length (figure 5–3) has a greater value than an increase in diameter, although the surface area of earth contact might be the same. The longer the ground rod, the easier it is for it to conduct or spill the electrons into the earth.

Figure 5–4 (page 44) illustrates one theory of the ground rod and the resistance around it. There are three main points of resistance to be considered. These are:

1. Resistance of the ground rod material and the connection to the ground rod
2. Contact resistance between the ground rod and the earth
3. Resistance of the surrounding earth

The resistance of the material is usually not very great and is really negligible, because the mass of material used is usually sufficient to conduct the electrons into the earth.

When the ground rod is kept free of grease, paint, or other nonconductive materials, as required by *Sections 250-83* and *250-118*, and the earth is packed firmly against the ground rod, the contact resistance is rather low. Compare the contact surface between the grounding electrode and the earth to that between two bus bars being spliced together. The optimum situation is to have full surface-to-surface contact between the two bus bars. The better the joint, the less resis-

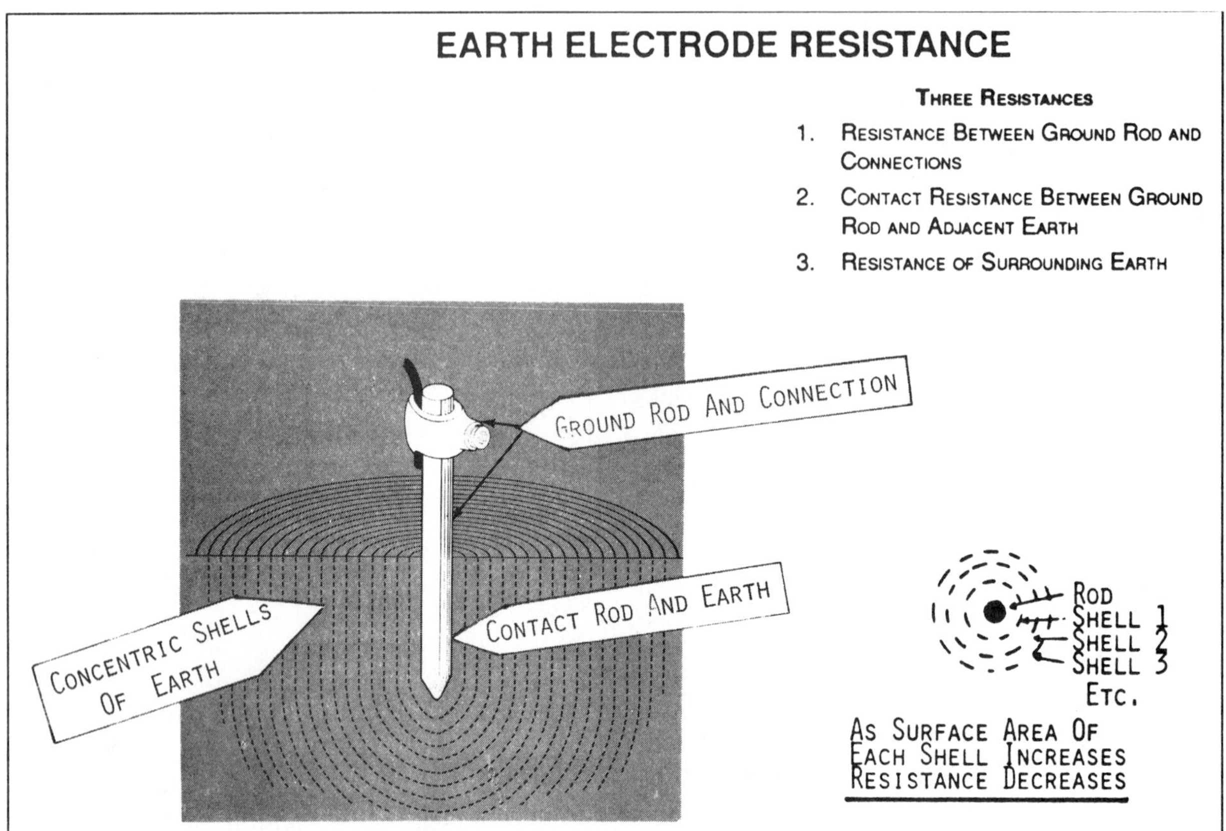

Fig. 5–4 The ground rod and earth electrode resistance. Earth shells are formed around the electrode. Courtesy FL Blackburn.

tance there will be to the flow of electrons. The more surface-to-surface contact the grounding electrode makes with the earth, the less resistance and the better the conductance (the ability to conduct current).

The resistance of the earth can be visualized by thinking of the ground rod as surrounded by shells of earth. Figure 5–4 shows a ground rod with shells of earth around it. Each shell wraps earth around the ground rod. The shell closest to the ground rod has the smallest surface area and the highest resistance.

Just as the length of tape required to wrap a connection increases with each lap, the size of the shell of earth wrapped around the ground rod increases with each shell that is added. As the surface area of each shell increases, the cross-sectional area of the conducting earth covered by each shell increases and there are now more paths for the electrons to travel. Therefore, there is a decrease in opposition to the current flow. The farther and farther away from the electrode the electrons travel, the more paths there are for the electrons to travel on and the lower the resistance (figure 5–5).

This example can be compared to an electrical conductor. The greater the cross-sectional area of the conductor, the lower the resistance of

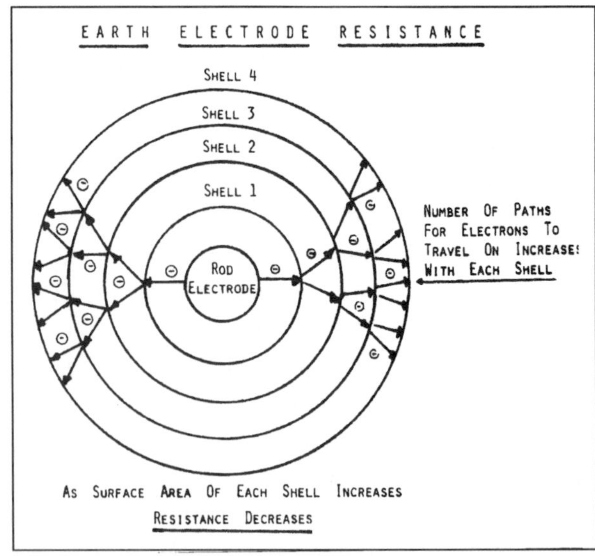

Fig. 5–5 The shells form an increasing number of paths and decrease resistance to the flow of current.

the conductor. Using the theory of the shells around the grounding electrode also helps to illustrate how a longer ground rod would disperse the electrons into the earth, through the shells around the electrode, quicker than a shorter one.

Figure 5–5 shows a grounding electrode surrounded by the same type of earth in all directions. The first shell shows only one path for the electrons to flow on from the grounding electrode. Each shell thereafter doubles the number of paths for the electrons, until in the fourth shell there are eight times as many parallel paths as there were in the first shell for the electrons to flow on and be dispersed into the earth. Eight parallel paths also offer considerably less opposition to the flow of electrons than one path.

Doubling the number of paths in each shell, as shown in this figure, is only an illustration. In reality, the number of paths would be increased many more times, rather than just doubled.

The grounding electrode might be compared to a sprinkler system spewing water out through many little holes or paths into the air. The electrode has an almost unlimited number of potential paths or spray points for the electrons to leave it and enter the earth, as long as the grounding electrode is in good contact with the earth.

Figure 5–6 is a vertical and horizontal view of an electrode. It illustrates this spraying effect or the many paths the electrons have for leaving

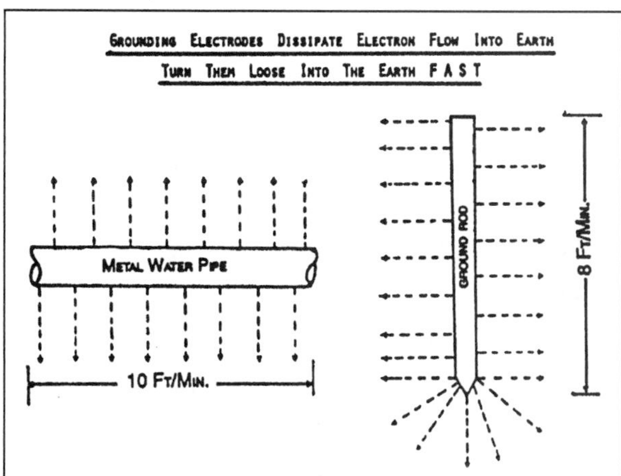

Fig. 5–6 A water pipe and a ground rod used as grounding electrodes to dissipate electrons into the earth.

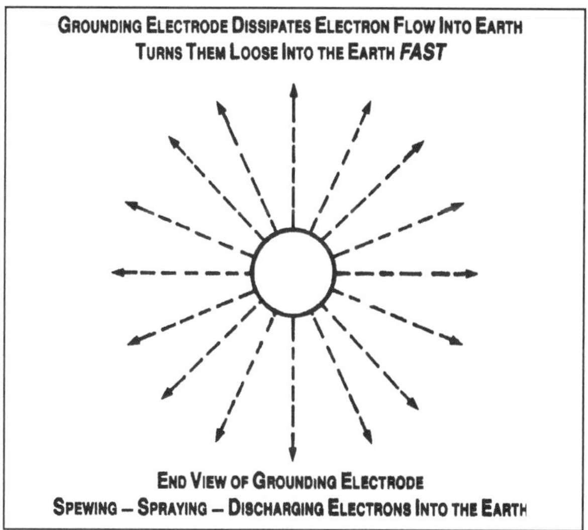

Fig. 5–7 Cross-sectional view of an electrode discharging electrons into the earth.

the grounding electrode and entering the earth. Figure 5–7 gives a cross-sectional view of the same thing. Imagine that this illustration is one electron thick, then stack up enough to make an 8-foot ground rod; there will be a lot of potential paths for electrons to enter the earth.

The grounding electrode has also been compared to the roots of a tree (figure 5–8, page 46), with the branches being the distribution system of the electrical installation. The root system plays a very important part in the life of the tree, just as the grounding electrode plays a very important part in the electrical protection system.

The grounding electrode can be even better compared to a tree with a tap root, such as a pecan tree (figure 5–9, page 46). The tap root is the long center root of the tree, and the life of the tree depends on the tap root. By cutting off the tree's tap root, its life is endangered. Likewise, cutting off an 8-foot ground rod at 4 feet or 2 feet is like cutting off the tap root of the electrical system. The people using the electrical equipment, thinking the electrical distribution system is properly grounded, can be put in some real hazardous situations.

When the grounding electrode is not in good contact with the earth, the contact between the two acts as a high-resistance joint and will heat, just as any other high-resistance joint will do. In areas where the earth is composed of sand, the heat generated by the electrons trying to

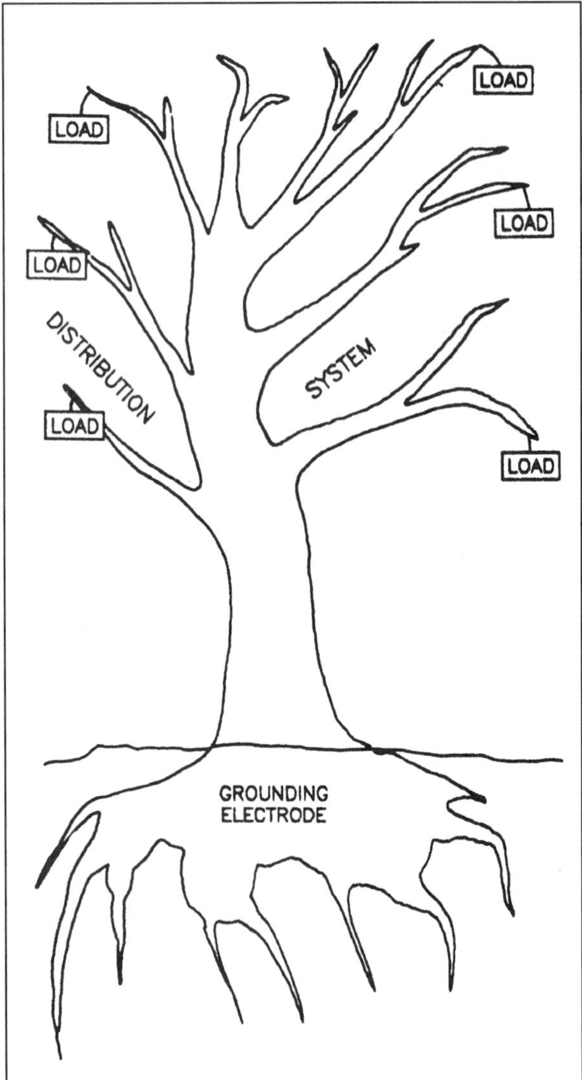

Fig. 5–8 Comparison of a grounding electrode to a tree. The branches of the tree are the distribution system and the root is the grounding electrode.

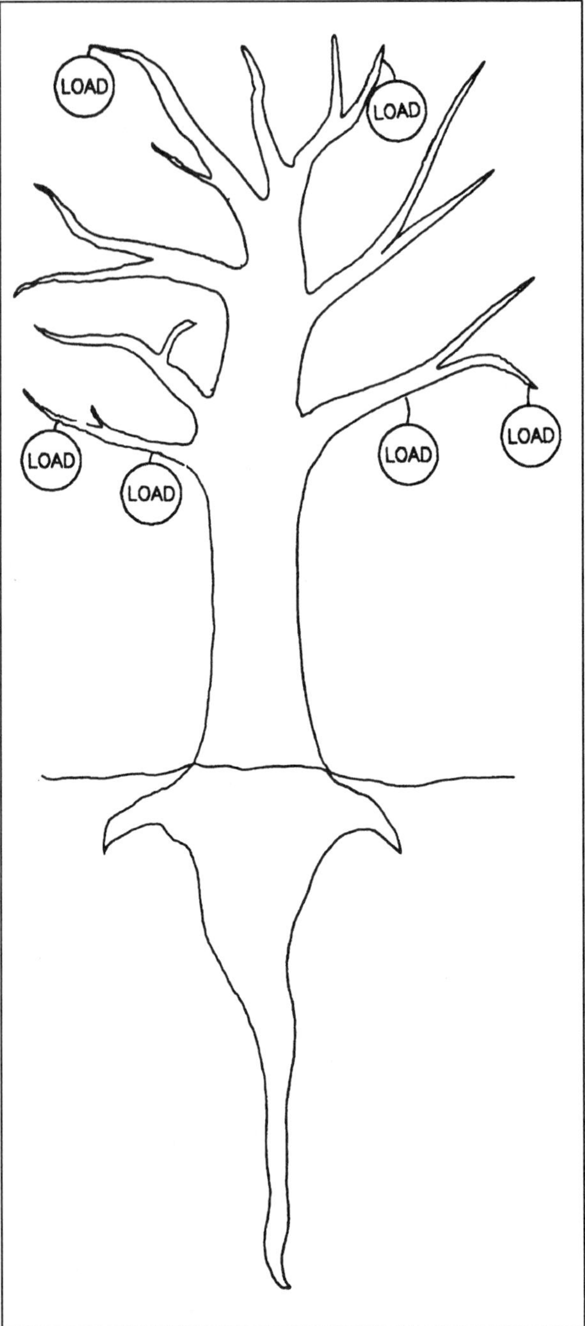

Fig. 5–9 Comparison of a grounding electrode to the tap root of a tree.

enter the earth has been known to be of sufficient temperature to crystallize the sand surrounding an electrode into glass.

Although there are numerous paths by which the electrons can enter the earth from the grounding electrode, most of the electrons will leave via the bottom of the electrode. High voltages and lightning prefer to travel in a straight line. Sometimes when there is a lot of high-voltage pressure behind an electron and it comes to a corner, it doesn't quite make the turn and damage results. High-voltage surges make a straight-line dive toward the bottom of the grounding electrode.

Grounding Electrodes Bonded Together

Part H of *Article 250* is directed at the grounding electrode system. *Section 250-81* starts with the word *if*. If available, all of the following shall be bonded together:

1. Metal underground water pipe
2. Metal frame of the building

3. Concrete-encased electrode
4. Ground ring
5. Any made electrodes

The section states "if available" (there is that big word *if*); if they are all not available, don't worry about it. The word "available" as used by the Code has a general meaning. If any of the electrodes are present or installed as the building is being built, they are considered available. Figure 5–10 illustrates all of the four potential grounding electrodes bonded together, as required when all are available. The sequence of bonding is for illustration only. The actual bonding connections will vary with the electrodes available.

Reason: When there are several separate effectively grounded electrodes on the same premises, there will be a potential difference between any two of them. When all the grounding electrodes are connected together, it results in a zero potential to ground on all systems.

METAL WATER PIPE ELECTRODE

The bonding together of existing electrodes is very often overlooked, for example, making sure the metal water piping is bonded to the effectively grounded building steel, other than through ground. When a grounding electrode is installed for computer grounding, it shall be bonded to the existing grounding electrodes. When a separate ground rod is driven for cable television, it shall be bonded to all other existing grounding electrodes.

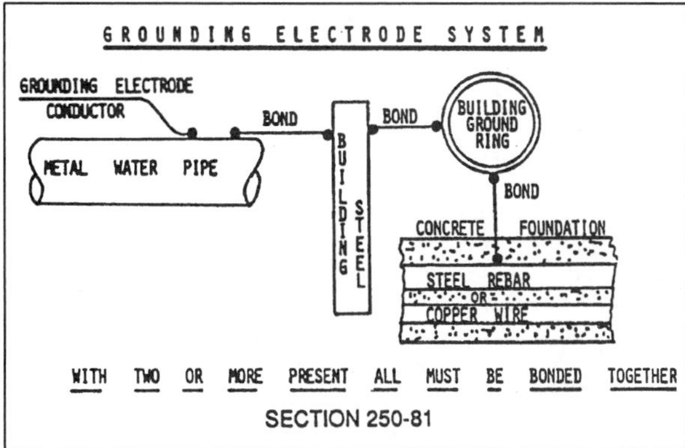

Fig. 5–10 The grounding electrode system bonding, as specified in *Section 250-81*.

The following is a general outline of *Section 250-81(a)*, because it contains a lot of specific information.

Section 250-81(a), Metal Underground Water Pipe

1. Shall be metal.
2. Shall be underground in direct contact with the earth.
3. Shall be 10 feet or more in length (including well casing effectively bonded to the pipe).
4. Shall be electrically continuous (bonding around insulated joints or sections permitted to secure continuity).
5. Shall not rely on water meters, filtering devices, or similar equipment for electrical continuity of grounding path.
6. Shall not rely on water meters, filtering devices, and similar equipment for bonding connection to interior metal water piping.
7. Metal water pipe shall be supplemented by an additional electrode as listed in the Code.
8. The supplemental electrode is permitted to be bonded to the grounding electrode conductor, the grounded service conductor, the grounded service raceway, or the grounded service enclosure.

Figure 5–11 (page 48) illustrates points 3 and 4 that are required for the underground water pipe to be used for a grounding electrode. Note the jumper around the insulated coupling to maintain 10 feet of required continuity of the grounding electrode. These bonding jumpers are also required by *Section 250-112*. *Section 250-112* further requires the bonding jumper around the meter filtering devices, and similar equipment to be of sufficient length to allow removal of the meter filtering devices, and similar equipment. The same holds true for bonding around insulated joints as illustrated in figure 5–11 (page 48).

Figure 5–12 (page 48) illustrates that with 10 feet or more of metal water pipe underground between the water meter and the premises wiring, no bonding jumper is required

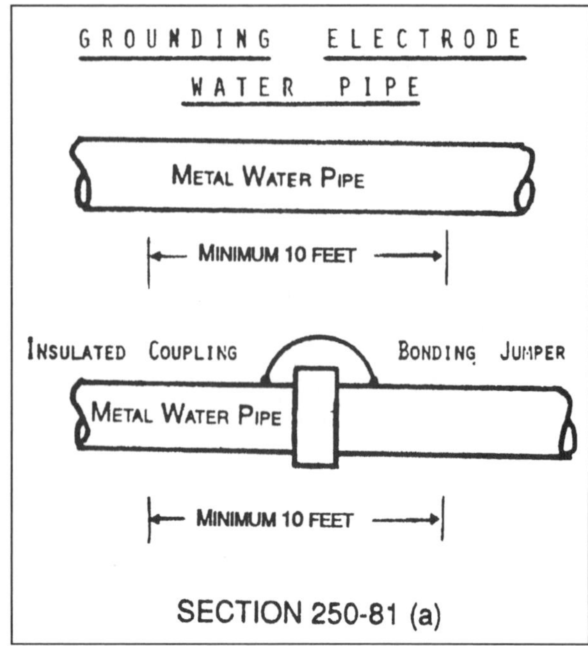

Fig. 5–11 Requirements for a grounding electrode water pipe.

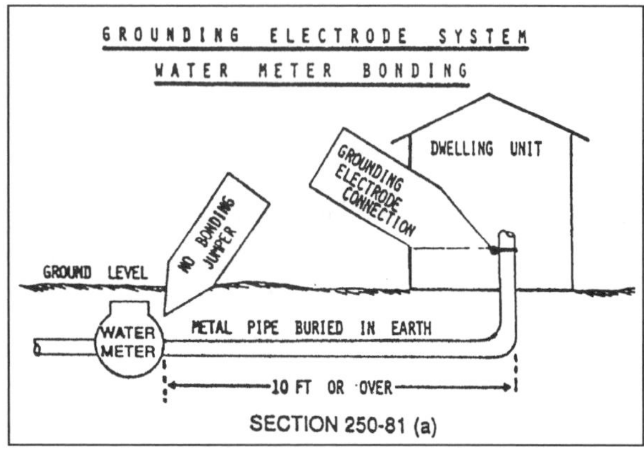

Fig. 5–12 Requirements for a grounding electrode system with a water meter.

around the water meter. This situation is found where the water meter is located outside near the property line.

Figure 5–13 shows a different situation. Now the water meter filtering devices, and similar equipment are installed inside the building and the 10 feet of water pipe in contact with the earth is outside the building. If the water meter filtering devices, and similar equipment are removed for any reason, the continuity of the grounding electrode would be broken. Therefore, *Section 250-81(a)* requires that a bonding

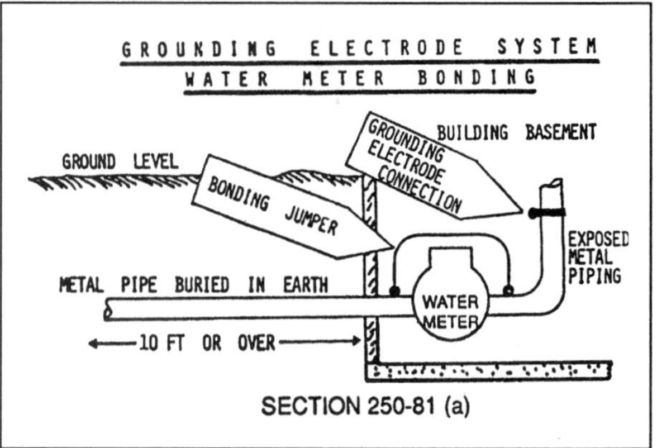

Fig. 5–13 A grounding electrode system with a water meter installed inside a building. Requirements for bonding.

jumper be installed around the water meter filtering devices, and similar equipment.

Figure 5–14 illustrates a grounding electrode system consisting of a water pipe as the primary grounding electrode and a ground rod as the supplemental grounding electrode.

Reason: The thought here is that the metal water pipe can no longer be trusted to remain as a grounding electrode throughout the life of the installation. It is too easy to take out a section of metal water pipe and replace it with a section of plastic pipe, thereby destroying the electrical continuity of the grounding electrode or the path to the grounding electrode.

However, when the underground metal water piping is present, it shall be used as a grounding electrode and shall be supplemented

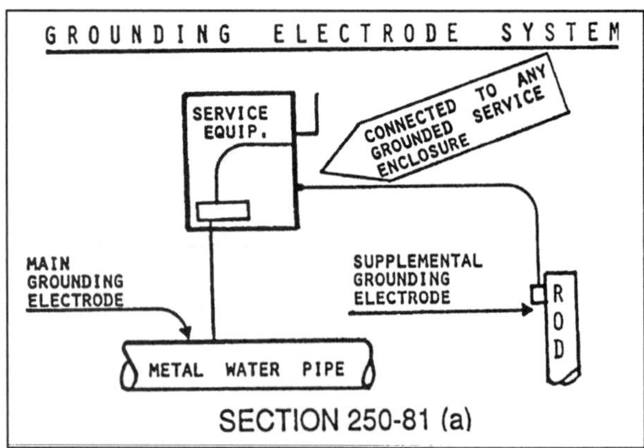

Fig. 5–14 A grounding electrode system using a water pipe and a ground rod.

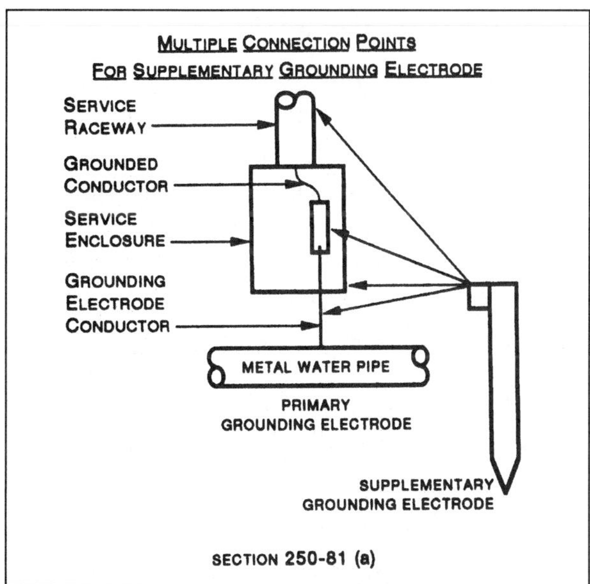

Fig. 5–15 The multitude of connections allowed for a supplemental grounding electrode.

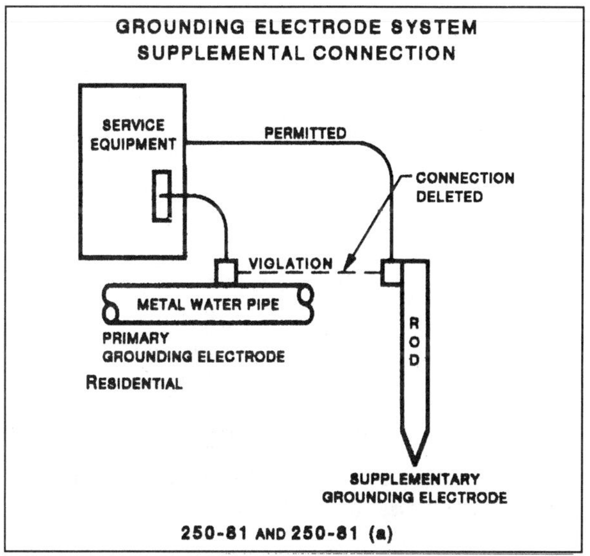

Fig. 5–16 Violation for connecting the supplemental grounding electrode conductor, and proper connection.

by another grounding electrode. Figure 5–15 illustrates a multitude of connection points permitted for the secondary grounding electrode.

Section 250-81(a) permits the supplemental grounding electrode to be connected to the:

a. grounding electrode conductor
b. grounded service entrance conductor
c. grounded service raceway
d. any grounded service enclosure

It is not permitted to be connected to the interior metal water piping system.

The interior metal water piping within a building is not to be used as a grounding conductor, per *Section 250-81(a)*. Therefore, the supplemental grounding electrode is not permitted to use the interior metal water piping as a grounding conductor to connect to the primary grounding electrode. The possibility of the insertion of a nonmetallic section of water piping destroys the continuity of the water piping as a conductor. The illustrated connection often is used for residential installations. The proper residential installation is to install the supplemental grounding electrode, as indicated in figure 5–16. The first five feet of metal water piping entering the building are not considered inside the building. The supplemental grounding electrode conductor is not to be connected to the water pipe at any location, except the first five feet that enter the building. The reason is to eliminate the use of the metal water pipe as a bonding jumper or equipment grounding conductor at any time.

BUILDING STEEL AS AN ELECTRODE

The Code recognizes effectively grounded building steel as a grounding electrode. When a metal water pipe is the primary grounding electrode, the effectively grounded building steel can be the supplementary grounding electrode.

The Code includes no provisions on how the building steel shall be effectively grounded, other than the requirements for effective grounding given in *Section 250-51*. When a building is set on steel-reinforced concrete piers, it is effectively grounded. However, some building specifications require a bare copper conductor to be installed in the piers and connected to the steel columns. The designing engineer determines the size and length of the copper conductor.

Figure 5–17 (page 50) illustrates a grounding electrode system using a metal water pipe as the primary grounding electrode and the effectively grounded metal frame of a building as the supplemental grounding electrode.

The basic rule, in *Section 250-81(a)*, requires the bonding of the supplemental grounding electrode to be carried back to the service

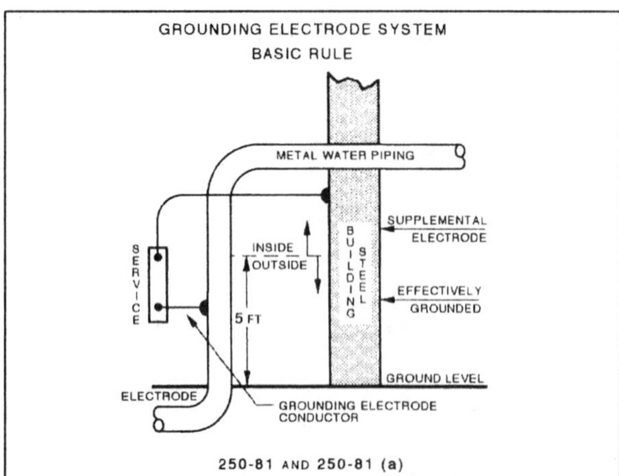

Fig. 5–17 Effectively grounded building steel used as the supplemental grounding electrode.

equipment or to the grounding electrode conductor as illustrated in figure 5–18.

Section 250-81, Exception No. 2, permits the supplemental grounding electrode to utilize the interior metal water piping as a conductor to connect to the primary grounding electrode, provided:

1. It is a commercial or industrial installation.
2. Conditions of maintenance assure only qualified persons will service the installation.
3. The water piping is exposed for its entire length.

When the Code uses the word exposed in the rule, it permits the metal water piping to be installed behind a lift-out ceiling.

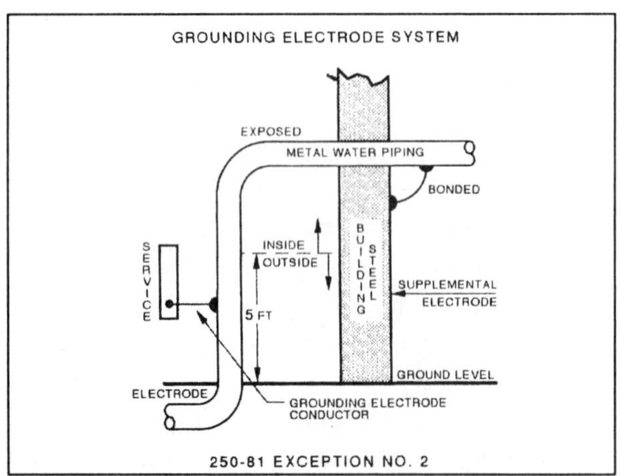

Fig. 5–18 Exception for commercial and industrial installations.

CONCRETE-ENCASED ELECTRODE

Figure 5–19 illustrates a grounding electrode system using a metal water pipe as the primary grounding electrode and a concrete-encased electrode as the supplemental grounding electrode. This is often referred to as a "Ufer" ground. The Ufer ground is named in honor of Mr. Ufer, who did much research in grounding and the concrete-encased grounding electrode.

Although both rebar and wire are illustrated, use of both is not required. Either can be used as the grounding electrode. However, the rebar is required to be bare or zinc-coated. A reinforcing rod coated with a nonconductive material is not suitable for use as a grounding electrode.

Section 250-81(c)(Concrete-Encased Electrode, or Ufer Electrode*)* allows the use of either one or more reinforcing bars (rebars) or a copper conductor, sized as specified in figure 5–19, encased in at least 2 inches of concrete. In addition, the concrete must be in direct contact with the earth.

The concrete-encased grounding electrode is becoming more and more popular. If you have ever had to break up some concrete, you may have noticed how the concrete clings to the steel

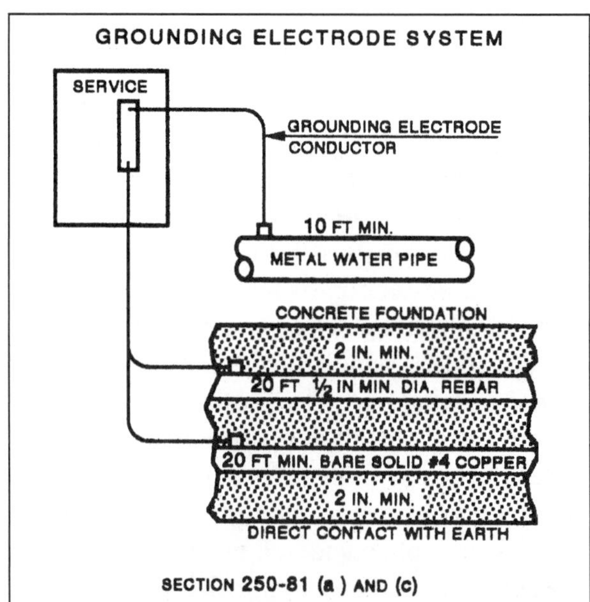

Fig. 5–19 A grounding electrode system using a water pipe and a concrete-encased electrode.

rebar. This could indicate that there is a very good surface-to-surface contact between the grounding electrode and the concrete encasing it. The rebar can also offer many parallel paths for the electrons to travel on, thereby decreasing the impedance of the ground path.

The concrete-encased electrode has several advantages. These include:

1. Concrete in contact with the earth tends to retain moisture.
2. A rebar could offer more than one path for electron flow.
3. The weight of the building maintains a steady pressure at the point of connection between the concrete and the earth.
4. The concrete provides a large surface-to-surface contact with the earth.
5. Many tests made with the concrete-encased electrode have proven it to be a very steady and successful grounding electrode.

Caution: When a vapor barrier, such as plastic, is used between the concrete and the earth, the concrete is no longer in direct contact with the earth and the value of the earth-to-concrete connection is destroyed. In this case, it could not be used for a concrete-encased electrode.

The Code considers concrete a grounded surface and so states in *Section 110-16(a).*

GROUND RING ELECTRODE

Figure 5–20 illustrates a grounding electrode system that uses a metal water pipe as the primary grounding electrode and a ground ring as the supplementary grounding electrode. The ground ring is required by *Section 250-81(d)* to be made of at least 20 feet of bare No. 2 copper and to be buried at a minimum depth of 2 1/2 feet.

A computer installation might specify a separate ground ring in addition to the existing grounding electrode installed for the power system. More often than not, the specification of the ground ring is more than the minimum specified by the Code. However, it still shall be

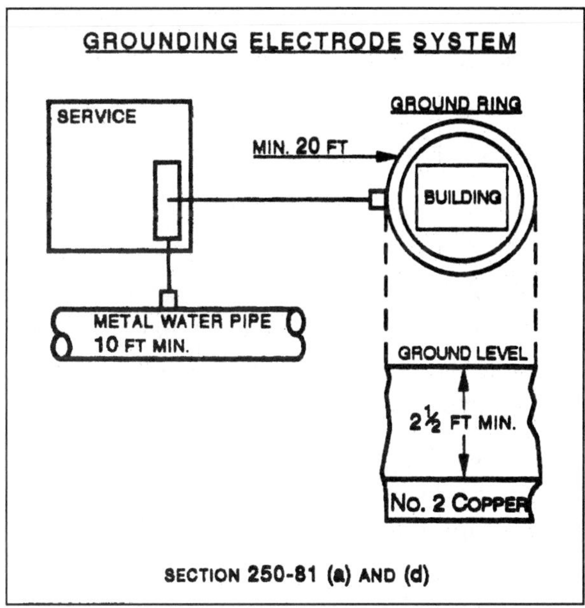

Fig. 5–20 A grounding electrode system using a water pipe and ground ring.

bonded to other existing grounding electrodes for the building.

MADE ELECTRODES

Section 250-83 lists the made electrodes; they are illustrated in figure 5–21. A sentence-by-sentence look at *Section 250-83* lists some very important points.

1. Where a metal water pipe, building steel, concrete-encased electrode, or ground ring

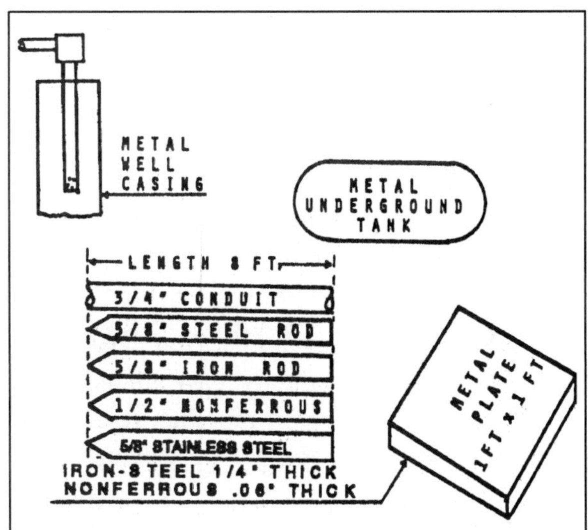

Fig. 5–21 Various grounding electrodes.

is not available, one of the made electrodes can be used.

2. For best results, made electrodes should be installed below permanent moisture level.
3. Made electrodes shall be free from paint, enamel, or other nonconductive coatings.

Comment: The Code is looking for as good a contact as possible between the grounding electrode and the earth. Grease, paint, and enamel can be considered insulators.

4. Grounding electrodes shall be separated by at least 6 feet. This also applies to grounding electrodes used for lightning rod grounding.

Comment: A little earlier we looked at the ground rod and the earth shells around it. Now there is the regulation that when there are two electrodes, they shall be at least 6 feet apart. One thought here is that if the electrodes are too close together, the shells of earth around an electrode will overlap, thereby increasing the opposition to the electron flow into the earth.

Section 250-83 covers what is permitted and what is not permitted to be used as grounding electrodes and the specification for each type of made electrode.

Specifically not permitted are:

1. the gas piping.
2. aluminum ground rods.

The gas companies do not want the gas lines used a grounding electrodes. In the past, the Code permitted the gas piping to be used as the grounding electrode, with the gas company's permission, but such permission was rarely, if ever, granted. The deterioration of aluminum exposed directly to soil makes it unacceptable as a material for a ground rod.

Permitted as grounding electrodes are:

1. Other local metal underground systems. This could be an effectively grounded metal structure, a metal oil pipeline, or a metal underground storage tank. However, should any of these be used, all the provisions listed, such as no paint and good earth contact, will have to be fulfilled.
2. Rod and pipe electrodes.

Comment: This is the most commonly used of the made electrodes. Various types of rods or pipes are recognized for use as grounding electrodes. Figure 5–21 illustrates these pipes and rods and shows their size limitations.

3. Plate electrodes.

The size limitations for plate electrodes are also shown in figure 5–21. However, there is no specification listed for the depth at which the plate must be buried, other than in *Section 250-83*, which requires that when practicable, it should be installed below permanent moisture level.

Figure 5–22 (page 53) illustrates the requirement outlined in *Section 250-84* for spacing made electrodes when the resistance is more than 25 ohms. Two electrodes is the maximum required. This section only applies to rod, pipe, or plate electrodes; when the second electrode is installed, both are bonded together and treated as a single electrode from then on. Once again the 6-foot measurement between electrodes is mentioned and the FPN indicates that the efficiency will be even better if they are installed more than 6 feet apart. This will also help to keep the shells of earth around the grounding electrode from overlapping.

One grounding electrode system used with computer grounding consists of three ground rods located at each corner of a 10-foot triangle. They are then connected together as a grounding electrode system.

When two or more ground rods or grounding electrodes are installed and effectively bonded together, they shall be considered as a single electrode system.

Electrolytic Ground Rod

One variation of the ground rod is the electrolytic, tube-type ground rod. It is primarily used in conjunction with the installation of microelectronic equipment where a very low resistance to ground is required, or in poor soil conditions where low resistance is difficult to achieve. When properly installed, the tube-type grounding elec-

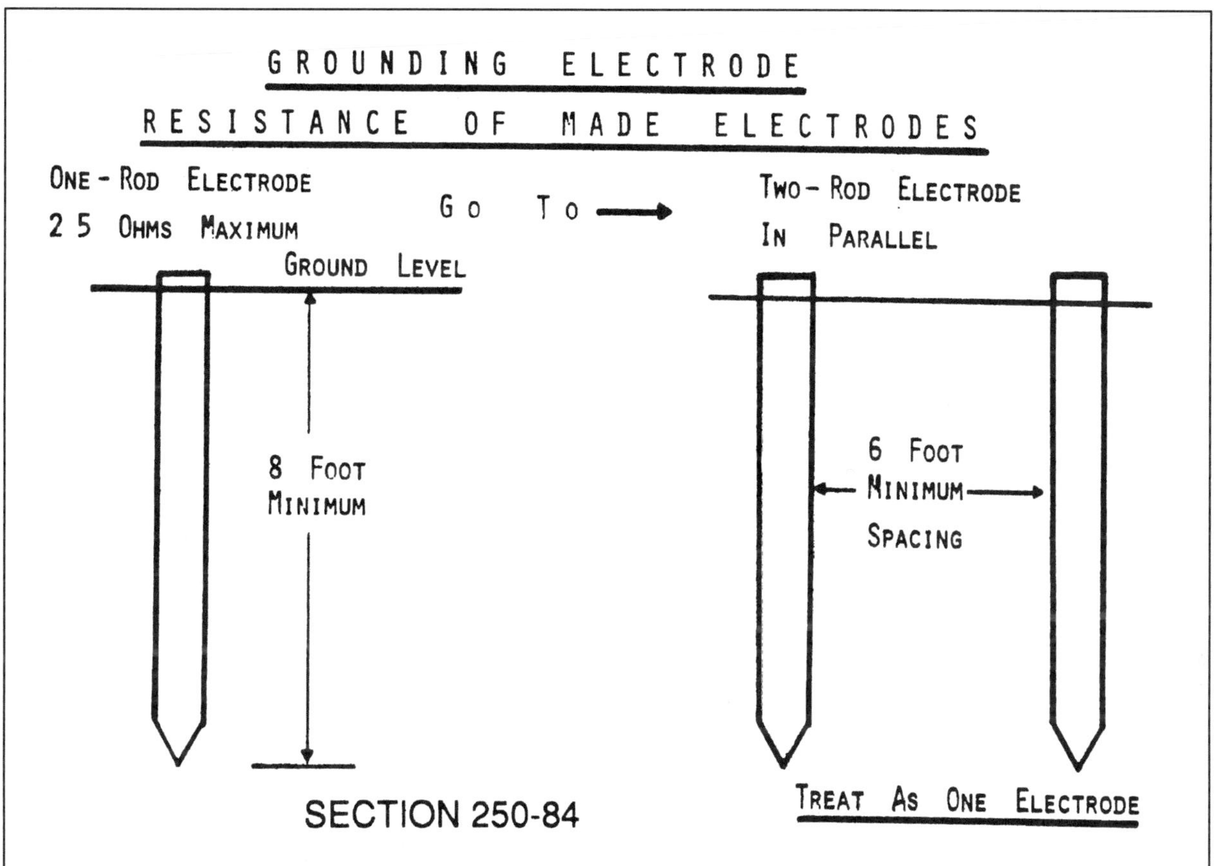

Fig. 5–22 Requirements for spacing made electrodes when the resistance is more than 25 ohms.

trode will produce an electrolyte with good conductivity, which seeps into the soil below and around the ground rod, thereby increasing the conductivity of the surrounding earth.

The Code permits the grounding electrode to have a resistance of 25 ohms to ground. Microelectronic manufacturers require a grounding electrode with much lower resistance to ground than 25 ohms. Some require 5 ohms or less. This can be achieved by using one or more electrolytic ground rods. In order to achieve the desired very low resistance to ground, it might be necessary to use an electrolytic ground rod longer than eight feet and/or a multitude of electrolytic ground rods. The electrolytic ground rod is illustrated in figure 5–23.

The electrolytic ground rod consists of a tube made of 95% copper and 5% nickel, eight feet six inches or more in length, about two inches in diameter, and filled with a mixture of calcium chloride ($CaCO_3$) and sodium chloride ($NaCl$), which are salts. The pipe has copper

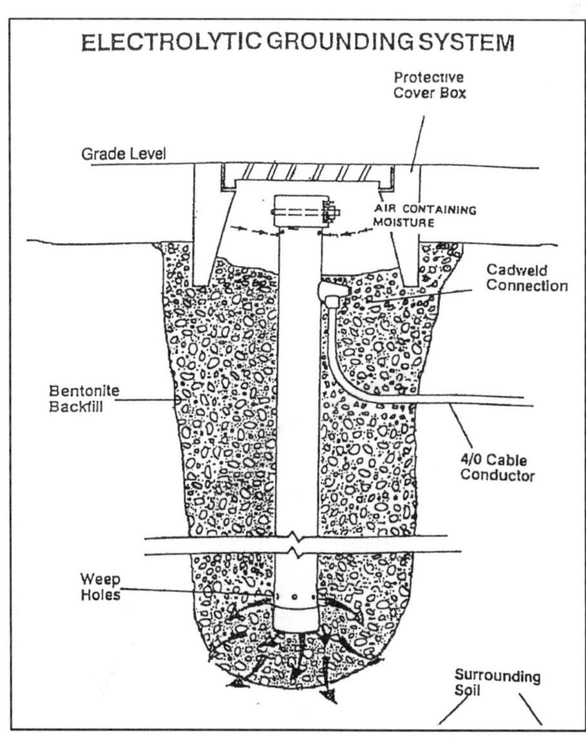

Fig. 5–23 Cutaway view of the installation of an electrolytic ground rod. Courtesy Lyncole XIT Grounding.

caps on the top and bottom with two breathing holes about two inches from the top and four weep holes about two inches from the bottom through which the electrolyte seeps into the soil.

The electrode is installed in a hole drilled into the earth; the hole is a minimum of six inches in diameter and six inches deeper than the length of the rod. The electrode is placed in the center of the hole with the top remaining six inches below the surface. After mixing with water, a slurry of bentonite (a natural volcanic clay with high conductivity) is used to fill the remaining space around the rod. A protected space is left at the top of the electrode for the connecting of the grounding electrode conductor and assuring the breathing holes at the top of the tube-type electrode are not closed up.

The principle of operation is based on the ability of the calcium chloride salt to extract moisture from the air through the two half-inch breathing holes near the top. Gravity causes the moisture taken from the air to pass down through the salt in the tube, where it becomes an electrolyte. An electrolyte is a good conductor for electrons. There is a small reservoir at the bottom of the tube in which the electrolyte accumulates. When a sufficient amount of electrolyte has accumulated in the bottom of the electrode, it will drain out the weep holes into the earth.

As the water is taken from the air filters down through the salts in the electrode pipe, it becomes rich in metallic salt ions. As the electrolyte seeps out from the electrode into the earth below, it moistens the earth with the rich metallic salt ions, resulting in an increase in the conductivity of the surrounding earth. It will also seep up the sides of the electrode through the bentonite.

The bentonite installed on all sides of the electrode is a good conductor. It has the quality of adherence when mixed with moisture. No matter how dry the weather may become, the bentonite will stick to the outside of the electrode on one side and to the existing earth on the other side. This eliminates the resistance between the electrode and the earth that is created when the earth separates from the electrode. The total result is lower resistance shells surrounding the grounding electrode.

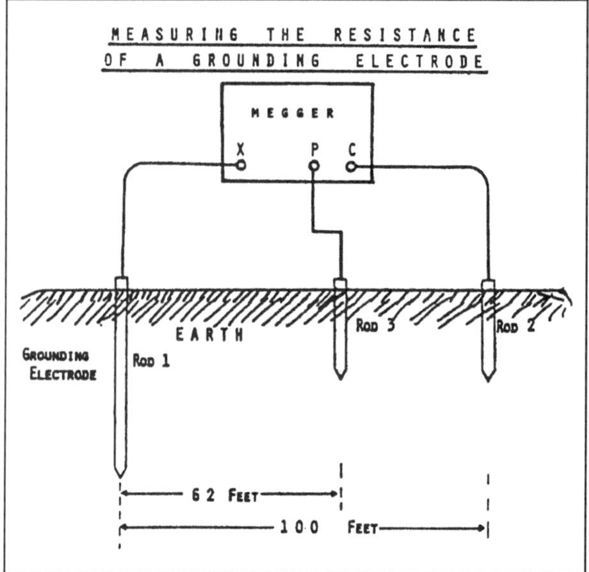

Fig. 5–24 Measuring the resistance of a grounding electrode.

The salt in the pipe electrode does not have to be replaced. It will not wash out nor dissipate with time. It can be installed indoors or outdoors and still function properly. Its estimated life is twenty-five years.

Grounding Electrode Resistance to Ground

Measuring resistance to ground (figure 5–24) illustrates how the resistance of a ground rod can be measured using a megger (an instrument used to measure resistance), two rods, and the grounding electrode. A megger actually generates voltage and causes a current flow. When the voltage and the current flow are known, the megger will calculate the resistance (Ohm's law: R = E/I).

Figure 5–25 (page 55) is a graph illustrating the relationship between the 62-foot measurement and the 25-ohm resistance the Code has set as the maximum resistance for a single ground rod. Note how the curve rises from zero to a flat spot, called a *plateau*. After passing the plateau, the resistance rises very rapidly.

So far, the resistance to ground of the grounding electrode at a residence has not been that big a problem. It may become one in the near future as the "Smart House" becomes more and more a reality and microelectronics move into

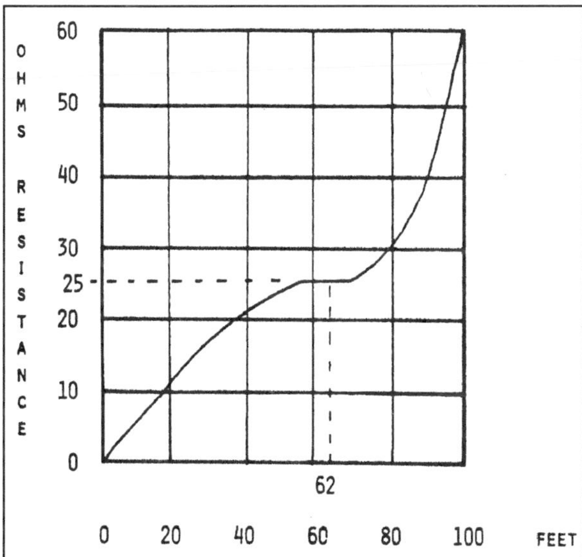

Fig. 5–25 Grounding electrode resistance graph.

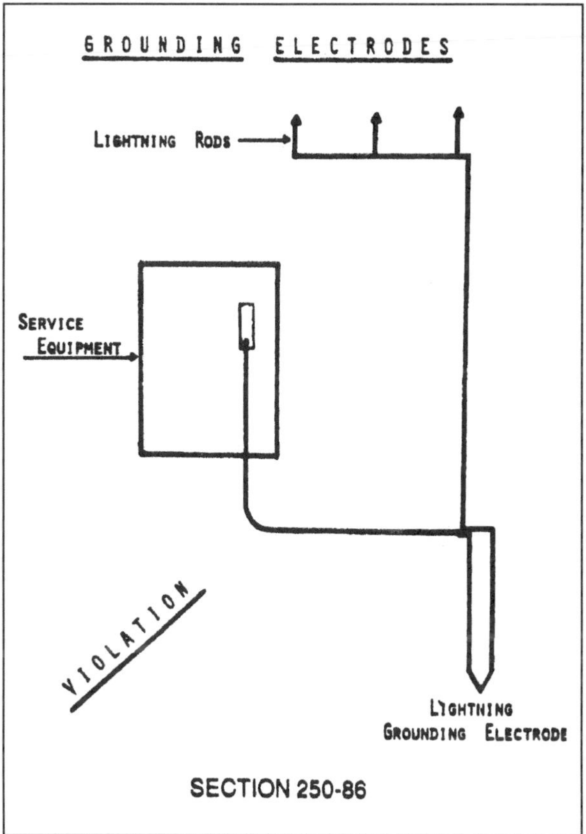

Fig. 5–26 A violation of *Section 250-86*, which prohibits using the same grounding electrode for a lightning rod system and a system supply.

the home. However, the demand for a very low resistance ground by the microelectronics branch of the electrical industry has made it mandatory that the resistance to ground of the grounding electrode be low and that it be checked periodically, due to changes in soil moisture, weather conditions, and age.

Bonding Grounding Electrodes

Figure 5–26 illustrates *Section 250-86*, which prohibits using a grounding electrode installed for a lightning rod system to be used for grounding wiring systems and equipment. The electrical supply must have a separate grounding electrode. However, as illustrated in figure 5–27 (page 56), the grounding electrode for the lightning and the one for the electrical supply system are permitted to be bonded together. The key is that one grounding electrode is not permitted to serve as the grounding electrode for lightning and for the electrical apply system. However, the Fine Print Note following *Section 250-86* calls attention to the fact that the safest installation is when all electrodes are bonded together.

There is an additional requirement in *Section 250-46* under bonding. When lightning rod conductors are within 6 feet of metal raceways, enclosures, frame, and other noncurrent carrying parts of electrical equipment or raceways, they are required to be bonded to the lightning rod conductor. The bonding jumper is to be installed at the point where the metal enclosure and lightning conductors are 6 feet or closer together.

Figure 5–28 (page 56) illustrates the value of bonding together all separate grounding electrodes, as recommended by the FPN No. 2 to *Section 250-86*. Doing so will limit the potential difference between them and between associated wiring of the different systems.

There are other electrical systems brought into a building that require a grounding electrode—the telephone system and cable television. Each is permitted to have its own grounding electrode. But to eliminate any potential differences between any of the grounding electrodes and any of the pieces of electrical equipment of each system, all the grounding electrodes should be bonded together.

When a separate grounding electrode is installed for other than the electrical system, it is

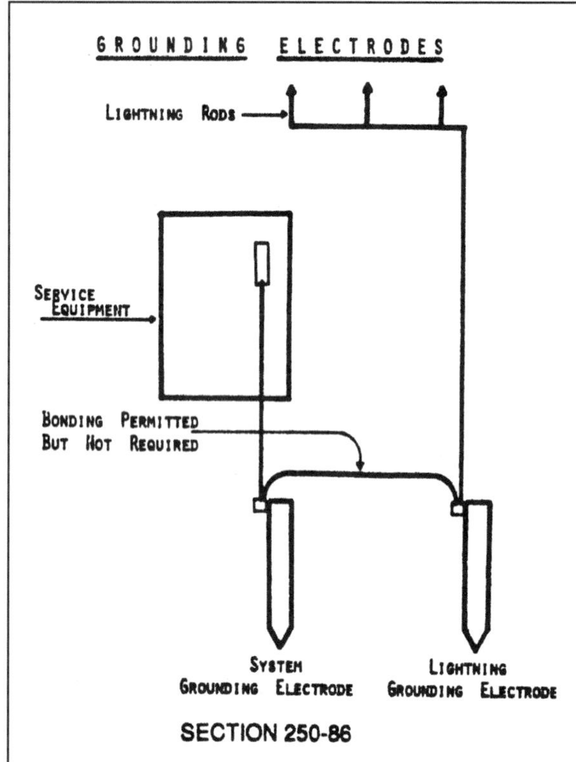

Fig. 5–27 Permitted connection of a system grounding electrode and a lightning rod grounding electrode.

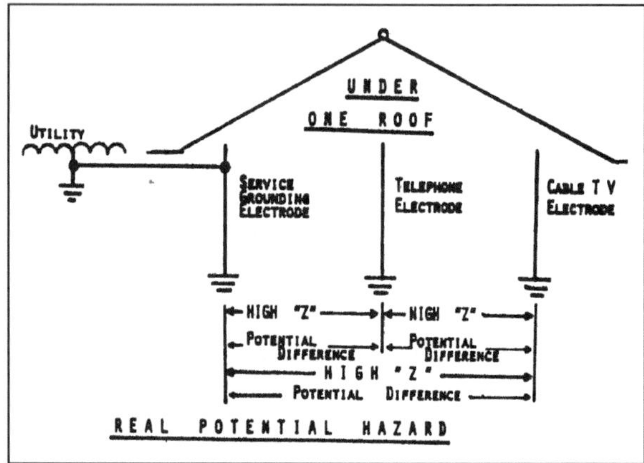

Fig. 5–28 When different grounding electrodes are used for a building and are not bonded together, a potential hazard will exist.

required to be bonded to the power grounding electrode by *Section 800-40(d),* for Telephone and Communication Circuits, *Section 810-21*(J), for Radio and Television systems, and Section *820-40(d),* for Cable TV systems. In each of these installations, the bonding jumper is required to be not smaller than No. 6 copper or

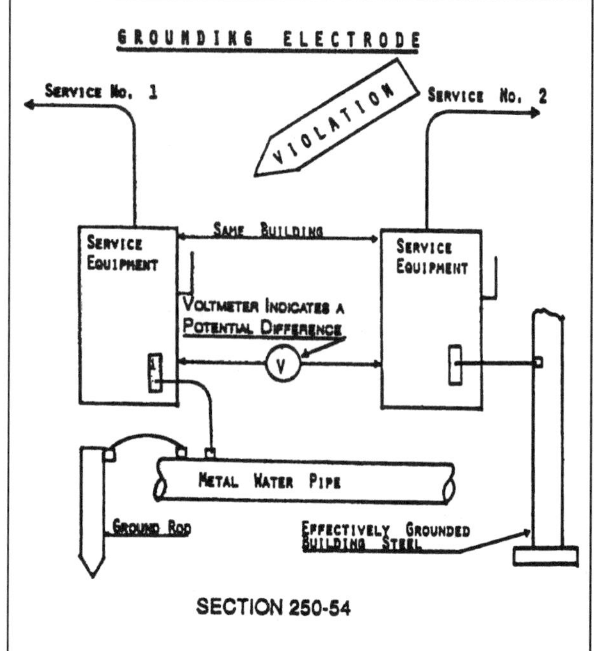

Fig. 5–29 A violation of *Section 250-84,* which specifies that two services to the same building must use the same grounding electrode.

equivalent. *Section 250-71(b)* requires that an external means be made available for this type of intersystem bonding.

One Building with Two Services

The exceptions to *Section 230-2 (Number of Services)* permit more than one service to the same building. Figure 5–29 illustrates a building being served by two separate services. Each service is required to have a grounding electrode. One service uses a metal water pipe as the primary electrode and a ground rod as a supplementary electrode. The second uses the effectively grounded building steel for the grounding electrode. Both are acceptable grounding electrode systems. When the two different grounding electrodes are used, however, a potential difference can be detected between the enclosures of service number one and the enclosures of service number two. Therefore, this is a violation of *Section 250-54,* which requires that when a building is supplied by two or more services and a grounding electrode is required, the same grounding electrode shall be used for both services.

Reason 1: By using one common grounding electrode, the potential difference caused by lightning or external power faults will limit the potential difference on metal enclosures and raceways.

Reason 2: By using one common grounding electrode, the potential difference between grounding electrode systems of different electrical power sources that supply the same premises will be reduced.

A building having two services will more than likely be a commercial or industrial installation with qualified maintenance persons. Figures 5–30 and 5–31 bond the supplemental electrode to the primary electrode using the water piping. According to *250-81 Exception No. 2*, the bonding of the grounding electrode to the water piping would only be permitted with proper supervision and if the water pipe is exposed inside the building. By using the word exposed, the metal water piping could be installed above a lift-out ceiling and meet the requirements in the definition.

Figure 5–30 illustrates two services using the same grounding electrode, as required by *Section 250-54*.

Figure 5–31 illustrates the use of a metal water pipe and a ground rod for one grounding electrode system and the building steel for the second service and second grounding electrode. When the two grounding electrodes are effectively bonded together, they are considered as one grounding electrode system.

SUMMARY

The grounding electrode is discussed first in this text because it is the vital point for all the grounding. Without the grounding electrode, there would be no place to connect the grounding electrode conductor.

Without the grounding electrode, there would be no place to connect the grounded conductor. Without the grounding electrode, there would be no place to connect the equipment grounding conductor. The grounding electrode is the drainpipe to earth from the bull's eye of the grounding target. The grounding electrode is the planned connection to earth to help the electrons enter the earth.

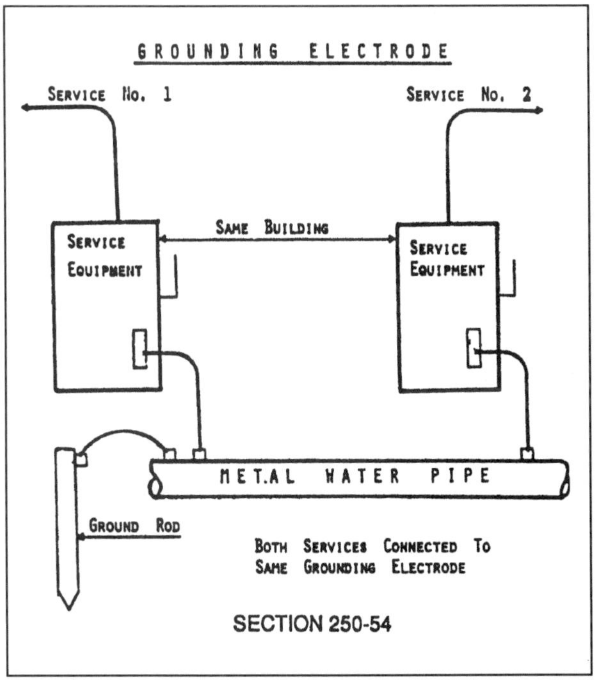

GROUNDING ELECTRODE
SERVICE No. 1
SERVICE No. 2
SAME BUILDING
SERVICE EQUIPMENT
SERVICE EQUIPMENT
METAL WATER PIPE
GROUND ROD
BOTH SERVICES CONNECTED TO SAME GROUNDING ELECTRODE
SECTION 250-54

Fig. 5–30 Two services to one building using the same grounding electrode system.

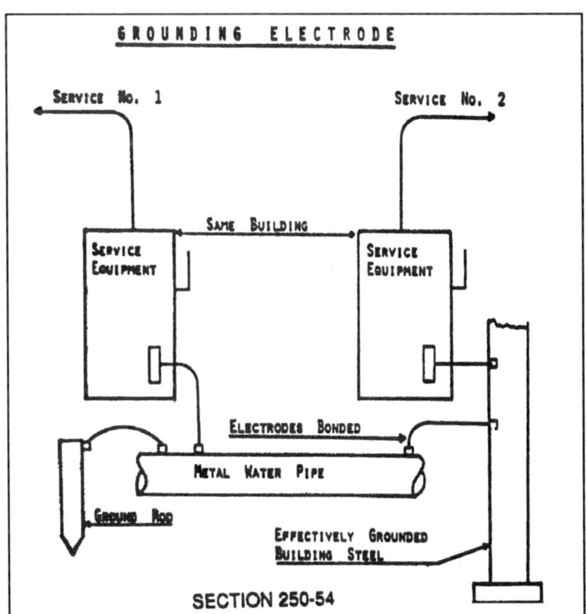

Fig. 5–31 Two services to one building using the same grounding electrode system and also connected to building steel.

FOLLOW UP

Topics for self-study, discussion, or questioning.

1. What is the responsibility of the grounding electrode?
2. Define the term *electrode*.
3. Discuss what constitutes a "grounding electrode system," and the installation requirements.
4. Discuss the use and requirements when a metal water pipe and a ground rod are used as the grounding electrode system.
5. Explain how the electrons are dissipated into the earth by the grounding electrode.
6. When is building steel permitted to be used as the grounding electrode?
7. Discuss the materials used for, and the requirements for the installation of, ground rods for grounding electrodes.
8. When two ground rods are installed, how far apart should they be installed?
9. Discuss the requirements and installation of a concrete-encased grounding electrode.
10. What is a "Ufer" ground?
11. Discuss the requirements and the installation of a ground-ring type grounding electrode.
12. Discuss some of the situations that can arise that will require bonding to maintain continuity of the grounding electrode.
13. Discuss the principle of operation of the electrolytic ground rod.
14. Discuss the installation of more than one grounding electrode for the building.
15. Discuss how the resistance of a grounding rod can be measured.
16. Discuss the points of connection for the supplemental grounding electrode conductor.
17. Discuss resistivity and conductivity of the earth and ground rods.

CHAPTER 6

Grounding Electrode Conductor

OBJECTIVES

After completing this chapter, the student should be able to:

- define a grounding electrode conductor.
- explain where and how a grounding electrode conductor shall be installed and connected.
- explain when and the conditions under which a grounding electrode conductor is permitted to be spliced.
- identify what materials are permitted to be used for grounding electrode conductors.
- discuss the protection of the grounding electrode conductor from a strong magnetic field when installed in a section of metal raceway.
- explain when the connection of the grounding electrode conductor shall be accessible and when it is permitted not to be accessible.
- calculate the minimum size grounding electrode conductor required for direct-current circuits.
- calculate the minimum size grounding electrode conductor permitted for a grounded or ungrounded alternating-current system, when one service-entrance conductor per phase is installed.
- calculate the minimum size grounding electrode conductor permitted for a grounded or ungrounded alternating-current system, when parallel service-entrance conductors are installed.
- identify when and where the minimum size equipment grounding conductor is permitted to be installed.
- use *Table 8* of Chapter 9 of the Code for converting circular mil area of conductors to standard size conductors.
- use *Table 250-94* for sizing copper or aluminum grounding electrode conductors.

This chapter focuses on the grounding electrode conductor (figure 6–1, page 60). Covered are its use, materials permitted, installations, protection, and sizing.

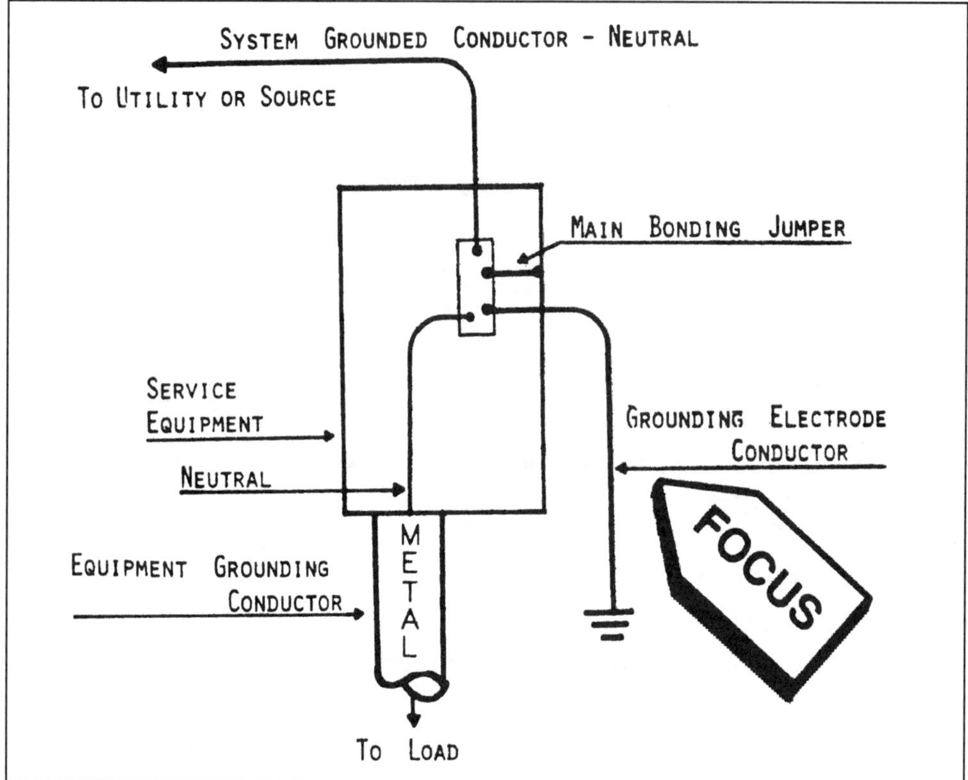

Fig. 6–1 Focus on the grounding electrode conductor.

DEFINITION OF *GROUNDING ELECTRODE CONDUCTOR*

The main points of the definition for the grounding electrode conductor are illustrated in figure 6–2.

1. The grounding electrode conductor will be connected to:

   The equipment grounding conductor.

   The grounded conductor when a grounded system is used.

   Both when both are present.

2. It will be connected at the service equipment, at the source for separately derived systems, or first disconnecting means.

The main purpose of the grounding electrode conductor is to connect the grounding electrode with the bull's eye of the grounding target. The grounding electrode conductor actually completes three grounding paths to the grounding electrode. These are:

1. The path from the grounded conductor

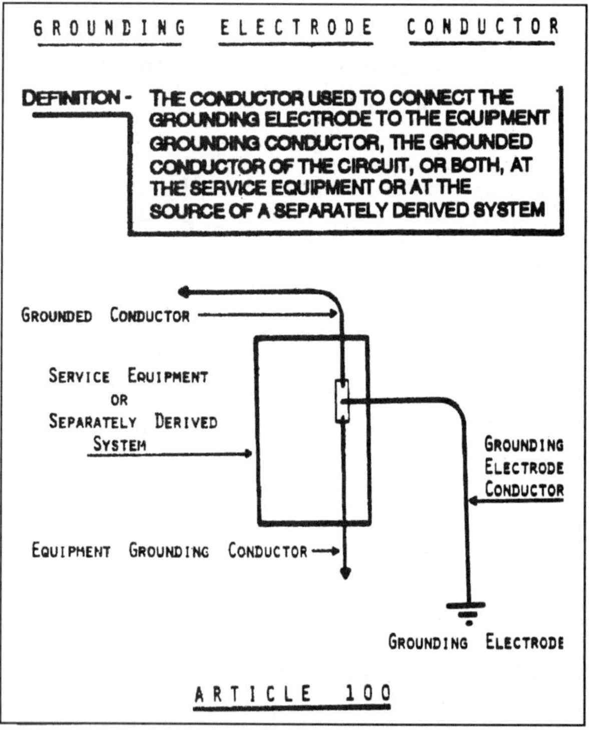

Fig. 6–2 Definition of *grounding electrode conductor.**

*Reprinted with permission from NFPA 70-1996, the National Electrical Code®, Copyright © 1995, National Fire Protection Association, Quincy, Massachusetts 02269. This reprinted material is not the complete and official position of the National Fire Protection Association, on the referenced subject, which is represented only by the standard in its entirety.

2. The path from the equipment grounding conductor when a wire is used as the equipment grounding conductor

3. The path from the main bonding jumper when raceways are used as the equipment grounding conductor

MATERIALS

When broken down, *Section 250-91(a)* shows the following requirements for the grounding electrode conductor:

1. Material
   a. Copper
   b. Aluminum
   c. Copper-clad aluminum
2. Material shall
   a. Resist corrosive conditions or
   b. Be protected from corrosion
3. Solid or stranded
4. Insulated, covered, or bare
5. Continuous length with no splices (three exceptions)

Splicing

Figure 6–3 illustrates one exception for splicing the grounding electrode conductor. Splicing is allowed when a bus bar is used for the grounding electrode conductor.

Figure 6–4 illustrates Exception No. 2, which permits the grounding electrode conductor to be spliced. Three things need to be noted here. These are:

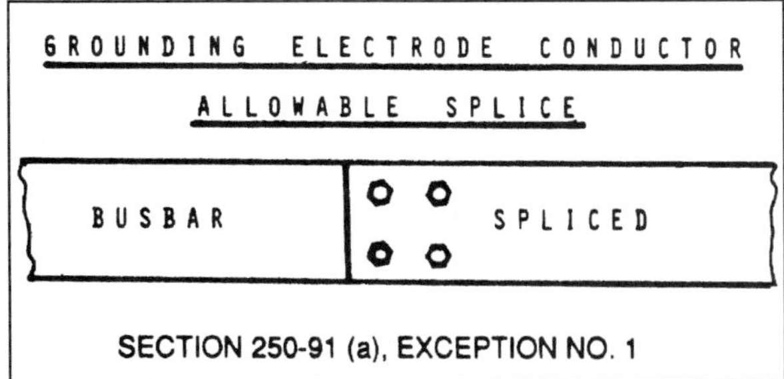

Fig. 6–3 Splicing the grounding electrode conductor using a bus bar.

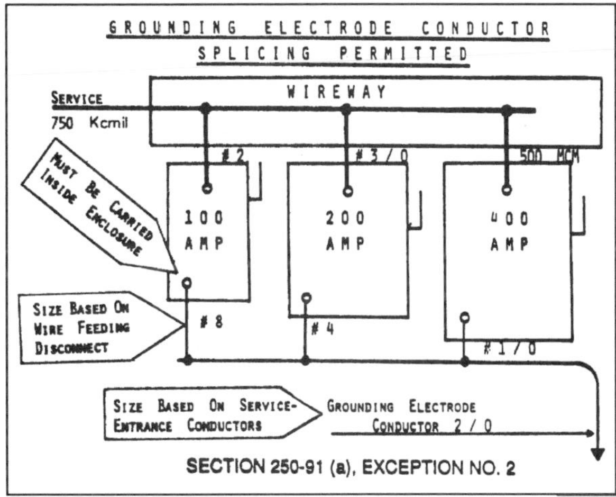

Fig. 6–4 Splicing the grounding electrode conductor when there is more than one service switch.

1. The grounding electrode conductor is sized according to the size of the service-entrance conductors.
2. The taps off the grounding electrode conductor are sized according to the size of the service feeder taps.
3. The tap must be carried inside the enclosure and is not connected to the outside of the enclosure.
4. The taps are so made that the grounding electrode conductor remains without splice.

Figure 6–5 (page 62) illustrates Exception No. 3, which permits the grounding electrode conductor to be spliced by means of exothermic weld or irreversible compression type connectors listed for the purpose. Thermoweld® and Cadweld® are trade names for exothermic welds. The irreversible compression type are installed with the use of a compression tool.

These two splicing methods are permitted for residential, commercial, or industrial installations. They offer some flexibility when extension or repair of the grounding electrode conductor is needed.

This exception covers the industry practice of installing a ground grid for an industrial plant that may require several splices or taps for the grounding electrode conductor.

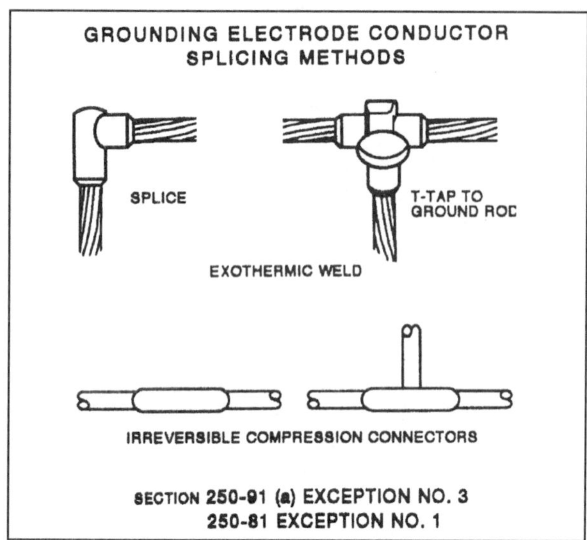

Fig. 6–5 Methods permitted for splicing the grounding electrode conductor.

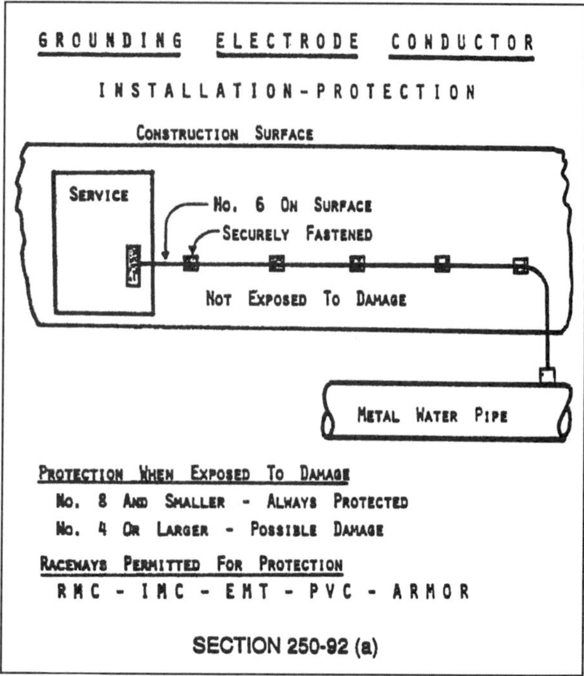

Fig. 6–6 Requirements for installing the grounding electrode conductor.

Natural disasters, such as tornadoes, hurricanes, earthquakes or other incidents, may cause the grounding electrode conductor to be broken. When this happens, repair can be made quickly with the use of a dependable splicing method identified for such use.

Some electrolytic type ground rods come from the factory with a short length of 4/0 bare copper exothermically welded to the casing of the ground rod. The factory instructions specify the use of exothermic welding when making the grounding electrode conductor connection to the short length of 4/0 copper.

INSTALLATION AND PROTECTION

Figure 6–6 illustrates the following items covered in *Section 250-92*. In this particular section, the term *grounding conductor* means the grounding electrode conductor.

1. The grounding electrode conductor, when installed without an enclosure, shall be securely fastened to the construction surface on which it is carried.
2. The enclosure for a grounding electrode conductor shall be securely fastened to the surface on which it is carried.
3. A No. 4 copper or aluminum or larger conductor shall be protected if exposed to severe physical damage.
4. A No. 6 grounding electrode conductor that is free from exposure to physical damage shall be permitted to be run along the surface of the building construction without metal covering or protection where it is securely fastened to the construction.
5. Raceways permitted for use to protect the grounding electrode conductor include the following:
   a. Rigid metal conduit (RMC)
   b. Intermediate metal conduit (IMC)
   c. Rigid nonmetallic conduit (PVC)
   d. Electrical metallic tubing (EMT)
   e. Cable armor.
6. A grounding electrode conductor smaller than No. 6 shall be protected by one of the raceways permitted for the protection of the grounding electrode conductor.

When aluminum or copper-clad aluminum is used for the grounding electrode conductor, insulated or bare, the following restrictions are placed on it (figure 6–7, page 63):

1. Shall not be used where in direct contact with masonry
2. Shall not be used where in direct contact with earth

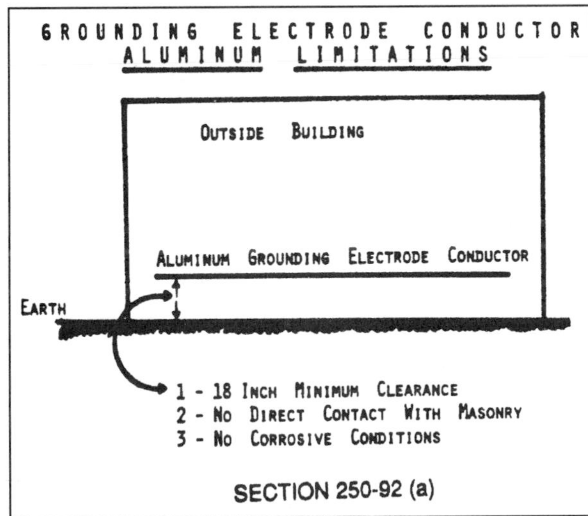

Fig. 6–7 Restrictions for using aluminum as the grounding electrode conductor.

3. Shall not be used where subjected to corrosive conditions
4. Where installed outside, shall not be within 18 inches of the earth.

Comment: The restrictions placed on aluminum and the copper-clad aluminum are part of the reason copper is usually specified for use as the grounding electrode conductor. The 18-inches-to-earth limitation eliminates using the aluminum or copper-clad aluminum as the grounding electrode conductor when the connection to the ground rod is either underground or less than 18 inches to earth.

Protection from a Magnetic Field

The protection of the grounding electrode conductor from destruction by a powerful magnetic field is covered in *Section 250-92(b)*. When metal enclosures are used for mechanical protection of the grounding electrode conductor, special precautions must be taken. These are set down in *Section 250-92(b)*.

1. The metal enclosure shall be electrically continuous from cabinets or equipment to the grounding electrode (figure 6–8).
2. The enclosure must be fastened securely to the ground clamp or fitting (figure 6–8).
3. Where the grounding electrode conductor is not protected the full length of the conductor and only for a small portion of it, both ends of the metal enclosure shall be bonded to the grounding electrode conductor (figure 6–9).

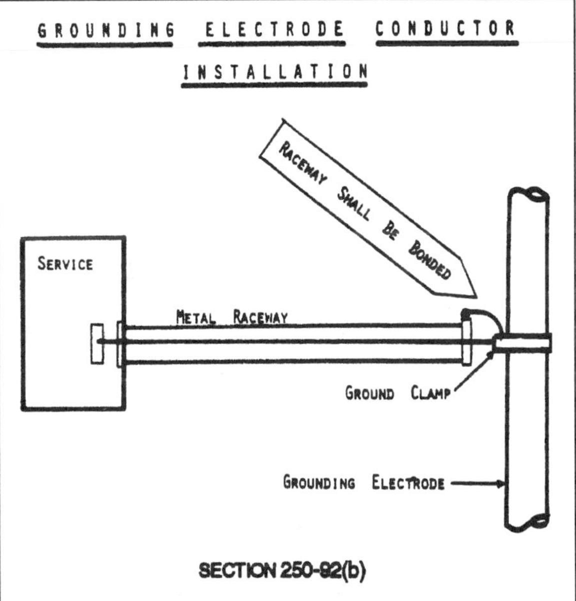

Fig. 6–8 Bonding the metal raceway enclosing the grounding electrode conductor to the grounding electrode.

All raceways used for protection of the grounding electrode conductor shall be installed considering the regulations set down in *Chapter 3, Wiring Methods and Materials.*

Figures 6–8 and 6–9 illustrate two very-often-overlooked Code regulations. Ignoring these regulations can result in severe damage to the grounding electrode conductor if a fault occurs.

When an electrical conductor carries current, it sets up a magnetic field around the

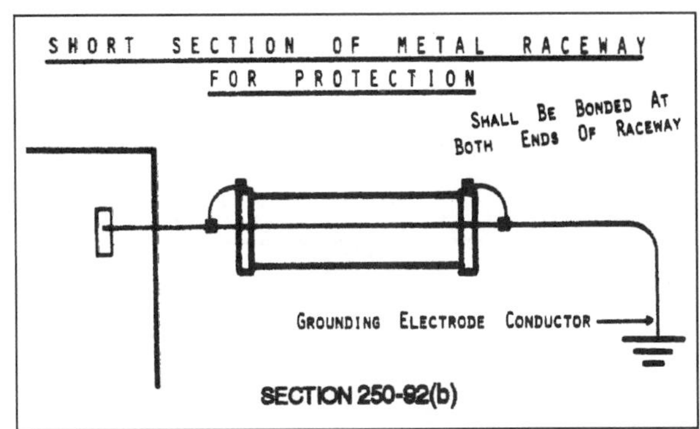

Fig. 6–9 Bonding both ends of short sections of a metal enclosure to the grounding electrode conductor.

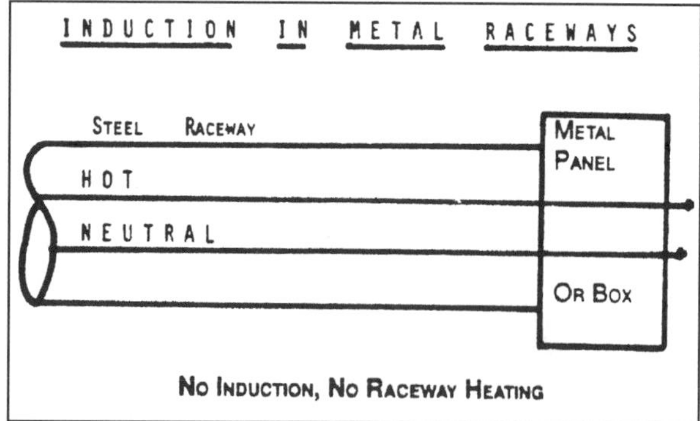

Fig. 6–10 Eliminating induction in metal raceways.

conductor. In the case of alternating current, it is an alternating magnetic field.

Figure 6–10 illustrates a hot conductor and a neutral conductor installed in the same metal raceway. Because the current is traveling in two different directions within the metal raceway, there is no induction in the metal raceway. The magnetic fields of the two currents flowing in opposite directions will cancel each other out.

When only one hot conductor or the neutral conductor figure (6–11) is installed in a metal raceway, there will be induction in the metal raceway and the metal raceway will become hot. The induction is due to the rise and fall of the alternating current's magnetic field.

The grounding electrode conductor for an alternating-current system is the only single alternating-current conductor that is run in a metal raceway. When only a short piece of metal raceway is used to protect the grounding electrode conductor, it must be bonded to the conductor, as shown in figure 6–9 (page 63), or there will be severe heating of the metal enclosure.

Figure 6–12 illustrates an installation without the required bonding jumpers. It also indicates some of the things that could take place should a ground fault occur.

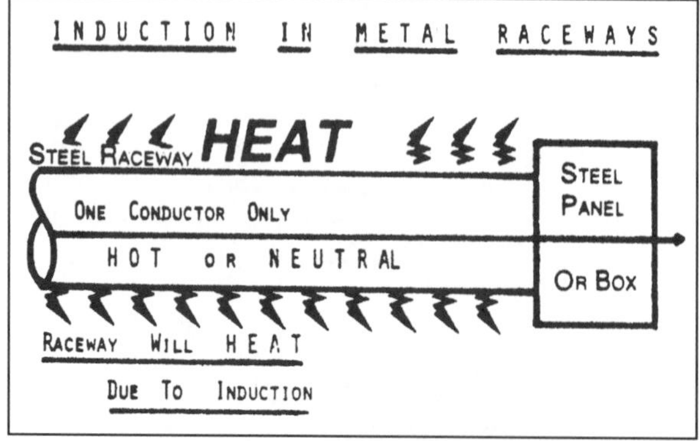

Fig. 6–11 Induction in metal raceways causes heat.

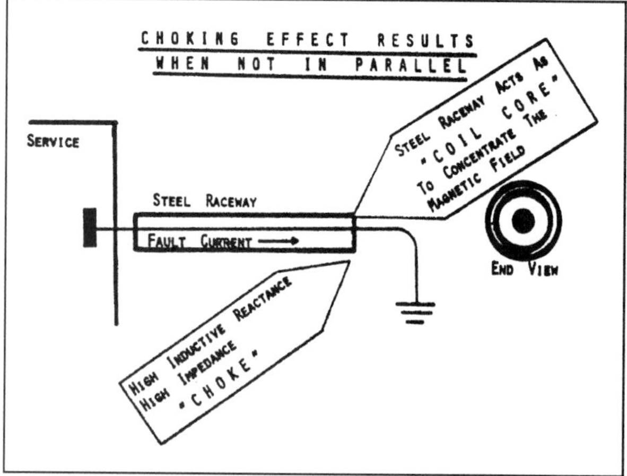

Fig. 6–12 Choking effect that occurs when a steel raceway is not bonded to the grounding electrode conductor.

When there is a fault current, it can be extremely high. The strength of the magnetic field set up by the current is directly proportional to the amount of current flowing in the conductor. A very high fault current will cause a very intense magnetic field in a very short period of time and the conduit enclosing the grounding electrode conductor will become extremely hot. The number of lines of force that are trying to flow in the steel raceway of the grounding electrode conductor enclosure far surpass the "saturation point" of the steel raceway. *Saturation point* means the number of lines of force a piece of steel can conduct, for its cross-sectional area, without dangerous overheating.

Magnetic lines of force like to flow in steel and will search out the steel for a path to travel on. Past the point where the steel raceway is terminated, the magnetic lines of force generated by the current in the conductor will all try to get back into the nearest edge of the steel conduit (figure 6–13, page 65). The saturation point for magnetic lines of force in the steel raceway is very much exceeded. Tremendous heat is generated at the point where the raceway is terminated.

The steel conduit acts like the steel core of a coil to concentrate the magnetic lines of force. It creates a high-impedance choke. Faults that have occurred when this happens have been known to melt the grounding electrode conduc-

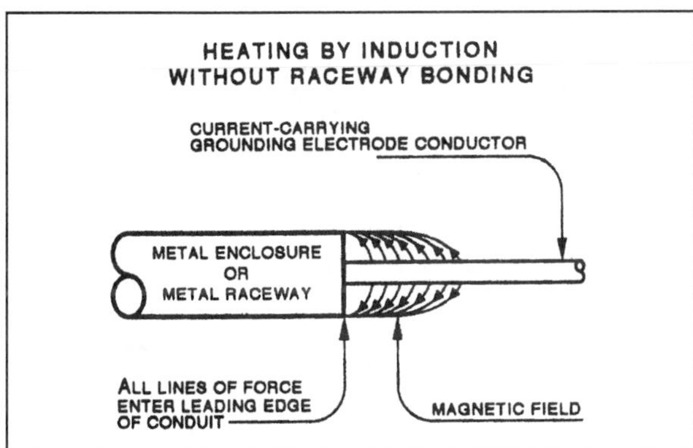

Fig. 6–13 Magnetic field at the termination of the steel raceway.

tor in two as smoothly as if it had been cut with a knife. This occurs at the point where the steel conduit is terminated. To avoid this situation, the Code is really saying to connect the conduit enclosing the grounding electrode conductor in parallel with the grounding electrode conductor.

Figure 6–14 illustrates an experiment conducted to show the relationship between the current flow in the conductor and the current flow in the conduit surrounding the conductor. A controlled supply is used that furnishes 100 amps, with the conductor and the conduit connected in parallel and an ammeter connected in series with both the conductor and the conduit. The result, as indicated, is very surprising.

When two service or feeder conductors are connected in parallel, they are expected to act as one conductor. In this case the conduit and the copper conductor act as one conductor. The current also looks at it as one conductor, which gives rise to the question, Why does so much more current flow in the steel conduit than in the copper wire conductor?

The answer is because of the "skin effect." The *skin effect* is the tendency for the current to flow on the outer edge of the conductor. Aluminum is a nonmagnetic material. PVC (nonmetallic conduit) is a nonmagnetic material. The magnetic-field problem does not exist when the grounding electrode conductor is installed in rigid nonmetallic conduit or aluminum conduit or aluminum electrical metallic tubing. Induction, as illustrated in figure 6–11 (page 64), will take place in an aluminum raceway when only one conductor is installed in it. However, when the grounding electrode conductor is installed in aluminum raceway, the aluminum raceway must be bonded to the grounding electrode conductor. When nonmetallic PVC is used, there is no induction, no need for bonding. It is not required.

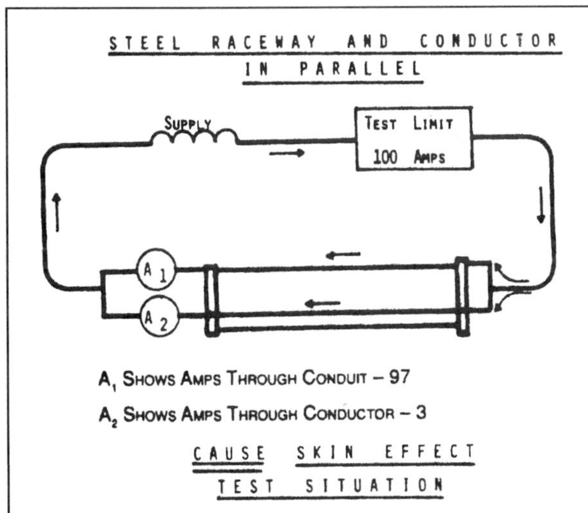

Fig. 6–14 Test showing the relationship between the current flow in the grounding electrode conductor and the metal conduit enclosure when they are bonded together.

Grounding Electrode Conductor Enclosure Bonding

When the grounding electrode conductor is bonded to the metal enclosure, it eliminates the heating at the raceway edge caused by the magnetic field. Therefore, bonding is required as set down in *Section 250-71(a)(3)* (figure 6–15):

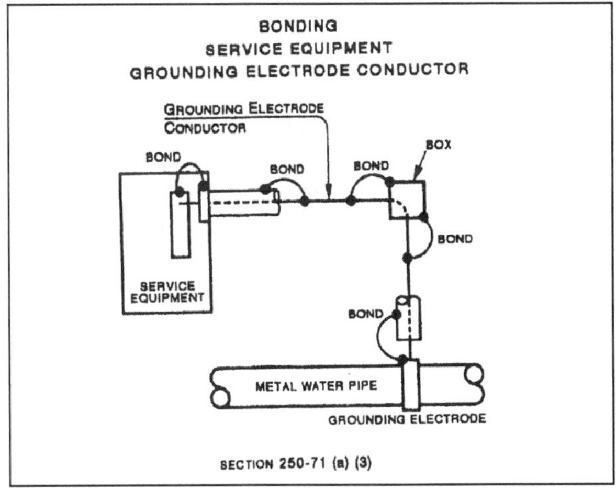

Fig. 6–15 All metal enclosing the grounding electrode conductor is required to be bonded to the grounding electrode conductor.

Bond at each end of raceway.

Bond at all intervening raceways.

Bond at all intervening boxes.

Bond at all enclosures.

When there is one continuous metal raceway from end to end, the bonding is at each end. When the raceway is not continuous, and there is the possibility of using one or more short sections of metal raceway, a metal box, or any kind of metal enclosure along the intervening length of the grounding electrode conductors, the metal enclosures must be bonded to the grounding electrode conductor.

Section 250-79(d) requires that the equipment bonding jumper used to bond the metal raceway, or armored cable that protects the grounding electrode conductor be the same size as or larger than the enclosed grounding electrode conductor, as illustrated in figure 6–16. The enclosure for the grounding electrode conductor is considered to be part of the service raceway. The bonding jumper is required to be the same size as the grounding electrode conductor or larger because of the skin effect of alternating current.

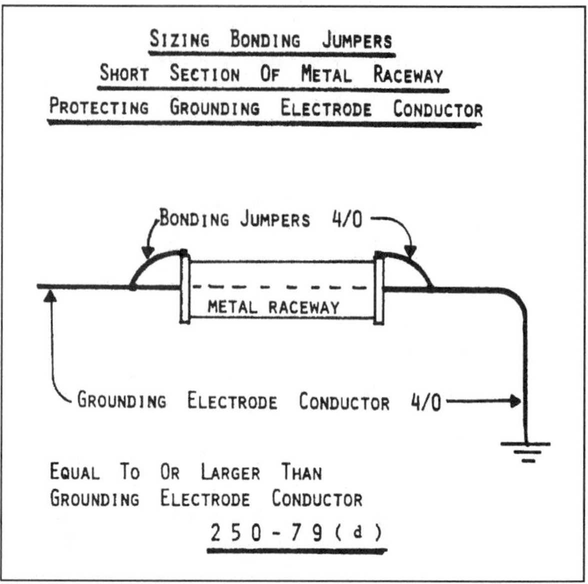

Fig. 6–16 Sizing bonding jumper for equipment grounding of metal enclosure containing the grounding electrode conductor.

CONNECTING THE GROUNDING ELECTRODE CONDUCTOR

Section 250-112, with its exceptions, lists the required accessible connections for the grounding electrode conductor. These are illustrated in figure 6–17. The basic rule for

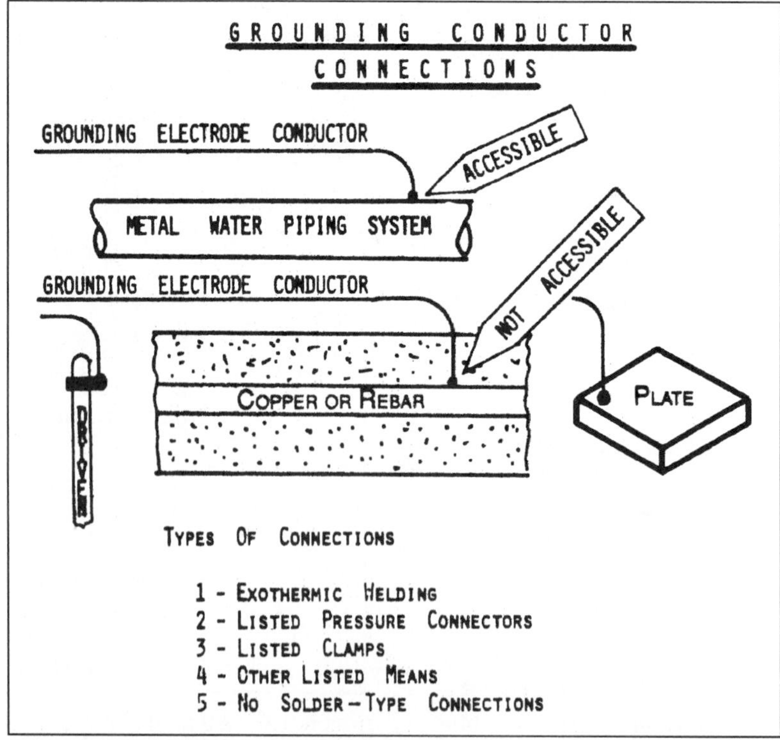

Fig. 6–17 Types and locations of connections for the grounding electrode conductor to a grounding electrode.

connecting the grounding electrode conductor to the grounding electrode is given in *Section 250-112*, with special emphasis on these points:

1. The connection shall be accessible.
2. The connection shall be made to assure a permanent and effective ground.

The exception to this section allows for some plain common sense. It states that when a buried electrode is used, the connection between the grounding electrode conductor and the grounding electrode need not be accessible, such as in the case of the following:

1. Concrete-encased grounding electrode
2. Driven grounding electrode
3. Buried grounding electrode

Comment: About the only electrode left that is required to be accessible is the metal water pipe and building steel.

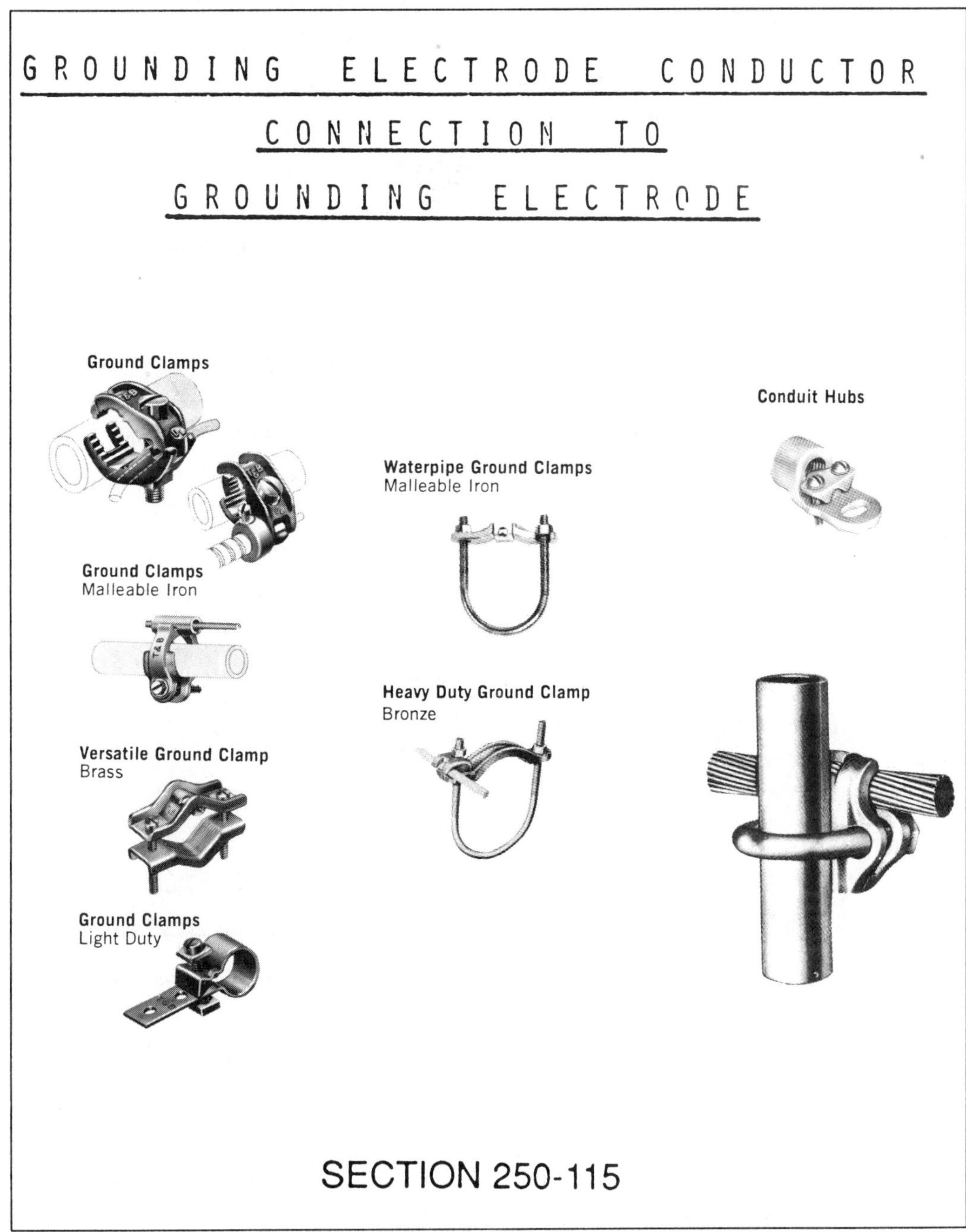

Fig. 6–18 Grounding electrode conductor connections to the grounding electrode. Photo courtesy Thomas & Betts Corporation.

The materials and methods for connecting the grounding electrode conductor to the grounding electrode are outlined in *Section 250-115*. Various types of these connections are illustrated in figure 6–18 (page 67). The following is an outline of the important points of *Section 250-115*:

1. Methods of making connections
   a. Exothermic welding
   b. Listed lug
   c. Listed pressure connector
   d. Listed clamp
   e. Other listed means

The word *listed* is very visible in this section and is defined in *Article 100.*

Quote – "Listed: Equipment or materials included in a list published by an organization acceptable to the authority having jurisdiction and concerned with product evaluation, that maintains periodic inspection of production of listed equipment or materials, and whose listing states either that the equipment or material meets designated standards or has been tested and found suitable for use in a specified manner."*

Comment: The means for identifying listed equipment may vary. It may be listed and it may be labeled.

2. No dependency on solder
3. Ground clamps to be material compatible with material they will clamp to; no aluminum ground clamps on copper piping
4. Where buried, connection listed for direct burial
5. Not more than one conductor per clamp
6. Clamps listed for more than one conductor permitted to have more than one conductor
7. Listed bolted clamps permitted: cast bronze, brass, plain iron, or malleable iron
8. Devices that screw into pipe: an approved or listed plug or fitting
9. Listed sheet-metal straps limitations
   a. Rigid metal base
   b. Seats on electrode
   c. Not liable to stretch during installation or with time
10. An equally substantial approved means substituted for any of the above.

SIZING THE DC GROUNDING ELECTRODE CONDUCTOR

There are three ways of sizing the direct-current grounding electrode conductor. These are:

1. Three-wire balancer set, with overcurrent protection in case of unbalanced condition. The grounding electrode conductor shall not be smaller than neutral (figure 6–19).
2. DC systems other than the three-wire balancer. The grounding electrode conductor shall not be smaller than the largest conductor (figure 6–20, page 69).
3. In no case shall the grounding electrode conductor be smaller than No. 8 copper or No. 6 aluminum (figure 6–21, page 69).

When the grounding electrode conductor is the sole connection to the grounding electrode,

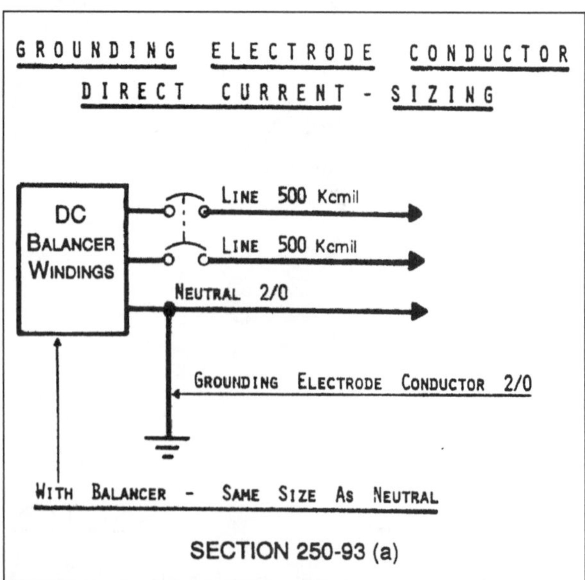

Fig. 6–19 Sizing a grounding electrode conductor for a DC system with balancer windings.

*Reprinted with permission from NFPA 70-1996, the National Electrical Code®, Copyright © 1995, National Fire Protection Association, Quincy, Massachusetts 02269. This reprinted material is not the complete and official position of the National Fire Protection Association, on the referenced subject, which is represented only by the standard in its entirety.

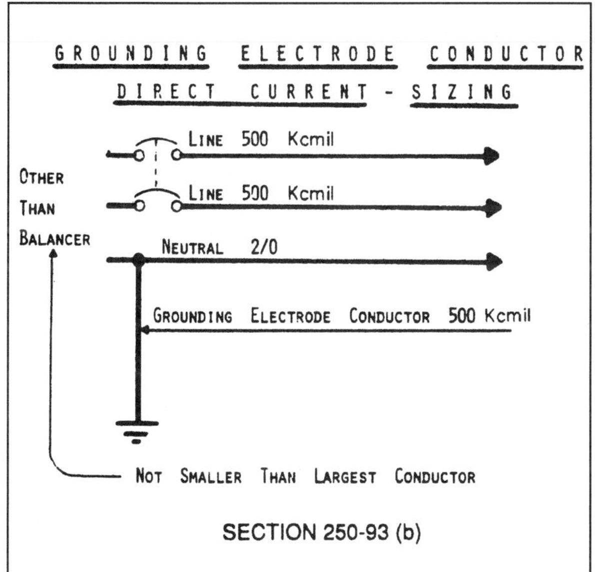

Fig. 6–20 Sizing a grounding electrode conductor for a DC system other than with a balancer winding.

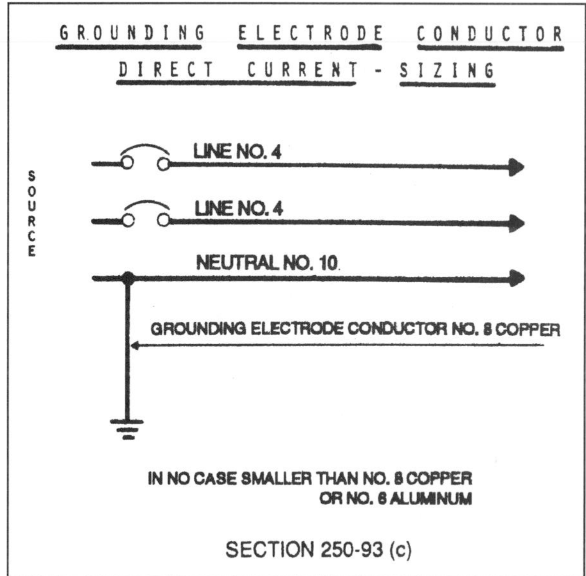

Fig. 6–21 The minimum size of a grounding electrode conductor permitted for a DC system.

there are three exceptions to the above basic rules listed:

1. When a rod, pipe, or plate electrode is being used as the grounding electrode, the grounding electrode conductor is not required to be larger than No. 6 copper or No. 4 aluminum wire.

   Note: Local authority having jurisdiction or a local ordinance may not allow the use of this exception.

2. When a concrete encased electrode is a being used as the grounding electrode, the grounding electrode conductor is not required to be larger than No. 4 copper wire.
3. When a ground ring is being used as the grounding electrode, the grounding electrode conductor is not required to be larger than the conductor used for the ground ring.

SIZING THE AC GROUNDING ELECTRODE CONDUCTOR

Section 250-94 states the basic rule for sizing the grounding electrode conductor for a grounded or ungrounded alternating-current system. "The size of the grounding electrode conductor of a grounded or ungrounded AC system shall not be less than that given in *Table 250-94*" (figure 6–22).

There are two exceptions to the basic rule. Each has three parts to it and is directed at a specific type of grounding electrode.

Exception No. 1 applies to grounded systems. Exception No. 2 applies to ungrounded systems. Exception No. 1a. lists the following requirements for a *grounded system* (figure 6–23, page 70):

1. Applies to made electrodes only, such as rod, pipe, or plate electrodes

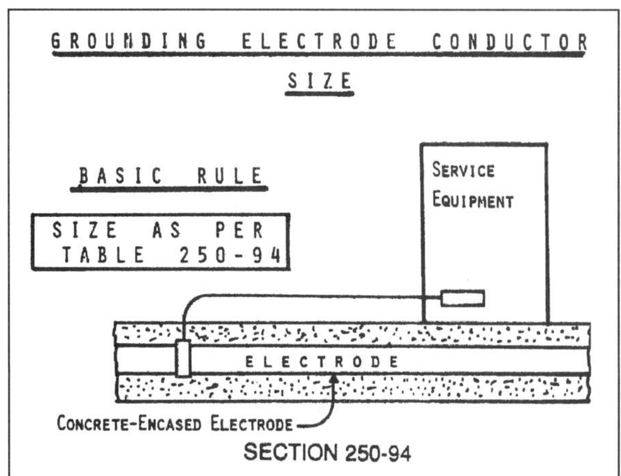

Fig. 6–22 Basic rule for sizing a grounding electrode conductor for an AC system.

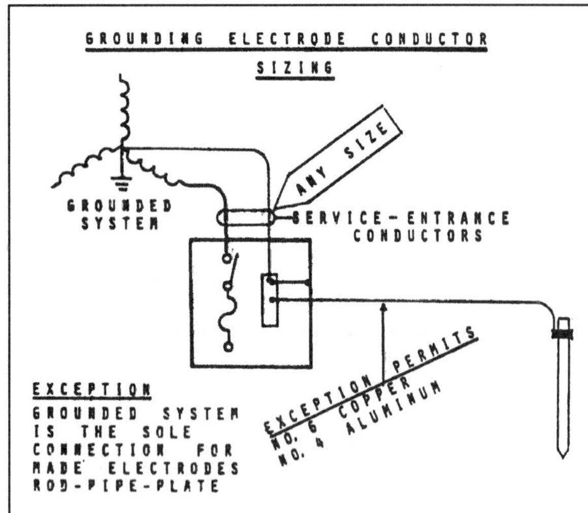

Fig. 6–23 Exception permitting a smaller grounding electrode conductor for a grounded AC system when the grounding electrode is a ground rod.

2. Requires a sole connection between the grounding electrode and the grounded conductor of the grounded system

Comment: Sole connection means there are no bonding jumpers in the circuit.

3. Is not required to be larger than No. 6 copper
4. Is not required to be larger than No. 4 aluminum

   Note: Local authority having jurisdiction or a local ordinance may not allow the use of the smaller conductors permitted by this exception

Exception No. 2, *Ungrounded Systems*, parallels the requirements for grounded systems in each of its four parts (figure 6–24).

Exception No. 2a. lists the following requirements for an *ungrounded system*:

1. Applies to made electrodes, such as rod, pipe, or plate electrodes
2. Requires a sole connection between the grounding electrode and service
3. Is not required to be larger than No. 6 copper
4. Is not required to be larger than No. 4 aluminum

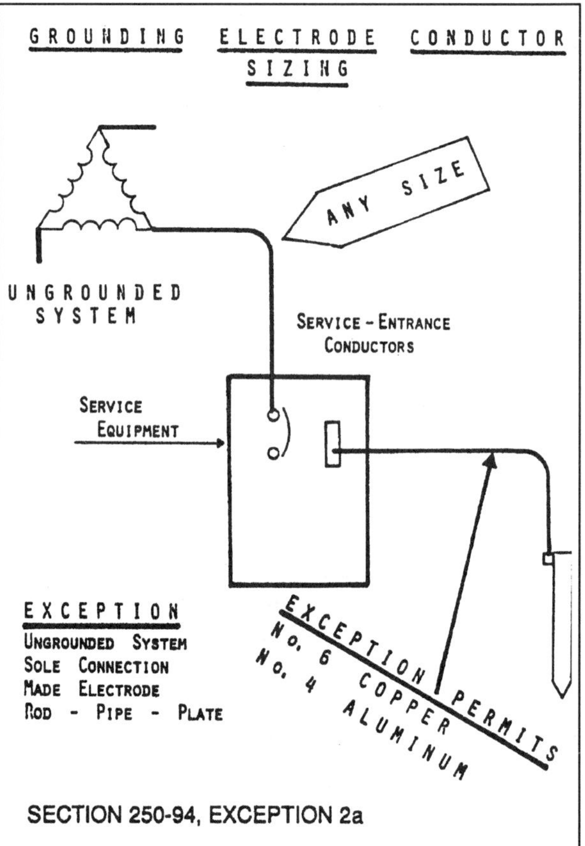

Fig. 6–24 Exception permitting a smaller grounding electrode conductor for an ungrounded AC system when the grounding electrode is a ground rod.

The smaller conductor is also permitted by *Section 250-81(a)*, last paragraph, when the water pipe is the primary electrode and is supplemented by a ground rod, pipe, or plate electrode, as illustrated in figure 6–25 (page 71).

Question: Why is this small conductor allowed for a grounding electrode conductor, regardless of the size of the service-entrance conductors?

Answer: Because the No. 6 copper or No. 4 aluminum will carry all the electrons the grounding electrode can dissipate into the earth in the given time limit. The grounding electrode is the limiting factor. When a larger conductor is used, the grounding electrode chokes down on the electron traffic and they all can't get through, so there is no need for a larger conductor.

Technical reports indicate the following theory was taken into consideration when establishing the minimum size of the grounding electrode conductor.

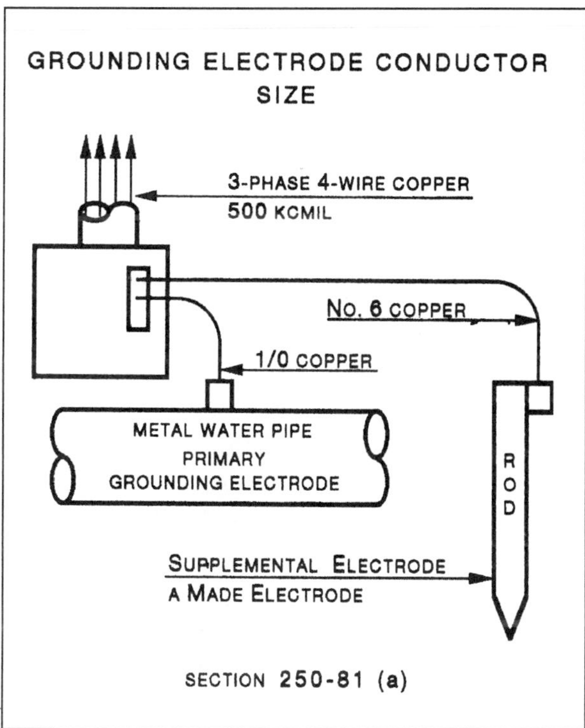

Fig. 6–25 Primary and supplemental grounding electrode conductors can be different sizes.

1. Bolted joint
2. Maximum fault current for 5 seconds
3. 1 amp allowed for each 42.25 circular mils (cmil) of conductor area
4. Voltage drop at maximum fault current limited to 40 volts per 100 feet
5. This is based on the theory that 42.25 cmil of copper conductor will carry one ampere of current for 5 seconds. After 5 seconds, it will rapidly destroy itself.

Example:

No. 6 copper = 26240 cmils (NEC® Chapter 9, *Table 8*)

1 amp per 42.25 cmils

26,240 cmils / 42.25 cmils = 621 amps current

Resistance of No. 6 = .491 ohms per 1000 feet (NEC® Chapter 9, *Table 8*)

Ohms per foot = .491 ohms / 1000 = .000491 ohms

Ohms per 100 feet = .000491 × 100 = .0491 ohms

Resistance per 100 feet = .0491 ohms

Voltage drop per 100 feet = amps × ohms

Voltage drop = 621 amps × .0491 ohms = 30.5 volts

This indicates the No. 6 copper will carry 621 amps for 5 seconds without a voltage drop of more than 40 volts per 100 feet. It is hoped the fault will be cleared, or will clear itself, in 5 seconds or less.

The second exception to the basic rule given in *Section 250-94*, Exception No. 1b., is for grounded systems; Exception No. 2b. is for ungrounded systems. The two exceptions parallel each other and are illustrated in figure 6–26. The following is a breakdown of the exceptions:

1. Applies only to concrete-encased electrodes
2. Sole connection to the grounding electrode
3. Not required to be larger than No. 4 copper
4. Only copper to be used for the grounding electrode conductor

When a supplemental electrode is used with a concrete-encased electrode, the maximum size conductor required is a No. 4 copper. However, note that the No. 4 copper grounding

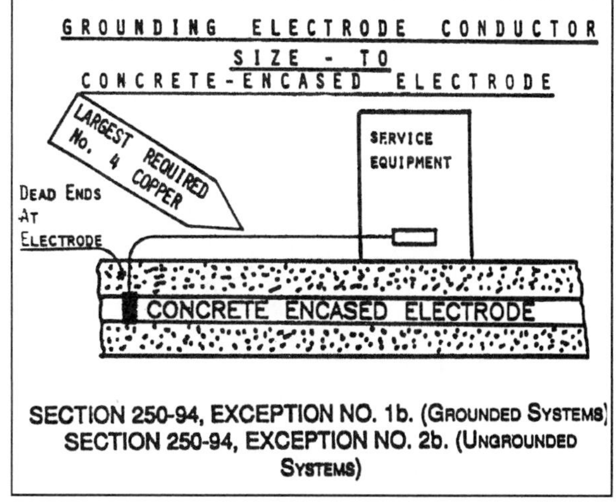

Fig. 6–26 The exception permitting a smaller grounding electrode conductor to be installed when a concrete-encased electrode is used.

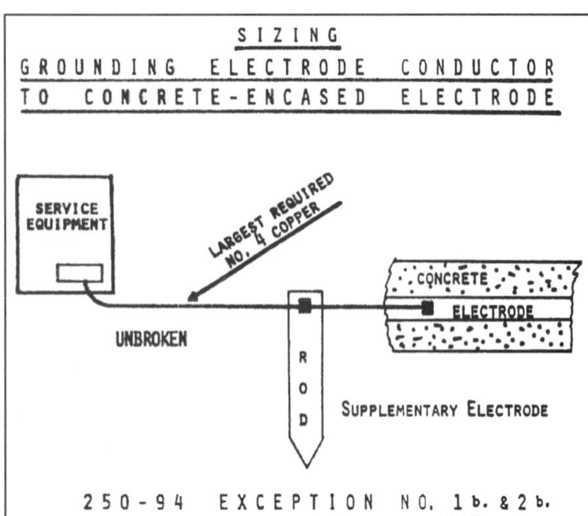

Fig. 6–27 Concrete-encased electrode with supplementary grounding electrode.

electrode conductor is unbroken at the supplementary ground rod. A No. 4 copper conductor is the smallest permitted for a concrete-encased electrode. This exception coordinates the size of the grounding electrode conductor with the size of the grounding electrode (figure 6-27).

The third exception to the basic rule, Exception No. 1c. for grounded systems and Exception No. 2c. for ungrounded systems, permits the use of a smaller grounding electrode conductor than that required by *Table 250-94* when a ground ring-type grounding electrode is installed. The two exceptions parallel each other and are illustrated in figure 6–28.

The special parts are:

1. Applies to the ground ring-type grounding electrode only
2. Requires a sole connection
3. Not required to be larger than the ground ring conductor, which is established as No. 2 copper by *Section 250-81(d)*
4. Only copper to be used for the grounding electrode conductor

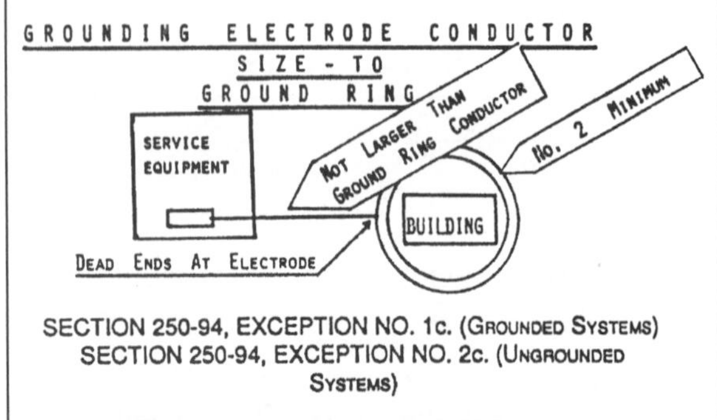

SECTION 250-94, EXCEPTION NO. 1c. (GROUNDED SYSTEMS)
SECTION 250-94, EXCEPTION NO. 2c. (UNGROUNDED SYSTEMS)

Fig. 6–28 The exception permitting a smaller grounding electrode conductor to be installed when a ground ring is the grounding electrode.

SIZING GROUNDING ELECTRODE CONDUCTORS

When sizing electrical conductors, the ampacity of the conductor is the main consideration. This is not the case when sizing the grounding electrode conductor; it is sized according to cross-sectional area. Figure 6–29 illustrates size 500 kcmil copper used as the service-entrance conductors for a grounded system with a copper grounding electrode conductor. Therefore, the basic rule applies. The size of the grounding electrode conductor is taken directly from *Table 250-94* and is No. 1/0 copper, as illustrated in figure 6–30 (page 73).

Figure 6–31 (page 73) illustrates 350 kcmil copper as the service-entrance conductors for a grounded system, and a copper grounding electrode conductor is being used. Therefore, the basic rule applies. The size of the grounding electrode conductor is taken directly from *Table 250-94,* as illustrated in figure 6–32 (page 73); a grounding electrode conductor of No. 2 copper is required.

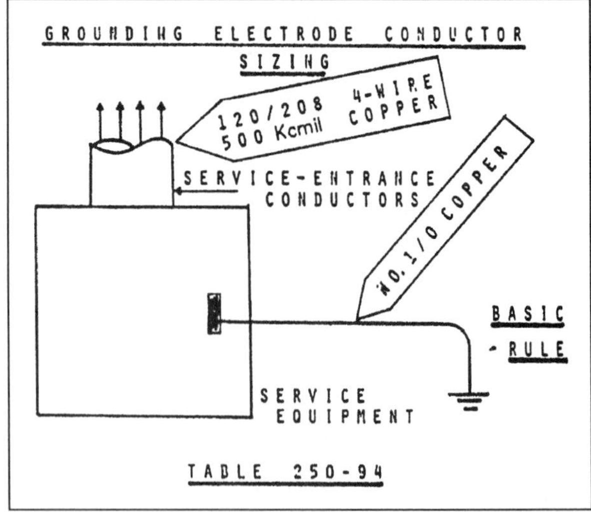

Fig. 6–29 Using 500 kcmil copper as the service conductors for a grounded AC system with a copper grounding electrode conductor.

Table 250-94.
Grounding Electrode Conductor for AC Systems

Size of Largest Service-Entrance Conductor or Equivalent Area for Parallel Conductors		Size of Grounding Electrode Conductor	
Copper	Aluminum or Copper-Clad Aluminum	Copper	*Aluminum or Copper-Clad Aluminum
2 or smaller	1/0 or smaller	8	6
1 or 1/0	2/0 or 3/0	6	4
2/0 or 3/0	4/0 or 250 kcmil	4	2
Over 3/0 thru 350 kcmil	Over 250 kcmil thru 500 kcmil	2	1/0
Over 350 kcmil thru 600 kcmil	Over 500 kcmil thru 900 kcmil	1/0	3/0
Over 600 kcmil thru 1100 kcmil	Over 900 kcmil thru 1750 kcmil	2/0	4/0
Over 1100 kcmil	Over 1750 kcmil	3/0	250 kcmil

Fig. 6–30 Reading *Table 250-94* for sizing the grounding electrode conductor for the service illustrated in figure 6–29.*

Table 250-94.
Grounding Electrode Conductor for AC Systems

Size of Largest Service-Entrance Conductor or Equivalent Area for Parallel Conductors		Size of Grounding Electrode Conductor	
Copper	Aluminum or Copper-Clad Aluminum	Copper	*Aluminum or Copper-Clad Aluminum
2 or smaller	1/0 or smaller	8	6
1 or 1/0	2/0 or 3/0	6	4
2/0 or 3/0	4/0 or 250 kcmil	4	2
Over 3/0 thru 350 kcmil	Over 250 kcmil thru 500 kcmil	2	1/0
Over 350 kcmil thru 600 kcmil	Over 500 kcmil thru 900 kcmil	1/0	3/0
Over 600 kcmil thru 1100 kcmil	Over 900 kcmil thru 1750 kcmil	2/0	4/0
Over 1100 kcmil	Over 1750 kcmil	3/0	250 kcmil

Fig. 6–32 Reading *Table 250-94* for sizing the grounding electrode conductor for the service illustrated in figure 6–31.*

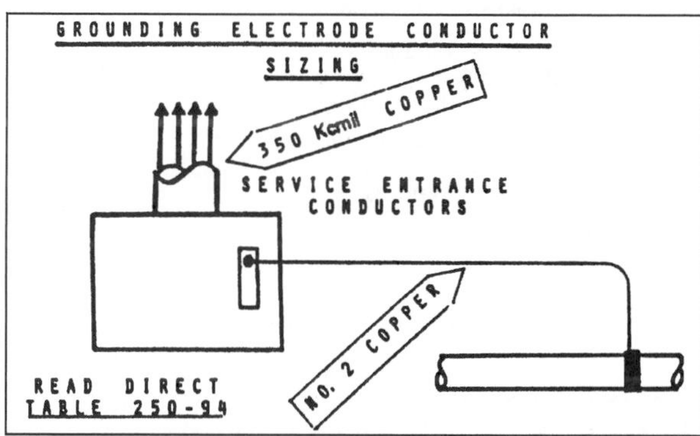

Fig. 6–31 Using 350 kcmil copper as the service conductors for a grounded AC system with a copper grounding electrode conductor.

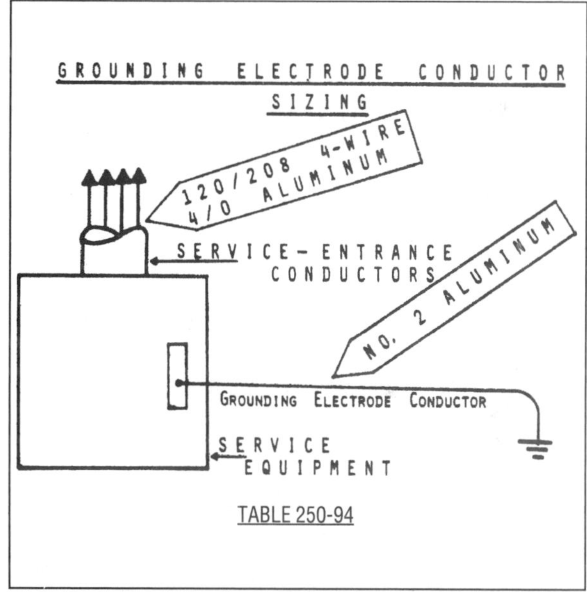

Fig. 6–33 Using No. 4/0 aluminum service conductors for a grounded AC system with an aluminum grounding electrode conductor.

Figure 6–33 illustrates size 4/0 aluminum service-entrance conductors for a grounded system; an aluminum grounding electrode conductor is used. Again, the basic rule applies. The size of the grounding electrode conductor is taken directly from *Table 250-94* and, as illustrated in figure 6–34, a grounding electrode conductor of No. 2 aluminum is required.

Figure 6–35 (page 74) illustrates the use of service-entrance conductors in parallel for a grounded system. There are two size 4/0 copper conductors, paralleled, per phase, and a copper grounding electrode conductor is used.

Table 250-94.
Grounding Electrode Conductor for AC Systems

Size of Largest Service-Entrance Conductor or Equivalent Area for Parallel Conductors		Size of Grounding Electrode Conductor	
Copper	Aluminum or Copper-Clad Aluminum	Copper	*Aluminum or Copper-Clad Aluminum
2 or smaller	1/0 or smaller	8	6
1 or 1/0	2/0 or 3/0	6	4
2/0 or 3/0	4/0 or 250 kcmil	4	2
Over 3/0 thru 350 kcmil	Over 250 kcmil thru 500 kcmil	2	1/0
Over 350 kcmil thru 600 kcmil	Over 500 kcmil thru 900 kcmil	1/0	3/0
Over 600 kcmil thru 1100 kcmil	Over 900 kcmil thru 1750 kcmil	2/0	4/0
Over 1100 kcmil	Over 1750 kcmil	3/0	250 kcmil

Fig. 6–34 Reading *Table 250-94* for sizing the grounding electrode conductor for the service illustrated in figure 6–33.*

*Reprinted with permission from NFPA 70-1996, the National Electrical Code®, Copyright © 1995, National Fire Protection Association, Quincy, Massachusetts 02269. This reprinted material is not the complete and official position of the National Fire Protection Association, on the referenced subject, which is represented only by the standard in its entirety.

Table 8, Conductor Properties (figure 6–36) is used to calculate the total circular-mil area of the service-entrance conductors. Then, the basic rule applies.

$$4/0 = 211{,}600 \text{ cmil} \times 2 \text{ conductors}$$
$$= 423{,}200 \text{ cmil}$$

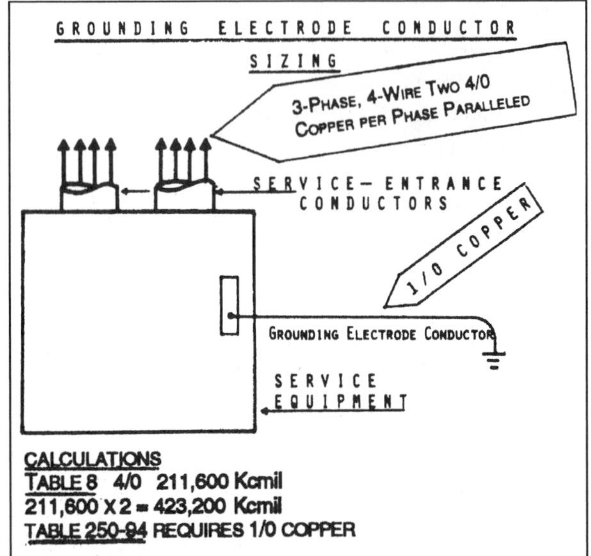

Fig. 6–35 Using two No. 4/0 copper conductors per phase, paralleled, as service conductors for a grounded AC system with a copper grounding electrode conductor.

Table 8. Conductor Properties

Size AWG/ kcmil	Area Cir. Mils	Conductors: Stranding Quantity	Conductors: Stranding Diam. in.	Conductors: Overall Diam. in.	Conductors: Overall Area in.²	DC Resistance at 75°C (167°F): Copper Uncoated ohm/kFT	DC Resistance at 75°C (167°F): Copper Coated ohm/kFT	DC Resistance at 75°C (167°F): Aluminum ohm/kFT
18	1620	1	—	0.040	0.001	7.77	8.08	12.8
18	1620	7	0.015	0.046	0.002	7.95	8.45	13.1
16	2580	1	—	0.051	0.002	4.89	5.08	8.05
16	2580	7	0.019	0.058	0.003	4.99	5.29	8.21
14	4110	1	—	0.064	0.003	3.07	3.19	5.06
14	4110	7	0.024	0.073	0.004	3.14	3.26	5.17
12	6530	1	—	0.081	0.005	1.93	2.01	3.18
12	6530	7	0.030	0.092	0.006	1.98	2.05	3.25
10	10380	1	—	0.102	0.008	1.21	1.26	2.00
10	10380	7	0.038	0.116	0.011	1.24	1.29	2.04
8	16510	1	—	0.128	0.013	0.764	0.786	1.26
8	16510	7	0.049	0.146	0.017	0.778	0.809	1.28
6	26240	7	0.061	0.184	0.027	0.491	0.510	0.808
4	41740	7	0.077	0.232	0.042	0.308	0.321	0.508
3	52620	7	0.087	0.260	0.053	0.245	0.254	0.403
2	66360	7	0.097	0.292	0.067	0.194	0.201	0.319
1	83690	19	0.066	0.332	0.087	0.154	0.160	0.253
1/0	105600	19	0.074	0.372	0.109	0.122	0.127	0.201
2/0	133100	19	0.084	0.418	0.137	0.0976	0.101	0.159
3/0	167800	19	0.094	0.470	0.173	0.0766	0.0797	0.126
→ 4/0	211600	19	0.106	0.528	0.219	0.0608	0.0626	0.100
250	—	37	0.082	0.575	0.260	0.0515	0.0535	0.0847
300	—	37	0.090	0.630	0.312	0.0429	0.0446	0.0707
350	—	37	0.097	0.681	0.364	0.0367	0.0382	0.0605
400	—	37	0.104	0.728	0.416	0.0321	0.0331	0.0529
500	—	37	0.116	0.813	0.519	0.0258	0.0265	0.0424
600	—	61	0.099	0.893	0.626	0.0214	0.0223	0.0353
700	—	61	0.107	0.964	0.730	0.0184	0.0189	0.0303
750	—	61	0.111	0.998	0.782	0.0171	0.0176	0.0282
800	—	61	0.114	1.030	0.834	0.0161	0.0166	0.0265
900	—	61	0.122	1.094	0.940	0.0143	0.0147	0.0235
1000	—	61	0.128	1.152	1.042	0.0129	0.0132	0.0212
1250	—	91	0.117	1.284	1.305	0.0103	0.0106	0.0169
1500	—	91	0.128	1.412	1.566	0.00858	0.00883	0.0141
1750	—	127	0.117	1.526	1.829	0.00735	0.00756	0.0121
2000	—	127	0.126	1.632	2.092	0.00643	0.00662	0.0106

Fig. 6–36 Reading *Table 8* (Chapter 9) for the circular-mil area of conductors when sized by number, as in figure 6–33.*

The total cross-sectional area is 423,200 circular mils per phase. The size of the grounding electrode conductor is taken directly from *Table 250-94* and is No. 1/0 copper, as indicated in figure 6–37. Note that in figure 6–37, part of the title of *Table 250-94* is *"Equivalent Area for Parallel Conductors."*

Figure 6–38 illustrates the use of service-entrance conductors in parallel for a grounded system, with a cross-sectional area exceeding the maximum listed in *Table 250-94*. The service

Table 250-94.
Grounding Electrode Conductor for AC Systems

Size of Largest Service-Entrance Conductor or Equivalent Area for Parallel Conductors: Copper	Size of Largest Service-Entrance Conductor or Equivalent Area for Parallel Conductors: Aluminum or Copper-Clad Aluminum	Size of Grounding Electrode Conductor: Copper	Size of Grounding Electrode Conductor: *Aluminum or Copper-Clad Aluminum
2 or smaller	1/0 or smaller	8	6
1 or 1/0	2/0 or 3/0	6	4
2/0 or 3/0	4/0 or 250 kcmil	4	2
Over 3/0 thru 350 kcmil	Over 250 kcmil thru 500 kcmil	2	1/0
Over 350 kcmil thru 600 kcmil	Over 500 kcmil thru 900 kcmil	1/0	3/0
Over 600 kcmil thru 1100 kcmil	Over 900 kcmil thru 1750 kcmil	2/0	4/0
Over 1100 kcmil	Over 1750 kcmil	3/0	250 kcmil

Fig. 6–37 Reading *Table 250-94* for sizing the grounding electrode conductor for the service illustrated in figure 6–35.*

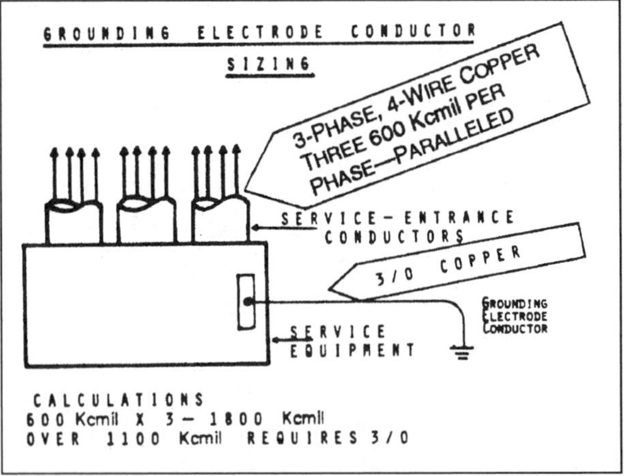

Fig. 6–38 Sizing the grounding electrode conductor for a grounded AC system with three conductors per phase, paralleled; all conductors are copper.

consists of three 600 kcmil copper conductors per phase for a three-phase, four-wire service. A copper grounding electrode conductor is used.

$$3 \times 600 \text{ kcmil} = 1800 \text{ kcmil per phase}$$

This exceeds the 1100 kcmil for the equivalent area of the service-entrance conductors listed in *Table 250-94*. In figure 6–39, the bottom line under "Copper" indicates that service-entrance conductors "over" 1100 kcmil are not required to be larger than No. 3/0 copper.

Figure 6–40 illustrates a three-phase, 480-volt, three-wire ungrounded service with one 750 kcmil copper conductor per phase. It is an ungrounded system and has no grounded service-entrance conductor. *Section 250-94* requires an

Table 250-94.
Grounding Electrode Conductor for AC Systems

Size of Largest Service-Entrance Conductor or Equivalent Area for Parallel Conductors		Size of Grounding Electrode Conductor	
Copper	Aluminum or Copper-Clad Aluminum	Copper	*Aluminum or Copper-Clad Aluminum
2 or smaller	1/0 or smaller	8	6
1 or 1/0	2/0 or 3/0	6	4
2/0 or 3/0	4/0 or 250 kcmil	4	2
Over 3/0 thru 350 kcmil	Over 250 kcmil thru 500 kcmil	2	1/0
Over 350 kcmil thru 600 kcmil	Over 500 kcmil thru 900 kcmil	1/0	3/0
Over 600 kcmil thru 1100 kcmil	Over 900 kcmil thru 1750 kcmil	2/0	4/0
Over 1100 kcmil	Over 1750 kcmil	3/0	250 kcmil

Fig. 6–39 Reading *Table 250-94* for sizing the grounding electrode conductor for the service illustrated in figure 6–38.*

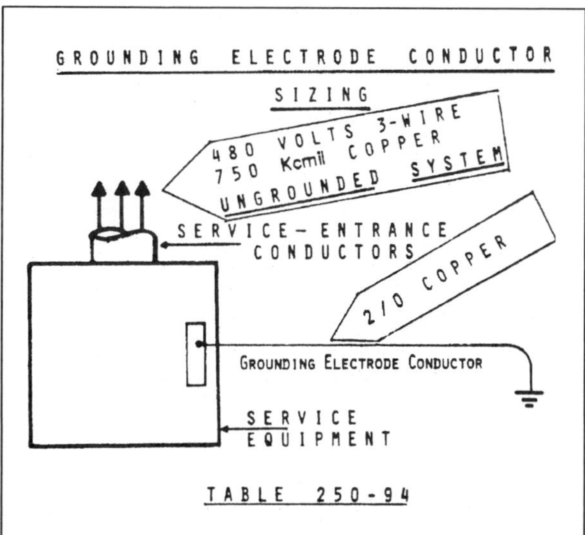

Fig. 6–40 Sizing the grounding electrode conductor for an ungrounded AC system with one conductor per phase and all copper conductors.

ungrounded system, as well as a grounded system, to have a grounding electrode conductor. As illustrated in figure 6–41, the grounding electrode conductor is read directly from *Table 250-94* and is No. 2/0 copper. Note the title of *Table 250-94*: *"Grounding Electrode Conductors for AC Systems."* The term *AC systems* will include both the grounded and ungrounded AC system.

Figure 6–42 illustrates a three-phase, 480-volt, three-wire ungrounded service with three 750

Table 250-94.
Grounding Electrode Conductor for AC Systems

Size of Largest Service-Entrance Conductor or Equivalent Area for Parallel Conductors		Size of Grounding Electrode Conductor	
Copper	Aluminum or Copper-Clad Aluminum	Copper	*Aluminum or Copper-Clad Aluminum
2 or smaller	1/0 or smaller	8	6
1 or 1/0	2/0 or 3/0	6	4
2/0 or 3/0	4/0 or 250 kcmil	4	2
Over 3/0 thru 350 kcmil	Over 250 kcmil thru 500 kcmil	2	1/0
Over 350 kcmil thru 600 kcmil	Over 500 kcmil thru 900 kcmil	1/0	3/0
Over 600 kcmil thru 1100 kcmil	Over 900 kcmil thru 1750 kcmil	2/0	4/0
Over 1100 kcmil	Over 1750 kcmil	3/0	250 kcmil

Fig. 6–41 Reading *Table 250-94* for sizing the grounding electrode conductor for the service illustrated in figure 6–40.*

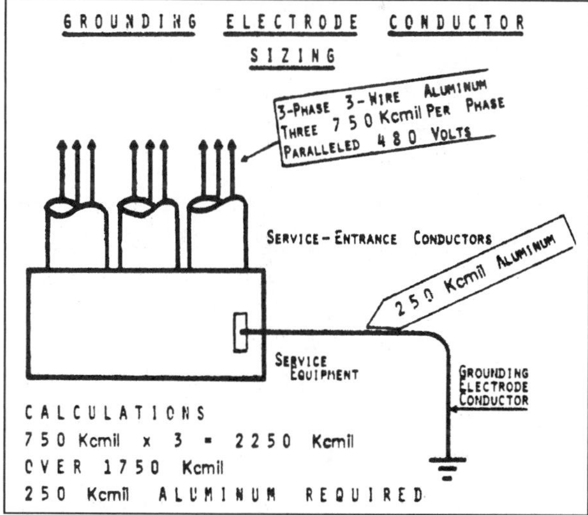

Fig. 6–42 Sizing the grounding electrode conductor for an ungrounded AC system with three conductors per phase, paralleled; all conductors are aluminum.

*Reprinted with permission from NFPA 70-1996, the National Electrical Code®, Copyright © 1995, National Fire Protection Association, Quincy, Massachusetts 02269. This reprinted material is not the complete and official position of the National Fire Protection Association, on the referenced subject, which is represented only by the standard in its entirety.

kcmil aluminum conductors in parallel per phase, with an aluminum grounding electrode conductor.

750 kcmil × 3 conductors = 2250 kcmil per phase

The size of the grounding electrode conductor is read directly from *Table 250-94* (figure 6–43). The 2250 kcmil is over the largest size listed for aluminum. Therefore, the grounding electrode conductor is 250 kcmil aluminum.

Figure 6–44 illustrates a three-phase, 240/120-volt grounded system with a high leg; all copper conductors are used. The high leg is calculated to be No. 2/0, the other two phase conductors are 500 kcmil, and the neutral is No. 4/0. The grounding electrode conductor is calculated on the largest service-entrance conductor, which in this case is 500 kcmil copper. The size of the copper grounding electrode conductor is read directly from *Table 250-94*, as illustrated in figure 6–45, and is No. 1/0 copper.

Figure 6–46 illustrates the use of aluminum service-entrance conductors and a different

Table 250-94.
Grounding Electrode Conductor for AC Systems

Size of Largest Service-Entrance Conductor or Equivalent Area for Parallel Conductors		Size of Grounding Electrode Conductor	
Copper	Aluminum or Copper-Clad Aluminum	Copper	*Aluminum or Copper-Clad Aluminum
2 or smaller	1/0 or smaller	8	6
1 or 1/0	2/0 or 3/0	6	4
2/0 or 3/0	4/0 or 250 kcmil	4	2
Over 3/0 thru 350 kcmil	Over 250 kcmil thru 500 kcmil	2	1/0
Over 350 kcmil thru 600 kcmil	Over 500 kcmil thru 900 kcmil	1/0	3/0
Over 600 kcmil thru 1100 kcmil	Over 900 kcmil thru 1750 kcmil	2/0	4/0
Over 1100 kcmil	Over 1750 kcmil	3/0	250 kcmil

Fig. 6–43 Reading *Table 250-94* for sizing the grounding electrode conductor for the service illustrated in figure 6–42.*

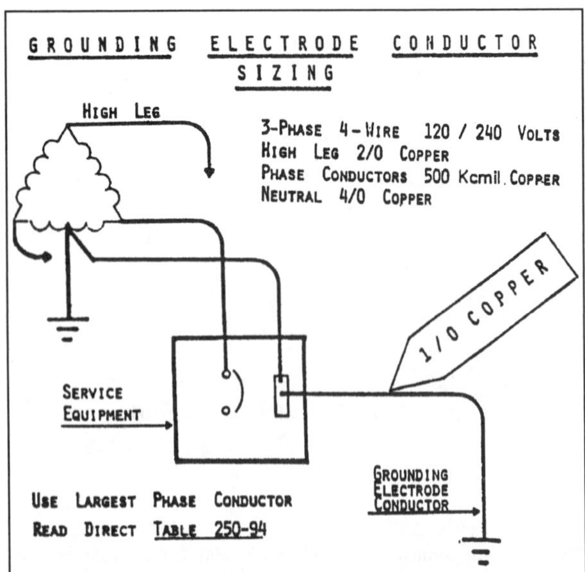

Fig. 6–44 Sizing the grounding electrode conductor for a delta with a high leg system with one conductor per phase and a neutral. All conductors are copper.

Table 250-94.
Grounding Electrode Conductor for AC Systems

Size of Largest Service-Entrance Conductor or Equivalent Area for Parallel Conductors		Size of Grounding Electrode Conductor	
Copper	Aluminum or Copper-Clad Aluminum	Copper	*Aluminum or Copper-Clad Aluminum
2 or smaller	1/0 or smaller	8	6
1 or 1/0	2/0 or 3/0	6	4
2/0 or 3/0	4/0 or 250 kcmil	4	2
Over 3/0 thru 350 kcmil	Over 250 kcmil thru 500 kcmil	2	1/0
Over 350 kcmil thru 600 kcmil	Over 500 kcmil thru 900 kcmil	1/0	3/0
Over 600 kcmil thru 1100 kcmil	Over 900 kcmil thru 1750 kcmil	2/0	4/0
Over 1100 kcmil	Over 1750 kcmil	3/0	250 kcmil

Fig. 6–45 Reading *Table 250-94* for sizing the grounding electrode conductor for the service illustrated in figure 6–44.*

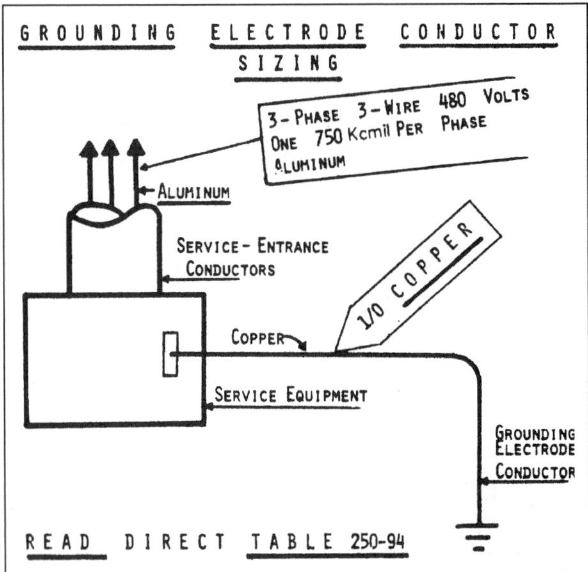

Fig. 6–46 Sizing the grounding electrode conductor for an ungrounded system with aluminum service-entrance conductors and a copper grounding electrode conductor.

metal, copper, for the grounding electrode conductor. It is a three-phase, three-wire, 480-volt system with one 750 kcmil aluminum conductor per phase, with a copper grounding electrode conductor. The Code makes no mention of this very common installation and *Table 250-94* can be used as illustrated in figure 6–47. The size of the service-entrance conductor is read under "Aluminum" and the size of the grounding electrode conductor is read under "Copper." It is No. 1/0 copper.

When there is more than one set of service-entrance conductors installed, as permitted by *Section 230-40*, Exception No. 2, the grounding electrode conductor is sized according to the largest conductor in each set of service entrance conductors.

Figure 6–48 illustrates three separate sets of service entrance conductors. They are all copper conductors, each is a three-phase, three-wire, 480-volt set of service entrance conductors. The grounding electrode conductor is sized according to the FPN to *Table 250-94*.

One of the 500 kcmil conductors	500,000 cmil
One of the 4/0 conductors (*Table 8*)	211,600 cmil
One of the 350 kcmil conductors	350,000 cmil
Total	1,061,600 cmil

1,061,600 cmil = 1061.6 kcmil

Using *Table 250-94* (figure 6–49), 2/0 copper is the size of the grounding electrode conductor.

Table 250-94.
Grounding Electrode Conductor for AC Systems

Size of Largest Service-Entrance Conductor or Equivalent Area for Parallel Conductors		Size of Grounding Electrode Conductor	
Copper	Aluminum or Copper-Clad Aluminum	Copper	*Aluminum or Copper-Clad Aluminum
2 or smaller	1/0 or smaller	8	6
1 or 1/0	2/0 or 3/0	6	4
2/0 or 3/0	4/0 or 250 kcmil	4	2
Over 3/0 thru 350 kcmil	Over 250 kcmil thru 500 kcmil	2	1/0
Over 350 kcmil thru 600 kcmil	Over 500 kcmil thru 900 kcmil	1/0	3/0
Over 600 kcmil thru 1100 kcmil	Over 900 kcmil thru 1750 kcmil	2/0	4/0
Over 1100 kcmil	Over 1750 kcmil	3/0	250 kcmil

Fig. 6–47 Reading *Table 250-94* for sizing the grounding electrode conductor for the service illustrated in figure 6–46.*

Figure 6–50 (page 78) illustrates two sets of copper service entrance conductors supplied from a three-phase, four-wire delta with a high leg bank of transformers. One set of the service-entrance conductors supplies the 120/240-volt, three-wire lighting and one set of the service-entrance conductors supplies the three-phase, three-wire, 240-volt power.

Power 2 × 300 kcmil =	600,000 cmil
Lighting No. 2 (from *Table 8*)	66,360 cmil
Total	666,360 cmil

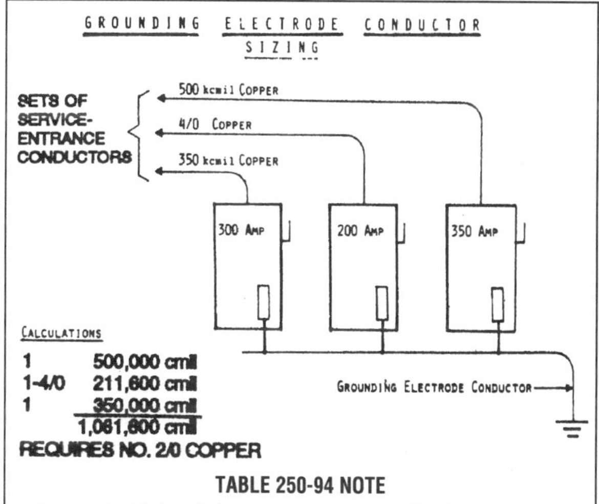

Fig. 6–48 Sizing grounding electrode conductor when there is more than one set of service-entrance conductors.

Table 250-94.
Grounding Electrode Conductor for AC Systems

Size of Largest Service-Entrance Conductor or Equivalent Area for Parallel Conductors		Size of Grounding Electrode Conductor	
Copper	Aluminum or Copper-Clad Aluminum	Copper	*Aluminum or Copper-Clad Aluminum
2 or smaller	1/0 or smaller	8	6
1 or 1/0	2/0 or 3/0	6	4
2/0 or 3/0	4/0 or 250 kcmil	4	2
Over 3/0 thru 350 kcmil	Over 250 kcmil thru 500 kcmil	2	1/0
Over 350 kcmil thru 600 kcmil	Over 500 kcmil thru 900 kcmil	1/0	3/0
Over 600 kcmil thru 1100 kcmil	Over 900 kcmil thru 1750 kcmil	2/0	4/0
Over 1100 kcmil	Over 1750 kcmil	3/0	250 kcmil

Fig. 6–49 Reading *Table 250-94* for sizing the grounding electrode conductor for the service illustrated in figure 6–48.*

Read the size of the grounding electrode conductor from *Table 250-94* (figure 6–51), which is 2/0 copper.

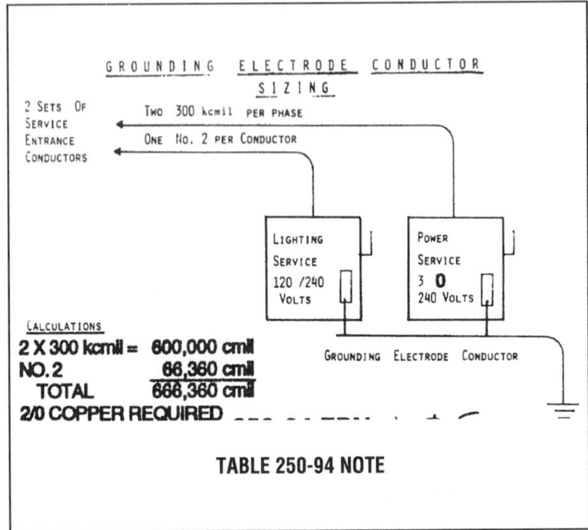

Fig. 6–50 Sizing grounding electrode conductor with two sets of service-entrance conductors.

SUMMARY

The grounding electrode conductor is the main highway the electrons travel to get to the grounding electrode and into the ground. All other grounding conductors are feeder lines to the main highway. Remember the "grounding target" in Chapter 1?

Table 250-94.
Grounding Electrode Conductor for AC Systems

Size of Largest Service-Entrance Conductor or Equivalent Area for Parallel Conductors		Size of Grounding Electrode Conductor	
Copper	Aluminum or Copper-Clad Aluminum	Copper	*Aluminum or Copper-Clad Aluminum
2 or smaller	1/0 or smaller	8	6
1 or 1/0	2/0 or 3/0	6	4
2/0 or 3/0	4/0 or 250 kcmil	4	2
Over 3/0 thru 350 kcmil	Over 250 kcmil thru 500 kcmil	2	1/0
Over 350 kcmil thru 600 kcmil	Over 500 kcmil thru 900 kcmil	1/0	3/0
Over 600 kcmil thru 1100 kcmil	Over 900 kcmil thru 1750 kcmil	2/0	4/0
Over 1100 kcmil	Over 1750 kcmil	3/0	250 kcmil

Fig. 6–51 Reading *Table 250-94* for sizing the grounding electrode conductor for the service illustrated in figure 6–50.*

FOLLOW UP

Topics for self-study, discussion, or questioning.

1. Define the grounding electrode conductor.
2. Discuss the materials permitted to be used for a grounding electrode conductor.
3. Explain when splicing the grounding electrode conductor is permitted.
4. Explain how the grounding electrode must be installed.
5. Explain why bonding the grounding electrode conductor to a metal raceway used for its protection is required.
6. What is the smallest grounding electrode conductor permitted? What is the largest required?
7. What is the maximum size grounding electrode conductor required for a concrete-encased grounding electrode for a grounded system?
8. Explain how the grounding electrode conductor should be connected to the grounding electrode.
9. Explain how to calculate the size of the bonding jumper when bonding the grounding electrode conductor to a metal enclosure used for mechanical protection.
10. Explain how to calculate the size of a copper grounding electrode conductor when three-phase, four-wire, 4/0 copper service-entrance conductors are installed.

11. Repeat number 10 above, this time using aluminum service-entrance conductors and an aluminum grounding electrode conductor.
12. Explain how to calculate the size of a copper grounding electrode conductor when two 500 kcmil copper service-entrance conductors are installed for a three-phase, four-wire service.
13. Do the same using aluminum service-entrance conductors and an aluminum grounding electrode conductor.
14. Discuss how the sizing of the grounding electrode conductor is the same for a grounded system and for an ungrounded system.
15. Explain how to calculate the size of a copper grounding electrode conductor for a service consisting of one 500 kcmil per phase, three-phase, four-wire, aluminum conductor.
16. Explain how to use *Table 8* of Chapter 9 to convert circular mil area to a standard conductor size.

CHAPTER 7

Circuit and System Grounding

OBJECTIVES

After completing this chapter, the student should be able to:

- make use of the cross-referencing *Table 250-2*.
- define the term *grounded conductor*.
- identify the neutral conductor as the grounded conductor and the systems in which it is used.
- explain why systems are grounded.
- explain why circuits are grounded.
- explain what is meant by electrical continuity of the grounding path.
- explain what the term "intentionally grounded" means.
- explain how the term "voltage to ground" applies to a grounded system and an ungrounded system.
- identify, with the use of Part B of *Article 250*, which systems and circuits shall be grounded and which are permitted to be grounded.
- interpret the exceptions to the basic rules for grounding systems and circuits.
- explain what is meant by an "isolated" system.
- interpret the requirements for impedance grounding for alternating-current circuits.
- explain the advantages of the impedance-grounded system.
- explain why no loads may be connected to the neutral of an impedance-grounded system.

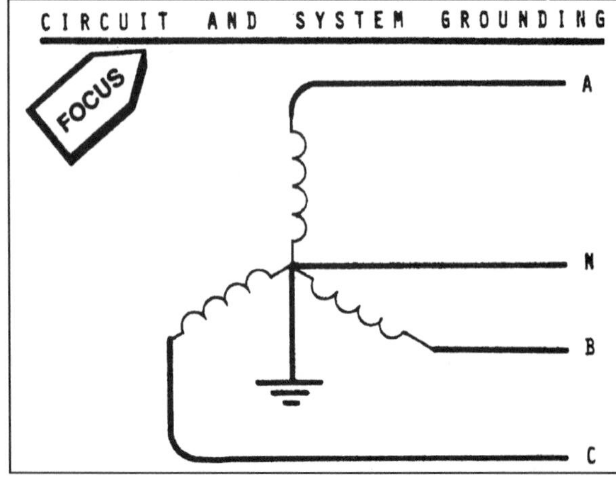

Fig. 7–1 Circuit and system grounding.

This chapter focuses on circuit and system grounding (figure 7–1) and the requirements are mostly covered in *Part B* of *Article 250.* Circuit and system grounding is a result of the way the source of supply is intentionally connected to ground. This can be a utility company connection or the connection at a separately derived system.

In the case of the direct-current generator, the connection is made at the generator. For alternating current, it is made at the transformer. When there is an alternating-current generator, the connection could be made at the generator or within the generator.

WHY GROUND CIRCUITS AND SYSTEMS?

Figure 7–2 illustrates five reasons that systems and circuits are grounded, as listed by the Code. These five reasons add up to one: safety of equipment and personnel. There are two other reasons for using the grounded system other than those listed in the Code. For example, two advantages of the 120/208-volt grounded system are:

1. Savings in wire cost—Four wires can be used to serve the same load that six wires, single phase would need.
2. Two voltages are available for use—120 volts for lighting, 208 volts for power.

Section 250-2, Application of Other Articles, is a very valuable section to become acquainted with. It is a cross-reference with other Code regulations applicable to grounding. It is usable as a table of content for locating specific grounding requirements for specific circuits or equipment.

DEFINITIONS

Grounded Conductor

When discussing systems and circuits, the term *grounded conductor* comes up very often because it plays such an important part in a grounded system. The definition for a grounded conductor (figure 7–3) needs to be reviewed before discussing grounded systems. The

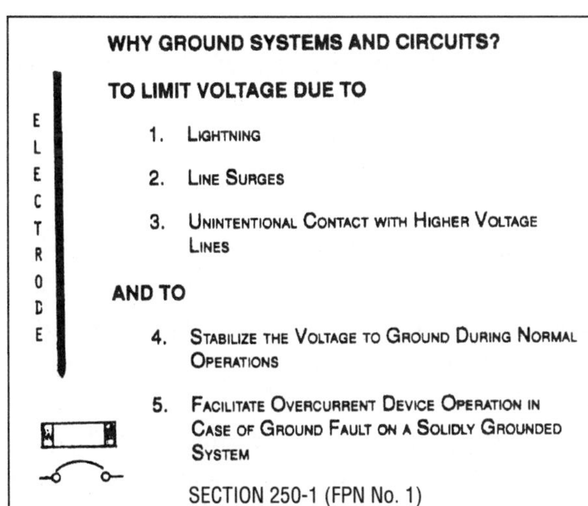

Fig. 7–2 Reasons for grounding systems and circuits.

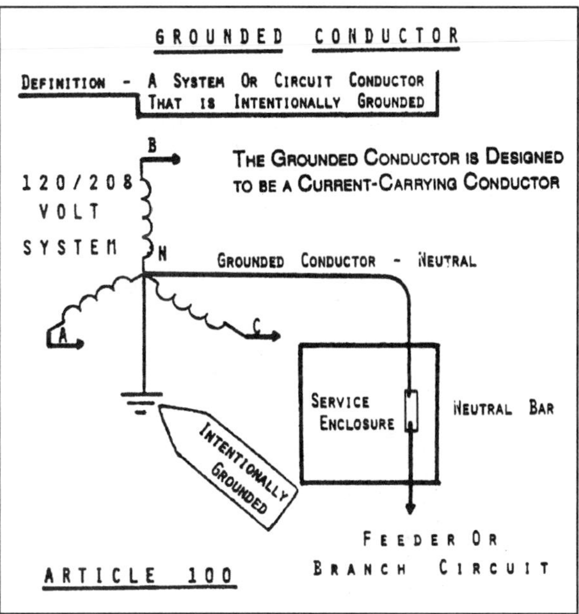

Fig. 7–3 Definition of *grounded conductor*. Reprinted with permission from NFPA 70-1996, the National Electrical Code®.*

grounded conductor will be discussed in detail in the next chapter. For simplicity and to keep the illustrations as uncluttered as possible, only one phase wire and the pertinent points will be shown on the figures in the rest of this text when possible.

The one word that really stands out in this definition, as shown in figure 7–3, is the word *intentionally*. There is no accident, no mistake; one conductor is intentionally grounded at the time of installation.

The Code sets down the regulations concerning when direct-current systems and alternating-current systems

1. shall be grounded,
2. are permitted to be grounded,
3. and are not permitted to be grounded.

Voltage Terminology

Two important terms used in conjunction with grounded systems are:

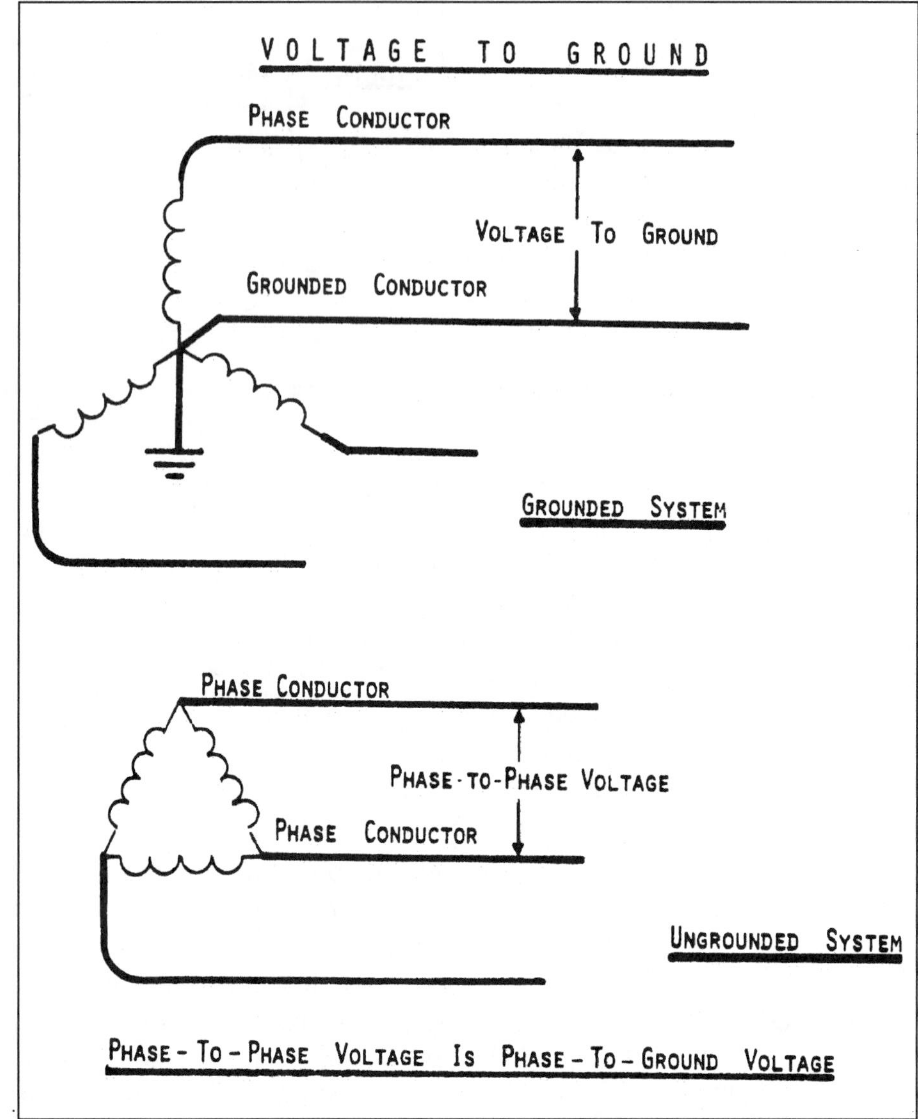

Fig. 7–4 Definition of *Voltage to Ground* in a grounded and ungrounded system.

1. *Voltage to Ground*
2. *Neutral*

Figure 7–4 illustrates the definition of voltage to ground (*Article 100*). There are two important parts to this definition. These are:

Quote – 1. "For grounded circuits, the voltage between the given conductor and that point or conductor of the circuit that is grounded.

2. For ungrounded circuits, the greatest voltage between the given conductor and any other conductor of the circuit."*

When the system is grounded so there is a neutral point, as in figure 7–4, the circuit conductor connected to the neutral point is called the *neutral*. With very few exceptions, the grounded conductor is the neutral conductor. The Code does not define the term *neutral* but refers to it, in Note 10 of *Tables 310-16*, as the conductor that carries the unbalanced load. *Section 250-25(2)* identifies the grounded conductor as the neutral of a single-phase, three-wire system.

*Reprinted with permission from NFPA 70-1996, the National Electrical Code®, Copyright © 1995, National Fire Protection Association, Quincy, MA 02269. This reprinted material is not the complete and official position of the National Fire Protection Association, on the referenced subject, which is represented only by the standard in its entirety.

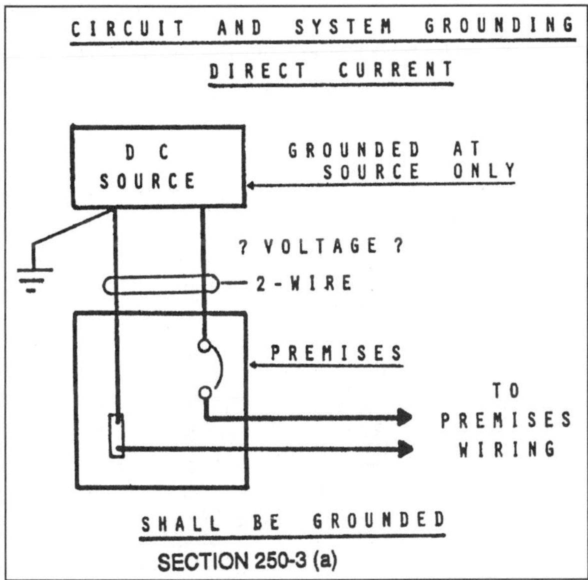

Fig. 7–5 Grounding a two-wire DC system.

DIRECT-CURRENT SYSTEMS

Figure 7–5 illustrates a two-wire, direct-current system with a grounded conductor. This system is required to be grounded when supplying premises wiring. In the basic rule, *Section 250-3(a)*, there is nothing mentioned concerning the minimum or maximum voltage. However, there are five exceptions that do take the voltage into consideration, and each of these five exceptions will be looked at.

One of the interesting things shown in figure 7–5 is that when the source of supply is located other than on the premises, the grounding electrode conductor is installed at the source. This regulation is set down in *Section 250-22*.

Exception No. 1 (figure 7–6) will permit an ungrounded, two-wire, direct-current system to be used where a system is installed that is equipped

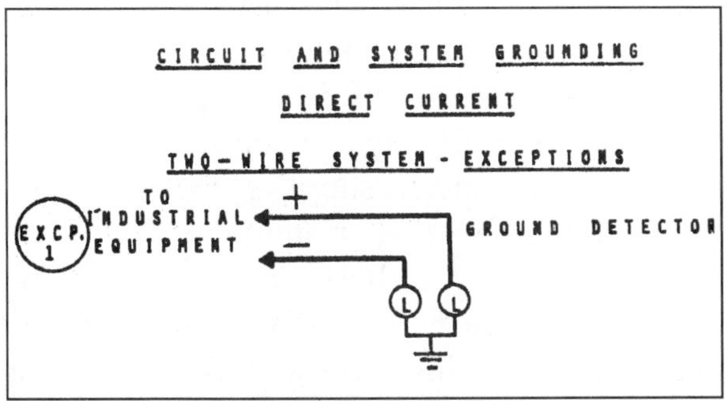

Fig. 7–6 An example of ground detectors for an ungrounded, two-wire DC system.

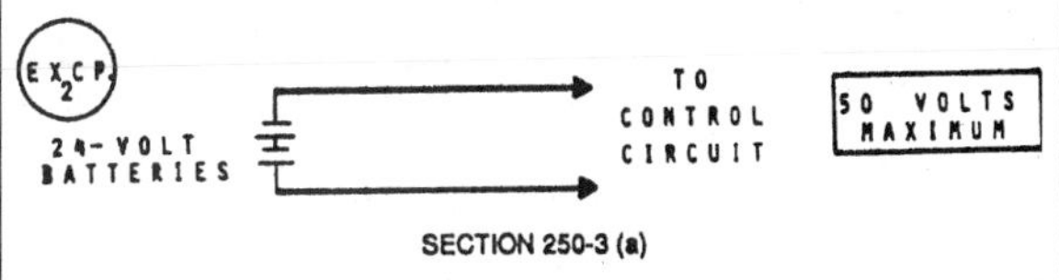

Fig. 7–7 An example of a low-voltage, ungrounded, two-wire DC system.

with ground detectors and supplies only industrial equipment in a limited area. For example, a manufacturing plant might use a two-wire, ungrounded DC system for production line control.

Exception No. 2 (figure 7–7) will permit an ungrounded, two-wire, direct-current system to be used where a system is operating at 50 volts or less between conductors. Such a system would exist where 24 volts direct current is used for controls in conjunction with a switchboard or similar equipment.

Exception No. 3 (figure 7–8) will permit an ungrounded, two-wire, direct-current system to be used where the equipment operates at more than 300 volts between conductors. Such a circuit might be a large, direct-current motor circuit.

Exception No. 4 (figure 7–9, page 84) will permit an ungrounded, two-wire, direct-current system to be used where the direct current is derived from a rectifier. However, the alternating-current system supplying the rectifier must meet the requirements set down for alternating-current systems. Such a system would exist where 120 volts alternating current is rectified for use as a 120-volt, direct-current control or signaling system.

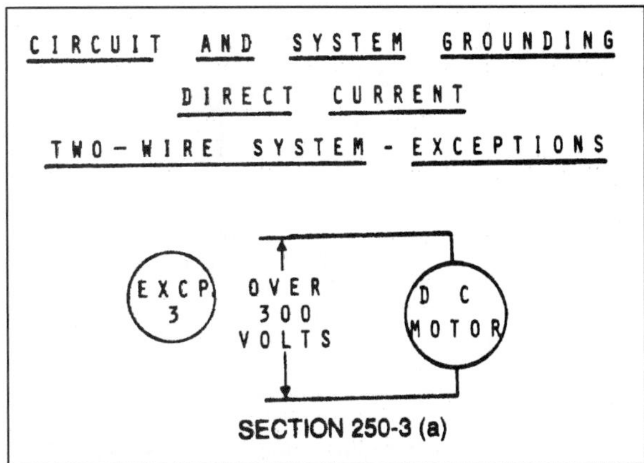

Fig. 7–8 An example of a higher-voltage, ungrounded, two-wire DC system.

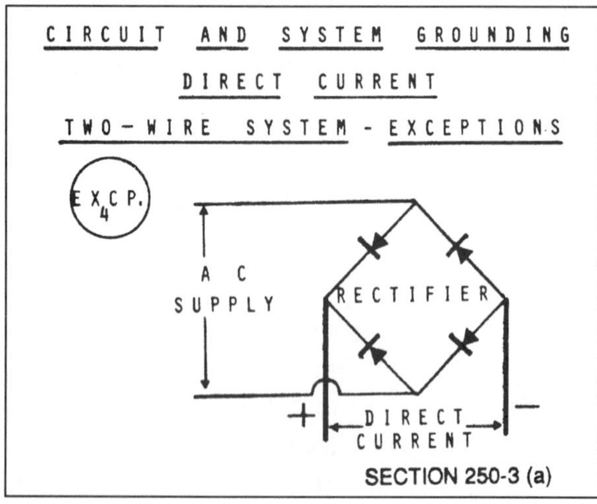

Fig. 7–9 An example of an ungrounded, two-wire DC system secured with the use of rectifiers.

Exception No. 5 (figure 7–10) will permit the use of an ungrounded, two-wire, direct-current system where the power supply is limited to a maximum of 30 milliamps (.030 amp) when used for direct-current, fire protection signal circuits. The 30 milliamps comes from *Article 760 (Fire Alarm Systems)*. This exception coordinates the Code regulations with *Article 760 (Fire Alarm Systems)*.

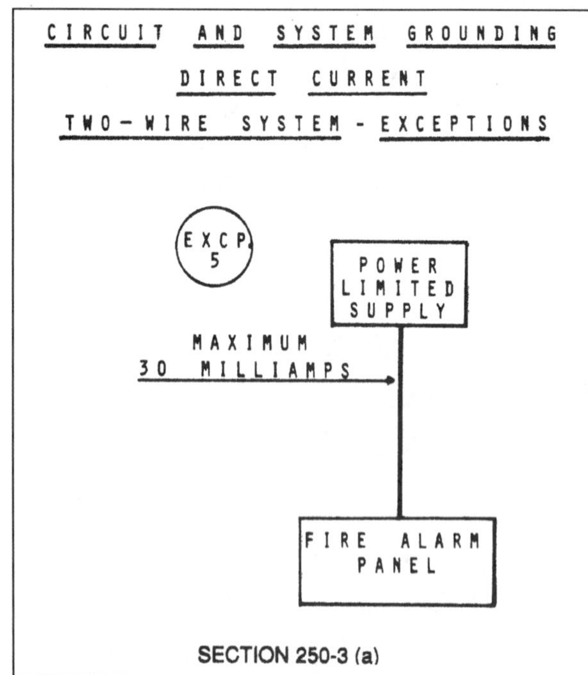

Fig. 7–10 An example of where a power-limited, ungrounded, two-wire DC supply is permitted.

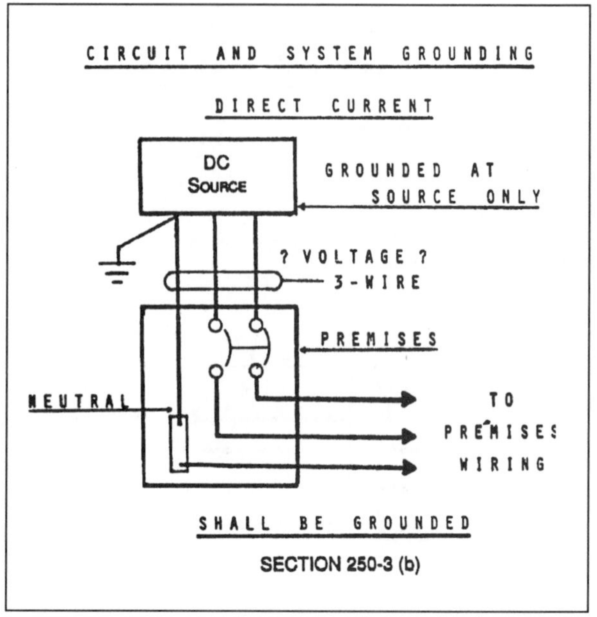

Fig. 7–11 Requirements for grounding a three-wire DC system.

Section 250-3(b) (figure 7–11) requires the neutral conductor of all three-wire, direct-current systems that supply premises wiring to be grounded. There are no minimum or maximum voltages mentioned, nor are there any exceptions listed. Once again, the grounding electrode conductor is installed at the source of supply only when it is located other than on the premises. The grounded conductor is not bonded to a second grounding electrode conductor at the service as it is in the case of alternating-current grounded systems.

Figure 7–12 (page 85) illustrates the exception to *Section 250-22*, which allows the grounding electrode conductor of direct-current systems to be installed at the direct-current generator, or at the first disconnecting means or overcurrent protective device. This applies when the direct-current source is located on the premises.

The second part of the exception to *Section 250-22* permits any other means of grounding the direct current supply provided it will accomplish the same system protection. It must use equipment listed and identified for this particular use. This second part of this exception takes into consideration sensitive electronic equipment that needs to be grounded

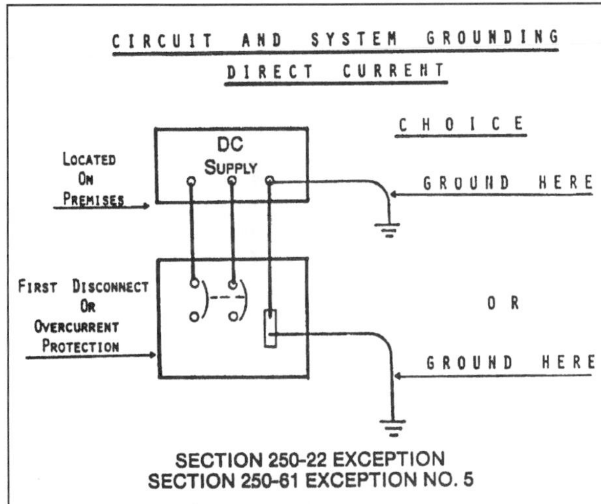

Fig. 7–12 Permitted locations for the grounding electrode conductor connection for an on-premises DC supply.

without establishing equipment grounding paths that could result in ground current paths through the building steel. (This exception is also coordinated with an Exception No. 5 to *Section 250-61*.)

ALTERNATING-CURRENT SYSTEMS

The Code divides the alternating-current systems to be grounded into three groups. These are:

1. Systems operating at less than 50 volts
2. Systems operating at 50 volts to 1000 volts
3. Systems operating at 1000 volts and over

Alternating-Current Systems of Less than 50 Volts

There are three situations under which alternating-current systems operating at less than 50 volts shall be grounded. The following paragraphs discuss these situations.

The first is where a system is supplied by a transformer and the transformer supply exceeds 150 volts to ground. In this case, it shall be grounded (figure 7–13). An example of this would be where one phase conductor and a neutral of a 277/480-volt system is used to supply the primary of a transformer, and the secondary of the transformer is used to supply 48 volts to operate small solenoid valves or some other low-voltage control circuit. The secondary is less than 50 volts and the primary is more than 150 volts to ground.

In the second situation, where a system is supplied by a transformer and the transformer supply is ungrounded, it shall be grounded (figure 7–14). An example of this is where one phase of a three-phase, 480-volt ungrounded system is used to supply the primary of a transformer, and the secondary of the transformer is less than 50 volts.

The third situation requiring that the system operating at less than 50 volts be grounded is when the system conductors are installed as overhead conductors outside a building. This is shown in figure 7–15 (page 86).

The Code is very specific when requiring that in these three situations, the systems be grounded. However, other alternating-current

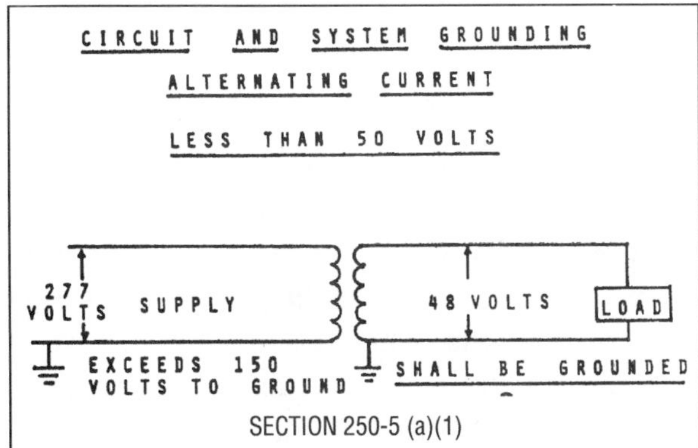

Fig. 7–13 An example of where an AC system of less than 50 volts is required to be grounded.

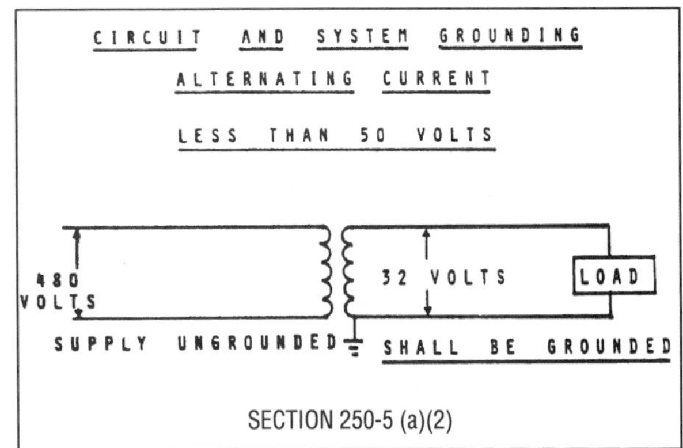

Fig. 7–14 Another example of where an AC system of less than 50 volts is required to be grounded.

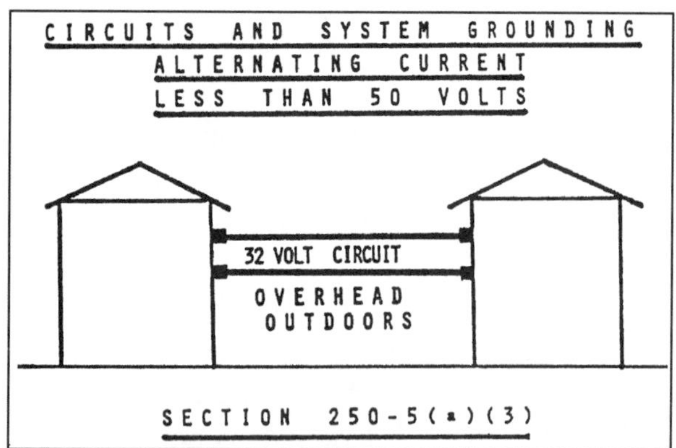

Fig. 7–15 Overhead conductors outdoors, less than 50 volts, shall be a grounded circuit or system.

systems operating at less than 50 volts are also permitted to be grounded. The electrical or design engineer should decide whether such a system should be grounded. An example here would be where the primary of a transformer is supplied with 120 volts, one hot wire, and a neutral, and the secondary is 32 volts. The secondary is less than 50 volts and the voltage supplying the transformers does not exceed 150 volts to ground (figure 7–16). In this case, the 32-volt secondary is not required to be grounded, but it is permitted to be grounded.

Alternating-Current Systems of 50 to 1000 Volts

Here the Code offers three electrical distribution systems and one situation under which the system shall be grounded. It should be kept in mind that these are not the only systems or

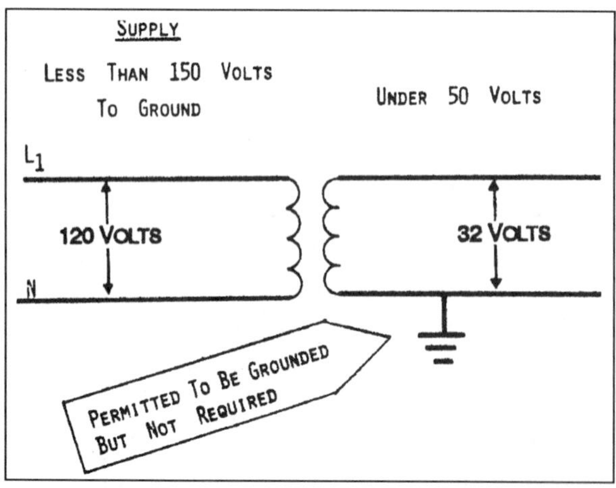

Fig. 7–16 AC system permitted to be grounded.

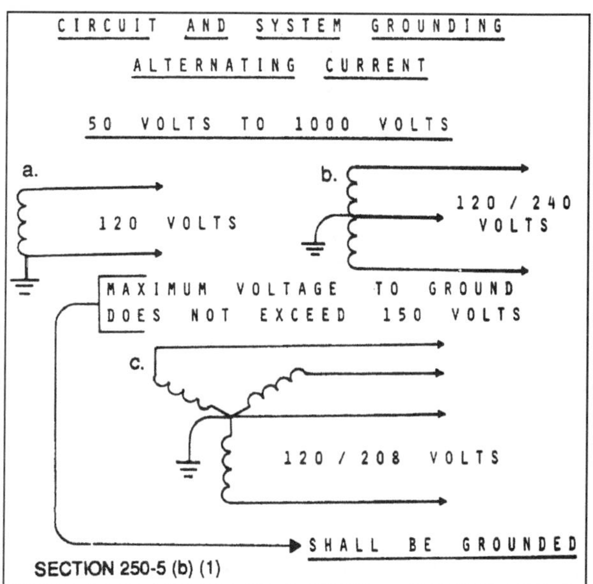

Fig. 7–17 AC systems required to be grounded: (a) two-wire system; (b) three-wire system; (c) four-wire system.

situations under which a grounded system is permitted to be installed. Rather, these are the "shall"-be-grounded systems, although other systems are permitted to be grounded.

Section 250-5(b)(1) requires that where the system can be so grounded, the maximum voltage to ground on the ungrounded conductors does not exceed 150 volts. Figure 7–17 illustrates the three most common applications of this regulation, which are the most common grounded systems the average electrician works on almost daily.

Figure 7–17 (a) shows the single-phase, 120-volt, two-wire system where one conductor is intentionally grounded and the voltage to ground does not exceed 150 volts. Such a system would be used for a small service with a single branch circuit.

In figure 7–17 (b), the single-phase, 120/240-volt, three-wire system is shown, with the center tap of the transformer intentionally grounded and used as the neutral conductor. Once again, the voltage to ground does not exceed 150 volts. This system is extensively used for residential services and in office areas where 120 volts is needed for receptacles.

The three-phase, 120/208-volt, four-wire system, which is a wye connected system with the wye point of the system intentionally grounded and used as the neutral conductor, is shown in figure 7–17 (c) (page 86). The voltage to ground does not exceed 150 volts. This system is used for services and distribution in office buildings, warehouses, shopping strips, schools, churches, multifamily dwellings, and many other locations.

In each of these three systems, the situation is such that the system can be grounded with the voltage to ground not exceeding 150 volts. Therefore, in each of the three systems, the system is "required" to be grounded.

Section 250-5(b)(2) requires the 480/277-volt, three-phase, four-wire system, where the neutral conductor is used as a circuit conductor, to be grounded (figure 7–18). This system is also a wye-connected system with the wye point of the system intentionally connected to ground and used as the neutral conductor. When the term *nominally rated* is used, it also means the rule covers the 460/266-volt system and the 440/254-volt system. This system is used extensively for lighting in schools, high-rise office buildings, and industrial areas.

Section 250-5(b)(3) applies to the three-phase, four-wire, delta-connected system, where the mid-point of one phase is used as the circuit conductor (figure 7–19). This system is the three-phase, delta, 120/240-volt, four-wire system, which is accomplished by intentionally grounding the center tap of one transformer of a three-

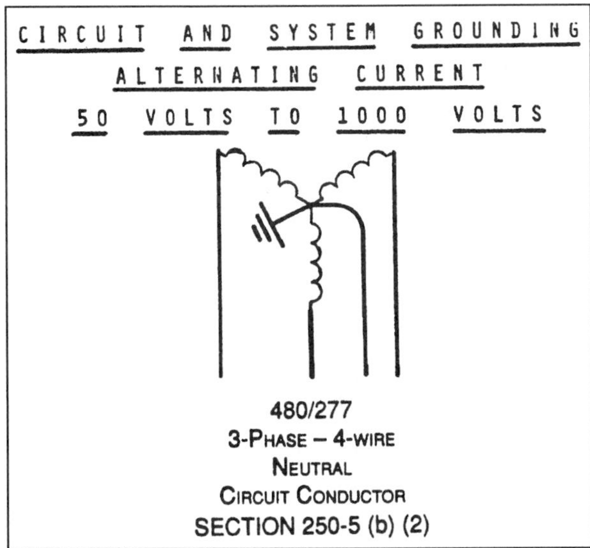

Fig. 7–18 Grounding a three-phase, four-wire AC system.

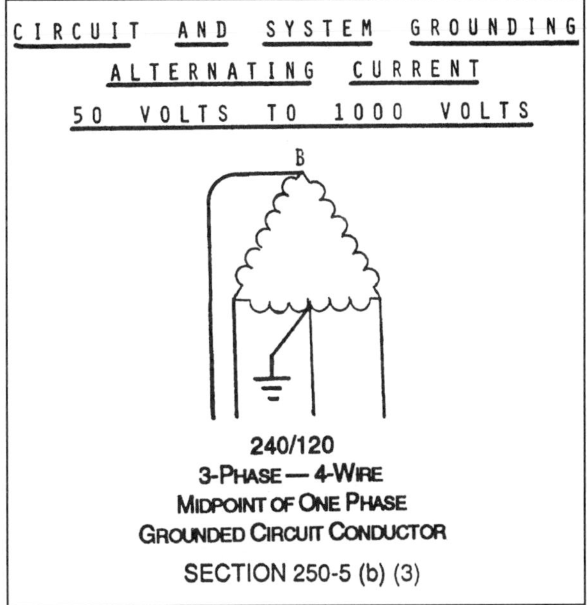

Fig. 7–19 Grounding a three-phase, four-wire, delta AC system with a high leg.

phase, delta-connected transformer bank. The system is known as a "high leg," "wild leg," or "red leg." The more technical identification is "delta with a high leg." The reason it is called the "high leg" is that one phase has a much higher voltage reading to ground than either of the other two legs. However, the voltage is still less than the phase-to-phase voltage. In *Section 384-3(f)*, the Code requires the high leg to be the "B" phase and when identified by color, *Section 384-3(e)* requires the color to be orange or identified by other effective means. The two most common system voltages for this connection are:

1. The 120/240-volt system will have a high-leg voltage of 208 volts.
2. The 110/220-volt system will have a high-leg voltage of 190 volts.

A simple way to calculate the high-leg voltage is to multiply half the phase voltage by 1.73.

(240/2 = 120 × 1.73 = 208 volts)
(220/2 = 110 × 1.73 = 190 volts)

The three-phase, four-wire system is used where there is a need for both power and lighting. The three-phase is used for power and the 120 volts is used for lighting.

CAUTION: No 120-volt lighting is to be connected to the high leg. The Code permits the

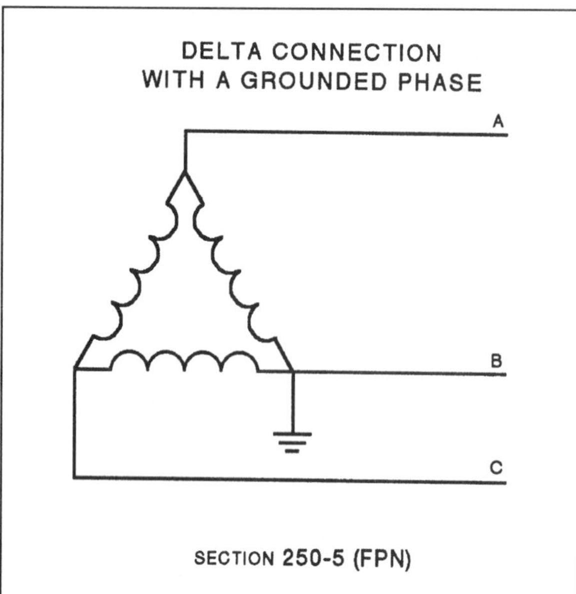

Fig. 7–20 Delta-connected system with a grounded phase.

use of the high-leg voltage, but there is seldom a situation where there is a need for a single-phase, 208-volt circuit

A grounded conductor is required to be brought to the service and connected to a grounding electrode, *Section 250-23(a)*, whenever the premises wiring system is supplied by an alternating current service that is grounded.

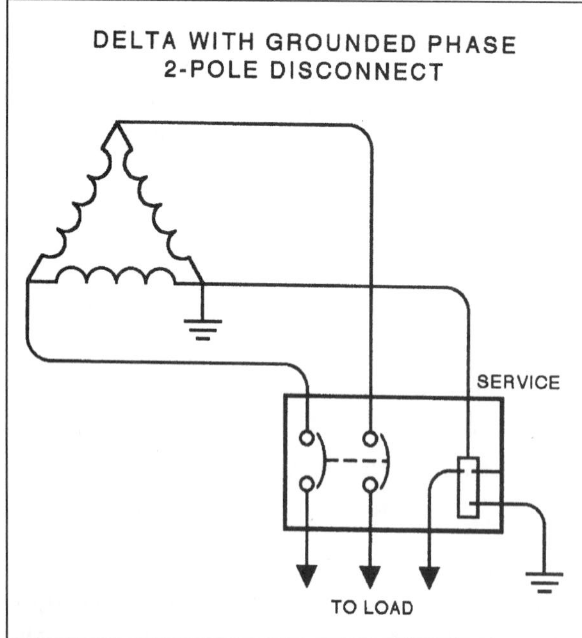

Fig. 7–21 Connections at service for delta with a grounded phase, with overcurrent protection in ungrounded conductors only.

Delta Connection with Grounded Phase

The Code requires the previously discussed systems to be grounded. But it also permits other alternating-current systems to be grounded. The FPN to *Section 250-5* (figure 7–20) identifies one of these systems as a corner-grounded delta connection. It also is referred to as a delta with a grounded leg, or a corner-grounded delta system.

Any premises wiring system supplied by an alternating current service that is grounded is required by *Section 250-23(a)* to have the grounded conductor connected to a grounding electrode at the service. This requires the corner-grounded delta system to have a grounding electrode system as illustrated in figures 7–21 and 7–22 (page 89).

Section 250-25(4) identifies the conductor to be grounded as a "phase conductor," indicating that any one of the three-phase conductors is permitted to be grounded. The phase to be grounded is usually established by the serving utility company. For a three-phase, 480-volt system with B phase as the grounded phase, the voltage readings would be as follows:

A - B	480 volts
B - C	480 volts
A - C	480 volts
A - gnd	480 volts
C - gnd	480 volts
B - gnd	0 volts

The phase conductor that is grounded is a grounded conductor as defined in *Article 100* and is handled as a grounded conductor throughout the system. It is identified as a circuit-grounded conductor using white or natural gray. This is one situation in which the grounded conductor is *not* the neutral conductor. It is carried as an insulated conductor throughout the system.

The basic rule, *Section 240-22*, does not permit an overcurrent device in a grounded conductor. Figure 7–21 illustrates the service overcurrent protection using a two-pole circuit breaker as the overcurrent protection and the means of disconnection. The grounded conductor is connected directly to the grounding electrode conductor and then carried throughout the

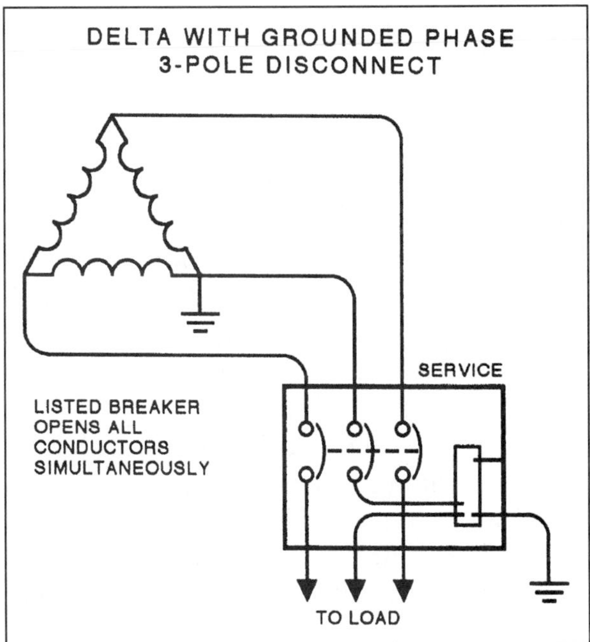

Fig. 7–22 Connections at service for delta with a grounded phase, with overcurrent protection in the grounded conductor.

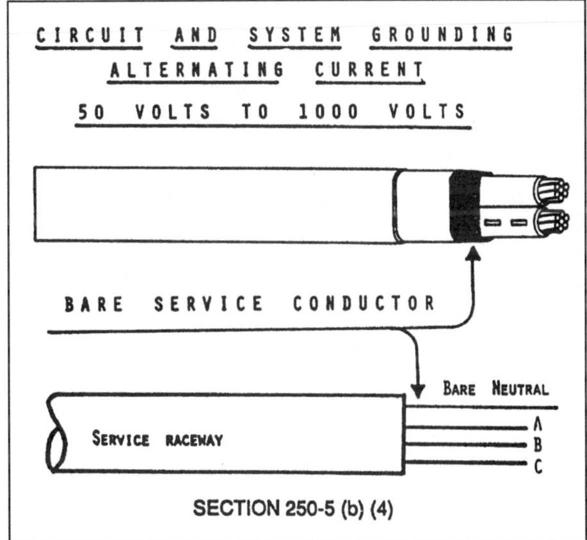

Fig. 7–23 The bare conductor in service-entrance cable is required to be grounded.

system. When a 2-pole switch is used with the corner-grounded delta system, it is required to be identified for this use.

A three-pole circuit breaker is permitted as the overcurrent protective device by *Section 240-22, Exception No. 1*, which requires the overcurrent device (to be listed for the purpose) to open all three circuit conductors simultaneously, figure 7–22. No phase overcurrent device operates separately. Circuit breakers are listed for this purpose.

A three-pole fused disconnect would not be permitted for use with the service or other feeders because it would not open all three circuit conductors simultaneously. However, when a motor circuit is supplied by a three-phase with a grounded phase, an overcurrent device is required in each phase. A fuse is permitted to be used in this case, *Section 430-36*.

The main bonding jumper and the grounding electrode conductor are installed per the requirements for these conductors.

Service Cable

Section 250-5(b)(4) has to do with uninsulated neutral service-entrance conductors (figure 7–23), and is one of the many common-sense rules in the Code. When an uninsulated grounded conductor is installed as a service-entrance conductor, the uninsulated or bare conductor shall be a grounded conductor. This also coordinates the Code with *Article 230 (230-22, 230-30, 230-41)*, which permits the use of an uninsulated neutral as a service-entrance conductor.

This regulation actually prohibits using a service-entrance cable with two insulated conductors, and one uninsulated conductor under a common jacket being used for the service-entrance conductors for a three-phase, three-wire, ungrounded system.

Section 250-5(b) lists five exceptions permitting 50-to-1000-volt systems to operate without a grounded conductor. These exceptions are discussed in the following paragraphs.

Exception No. 1 (figure 7–24, page 90) permits a system used exclusively to supply industrial electric furnaces for melting, refining, tempering, and the like to be installed without the system being grounded. Exception No. 2 (figure 7–25, page 90) permits a separately derived system used exclusively for rectifiers supplying only adjustable-speed industrial drives to be installed without the system being grounded.

Exception No. 3 (figure 7–26, page 90) permits a separately derived system supplied by transformers to be installed without the system being grounded, provided that all five of the conditions listed are fulfilled. One condition requires the use of ground detectors. Figure 7–26 also illustrates the use of ground detectors, with lights used to warn of a ground being detected.

In more than one place, the Code calls attention to the value of installing ground detectors. The ground detector can be used to give a visual warning, an audible warning, or a combination of both when there is an accidental ground on the circuit. This allows corrective measures to be taken before the ground can develop into a serious fault.

Isolated systems. Exception No. 4 coordinates the Code with two other Code articles—*Article 517 (Health Care Facilities)* and *Article 668 (Electrolytic Cells)*—that required isolated systems. These articles permit a system isolated from ground. In the health care facility, the isolated system is secured with the use of an isolating transformer. Figure 7–27 (page 91) illustrates the use of an isolating transformer. An isolating transformer is a two-winding transformer. The purpose of an isolating transformer is to protect against circulating ground currents and help to eliminate dirty electricity in computer and other electronic circuits.

A bank of electrolytic cells uses direct current to process a product such as metal. An electrolytic cell is like a large vat containing liquid. A bank of electrolytic cells is used to put metal coatings on objects and in the refining, or purifying, of certain metals such as copper. The direct current needed for its operation is permitted to be isolated from ground by insulating it from ground.

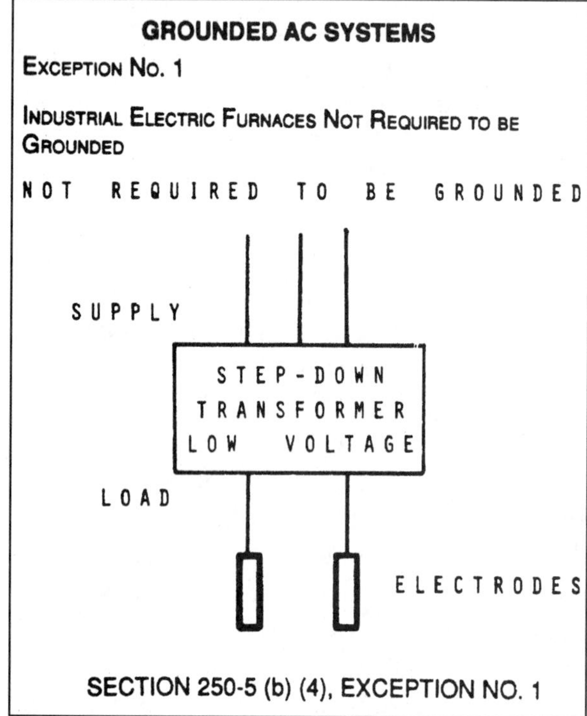

Fig. 7–24 An example of Exception No. 1, which permits an AC system of 50 to 1000 volts to be ungrounded.

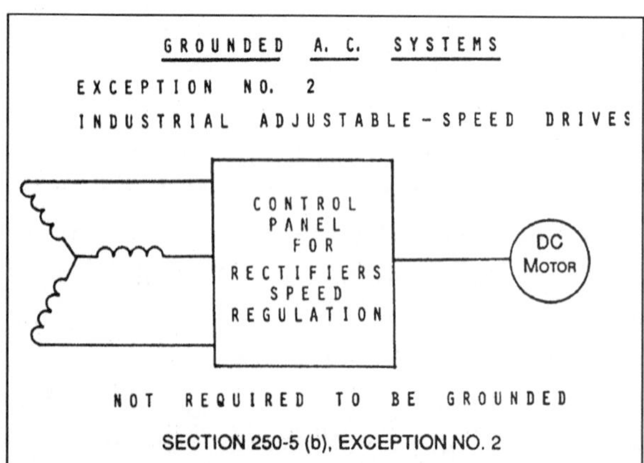

Fig. 7–25 An example of Exception No. 2, which permits a 50-1000-volt AC system to be ungrounded.

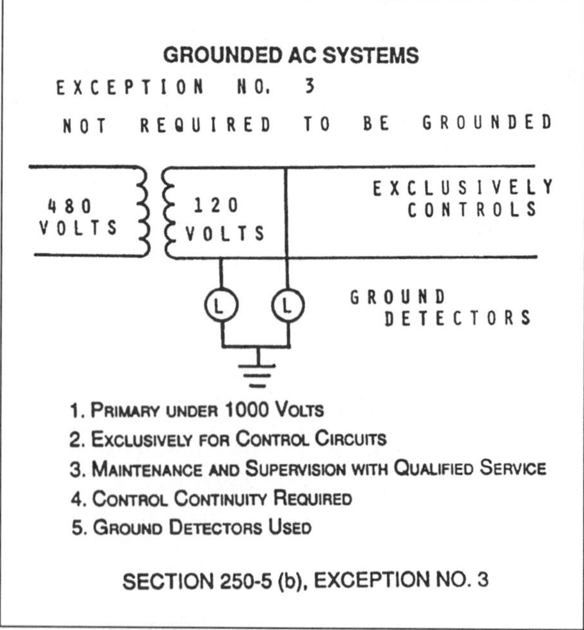

Fig. 7–26 Exception No. 3, which permits a separately derived AC system used exclusively for controls to be ungrounded.

High-impedance grounding. Exception No. 5 (figure 7–28) is an example of how impedance grounding is used to limit the ground fault current to a low value by the use of an impedance, which is usually a resistor. Exception No. 5 of *Section 250-5(b)* permits the use of a high-impedance grounded neutral system, but limits its use by requiring that all the following conditions be met.

1. It must be a three-phase AC system.
2. It must be 480 to 1000 volts.
3. Conditions of maintenance and supervision assure that only qualified persons service installation.
4. The installation requires continuity of power.
5. Ground detectors are required.
6. No line-to-neutral loads are served by the system. Further requirements are listed in *Section 250-27(b)*.
7. The neutral conductor is required to be insulated.
8. The neutral conductor has an ampacity not less than the current rating of the grounding impedance.

CIRCUIT AND SYSTEM GROUNDING
ALTERNATING CURRENT
ISOLATED TRANSFORMER FOR AN ISOLATED SYSTEM
120 VOLTS
120 VOLTS
NO ELECTRICAL CONNECTION BETWEEN PRIMARY AND SECONDARY
SECTION 250-5 (b), EXCEPTION NO. 4
EXAMPLE 517-63 (a) (2)

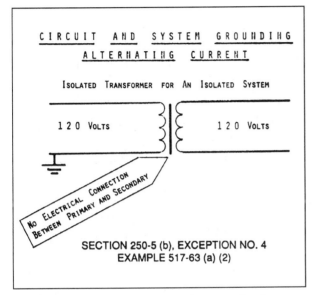

Fig. 7–27 Exception No. 4, which permits the use of an isolation transformer for an ungrounded AC system.

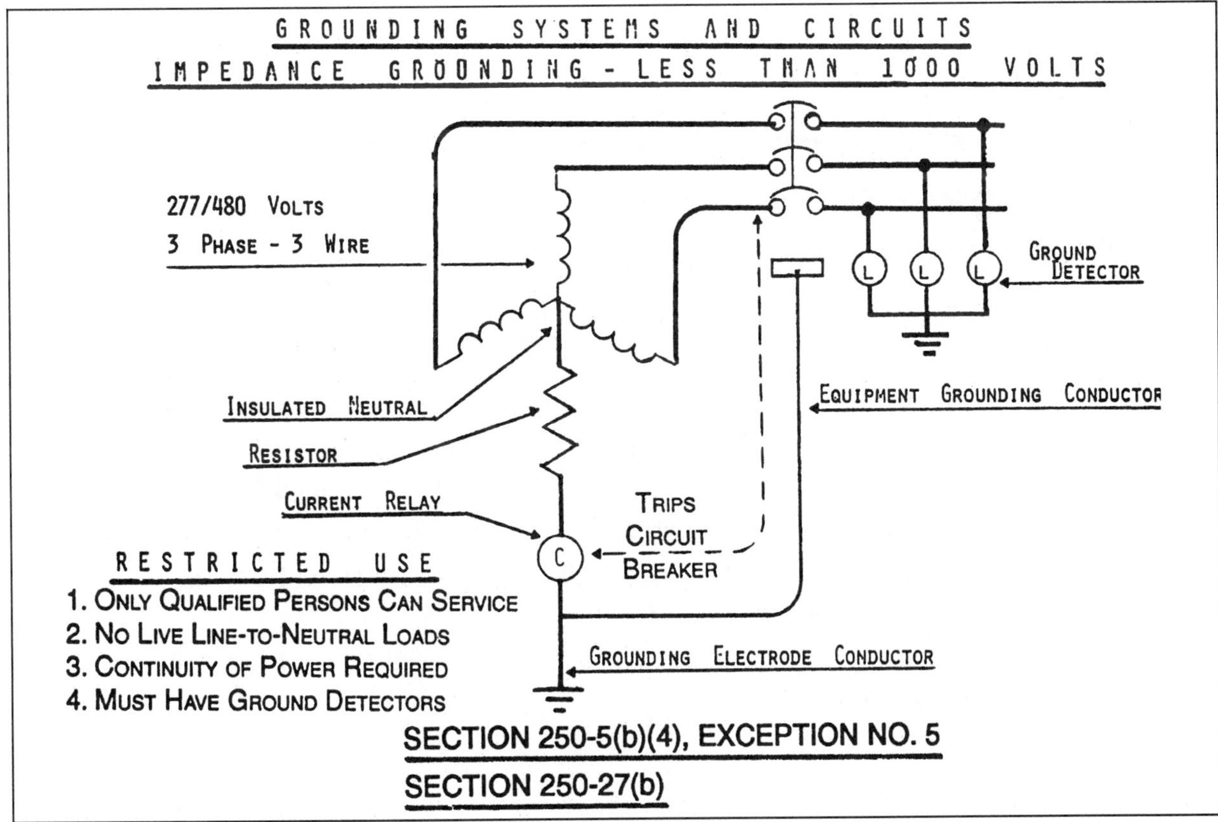

Fig. 7–28 Exception No. 5, which permits the use of impedance grounding for a 277/480-volt AC system.

9. The neutral is required to be not less than No. 8 copper or No. 6 aluminum or copper-clad aluminum. High-impedance grounding for nominal voltages over 600 volts is covered in Chapter 15 of this text.

Comments: High-impedance grounding has been used with the higher voltage for some time, but not until in the 1987 Code has it been recognized for anything under 1000 volts. Note how restrictive the regulations are.

The three-phase requirement eliminates all single-phase systems. The 480-to-1000-volt limitation eliminates the 120/208-volt, three-phase, four-wire wye system and the three-phase, 120/240-volt, four-wire delta with the high-leg system. The voltage limitation almost zeros in on the three-phase, 277/480-volt, wye-connected, four-wire system.

Where continuity of power is required, it indicates an orderly shutdown is required to minimize personnel hazard and equipment damage. One of the reasons for having a grounded system with a very low impedance to ground was to allow the overcurrent protection device to operate quickly. Now there develops a situation where the tripping of the overcurrent protective device could create more of a hazard than a protection.

Example: A manufacturing plant, operating with a sequence-control process to produce either a perishable or nonperishable product, needs an orderly shutdown to protect personnel, equipment, and materials.

A second advantage of the impedance-grounded system is its ability to limit the current flow to ground and to reduce or eliminate the arc at the point of fault, thereby reducing the fire hazard caused by an arcing fault. Impedance grounding has been given credit for protecting a service from a serious explosion or burn down.

Ground detectors are required to be installed on the system so they can warn of an unintentional ground on the system. Using the 277/480-volt system as an example, the line-to-neutral voltage of 277 is normally used for lighting. With the impedance-grounded system, no line-to-neutral loads are used. All connected loads will be 480 volts.

Reason: After being grounded through an impedance, the neutral is no longer at ground potential. There will be a voltage between the neutral and ground.

FOLLOW UP

Topics for self-study, discussion, or questioning.

1. Discuss why systems and circuits are grounded.
2. Define *grounded conductor*.
3. Discuss how the voltage to ground is arrived at for both grounded and ungrounded systems.
4. Discuss what direct-current circuits are required to be grounded.
5. Discuss the exceptions to the requirements for grounding direct-current circuits.
6. Discuss what alternating-current circuits operating at 50 volts or less are required to be grounded.
7. Discuss what alternating-current circuits operating at 50 to 1000 volts are required to be grounded.

8. Discuss the grounding of a delta system with a high leg.
9. Discuss a delta system with a grounded phase.
10. Explain where and why isolated systems are used.
11. Discuss the requirements for impedance grounding of an alternating-current system.
12. Why is the neutral not permitted to be used as a circuit conductor on an impedance-grounded system?

CHAPTER 8

Grounded Conductor

OBJECTIVES

After completing this chapter, the student should be able to:

- distinguish when a grounded conductor is, and when it is not, a neutral conductor.
- identify when the grounded conductor is required to be brought to the service although it is not used as a circuit conductor.
- explain where the grounded conductor is required to be connected at the service equipment.
- explain the installation of the grounded conductor when the service contains a multitude of service disconnecting means.
- explain how the grounded conductor should be installed for a three-phase, four-wire delta system with a high leg, and a separate disconnecting switch for power and for lighting.
- use *Table 250-94* to explain how the grounded conductor is sized when brought to the service equipment, but not used as a circuit conductor.
- explain the 12 1/2 percent rule used for sizing a grounded conductor that is brought to the service equipment but not used as a circuit conductor.
- explain the sizing of the grounded conductor when a) it is brought to the service and not used for a circuit conductor, and b) the service-entrance conductors consist of parallel conductors installed in the same conduit.
- identify the color dedicated to the grounded conductor and explain when a color other than the dedicated one is permitted to be used for the grounded conductor.
- identify the locations in which a conductor identified as the grounded conductor can be used other than as the neutral conductor.
- explain when the grounded conductor is permitted to have overcurrent protection.

This chapter focuses on the system grounded conductor (figure 8–1, page 95). Discussions will cover identifying it, determining where and when it is used and how it is connected to other grounding conductors, and installing it.

DEFINITION OF *GROUNDED CONDUCTOR*

The grounded conductor is part of the overall grounding system and, as previously illustrated, under ground fault conditions it becomes an equipment grounding conductor from the service back to the source. The grounded conductor installed in the service raceway is used as the equipment grounding conductor between the utility company and the service-disconnecting means. An additional equipment grounding conductor is not required.

The grounded circuit conductor of a single-phase, three-wire system, and the grounded cir-

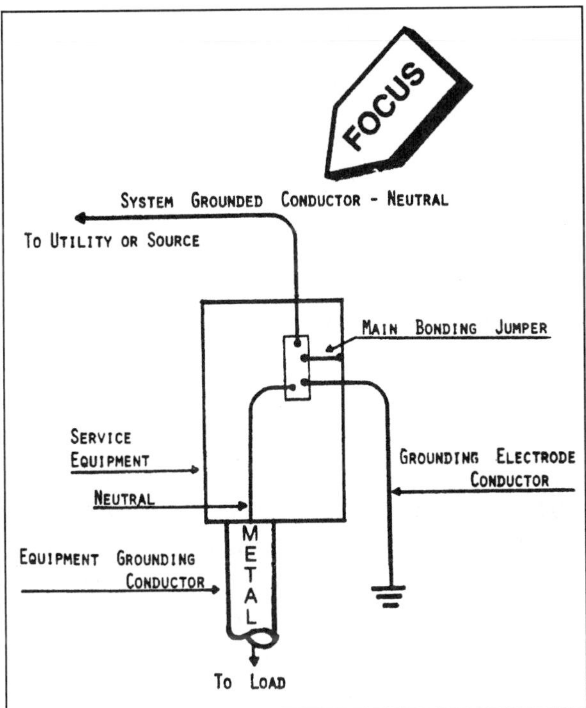

Fig. 8–1 Focusing on the system grounded conductor (neutral).

cuit conductor of a three-phase, four-wire system, are referred to as the neutral.

Question: Is every grounded conductor a neutral conductor?

Answer: NO. Figure 8–2 illustrates a three-phase, delta-connected system with an intentionally grounded phase conductor. The grounded phase conductor is not a neutral conductor.

In *Part C (Location of System Grounding Connections)* of *Article 250*, there is considerable information given about connecting the

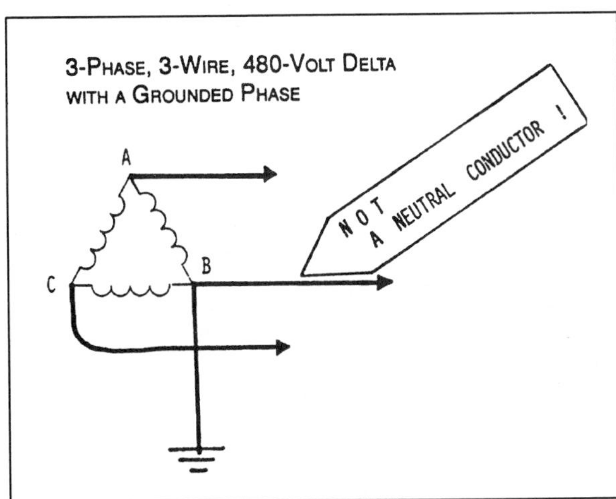

Fig. 8–2 A delta with a grounded leg that is not a neutral.

grounded conductor to the grounding electrode conductor. This requires a lot of interlocking and referencing with other parts of *Article 250*.

GROUNDED CONDUCTOR CONNECTION IN A DIRECT-CURRENT SYSTEM

The point at which the grounded circuit conductor is grounded is different for direct current than it is for alternating current. When a direct-current system is grounded, it shall be grounded only at the source of supply. In this book, this is illustrated in Chapter 7, figure 7–5 (page 83) for a two-wire, direct-current system and in figure 7–11 (page 84) for a three-wire, direct-current system.

When the direct-current supply is located on the premises, as illustrated in figure 7–12 (page 85) of Chapter 7, the exception to *Section 250-22* permits the grounded conductor to be connected to the grounding electrode conductor at the supply or at the first system disconnecting means or overcurrent protective device.

GROUNDED CONDUCTOR CONNECTION IN AN ALTERNATING-CURRENT SYSTEM

When a grounded AC system is used, *Section 250-23(a)* requires the grounded conductor to be connected to the grounding electrode system by means of the grounding electrode conductor. Figure 8–3 (page 96) illustrates where the connection shall be made. Some of the main points of *Section 250-23(a)* that apply to the grounded conductor are as follows:

1. The grounded conductor shall be connected to the grounded (neutral) service conductor.
2. The connection must be at an accessible point.
3. That accessible point can be anywhere from the load end of the service drop or service lateral to and including the neutral bar in the service disconnecting means or service switchboard.

Comment: This connection is more often referred to as being on the line side (also referred to as the supply side) of the service switch, or the line side of the service equipment. It permits a mul-

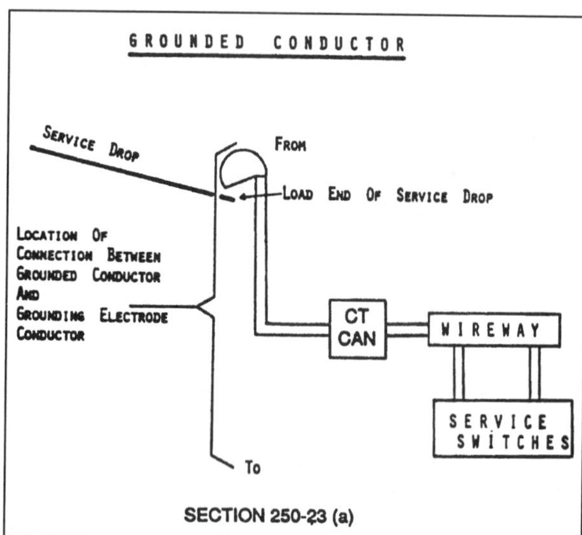

Fig. 8–3 Location of connection between the grounded conductor and the grounding electrode conductor.

titude of places where the connection can be made between the system grounded conductor and the grounding electrode conductor. The following are some of the main points concerning where the connection is usually made (figure 8–3).

1. Residential installations
   a. Service equipment neutral bar
   b. Also permitted in meter base
      Note: Some utility companies do not permit the connection in the meter base.
2. Commercial and industrial installations
   a. Service equipment
   b. CT (current transformer) can
   c. Metal gutter or wireway containing service-entrance conductors

BRINGING THE GROUNDED CONDUCTOR TO SERVICE

Quote – *"Section 250-23(b).* Where an AC system operating at less than 1000 volts is grounded at any point, the grounded conductor shall be run to each service disconnecting means and shall be bonded to each disconnecting means enclosure."*

* Reprinted with permission from NFPA 70-1996, the National Electrical Code®, Copyright © 1995, National Fire Protection Association, Quincy, Massachusetts 02269. This reprinted material is not the complete and official position of the National Fire Protection Association, on the referenced subject, which is represented only by the standard in its entirety.

Reason: Under fault conditions, the grounded conductor becomes the equipment grounding conductor and furnishes the path for the fault current, which causes the circuit overcurrent protective device to operate. This is illustrated and explained under *Faults* (Chapter 4, figures 4–7, page 34, 4–8, and 4–9, page 35).

Where an alternating-current system operating at less than 1000 volts is grounded at any point, the grounded conductor shall be run to and bonded to the service disconnecting means, as illustrated in figure 8–4. Therefore any time the utility source of supply has an established ground point at the supply transformer, a grounded conductor must be brought to the service disconnecting means, regardless of whether it is used as a circuit conductor or not. The grounded conductor is also required to be run with the phase conductors.

The supply transformer illustrated in figure 8–4 is a wye connection with the center tap grounded. Therefore a grounded conductor must be brought to the service disconnecting means. This would be applicable to a 120/208-volt wye connection, a 277/480-volt wye connection, or a 220/380-volt wye connection when there is no lighting load and only three conductors are needed for a three-phase, three-wire power load. The grounded conductor is brought to the service, although it is not used as a circuit conductor.

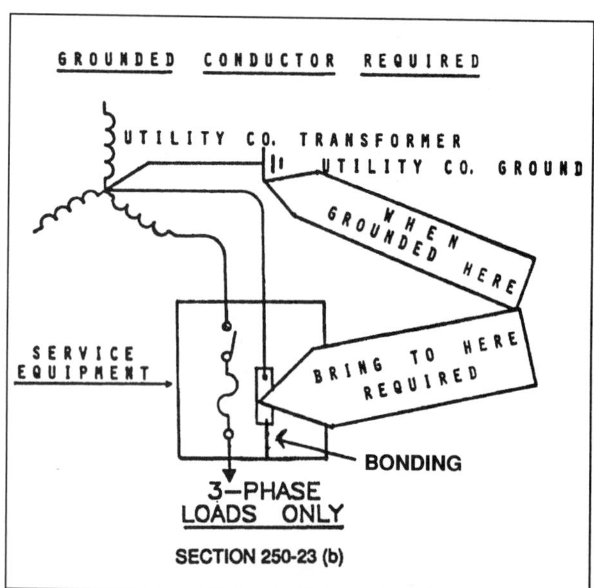

Fig. 8–4 When the supply is grounded, the grounded conductor is required to be brought to the service disconnecting means.

When the grounded conductor is brought into the service switch enclosure, it offers a lower-impedance path for the fault current than that which exists if the grounded conductor is not brought into the disconnect switch. This is really establishing an equipment grounding point and utilizing the grounded conductor as an equipment grounding conductor under fault conditions. All equipment grounding conductors extending beyond any of the switches will be connected to the grounded conductor at the service disconnecting means.

Multiple Service Disconnecting Means

When multiple disconnecting switches are used for the service disconnecting means, *Section 250-23(b)* requires the grounded conductor (neutral) to be brought into each service disconnecting switch and bonded to the metal service switch enclosure. The grounded conductor is brought into every switch even though the grounded conductor does not extend beyond the service equipment. *Section 250-23(b) Exception No. 3* permits a single grounded conductor to be brought into the service where there is an assembly of switches within the same enclosure, listed for use as service equipment.

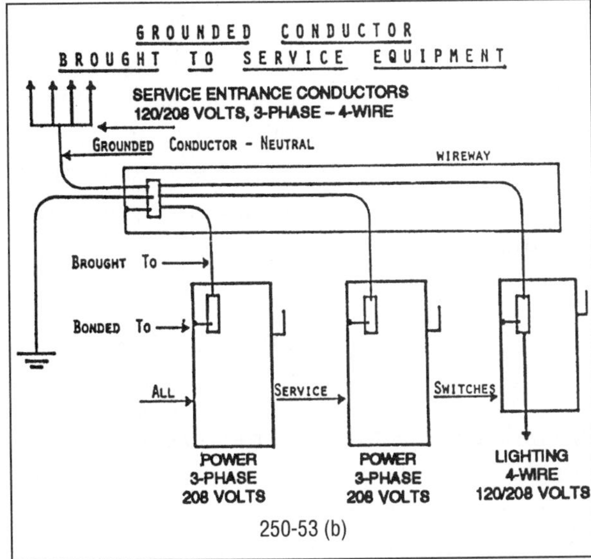

Fig. 8–5 Grounded conductor brought to all service disconnecting means and bonded to disconnecting means enclosure.

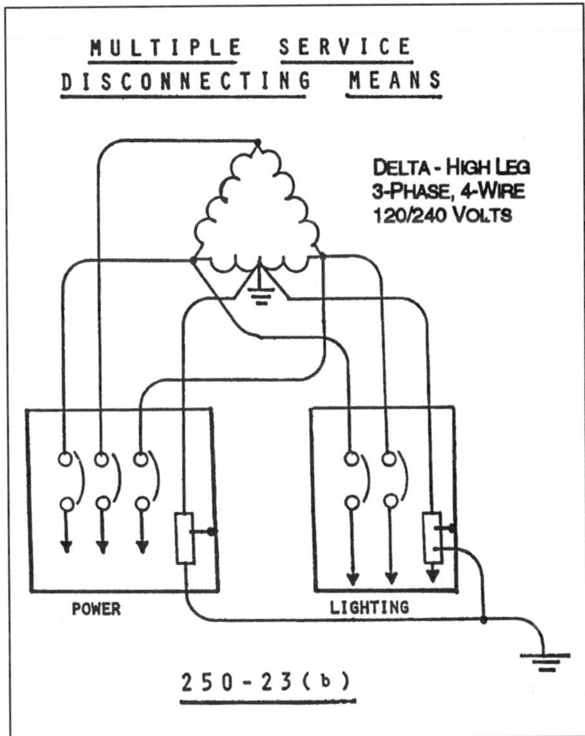

Fig. 8–6 Grounded conductor brought to each service disconnecting means. Also utilize common grounding electrode system.

Three-phase wye connections. Figure 8–5 illustrates the use of more than one service disconnecting switch for one set of service-entrance conductors. One disconnecting switch serves the 120/208-volt lighting load and two disconnecting switches serve the 208-volt, three-phase power loads. The grounded conductor (neutral) is brought into the lighting switch and extends beyond the lighting disconnecting means. The grounded conductor will also be brought into the disconnecting means for the power. Note in figure 8–5 that each switch enclosure is bonded to the grounded conductor.

Three-phase delta with a high leg. Figure 8–6 illustrates a situation where the three-phase power and the single-phase lighting service-entrance conductors are brought into the service equipment separately from a three-phase, four-wire delta with a high leg. Note that the grounded conductor is brought with the power conductors to the power service disconnecting means and bonded to the disconnecting means enclosure. It is also brought to the lighting service disconnecting means and bonded to the disconnecting means enclosure. Both are connected to, and use, the same grounding electrode system.

Figure 8–7 illustrates a second method of grounding a three-phase, four-wire delta system with a high leg. In this case there is a separate service disconnect for three-phase power and a separate disconnect for the single-phase lighting. Here the three phase conductors and the grounded conductor are brought into a wireway, or auxiliary gutter; the grounded conductor is connected to the grounding electrode conductor in the auxiliary gutter and then carried into both the power service and the lighting service equipment. This same system of connection could be used with a CT can, in which case the connections made in the CT can are like those made in the auxiliary gutter. In each case note the bonding of the service equipment enclosure to the grounded conductor.

The basic rule for bringing the grounded conductor to the service disconnecting means applies only to solidly grounded systems; an impedance-grounded system is a very different situation. Exception No. 2 of *Section 250-23(b)* permits an impedance-grounded system to be installed without bringing the grounded conductor to the service disconnecting means.

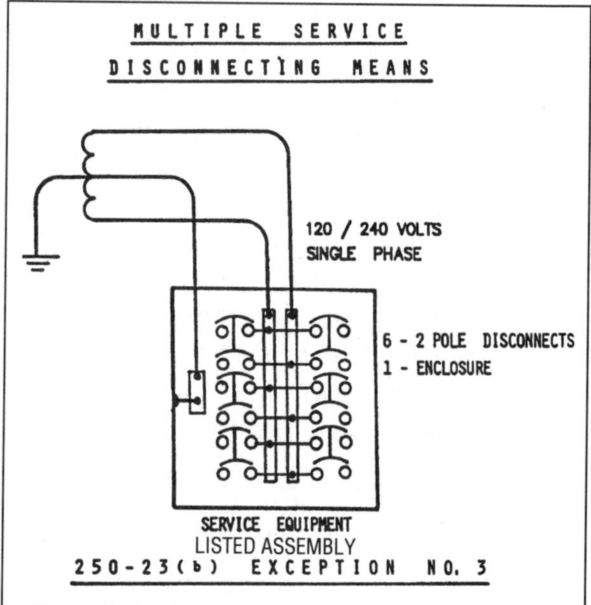

Fig. 8–8 A multiple of service disconnecting means within one listed assembly.

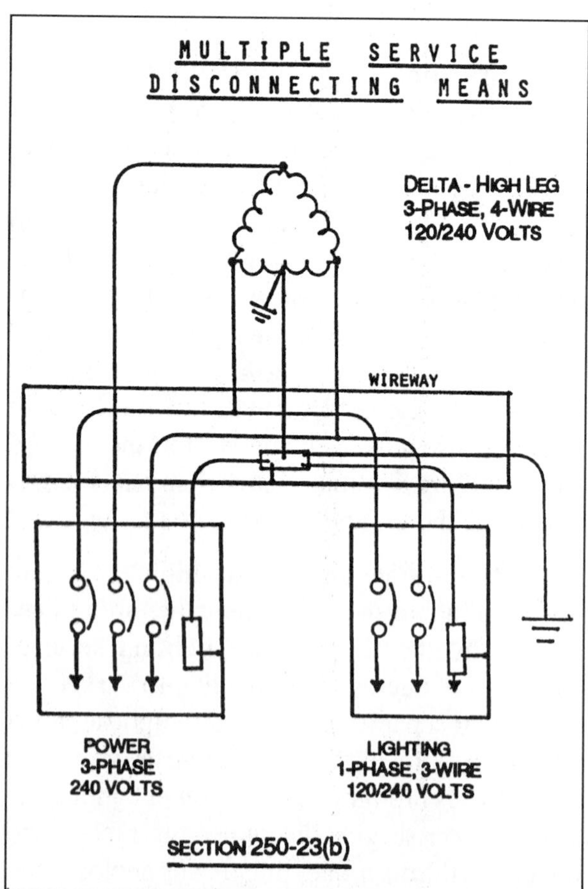

Fig. 8–7 Grounded conductor brought to service disconnecting switches via an auxiliary gutter.

The basic rule requires the grounded conductor to be brought to each service disconnecting means. A service is permitted to have as many as six disconnecting means; these can also all be in one enclosure. When there is an installation consisting of a multitude of service disconnecting means in a listed assembly, Exception No. 3 of *Section 250-23(b)* (figure 8–8) permits the grounded conductor to be brought to the common enclosure and bonded *to the common enclosure*. This exception is an example of where the Code uses an exception to apply a little common sense.

SIZING THE GROUNDED CONDUCTOR

Now that the Code has required the grounded conductor to be brought to the service, whether it is used or not, the Code follows up with a regulation on how to size the grounded conductor when it is not used as a circuit conductor. *Section 250-23(b)* gives the rules for sizing the grounded conductor. The sizing of the grounded conductor illustrated in this Code

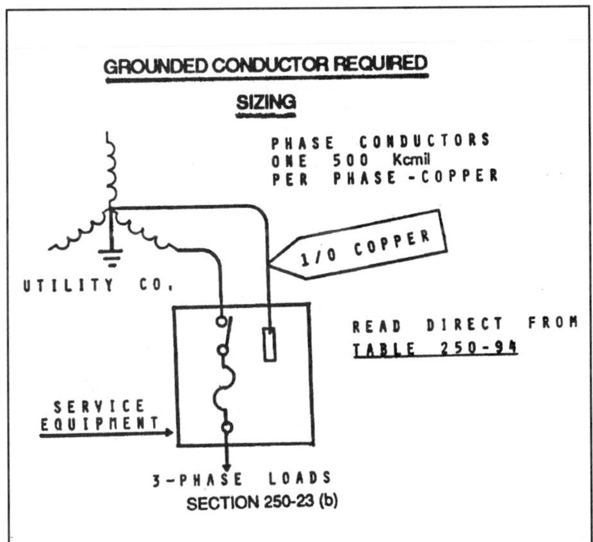

Fig. 8–9 Sizing a copper grounded conductor brought to the service but not used as a circuit conductor.

Table 250-94.
Grounding Electrode Conductor for AC Systems

Size of Largest Service-Entrance Conductor or Equivalent Area for Parallel Conductors		Size of Grounding Electrode Conductor	
Copper	Aluminum or Copper-Clad Aluminum	Copper	*Aluminum or Copper-Clad Aluminum
2 or smaller	1/0 or smaller	8	6
1 or 1/0	2/0 or 3/0	6	4
2/0 or 3/0	4/0 or 250 kcmil	4	2
Over 3/0 thru 350 kcmil	Over 250 kcmil thru 500 kcmil	2	1/0
Over 350 kcmil thru 600 kcmil	Over 500 kcmil thru 900 kcmil	1/0	3/0
Over 600 kcmil thru 1100 kcmil	Over 900 kcmil thru 1750 kcmil	2/0	4/0
Over 1100 kcmil	Over 1750 kcmil	3/0	250 kcmil

Fig. 8–10 Reading *Table 250-94* for sizing a copper grounded conductor brought to the service but not used as a circuit conductor, as in figure 8–9.*

section applies only when the grounded conductor is required to be brought to the service and is not used as a circuit conductor. When the grounded conductor is used as a circuit conductor, it is sized according to *Article 220 (Branch-Circuit, Feeder, and Service Calculations).*

The FPN to *Section 230-23(b)* calls attention to *Section 310-4*, which covers conductors installed in parallel. The smallest conductor permitted to be installed in parallel is 1/0; this applies to the grounded conductor when parallel conductors are installed. This requirement applies to two installations: 1) when the grounded conductor is used as a circuit conductor and 2) when the grounded conductor is not a circuit conductor and is brought to the service.

Section 250-23(b) goes on to list ways to calculate the size of the grounded conductor. These are:

1. The basic rule is to read the size directly from *Table 250-94* when the size of the service-entrance conductors is not larger than 1100 kcmil copper or 1750 kcmil aluminum.
2. When the service-entrance conductors are larger than 1100 kcmil copper or 1750 kcmil aluminum, the grounded conductor shall be $12^1/_2$ percent of the largest phase conductor.
3. Where the service phase conductors are paralleled, the size of the grounded conductor shall be based on the total cross-sectional area of any one phase.

When the service-entrance phase conductors are not over 1100 kcmil copper or 1750 kcmil aluminum, *Table 250-94* is used. Figure 8–9 illustrates a three-phase, wye connected service with the center of the wye grounded. The load consists of three-phase loads only and the neutral or grounded conductor is not needed. Only the three-phase conductors are used to service the load. The service-entrance phase conductors are 500 kcmil copper. The size of the copper grounded conductor can be read directly from *Table 250-94* (figure 8–10). The grounded conductor size can be found under the column entitled "Size of Grounding Electrode Conductor." *Table 250-94* indicates that 500 kcmil copper will require a No. 1/0 copper grounded conductor.

For comparison's sake, if the service-entrance phase conductors are aluminum, including the grounded conductor, the information in the two aluminum columns of *Table 250-94* will be used. *Table 250-94* indicates that 500 kcmil aluminum will require a No. 1/0 aluminum grounded conductor, as illustrated in figure 8–11.

When the service-entrance phase conductors are over 1100 kcmil copper or 1750 kcmil aluminum, *Table 250-94* cannot be used for sizing the grounded conductor. The grounded conductor is required to be not less than 12$^1/_2$ percent of the total cross-sectional area of any one phase conductor.

A special regulation for paralleling the grounded conductor is also included in *Section 250-23(b)*. When parallel conductors are used for the grounded conductor, the minimum size to be installed is No. 1/0.

Figure 8–12 illustrates a service that consists of three 600 kcmil copper conductors per phase. For this example, consider all the service-entrance phase conductors to be installed in a common raceway with one grounded conductor installed.

600 kcmil = 1800 kcmil per phase copper

The 1800 kcmil per phase exceeds the 1100 kcmil for copper listed in *Table 250-94*. Therefore, the size of the copper grounded conductor will be calculated using the 12$^1/_2$ percent requirement.

12$^1/_2$ percent of 1800 kcmil is 225 kcmil.

The 225 kcmil required is not a standard-size conductor; therefore, it is necessary to go to the next higher standard-size copper conductor,

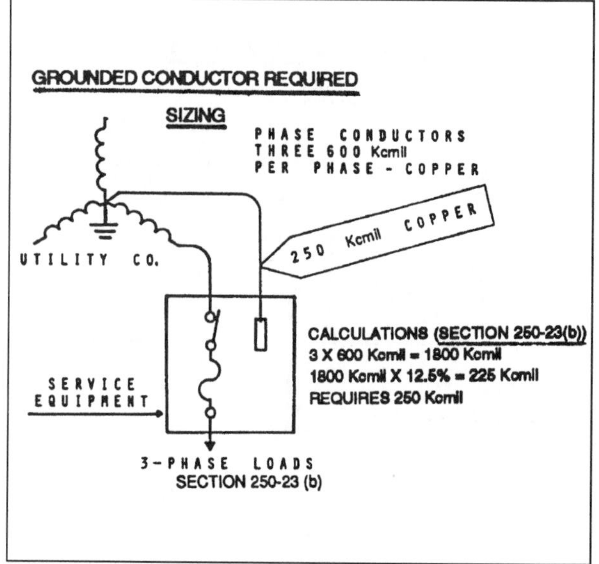

Fig. 8–12 Using the 12$^1/_2$ percent rule to size a copper grounded conductor brought to the service but not used as a circuit conductor.

Table 8. Conductor Properties

Size AWG/ kcmil	Area Cir. Mils	Conductors: Stranding Quantity	Conductors: Stranding Diam. in.	Conductors: Overall Diam. in.	Conductors: Overall Area in.²	DC Resistance at 75°C (167°F): Copper Uncoated ohm/kFT	DC Resistance at 75°C (167°F): Copper Coated ohm/kFT	DC Resistance at 75°C (167°F): Aluminum ohm/kFT
18	1620	1	—	0.040	0.001	7.77	8.08	12.8
18	1620	7	0.015	0.046	0.002	7.95	8.45	13.1
16	2580	1	—	0.051	0.002	4.89	5.08	8.05
16	2580	7	0.019	0.058	0.003	4.99	5.29	8.21
14	4110	1	—	0.064	0.003	3.07	3.19	5.06
14	4110	7	0.024	0.073	0.004	3.14	3.26	5.17
12	6530	1	—	0.081	0.005	1.93	2.01	3.18
12	6530	7	0.030	0.092	0.006	1.98	2.05	3.25
10	10380	1	—	0.102	0.008	1.21	1.26	2.00
10	10380	7	0.038	0.116	0.011	1.24	1.29	2.04
8	16510	1	—	0.128	0.013	0.764	0.786	1.26
8	16510	7	0.049	0.146	0.017	0.778	0.809	1.28
6	26240	7	0.061	0.184	0.027	0.491	0.510	0.808
4	41740	7	0.077	0.232	0.042	0.308	0.321	0.508
3	52620	7	0.087	0.260	0.053	0.245	0.254	0.403
2	66360	7	0.097	0.292	0.067	0.194	0.201	0.319
1	83690	19	0.066	0.332	0.087	0.154	0.160	0.253
1/0	105600	19	0.074	0.372	0.109	0.122	0.127	0.201
2/0	133100	19	0.084	0.418	0.137	0.0976	0.101	0.159
3/0	167800	19	0.094	0.470	0.173	0.0766	0.0797	0.126
4/0	211600	19	0.106	0.528	0.219	0.0608	0.0626	0.100
250	—	37	0.082	0.575	0.260	0.0515	0.0535	0.0847
300	—	37	0.090	0.630	0.312	0.0429	0.0446	0.0707
350	—	37	0.097	0.681	0.364	0.0367	0.0382	0.0605
400	—	37	0.104	0.728	0.416	0.0321	0.0331	0.0529
500	—	37	0.116	0.813	0.519	0.0258	0.0265	0.0424
600	—	61	0.099	0.893	0.626	0.0214	0.0223	0.0353
700	—	61	0.107	0.964	0.730	0.0184	0.0189	0.0303
750	—	61	0.111	0.998	0.782	0.0171	0.0176	0.0282
800	—	61	0.114	1.030	0.834	0.0161	0.0166	0.0265
900	—	61	0.122	1.094	0.940	0.0143	0.0147	0.0235
1000	—	61	0.128	1.152	1.042	0.0129	0.0132	0.0212
1250	—	91	0.117	1.284	1.305	0.0103	0.0106	0.0169
1500	—	91	0.128	1.412	1.566	0.00858	0.00883	0.0141
1750	—	127	0.117	1.526	1.829	0.00735	0.00756	0.0121
2000	—	127	0.126	1.632	2.092	0.00643	0.00662	0.0106

Fig. 8–13 Using *Table 8* (Chapter 9) to determine the nearest conductor size when the 12$^1/_2$ percent rule is applied.*

Table 250-94.
Grounding Electrode Conductor for AC Systems

Size of Largest Service-Entrance Conductor or Equivalent Area for Parallel Conductors: Copper	Size of Largest Service-Entrance Conductor or Equivalent Area for Parallel Conductors: Aluminum or Copper-Clad Aluminum	Size of Grounding Electrode Conductor: Copper	Size of Grounding Electrode Conductor: *Aluminum or Copper-Clad Aluminum
2 or smaller	1/0 or smaller	8	6
1 or 1/0	2/0 or 3/0	6	4
2/0 or 3/0	4/0 or 250 kcmil	4	2
Over 3/0 thru 350 kcmil	Over 250 kcmil thru 500 kcmil	2	1/0
Over 350 kcmil thru 600 kcmil	Over 500 kcmil thru 900 kcmil	1/0	3/0
Over 600 kcmil thru 1100 kcmil	Over 900 kcmil thru 1750 kcmil	2/0	4/0
Over 1100 kcmil	Over 1750 kcmil	3/0	250 kcmil

Fig. 8–11 Reading *Table 250-94* for sizing an aluminum grounded conductor brought to the service but not used as a circuit conductor, as in figure 8–9.*

which in this case is 250 kcmil copper. *Table 8* in Chapter 9 of the Code (figure 8–13, page 100) gives the circular-mil area of conductors and is used to convert circular mils into a standard conductor size when the 12½ percent rule is applied. In this case the 225 kcmil is larger than No. 4/0; therefore, the next larger size, 250 kcmil, is used.

Had the conductors been aluminum and the service-entrance conductors exceeded 1750 kcmil, the procedure for calculating the size of the grounded conductor would have been the same. *Table 8* would also be used.

Table 250-94 is entitled *Grounding Electrode Conductor for AC Systems.* According to the table, the maximum size ever required for a grounding electrode conductor is No. 3/0 copper or 250 kcmil aluminum. This means that when it is necessary to apply the 12½ percent rule to establish the size of the grounded conductor, the grounded conductor can be larger than the grounding electrode conductor for the same service. However, the grounded conductor is never required to be larger than the phase conductors *(Section 250-23(b),* Exception No. 1).

Figure 8–14 uses the same size conductors as the previous example. In this example, however, the installation consists of three parallel conduits with one conductor of phase A, B, and C in each conduit with a grounded conductor, and the three grounded conductors are paralleled.

$$600 \text{ kcmil} \times 3 = 1800 \text{ kcmil per phase}$$

The 1800 kcmil per phase exceeds the 1100 kcmil for copper listed in *Table 250-94*. Therefore, the size of the copper grounded conductor will be calculated using the 12½ percent requirement.

12½ percent of 1800 kcmil is 225 kcmil.

One grounded conductor in each of three conduits to be paralleled.

225 kcmil divided by 3 = 75 kcmil or 75,000 cmil

From *Table 8*, the next largest standard size for 75,000 cmil is No. 1. The minimum size permitted to be paralleled by *Section 250-23(b)* and *310-4* is No. 1/0. Therefore, each of the paralleled grounded conductors must be a minimum of No. 1/0 copper. One 1/0 should be installed in each of the three paralleled conduits.

CAUTION: These illustrated calculations only apply when there is a grounded system and the grounded conductor is brought to the service equipment but is not used as a circuit conductor. When the grounded conductor is used as a circuit

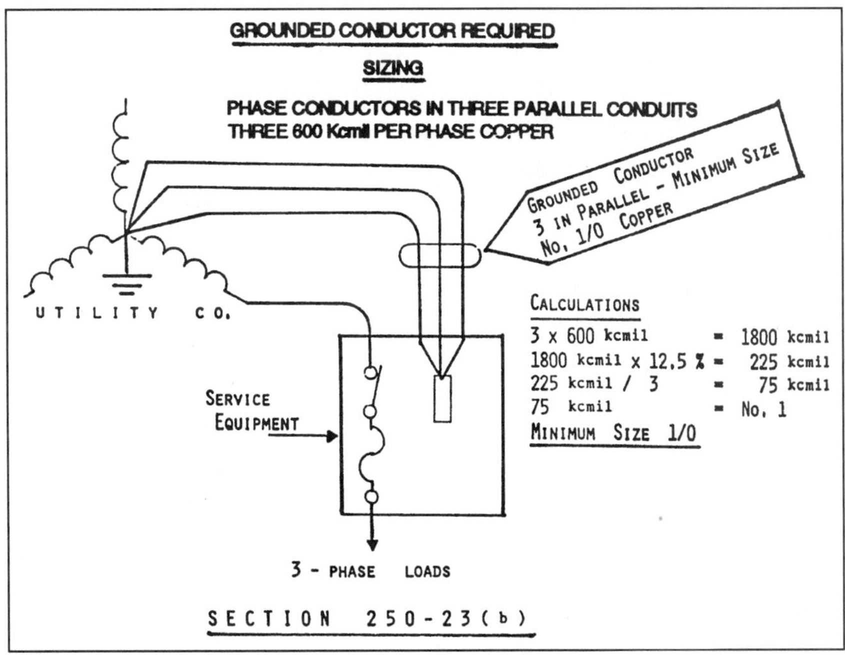

Fig. 8–14 Paralleled grounded conductors brought to service in separate conduits, minimum size 1/0 copper.

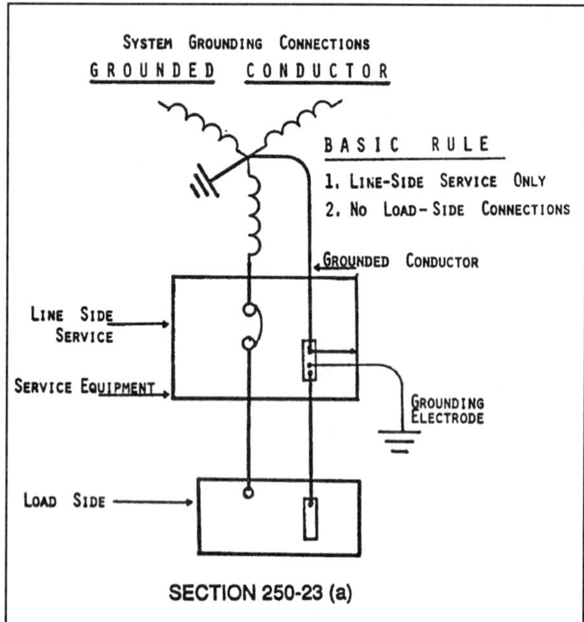

Fig. 8–15 Basic rule for making grounding connections to the system grounded conductor.

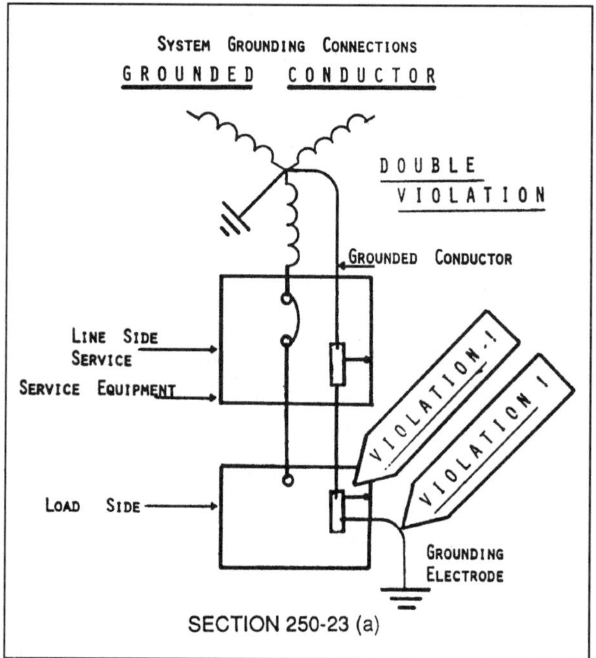

Fig. 8–16 Violation of basic rule for making a grounding connection to the grounded conductor.

conductor and called the neutral, then the grounded conductor is calculated as the neutral and it must be calculated according to *Article 220 (Branch-Circuit, Feeder, and Service Calculations).*

INSTALLING THE GROUNDED CONDUCTOR

Figure 8–15 illustrates one basic rule for installing the system grounded conductor (neutral). *Section 250-23(a)* prohibits a grounding connection to be made to any grounded circuit conductor on the load side of the service disconnecting means. This means that the neutral cannot be used to ground the noncurrent-carrying metal parts of electrical equipment on the load side of the service disconnecting means. However, the Code does make a few exceptions to the rule. Figure 8–16 illustrates a violation. The rule has two basic requirements.

1. The neutral cannot be used as the equipment grounding conductor to ground any metal enclosure on the load side of the service equipment.
2. The grounded conductor (neutral) shall be connected to the grounding electrode conductor at the service and not at any convenient location on the premises wiring.

Figure 8–17 illustrates the connection allowed by Exception No. 4 of *Section 250-23(a).* When a dual-fed system is grouped together in a common enclosure or in separate enclosures with a secondary tie, it is permitted to have one common point for the two grounded conductors (neutrals) and the grounding electrode conductor to be connected together.

Figure 8–18 (page 103) illustrates the connection allowed by Exception No. 5 of *Section 250-23.* In a practical way, this exception is

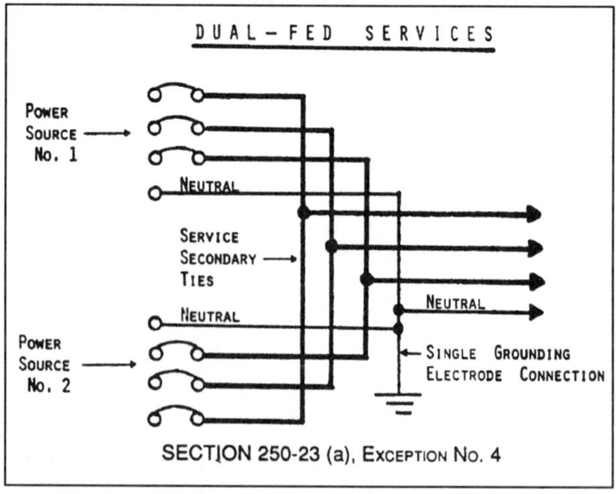

Fig. 8–17 Exception No. 4 to the basic rule for connecting the grounded conductor for a dual-fed system.

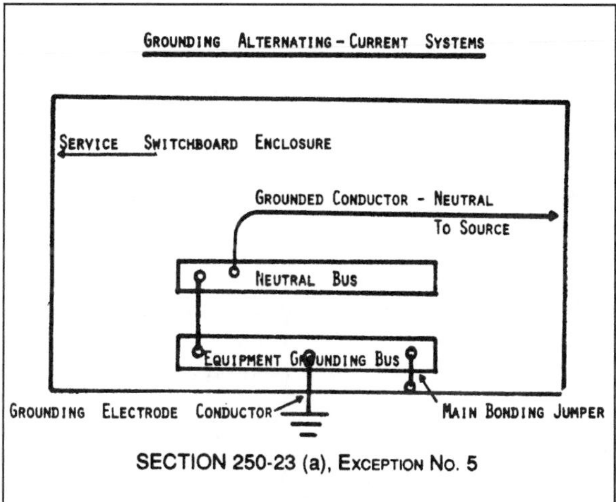

Fig. 8–18 An example of Exception No. 5 for connecting the grounded conductor to a service switchboard.

saying that when there is a neutral bus and an equipment grounding bus in the same piece of service equipment, the grounded conductor does not have to be directly connected to the grounding electrode conductor. When the neutral bus and the equipment grounding bus are bonded together, the grounded conductor is permitted to be connected to either bus.

SYSTEM OR CIRCUIT CONDUCTOR TO BE GROUNDED

Figure 8–19 illustrates the conductors that shall be grounded for the various systems listed in *Section 250-25* of the Code. The five systems are:

1. Single-phase, two-wire—one conductor is grounded.
2. Single-phase, three-wire—one conductor is grounded.
3. Multiphase system with one wire common to all phases—the common conductor is grounded.
4. Multiphase system with one phase grounded—one phase conductor is grounded.

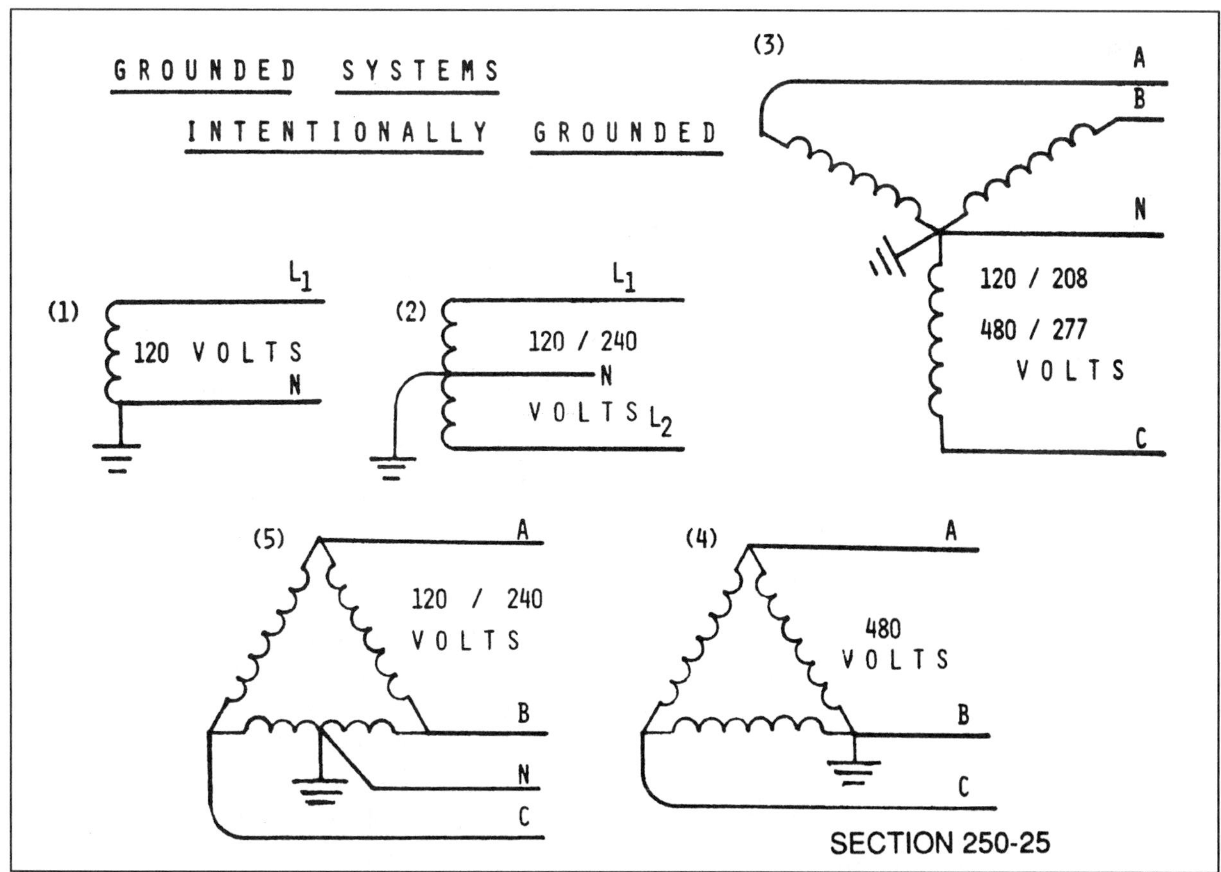

Fig. 8–19 Conductors that are required to be grounded, according to *Section 250-25*.

5. Multiphase system from which a single-phase, three-wire system is derived—the neutral conductor is grounded.

IDENTIFYING THE GROUNDED CONDUCTOR

Not all the information needed to identify the grounded conductor is in *Article 250*. Identification of the grounded conductor is made in *Article 200*, which dedicates the color white or natural gray to the grounded (neutral) conductor *(Section 200-7).*

This section also prohibits a conductor with white or natural gray insulation from being used as an ungrounded conductor. However, there are a few exceptions.

Exception No. 1 permits an insulated conductor with a white outer finish to be used as an ungrounded circuit conductor when it is permanently reidentified to indicate its use, by painting or other effective means, at each location the conductor is visible and accessible. Figure 8–20 illustrates an insulated conductor with a white finish being used as the ungrounded conductor to supply a 240-volt, single-phase motor. The white conductor is reidentified at the panel and the motor.

Exception No. 2 permits an insulated conductor with a white or natural gray finish to be used for switch loops for single-pole, three-way, and four-way switches when the conductors are part of a cable assembly. An example would be nonmetallic sheath cable or Romex. Figure 8–21 illustrates the use of the insulated conductor with a white finish with a single-pole switch; figure 8–22 (page 105) shows use with three- and four-way switches. When the white conductor is used as switch loops, it is not reidentified.

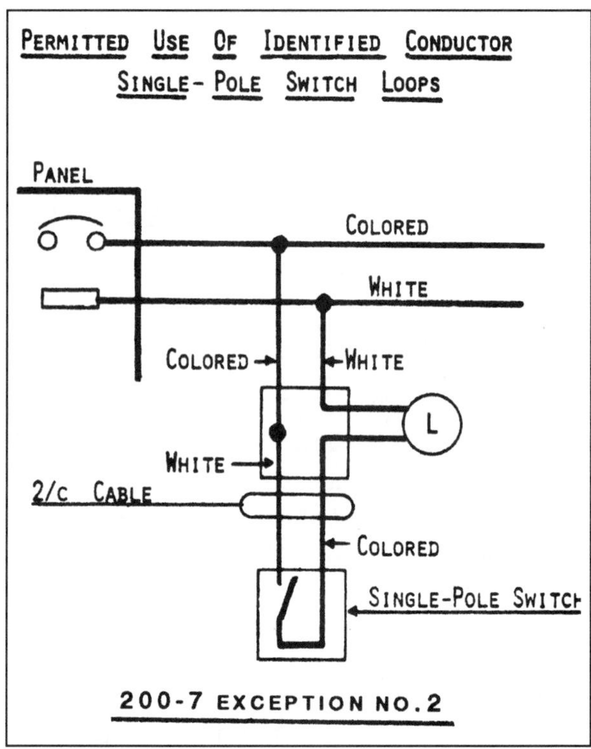

Fig. 8–21 Permitted use of a grounded conductor as an ungrounded conductor using a single-pole switch loop as an example.

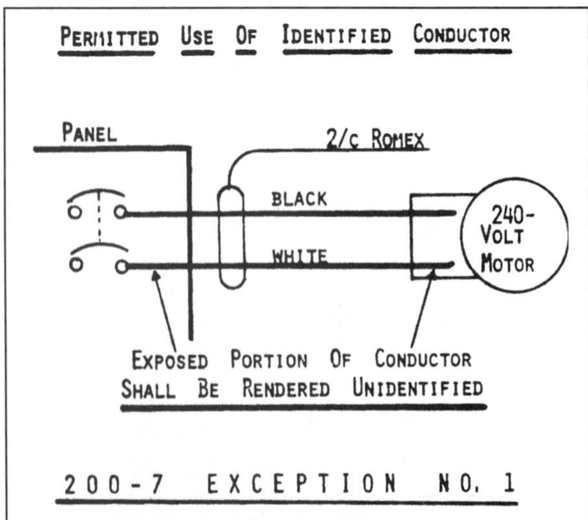

Fig. 8–20 An example of permitted use of a white conductor as an ungrounded conductor.

There are three recognized means for identifying a grounded conductor *(Section 200-6(a))* for No. 6 and smaller conductors (figure 8–23, page 105). The identification must extend the entire length of the conductor.

1. No. 6 and smaller—white or natural gray
2. Aerial cable—ridge on exterior of cable
3. An outer covering of white insulation with colored tracer threads permitted

There are four exceptions listed to the requirement that the conductor be white. These are some common-sense exceptions that have to do with special cable assemblies or special installations. For example, in Exception No. 4 (figure 8–24, page 105) when mineral-insulated cable (Type MI) is used, it does not have to have a white outer finish. But some distinctive marking

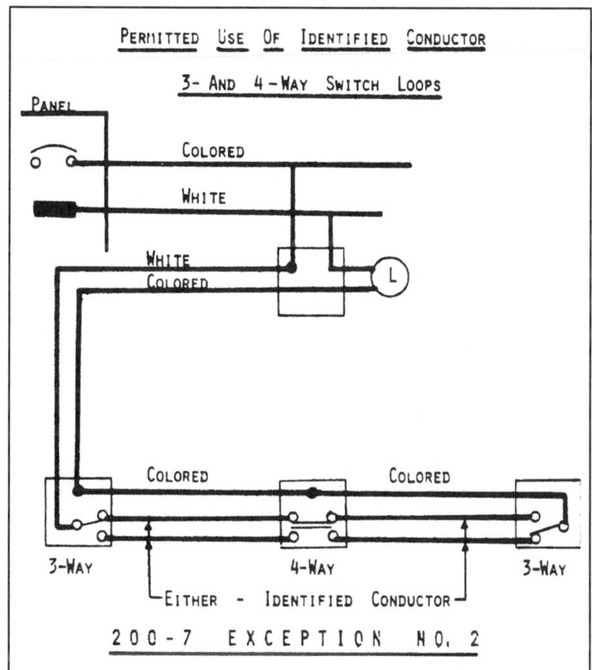

Fig. 8–22 Permitted use of a grounded conductor as an ungrounded conductor using three-way and four-way switch loops as an example.

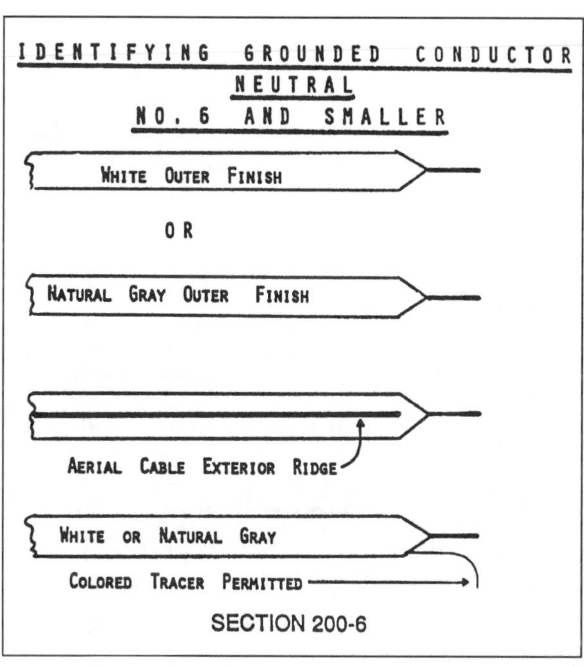

Fig. 8–23 Identifying a grounded conductor No. 6 and smaller.

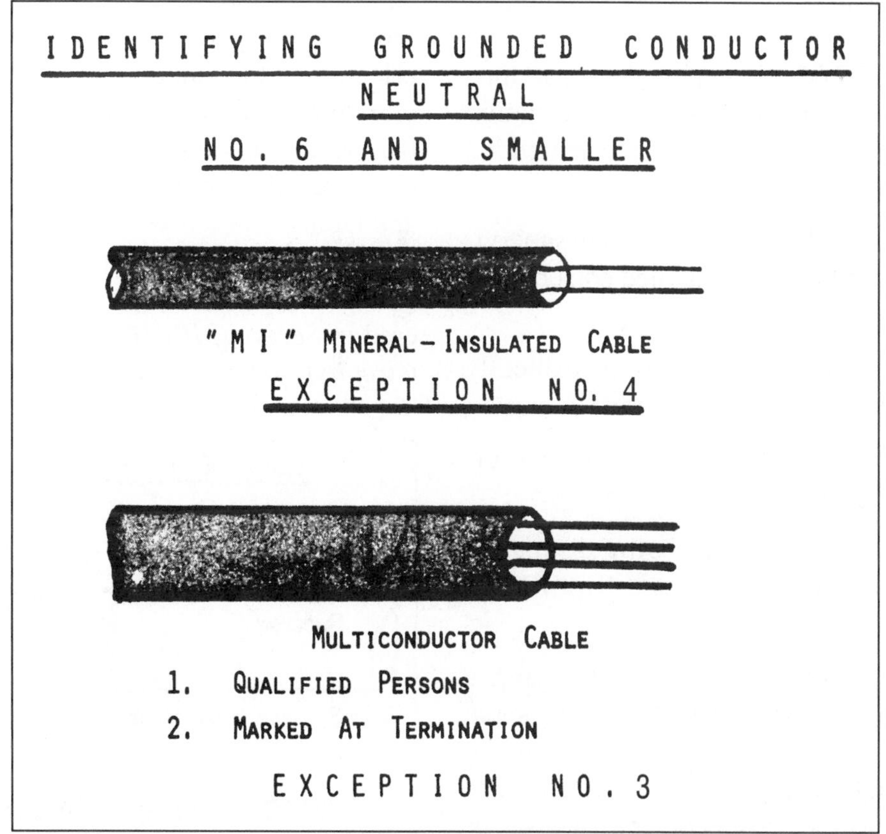

Fig. 8–24 Two exceptions to identifying a grounded conductor No. 6 and smaller.

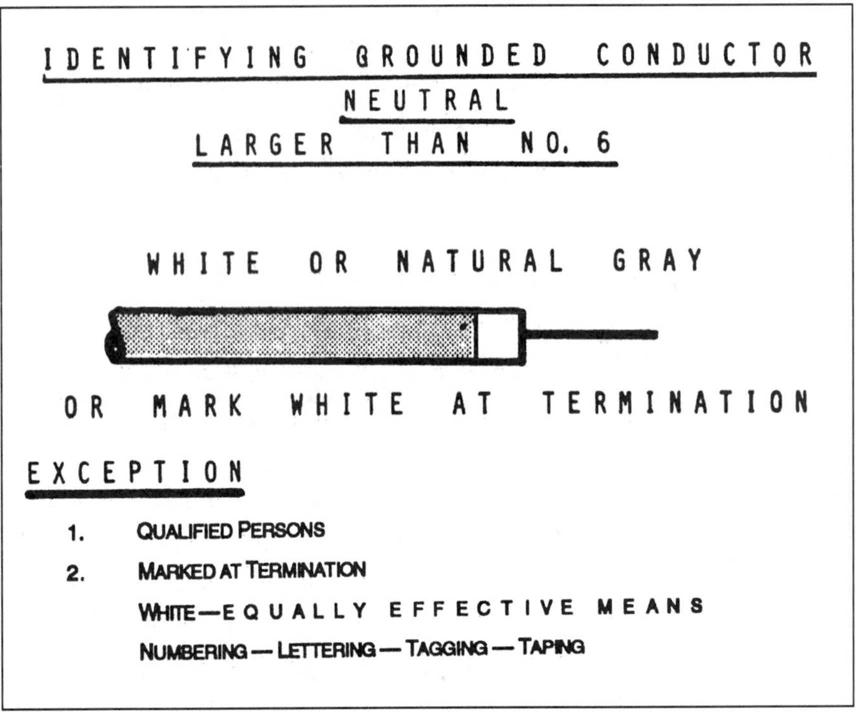

Fig. 8–25 Identifying a grounded conductor larger than No. 6. Includes exceptions to the requirement.

shall be used to identify the grounded conductor at its terminations or exposures.

Section 200-6(a), Exception No. 3, permits a conductor without a white-colored insulation to be used as the grounded conductor, provided the following conditions are met:

1. Conditions of maintenance and supervision assure that only qualified persons will service the installation.
2. The grounded conductor is permanently identified at its terminations.
3. Identification of the grounded conductor is done at the time of installation.
4. The identification shall be by distinctive white markings or other equally effective means.

The basic requirement for identifying a grounded conductor larger than No. 6 is the same as for the smaller conductor: it must have a white or natural gray outer finish (figure 8–25). The exception allows something other than white or natural gray to be used when only qualified persons will service it under proper maintenance and supervision. Then the grounded conductor must be identified by some means that will be as effective as the outer white finish. Some of the effective means permitted to be used to identify the grounded conductor at its terminations include painting, numbering, lettering, tagging, and taping.

The use of the color white to identify the grounded conductor of a branch circuit is covered in *Section 210-5 (Color Code for Branch Circuits)* and is illustrated in figure 8–26. It

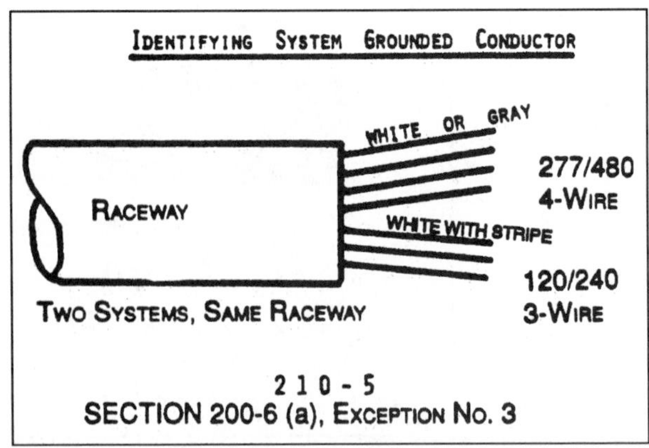

Fig. 8–26 Identifying the grounded conductor of two different systems in the same raceway.

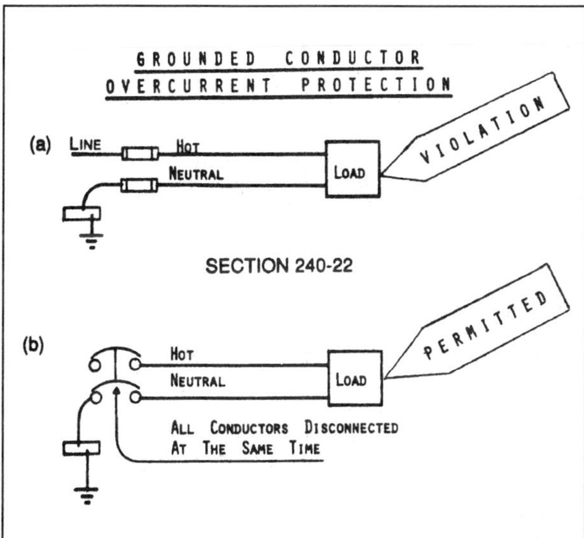

Fig. 8–27 (a) A violation of the grounded conductor overcurrent protection rule; (b) an example of overcurrent protection permitted by an exception.

considers the installation of two different grounded systems in the same raceway and then requires the grounded conductor of one to be white or natural gray and the other to be white with a colored tracer (other than green) or other means of identification on the outside of the conductor. As an example, a 277/480-volt, four-wire grounded system for lighting is installed in the same raceway with a 120/240-volt, three-wire grounded system for receptacles. There will be two neutrals installed. One neutral will be either white or gray and the second neutral could be white with a stripe, other than green.

GROUNDED CONDUCTOR OVERCURRENT PROTECTION

Figure 8–27 (a) illustrates the use of a fuse as an overcurrent protective device connected in series with a neutral conductor. This is a violation of *Section 240-22*; it prohibits using an overcurrent device in series with an intentionally grounded conductor. This means no overcurrent device in the neutral.

However, there are a couple of exceptions. The first is illustrated in figure 8–27 (b), where a circuit breaker will open the neutral and all other conductors at the same time and is permitted to be used as an overcurrent device connected in series with the neutral.

A circuit breaker with a handle tie would not be permitted, because it is possible for such a breaker to trip only one pole of the breaker. However, there are some circuit breakers on the market that will trip all poles when they are connected with a handle tie. Fuses do not trip all poles. The exception requires all poles to be opened by the overcurrent protective device.

FOLLOW UP

Topics for self-study, discussion, or questioning.

1. Discuss when the grounded conductor is, and when it is not, a neutral conductor.
2. Discuss the point of connection of the grounded conductor at the service equipment for an alternating-current system.
3. Using *Table 250-94*, discuss how the grounded conductor is sized.
4. Discuss how the grounded conductor is sized using the $12^1/_2$ percent rule.
5. Discuss how the grounded conductor is sized when the service-entrance conductors are paralleled in the same conduit.
6. Discuss how the grounded conductor is sized when the service-entrance conductors are paralleled in two or more conduits and the grounded conductor is also paralleled.
7. Discuss how to identify the grounded conductor.
8. Discuss when a white conductor can be used for other than the grounded conductor.
9. Explain when overcurrent protection is permitted to be installed in series with the grounded conductor.

CHAPTER 9

Main Bonding Jumper

OBJECTIVES

After completing this chapter, the student should be able to:

- define the main bonding jumper.
- describe the location of the main bonding jumper.
- describe how the main bonding jumper is connected.
- explain when the main bonding jumper is installed.
- identify the materials permitted to be used for the main bonding jumper.
- explain what precautions must be taken when a screw is used as the equipment bonding jumper.
- explain the importance of correctly installing the main bonding jumper.
- use *Table 250-94* to calculate the size of the main bonding jumper, when both the main bonding jumper and the service-entrance conductors are of the same material.
- calculate the size of the main bonding jumper using the $12^1/_2$ percent rule, when both the main bonding jumper and the service-entrance conductors are of the same material.
- calculate the size of the main bonding jumper when the service-entrance conductors are installed in parallel.
- calculate the size of the main bonding jumper when the service-entrance conductors are aluminum and the main bonding jumper is copper.

This chapter focuses on the main bonding jumper (figure 9–1). Covered are its purpose, its location in the ground path, the materials used, connections, and sizing. The main bonding jumper is a very important link in the overall grounding system. Information presented in *Article 250* for the main bonding jumper is also coordinated in *Section 384-3(c)*, which discusses switchboards and panelboards used as service equipment.

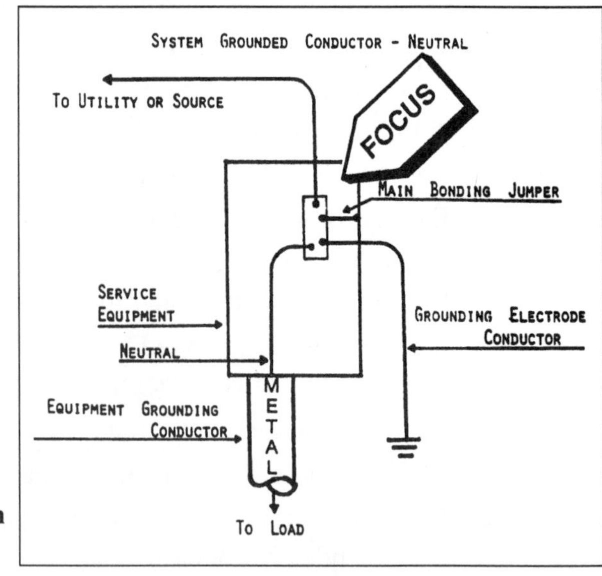

Fig. 9–1 Focus on the main bonding jumper.

DEFINITION OF *MAIN BONDING JUMPER*

Article 100 defines the main bonding jumper as follows (figure 9–2):

Quote – "The connection between the grounded circuit conductor and the equipment grounding conductor at the service."*

Comment: This definition makes two very important points. These are:

1. Two specific conductors are connected together.
2. The connection is made at the service.

As illustrated earlier (Chapter 4, figure 4–9, page 35), under fault conditions, the grounded circuit conductor becomes the equipment grounding conductor, through the main bonding jumper.

*Reprinted with permission from NFPA 70-1996, the National Electrical Code®, Copyright © 1995, National Fire Protection Association, Quincy, Massachusetts 02269. This reprinted material is not the complete and official position of the National Fire Protection Association, on the referenced subject which is represented only by the standard in its entirety.

Although it is not specifically stated in the definition, there is another important connection the main bonding jumper makes. When the metal enclosures and metal raceways are used for the equipment grounding conductor, the main bonding jumper is in series with the grounding electrode conductor and connects the equipment grounding conductor to the grounding electrode system. This connection, required by *Section 250-23(b)*, provides the zero-to-ground potential for equipment connected to the equipment grounding conductor.

Comment: Note the use of the terminology "grounded circuit conductor" in the definition. This means there is no main bonding jumper for an ungrounded system. For example, a three-phase, three-wire, 480-volt, wye connected system would have no grounded conductor and no main bonding jumper. However, it would have an equipment bonding jumper.

When the metal equipment enclosures and metal raceways are used as the equipment grounding conductor, the main bonding jumper is the direct link to the system grounded conductor and

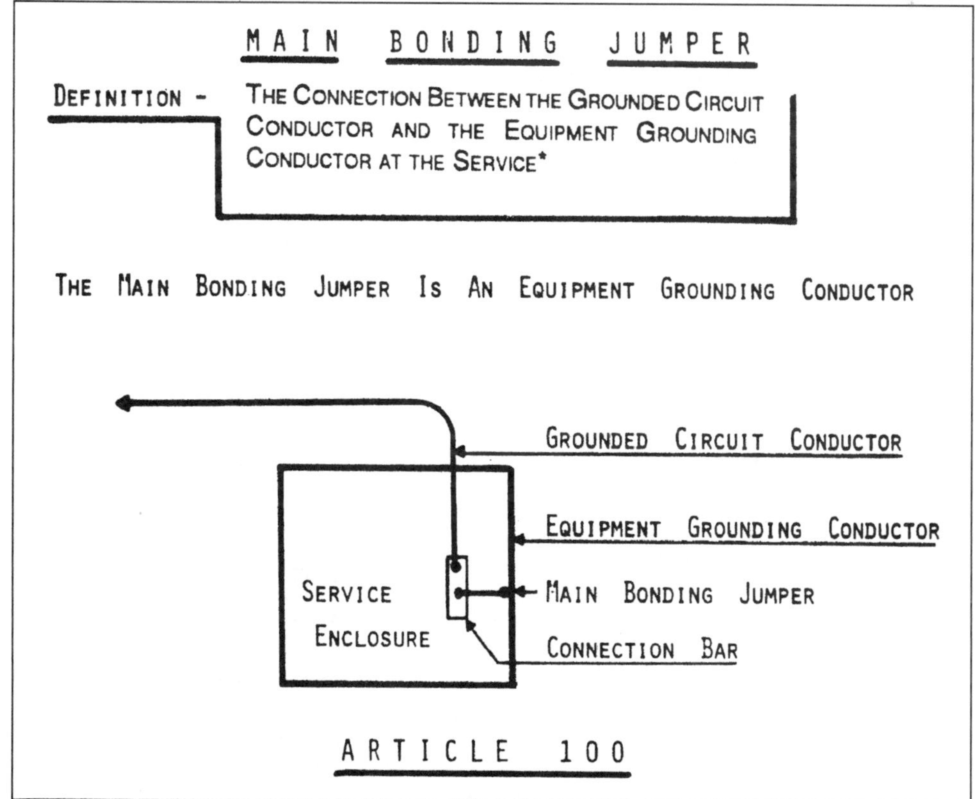
MAIN BONDING JUMPER
DEFINITION - THE CONNECTION BETWEEN THE GROUNDED CIRCUIT CONDUCTOR AND THE EQUIPMENT GROUNDING CONDUCTOR AT THE SERVICE*
THE MAIN BONDING JUMPER IS AN EQUIPMENT GROUNDING CONDUCTOR
GROUNDED CIRCUIT CONDUCTOR
EQUIPMENT GROUNDING CONDUCTOR
SERVICE ENCLOSURE
MAIN BONDING JUMPER
CONNECTION BAR
ARTICLE 100

Fig. 9–2 Definition of *main bonding jumper*.

the grounding electrode system. When the main bonding jumper is left out, it is the missing link, creating an open circuit and an invitation to a dangerous situation.

LOCATION OF THE MAIN BONDING JUMPER

As illustrated in figure 9–3, the main bonding jumper is installed in the service disconnect enclosure. The main bonding jumper is used only with a grounded system. Its purpose is to connect the equipment grounding conductor to the system grounded conductor. *Section 250-53(b)* contains regulations applying to the main bonding jumper. These include:

1. The main bonding jumper is used only with grounded systems.
2. The main bonding jumper shall be unspliced.

Comment: Note how this section mentions "for a grounded system," just as the definition in *Article 100* did. Also, there are no exceptions listed for splicing the main bonding jumper.

3. The purpose of the main bonding jumper is to connect the equipment grounding conductor to the grounded conductor.
4. The main bonding jumper shall be installed in *each* service disconnect switch.

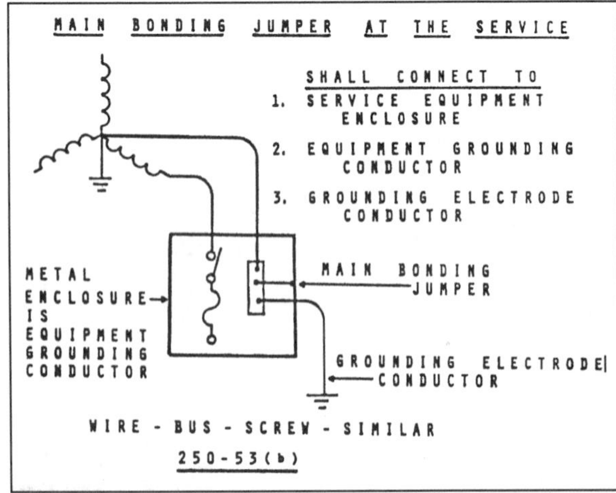

Fig. 9–3 Installation of the main bonding jumper at the service.

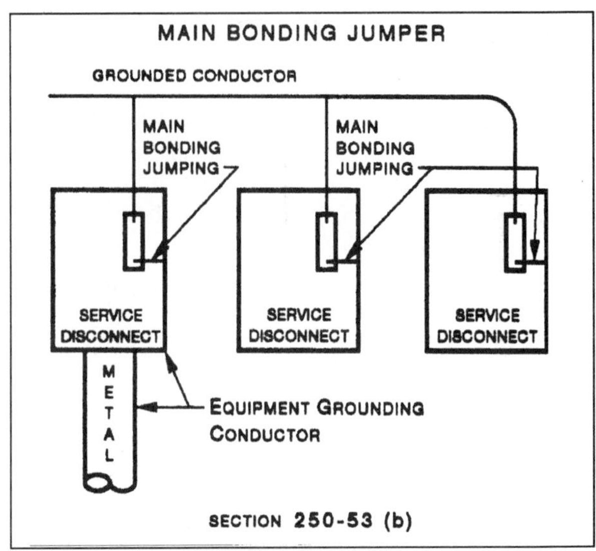

Fig. 9–4 A main bonding jumper is required in each service disconnecting switch.

5. One main bonding jumper is permitted when more than one service disconnect switch is installed in the same enclosure.

Section 250-53(b) requires an unspliced main bonding jumper to connect the equipment grounding conductor and the service disconnect enclosure to the grounded conductor of the system at each disconnect. Note in figure 9–4 how the metal conduit and the metal switch enclosure, which make up the equipment

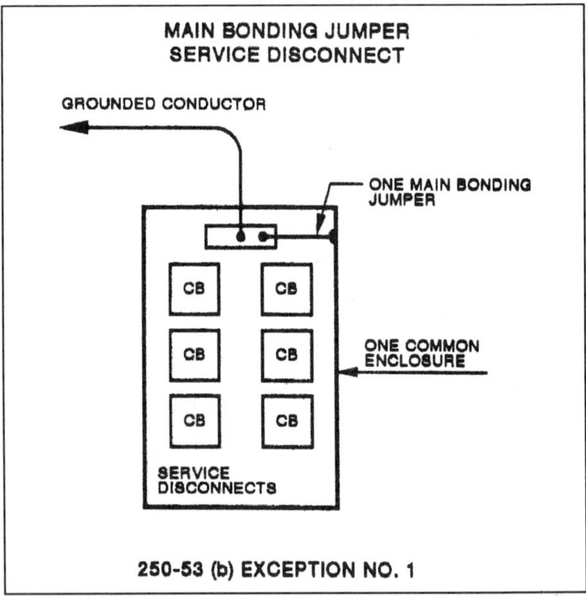

Fig. 9–5 One main bonding jumper for more than one service disconnect in the same listed assembly.

grounding conductor, are connected to the grounded conductor by way of the main bonding jumper.

Exception No. 1 to *Section 250-53(b)* permits the use of a single main bonding jumper when more than one service disconnect switch is installed in the same listed assembly. The Code permits a maximum of six disconnecting means for one service. Therefore, it is not unusual to have six circuit breakers installed within the same enclosure (figure 9–5, page 110).

MATERIALS FOR THE MAIN BONDING JUMPER

Section 250-79(a) gives information on what materials can be used for the main bonding jumper.

1. The material can be
   a. copper
   b. other corrosion-resistant material
2. It is permitted to be
   a. wire
   b. bus bar
   c. screw
   d. similar suitable conductor

Where the main bonding jumper is a screw only, *Section 250-79(b)* requires the screw be identified with a green finish that will be visible with the screw installed. When a main bonding jumper is not a screw, e.g., a ground strap used as a main bonding jumper in a switchboard, it is not required to be green in color.

Comment: Although copper is specifically mentioned, the phrase "other corrosion-resistant materials" allows the use of aluminum for the main bonding jumper.

A group of electrical inspectors was asked the question, What one Code rule do you find most violated? The answer was, The screw for the main bonding jumper in the service switch is not properly installed or not used when making a residential or small commercial installation.

When equipment is approved for service equipment, there will be provisions for the main bonding jumper. Often it is a screw that, when tightened, will make contact with the metal enclosure. However, the service equipment does not always come with this screw grounded to the metal enclosure. By not grounding the metal enclosure at the factory, it makes the piece of equipment more versatile for use other than for service equipment. Therefore, it is necessary for the electrician to make sure the screw is screwed all the way in and makes a good connection to the metal enclosure.

The screw is the main bonding jumper and plays an important part in the overall grounding. It is also an important link in the ground path, as illustrated in figure 9–6.

For a large service where a switchboard is installed, a screw is not used as the main bonding jumper. The switchboard may or may not come with a main bonding jumper installed. It is necessary to make sure that the main bonding jumper is there and is installed properly.

CAUTION: Equipment is manufactured with the screw available for grounding the equipment, thereby making it approved for service equipment. However, it can be used for other than service equipment. For example, when used for a distribution panel, other than the service, the screw must not be installed. In this case it is safer to discard the screw so that no one looks at the panel, possibly thinks it should be making a connection, and screws the screw down. This is

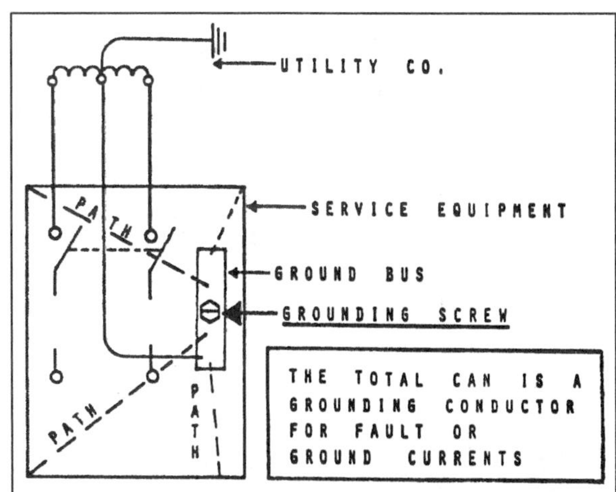

Fig. 9–6 Total metal enclosure, including grounding screw, is equipment grounding conductor to main bonding jumper.

explained and illustrated in the next chapter, "Equipment Grounding Conductor."

When the ground bus is connected to the service enclosure, the entire enclosure becomes a conductor with a considerable amount of cross-sectional area for conducting fault current.

CONNECTIONS

Section 250-113 covers the methods permitted for connecting the main bonding jumper. The connection is permitted to be made by any of the following:

1. Exothermic welding
2. Listed pressure connectors
3. Listed clamps
4. Other listed means

Devices depending solely on solder are not permitted. *Reason:* Solder has a low melting point. When there is a very high fault current, heat is developed. Enough heat could be generated to melt the solder. Depending on the position of the solder-type lug used for the connection, the melting solder could easily run out of the lug and cause the grounding circuit to open. The solder also may be blown out of the lug by magnetic motor action of fault current.

SIZING THE MAIN BONDING JUMPER

Section 250-79(c) gives three methods for sizing the main bonding jumper. When sizing the main bonding jumper, the size and material of the service-entrance conductors and the material used for the main bonding conductor are taken into consideration. Each of the three methods and some variations of the three methods are illustrated.

Method	Requirement
1. Basic Rule: Use *Table 250-94*	*Table 250-94*, the grounding electrode conductor table, is also used for sizing the main bonding jumper, which is required to be not smaller than the size given in *Table 250-94*.
2. 12½ Percent Rule for Large Conductors	When the total circular-mil area of any service-entrance phase conductor exceeds the maximum circular-mil area listed in *Table 250-94* (1100 kcmil for copper and 1750 kcmil for aluminum), the main bonding jumper shall not be smaller than 12½ percent of the service-entrance phase conductors.
3. Rule for Using Different Materials	This rule applies when the main bonding jumper is a different material than the service-entrance conductors. One could be aluminum and the other copper, for example. In this case, the minimum size of the main bonding jumper is based on assuming that the service-entrance conductors are of the same material as the main bonding jumper and that the ampacity is equivalent to the installed phase conductors.

CAUTION: Take particular note that in method 1, the same table is used to size the main bonding jumper and the grounding electrode conductor up to the maximum size listed in the table, even though *Table 250-94* makes no mention of the main bonding jumper. Also in method 1, the phrase "not smaller than" indicates that a conductor larger than the conductor required by *Table 250-94* is permitted.

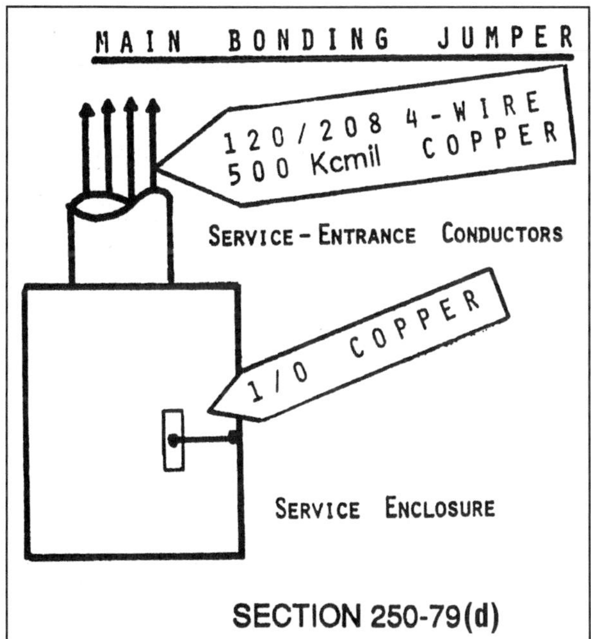

Fig. 9–7 Using one copper conductor per phase as the service conductors for a grounded AC system with a copper main bonding jumper.

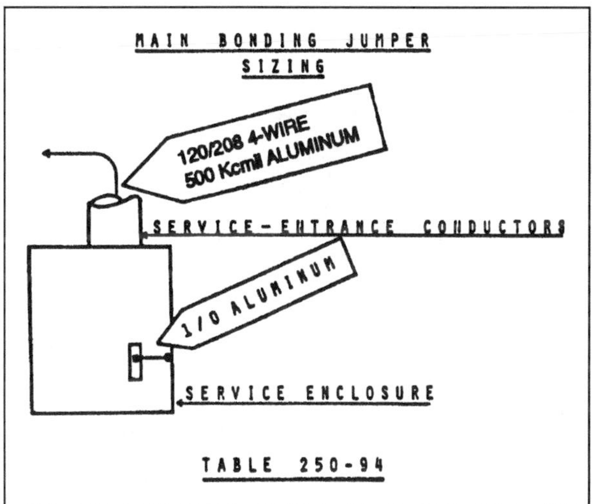

Fig. 9–9 Using one aluminum conductor per phase as the service conductors for a grounded AC system with a copper main bonding jumper.

Figure 9–7 illustrates the first method for calculating the size of the main bonding jumper. It shows the use of single conductor, 500 kcmil copper for the service-entrance conductors and a copper conductor for the main bonding jumper. For this installation, the size of the main bonding jumper is read directly from *Table 250-94* (figure 9–8) under the heading for the copper service-entrance conductors and copper grounding electrode conductor. The minimum size of the main bonding jumper is No. 1/0 copper.

TABLE ALSO USED FOR SIZING MAIN BONDING JUMPER

Table 250-94.
Grounding Electrode Conductor for AC Systems

Size of Largest Service-Entrance Conductor or Equivalent Area for Parallel Conductors		Size of Grounding Electrode Conductor	
Copper	Aluminum or Copper-Clad Aluminum	Copper	*Aluminum or Copper-Clad Aluminum
2 or smaller	1/0 or smaller	8	6
1 or 1/0	2/0 or 3/0	6	4
2/0 or 3/0	4/0 or 250 kcmil	4	2
Over 3/0 thru 350 kcmil	Over 250 kcmil thru 500 kcmil	2	1/0
Over 350 kcmil thru 600 kcmil	Over 500 kcmil thru 900 kcmil	1/0	3/0
Over 600 kcmil thru 1100 kcmil	Over 900 kcmil thru 1750 kcmil	2/0	4/0
Over 1100 kcmil	Over 1750 kcmil	3/0	250 kcmil

Fig. 9–8 Reading *Table 250-94* for sizing the main bonding jumper for the service illustrated in figure 9–7.*

Figure 9–9 illustrates method 1 with the use of single-conductor, 500 kcmil aluminum service-entrance conductors and an aluminum conductor for the main bonding jumper. For this installation, the size of the main bonding jumper is read directly from *Table 250-94* (figure 9–10, page 114) under the heading for the aluminum service-entrance conductors and aluminum grounding electrode conductor. The minimum size of the main bonding jumper is No. 1/0 aluminum.

Figure 9–11 (page 114) illustrates method 1 with the use of two 500 kcmil copper conductors per phase, connected in parallel, for the service-entrance conductors and a copper conductor for the main bonding jumper. The parallel conductors are treated as one conductor and the total kcmil of the two paralleled 500 kcmil conductors is:

500 kcmil + 500 kcmil = 1000 kcmil per phase

The size of the main bonding jumper is read directly from *Table 250-94* (figure 9–12, page 114) under the heading for the copper service-

*Reprinted with permission from NFPA 70-1996, the National Electrical Code®, Copyright © 1995, National Fire Protection Association, Quincy, Massachusetts 02269. This reprinted material is not the complete and official position of the National Fire Protection Association, on the referenced subject, which is represented only by the standard in its entirety.

Table 250-94.
Grounding Electrode Conductor for AC Systems

Size of Largest Service-Entrance Conductor or Equivalent Area for Parallel Conductors		Size of Grounding Electrode Conductor	
Copper	Aluminum or Copper-Clad Aluminum	Copper	*Aluminum or Copper-Clad Aluminum
2 or smaller	1/0 or smaller	8	6
1 or 1/0	2/0 or 3/0	6	4
2/0 or 3/0	4/0 or 250 kcmil	4	2
Over 3/0 thru 350 kcmil	Over 250 kcmil thru 500 kcmil	2	1/0
Over 350 kcmil thru 600 kcmil	Over 500 kcmil thru 900 kcmil	1/0	3/0
Over 600 kcmil thru 1100 kcmil	Over 900 kcmil thru 1750 kcmil	2/0	4/0
Over 1100 kcmil	Over 1750 kcmil	3/0	250 kcmil

Fig. 9–10 Reading *Table 250-94* for sizing the main bonding jumper for the service illustrated in figure 9–7.*

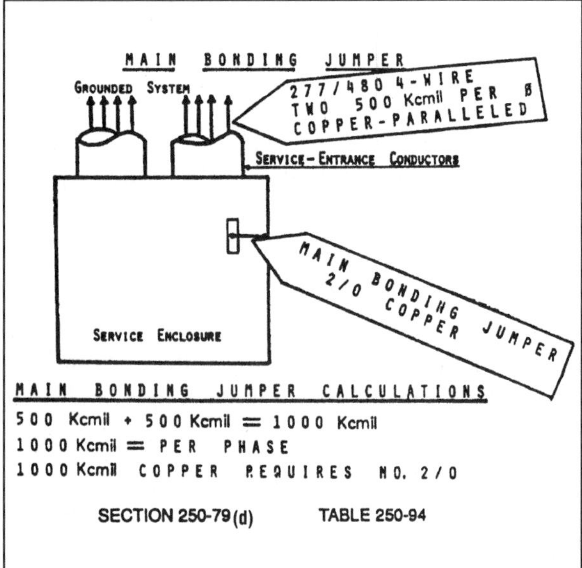

Fig. 9–11 Using two copper conductors per phase, paralleled, as service conductors for a grounded AC system with a copper main bonding jumper.

Table 250-94.
Grounding Electrode Conductor for AC Systems

Size of Largest Service-Entrance Conductor or Equivalent Area for Parallel Conductors		Size of Grounding Electrode Conductor	
Copper	Aluminum or Copper-Clad Aluminum	Copper	*Aluminum or Copper-Clad Aluminum
2 or smaller	1/0 or smaller	8	6
1 or 1/0	2/0 or 3/0	6	4
2/0 or 3/0	4/0 or 250 kcmil	4	2
Over 3/0 thru 350 kcmil	Over 250 kcmil thru 500 kcmil	2	1/0
Over 350 kcmil thru 600 kcmil	Over 500 kcmil thru 900 kcmil	1/0	3/0
Over 600 kcmil thru 1100 kcmil	Over 900 kcmil thru 1750 kcmil	2/0	4/0
Over 1100 kcmil	Over 1750 kcmil	3/0	250 kcmil

Fig. 9–12 Reading *Table 250-94* for sizing the main bonding jumper for the service illustrated in figure 9–11.*

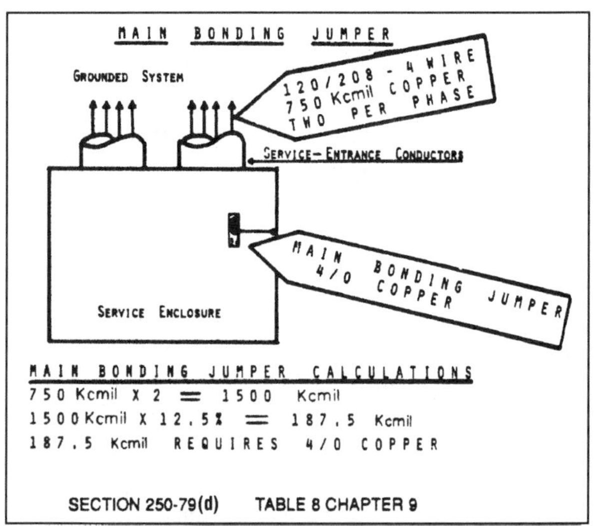

Fig. 9–13 Using the 12½ percent rule to size a copper main bonding jumper for a grounded AC system.

entrance conductors and copper grounding electrode conductor. The minimum size of the main bonding jumper is No. 2/0.

Figure 9–13 illustrates method 2 with the use of two 750 kcmil copper conductors per phase, connected in parallel:

> 750 kcmil + 750 kcmil = 1500 kcmil per phase

This is larger than the 1100 kcmil maximum listed in *Table 250-94*. Therefore, the 12½ percent rule shall be used.

> 1500 kcmil × 12½% = 187.5 kcmil or 187,500 circular mils

Table 8 (Chapter 9) *Conductor Properties* (figure 9–14, page 115) is used to convert the calculated circular-mil area into a standard wire size. In this case it is a little less than No. 4/0 but a little more than No. 3/0; therefore, the No. 4/0 must be used. The minimum size main bonding jumper required for this service is No. 4/0.

Question: Is the main bonding jumper ever required to be larger than the grounding electrode conductor?

187,500 cmil REQUIRES 4/0

Table 8. Conductor Properties

Size AWG/ kcmil	Area Cir. Mils	Conductors				DC Resistance at 75°C (167°F)		
		Stranding		Overall		Copper		Aluminum
		Quan-tity	Diam. in.	Diam. in.	Area in.²	Uncoated ohm/kFT	Coated ohm/kFT	ohm/ kFT
18	1620	1	—	0.040	0.001	7.77	8.08	12.8
18	1620	7	0.015	0.046	0.002	7.95	8.45	13.1
16	2580	1	—	0.051	0.002	4.89	5.08	8.05
16	2580	7	0.019	0.058	0.003	4.99	5.29	8.21
14	4110	1	—	0.064	0.003	3.07	3.19	5.06
14	4110	7	0.024	0.073	0.004	3.14	3.26	5.17
12	6530	1	—	0.081	0.005	1.93	2.01	3.18
12	6530	7	0.030	0.092	0.006	1.98	2.05	3.25
10	10380	1	—	0.102	0.008	1.21	1.26	2.00
10	10380	7	0.038	0.116	0.011	1.24	1.29	2.04
8	16510	1	—	0.128	0.013	0.764	0.786	1.26
8	16510	7	0.049	0.146	0.017	0.778	0.809	1.28
6	26240	7	0.061	0.184	0.027	0.491	0.510	0.808
4	41740	7	0.077	0.232	0.042	0.308	0.321	0.508
3	52620	7	0.087	0.260	0.053	0.245	0.254	0.403
2	66360	7	0.097	0.292	0.067	0.194	0.201	0.319
1	83690	19	0.066	0.332	0.087	0.154	0.160	0.253
1/0	105600	19	0.074	0.372	0.109	0.122	0.127	0.201
2/0	133100	19	0.084	0.418	0.137	0.0976	0.101	0.159
3/0	167800	19	0.094	0.470	0.173	0.0766	0.0797	0.126
4/0	211600	19	0.106	0.528	0.219	0.0608	0.0626	0.100
250	—	37	0.082	0.575	0.260	0.0515	0.0535	0.0847
300	—	37	0.090	0.630	0.312	0.0429	0.0446	0.0707
350	—	37	0.097	0.681	0.364	0.0367	0.0382	0.0605
400	—	37	0.104	0.728	0.416	0.0321	0.0331	0.0529
500	—	37	0.116	0.813	0.519	0.0258	0.0265	0.0424
600	—	61	0.099	0.893	0.626	0.0214	0.0223	0.0353
700	—	61	0.107	0.964	0.730	0.0184	0.0189	0.0303
750	—	61	0.111	0.998	0.782	0.0171	0.0176	0.0282
800	—	61	0.114	1.030	0.834	0.0161	0.0166	0.0265
900	—	61	0.122	1.094	0.940	0.0143	0.0147	0.0235
1000	—	61	0.128	1.152	1.042	0.0129	0.0132	0.0212
1250	—	91	0.117	1.284	1.305	0.0103	0.0106	0.0169
1500	—	91	0.128	1.412	1.566	0.00858	0.00883	0.0141
1750	—	127	0.117	1.526	1.829	0.00735	0.00756	0.0121
2000	—	127	0.126	1.632	2.092	0.00643	0.00662	0.0106

Fig. 9–14 Using *Table 8* (Chapter 9) to convert circular mils to a numbered wired size.*

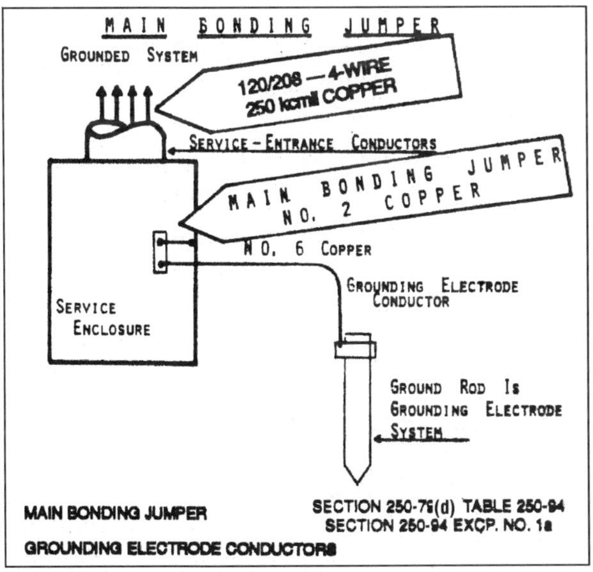

Fig. 9–15 Comparing the size of the main bonding jumper to the grounding electrode conductor.

Answer: Yes. Figure 9–15 illustrates the use of a ground rod for the grounding electrode. Because of an exception, a No. 6 copper conductor is permitted to be installed as the grounding electrode conductor. *Table 250-94* requires that No. 2 copper be used for the main bonding jumper.

Reason: Under fault conditions where the equipment grounding conductor consists of metal enclosures for electrical equipment and electrical conductors, such as a steel conduit installation, the main bonding jumper is required to carry the total fault current to the system grounded conductor for the quick operation of the overcurrent protective device, as illustrated in figure 9–16 (page 116).

Figure 9–16 illustrates the low-impedance path for current flow through the main bonding jumper. At the same time, however, there is also a high-impedance parallel path for current flow via the system grounding electrode conductor and the grounding electrode for the supply transformer.

Note the following in figure 9–16:

1. Under fault conditions the metal raceway and metal enclosure are the equipment grounding conductors.
2. Watch the electron flow under fault conditions.
3. The electrons travel on the main bonding jumper.
4. Under fault conditions the system grounded conductor becomes an equipment grounding conductor.
5. The path of the fault current is channelled back through the overcurrent protective device.

Figure 9–17 gives a second example where the grounding electrode conductor will be smaller than the main bonding jumper. When using the $12^1/_2$ percent rule, the required main bonding jumper is 250 kcmil. The grounding electrode conductor is read directly from *Table 250-94*. The 1800 kcmil per phase is over the maximum 1100 kcmil listed. It needs to be at least No. 3/0 copper, although it is not required to be larger than that.

It is not unusual for an installation to utilize aluminum service-entrance conductors and a

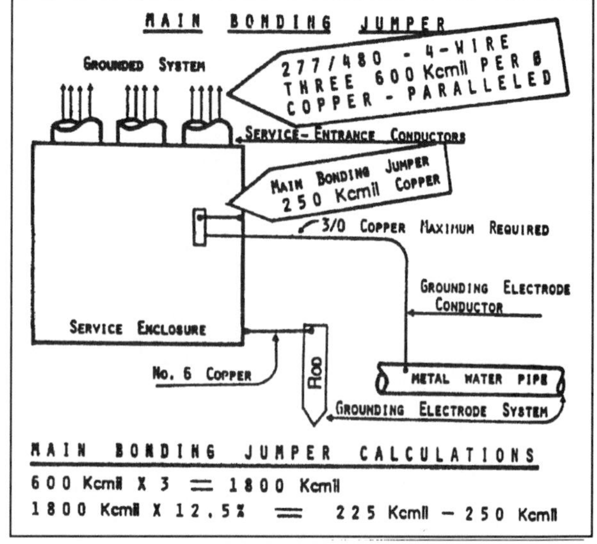

Fig. 9–17 Sizing the main bonding jumper. A case where the grounding electrode conductor can be smaller than the main bonding jumper.

copper main bonding jumper. Two different materials have been used and the ampacity of copper and aluminum is different.

Figure 9–18 illustrates a service with aluminum service-entrance conductors and a copper main bonding jumper. The size of the main bonding jumper is read directly from *Table 250-94* (figure 9–19, page 117). Use the aluminum column for the service-entrance conductors, and the copper column for the size of the main bonding jumper.

Figure 9–20 (page 117) illustrates method 3 for calculating the main bonding jumper size with the use of three 750 kcmil, type THW,

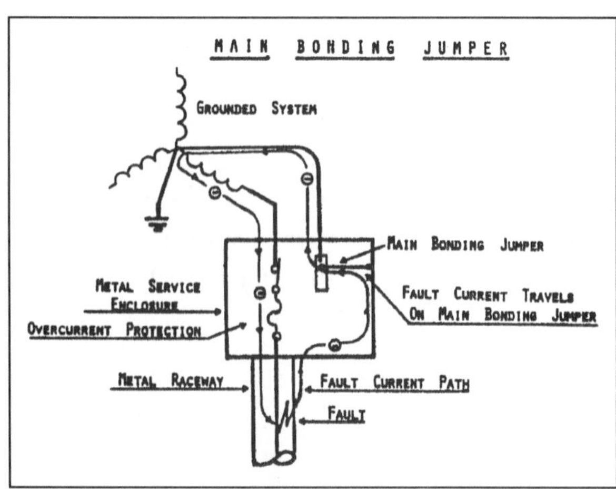

Fig. 9–16 The path of the fault current through the main bonding jumper.

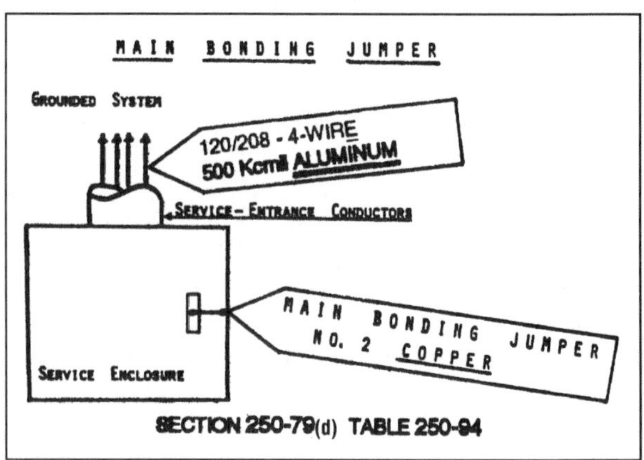

Fig. 9–18 Sizing the main bonding jumper using 500 kcmil aluminum service conductors with a copper main bonding jumper.

Table 250-94.
Grounding Electrode Conductor for AC Systems

Size of Largest Service-Entrance Conductor or Equivalent Area for Parallel Conductors		Size of Grounding Electrode Conductor	
Copper	Aluminum or Copper-Clad Aluminum	Copper	*Aluminum or Copper-Clad Aluminum
2 or smaller	1/0 or smaller	8	6
1 or 1/0	2/0 or 3/0	6	4
2/0 or 3/0	4/0 or 250 kcmil	4	2
Over 3/0 thru 350 kcmil	Over 250 kcmil thru 500 kcmil	2	1/0
Over 350 kcmil thru 600 kcmil	Over 500 kcmil thru 900 kcmil	1/0	3/0
Over 600 kcmil thru 1100 kcmil	Over 900 kcmil thru 1750 kcmil	2/0	4/0
Over 1100 kcmil	Over 1750 kcmil	3/0	250 kcmil

Fig. 9–19 Using *Table 250-94* for sizing the main bonding jumper with aluminum service entrance conductors and copper main bonding jumper.*

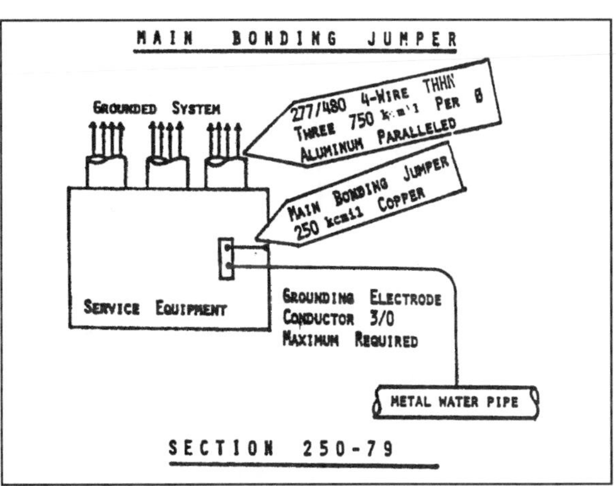

Fig. 9–20 Aluminum service entrance conductors with a copper main bonding jumper, when kcmil of service entrance conductors exceed *Table 250-94*.

Table 310-16. Allowable Ampacities of Insulated Conductors Rated 0-2000 Volts, 60° to 90°C (140° to 194°F) Not More Than Three Current-Carrying Conductors in Raceway or Cable or Earth (Directly Buried), Based on Ambient Temperature of 30°C (86°F)

Size	Temperature Rating of Conductor. See Table 310-13.						Size
	60°C (140°F)	75°C (167°F)	90°C (194°F)	60°C (140°F)	75°C (167°F)	90°C (194°F)	
AWG kcmil	TYPES TW†, UF†	TYPES FEPW†, RH†, RHW†, THHW†, THW†, THWN†, XHHW† USE†, ZW†	TYPES TBS, SA SIS, FEP†, FEPB†, MI RHH†, RHW-2, THHN†, THHW†, THW-2†, THWN-2†, USE-2, XHH, XHHW†, XHHW-2, ZW-2	TYPES TW†, UF†	TYPES RH†, RHW†, THHW†, THW†, THWN†, XHHW†, USE†	TYPES TA, TBS, SA, SIS, THHN†, THHW†, THW-2 THWN-2, RHH†, RHW-2, USE-2 XHH, XHHW, XHHW-2, ZW-2	AWG kcmil
	COPPER			ALUMINUM COPPER-CLAD ALUMINUM			
18	....	....	14	....	....	....	....
16	....	....	18	....	....	....	....
14	20†	20†	25†	....	....	....	....
12	25†	25†	30†	20†	20†	25†	12
10	30	35†	40†	25	30†	35†	10
8	40	50	55	30	40	45	8
6	55	65	75	40	50	60	6
4	70	85	95	55	65	75	4
3	85	100	110	65	75	85	3
2	95	115	130	75	90	100	2
1	110	130	150	85	100	115	1
1/0	125	150	170	100	120	135	1/0
2/0	145	175	195	115	135	150	2/0
3/0	165	200	225	130	155	175	3/0
4/0	195	230	260	150	180	205	4/0
250	215	255	290	170	205	230	250
300	240	285	320	190	230	255	300
350	260	310	350	210	250	280	350
400	280	335	380	225	270	305	400
500	320	380	430	260	310	350	500
600	355	420	475	285	340	385	600
700	385	460	520	310	375	420	700
750	400	475	535	320	385	435	750
800	410	490	555	330	395	450	800
900	435	520	585	355	425	480	900
1000	455	545	615	375	445	500	1000
1250	495	590	665	405	485	545	1250
1500	520	625	705	435	520	585	1500
1750	545	650	735	455	545	615	1750
2000	560	665	750	470	560	630	2000

750 kmil THW ALUMINUM 385 AMPS

385 AMPS THW COPPER 600 kcmil

Fig. 9–21 Using *Table 310-16* to assume replacement of aluminum service entrance conductors with copper service entrance conductors.*

Table 8. Conductor Properties

Size AWG/ kcmil	Area Cir. Mils	Conductors				DC Resistance at 75°C (167°F)		
		Stranding		Overall		Copper		Aluminum
		Quantity	Diam. in.	Diam. in.	Area in.²	Uncoated ohm/kFT	Coated ohm/kFT	ohm/ kFT
18	1620	1	—	0.040	0.001	7.77	8.08	12.8
18	1620	7	0.015	0.046	0.002	7.95	8.45	13.1
16	2580	1	—	0.051	0.002	4.89	5.08	8.05
16	2580	7	0.019	0.058	0.003	4.99	5.29	8.21
14	4110	1	—	0.064	0.003	3.07	3.19	5.06
14	4110	7	0.024	0.073	0.004	3.14	3.26	5.17
12	6530	1	—	0.081	0.005	1.93	2.01	3.18
12	6530	7	0.030	0.092	0.006	1.98	2.05	3.25
10	10380	1	—	0.102	0.008	1.21	1.26	2.00
10	10380	7	0.038	0.116	0.011	1.24	1.29	2.04
8	16510	1	—	0.128	0.013	0.764	0.786	1.26
8	16510	7	0.049	0.146	0.017	0.778	0.809	1.28
6	26240	7	0.061	0.184	0.027	0.491	0.510	0.808
4	41740	7	0.077	0.232	0.042	0.308	0.321	0.508
3	52620	7	0.087	0.260	0.053	0.245	0.254	0.403
2	66360	7	0.097	0.292	0.067	0.194	0.201	0.319
1	83690	19	0.066	0.332	0.087	0.154	0.160	0.253
1/0	105600	19	0.074	0.372	0.109	0.122	0.127	0.201
2/0	133100	19	0.084	0.418	0.137	0.0976	0.101	0.159
3/0	167800	19	0.094	0.470	0.173	0.0766	0.0797	0.126
4/0	211600	19	0.106	0.528	0.219	0.0608	0.0626	0.100
250	—	37	0.082	0.575	0.260	0.0515	0.0535	0.0847
300	—	37	0.090	0.630	0.312	0.0429	0.0446	0.0707
350	—	37	0.097	0.681	0.364	0.0367	0.0382	0.0605
400	—	37	0.104	0.728	0.416	0.0321	0.0331	0.0529
500	—	37	0.116	0.813	0.519	0.0258	0.0265	0.0424
600	—	61	0.099	0.893	0.626	0.0214	0.0223	0.0353
700	—	61	0.107	0.964	0.730	0.0184	0.0189	0.0303
750	—	61	0.111	0.998	0.782	0.0171	0.0176	0.0282
800	—	61	0.114	1.030	0.834	0.0161	0.0166	0.0265
900	—	61	0.122	1.094	0.940	0.0143	0.0147	0.0235
1000	—	61	0.128	1.152	1.042	0.0129	0.0132	0.0212
1250	—	91	0.117	1.284	1.305	0.0103	0.0106	0.0169
1500	—	91	0.128	1.412	1.566	0.00858	0.00883	0.0141
1750	—	127	0.117	1.526	1.829	0.00735	0.00756	0.0121
2000	—	127	0.126	1.632	2.092	0.00643	0.00662	0.0106

Fig. 9–22 Using *Table 8*, Chapter 9, to select standard size conductors, when kcmil is known.*

aluminum per phase, paralleled service-entrance conductors.

Three times 750 kcmil equals 2250 kcmil, which is more than the maximum listed in *Table 250-94*. Therefore, the 12½ percent rule comes into play.

When making this calculation, the ampacity of the two different metals is taken into consideration. In this case the service-entrance conductors are assumed, or visualized, to be copper instead of aluminum while making this calculation for the main bonding jumper. *Table 310-16* (figure 9–21, page 117) is used for making the transition from aluminum to the equivalent copper conductors.

There could be situations where an ampacity table other than *Table 310-16* would be used, but this installation fits into *Table 310-16*.

750 kcmil aluminum THW insulation is rated 385 amps

385 amps copper will only require 600 kcmil THW copper

600 kcmil copper × 3 paralleled = 1800 kcmil

1800 kcmil × 12½ percent = 225 kcmil

Next standard size given in *Table 8*, Chapter 9 (figure 9–22)

Next larger standard size to 225 kcmil is 250 kcmil copper

Note from figure 9–20 (page 117) that the main bonding jumper is once again larger than the grounding electrode conductor.

FOLLOW UP

Topics for self-study, discussion, or questioning.

1. Define what the *main bonding jumper* is.
2. Discuss the location of the main bonding jumper.
3. Discuss what other conductors the main bonding jumper must be connected to.
4. Discuss number of main bonding jumpers needed when more than one disconnecting switch is used.
5. Discuss what precautions must be taken when a screw serves as the main bonding jumper.
6. When the main bonding jumper is a screw and is installed in the service equipment by the manufacturer, how is it required to be identified?
7. Discuss calculating the size of the main bonding jumper, using the basic rule and *Table 250-94*, when both the main bonding jumper and the service-entrance conductors are of the same material.
8. Discuss calculating the size of the main bonding jumper, using the $12^1/_2$ percent rule, when both the main bonding jumper and the service-entrance conductors are of the same material.
9. Discuss calculating the size of the main bonding jumper when the main bonding jumper and the service-entrance conductors are of different materials.

CHAPTER 10

Equipment Grounding Conductor

OBJECTIVES

After completing this chapter, the student should be able to:

- define what an equipment grounding conductor is.
- identify where the highest number of faults occur in an electrical installation.
- identify what an effective grounding path is.
- explain what must be done to maintain continuity of the equipment grounding path, when a system of metal raceways and enclosures is used as the equipment grounding conductor.
- identify the various ways the equipment grounding conductor is identified.
- identify the various wires and materials permitted to be used as equipment grounding conductors.
- explain the proper installation of the equipment grounding conductor under various conditions.
- explain the limitations on the use of flexible metal conduit, when it is permitted to be used as the equipment grounding conductor.
- explain the importance of continuity when installing any type of equipment grounding conductor.
- use *Table 250-95* for calculating the size of the equipment grounding conductor, when conductors are installed in a single raceway.
- use *Table 250-95* for calculating the size of the equipment grounding conductor, when conductors are installed in parallel conduits.
- calculate the size of the equipment grounding conductor when the circuit is protected by an instantaneous circuit breaker.
- calculate the size of the equipment grounding conductor, when the circuit conductors are enlarged to compensate for voltage drop.
- explain how continuity is maintained when equipment grounding conductors pass through a box or the box is part of the equipment grounding conductor path.

This chapter focuses on the equipment grounding conductor (figure 10–1, page 121). Discussed are its purpose, use, types, identification, installation, connection, and sizing.

The equipment grounding conductor is one of the conductors that ties into the bull's eye of the overall grounding system at the service equipment. It is used for grounding metal enclosures

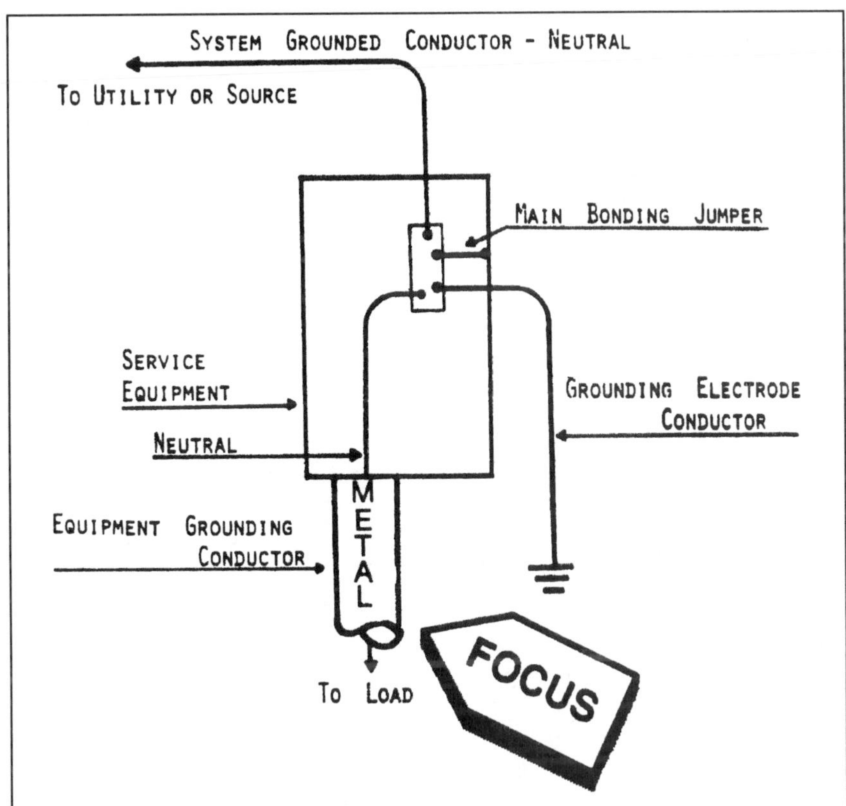

Fig. 10–1 Focus on the equipment grounding conductor.

containing current-carrying conductors and metal enclosures of electrical equipment.

DEFINITION OF *EQUIPMENT GROUNDING CONDUCTOR*

The equipment grounding conductor plays no part in delivering current in an electrical lighting or power circuit. But it plays a very important part in ensuring safety in the grounding system. "Equipment grounding conductor" is defined in *Article 100* (figure 10–2, page 122).

Quote – "The conductor used to connect the non-current-carrying metal parts of equipment, raceways, and other enclosures to the system grounded conductor, the grounding electrode conductor or both, at the service equipment or at the source of a separately derived system."*

Comment: The term *both* indicates that when there is a grounded system, the equipment grounding conductor is connected to the grounded conductor and the grounding electrode conductor. When there is an ungrounded system and no grounded conductor, the equipment grounding conductor is connected to the grounding electrode conductor.

DEFINITION OF *SYSTEM*

Figure 10–3 (page 122) is a very basic illustration of a *system.* The definition given is not taken from the Code.

> "A system is a group of electrical circuits connected in an orderly fashion to make the whole installation workable."

The term *system* is often used in the field just to indicate the connection at the source of supply—such as a three-wire system, a delta system, a wye system, or another type of connection—and not the entire system the supply feeds. One should not be misled into believing that the system is only the connection at the source of supply.

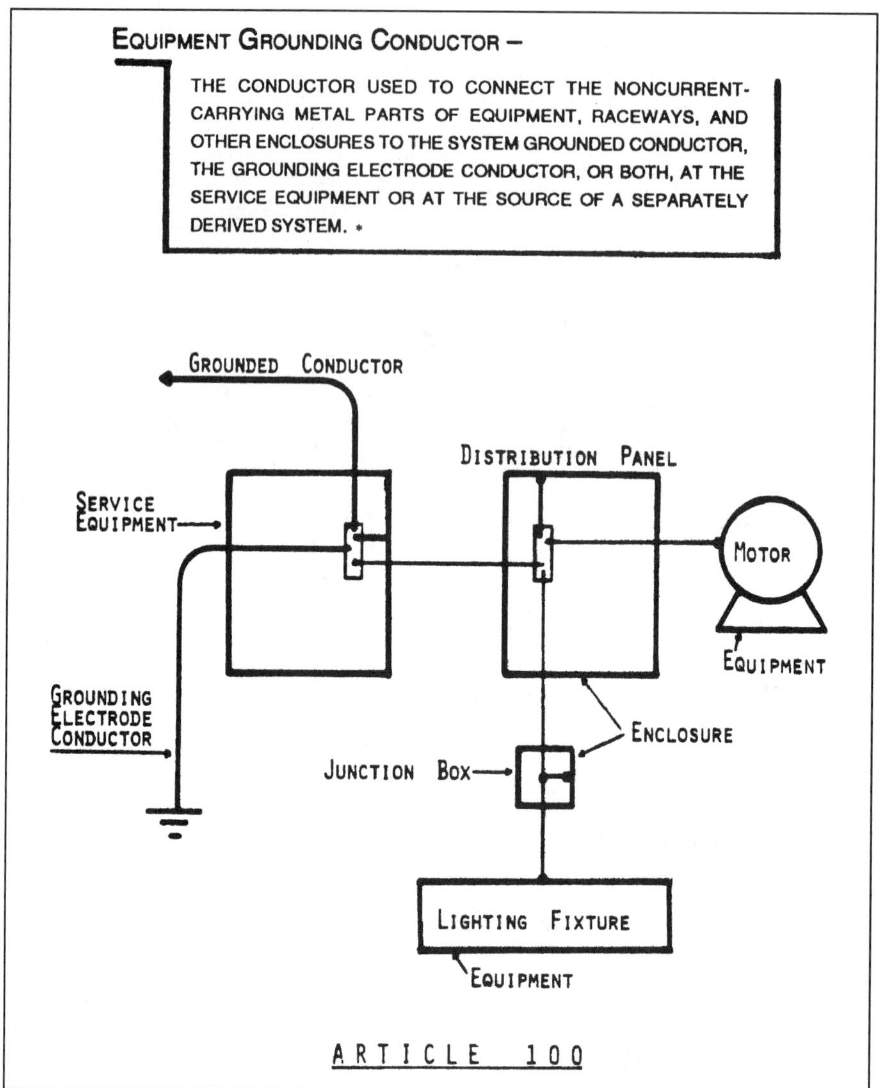
EQUIPMENT GROUNDING CONDUCTOR –
THE CONDUCTOR USED TO CONNECT THE NONCURRENT-CARRYING METAL PARTS OF EQUIPMENT, RACEWAYS, AND OTHER ENCLOSURES TO THE SYSTEM GROUNDED CONDUCTOR, THE GROUNDING ELECTRODE CONDUCTOR, OR BOTH, AT THE SERVICE EQUIPMENT OR AT THE SOURCE OF A SEPARATELY DERIVED SYSTEM. *
GROUNDED CONDUCTOR
DISTRIBUTION PANEL
SERVICE EQUIPMENT
MOTOR
EQUIPMENT
GROUNDING ELECTRODE CONDUCTOR
ENCLOSURE
JUNCTION BOX
LIGHTING FIXTURE
EQUIPMENT
ARTICLE 100

Fig. 10–2 Definition of *equipment grounding conductor*.*

The system includes all the distribution feeders, the branch circuit, all electrically operated equipment, and all electrical and mechanical connections.

Question: In a system as simple as the one illustrated, at how many points throughout the system would electrical connections be made?

Answer: When counting the electrical connections for the service-entrance conductor, the feeder, going to the lighting panel, the branch circuits going to the individual lights, the connections at the lighting fixture, feeder connections for the motor control center, the motor branch circuits, the motor connections, and control connections, the result would be a very large number. These electrical connections must be made with care to maintain continuity of the electrical circuit and make sure all the electrical equipment operates satisfactorily.

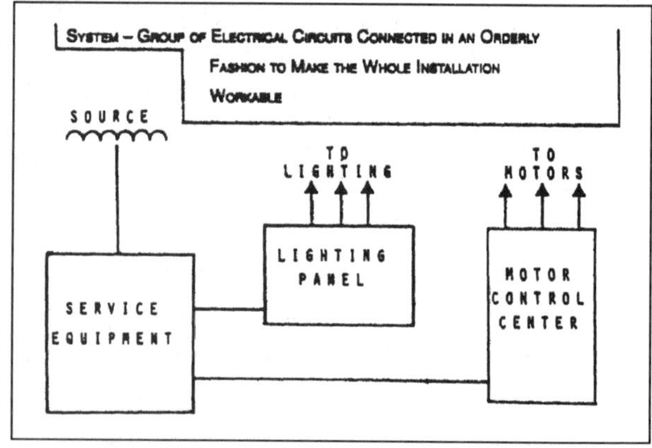
SYSTEM – GROUP OF ELECTRICAL CIRCUITS CONNECTED IN AN ORDERLY FASHION TO MAKE THE WHOLE INSTALLATION WORKABLE
SOURCE
TO LIGHTING
TO MOTORS
LIGHTING PANEL
SERVICE EQUIPMENT
MOTOR CONTROL CENTER

Fig. 10–3 Definition of *system*.

*Reprinted with permission from NFPA 70-1996, the National Electrical Code®, Copyright © 1995, National Fire Protection Association, Quincy, Massachusetts 02269. This reprinted material is not the complete and official position of the National Fire Protection Association, on the referenced subject, which is represented only by the standard in its entirety.

Section 300-13 requires the continuity of conductors to be maintained. There is another very good reason that every one of these connections should be made properly:

THE POINT OF CONNECTION IS THE POINT AT WHICH THE HIGHEST NUMBER OF FAULTS TAKES PLACE.

Very few faults take place between conductors in the middle of a conduit run. Most faults occur at or near the point of connection or termination.

Look once again at the same system (figure 10–3, page 122). Only this time, look at it from a mechanical viewpoint of the installation of the raceways and enclosures. How many "mechanical" connections will be made to complete the installation properly?

Each coupling, connector, locknut, and fitting, installed to make the installation complete, is a point of connection. Consider the service to be in metal conduit. The service equipment is a metal enclosure, the feeder to the lighting panel is in metal conduit, the lighting panel is a metal enclosure, the lighting branch circuits are all in metal conduit, the motor feeder is in metal conduit, the motor control center is a metal enclosure, and all of the motor branch circuits are in metal conduit. The answer would be a very large number of "mechanical" connections.

Question: Will these mechanical connections be made with the same care given to making the electrical connections?

Answer: Seldom, but they should be and must be, because these mechanical connections are the electrical connections of the grounding circuit. Each mechanical fitting is a part of the ground path for the grounding circuit.

Section 300-12 requires continuity of raceways and enclosures. It is just as important that the mechanical connections be made as properly as the electrical connections. Poor installation of the equipment grounding conductors results in "dirty, trashy" electricity. Figure 10–4 illustrates what sometimes happens. Too often someone will turn their head the other way or bury their head in the sand and comment: "It will never happen, so why worry about it or go to all that work to prepare for it?"

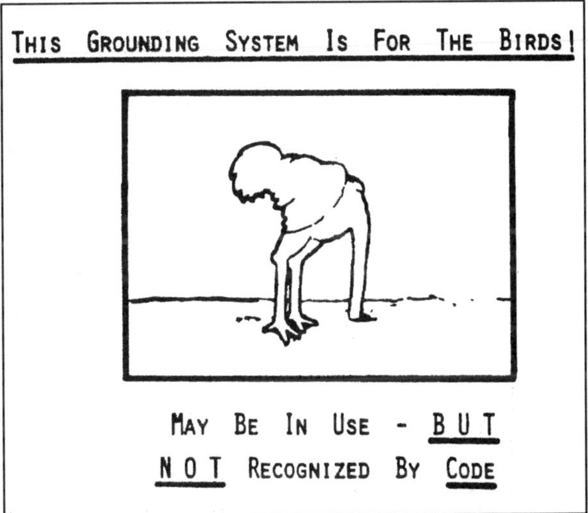

Fig. 10–4 A grounding system for the birds.

Equipment grounding is important in order to fulfill the purpose of the Code, which is the practical safeguarding of persons and property from hazards arising from the use of electricity. The Code gives the minimum requirements for an electrical installation and makes one think whether minimum is good enough or whether there is a need for maximum protection of human life. A mediocre grounding installation might have a few loose connections that could turn to open circuits when needed and would not even be the minimum Code requirement.

The equipment grounding conductor establishes a path for the electrons to travel under fault conditions, while at the same time it maintains grounded electrical equipment at zero potential. It will also act as a drain line for static electricity.

DEFINITION OF *CIRCUIT*

Figure 10–5 (page 124) defines a *circuit.* Once again, this is not a Code definition.

> "A circuit is the particular route the electrons will travel in order to accomplish certain work electrically."

The circuit is the path the electrons will take from the source to the utilization equipment (the load) and back to the source. All electrons will try to get back to the source by way of the path built for them, or they will try to get back to

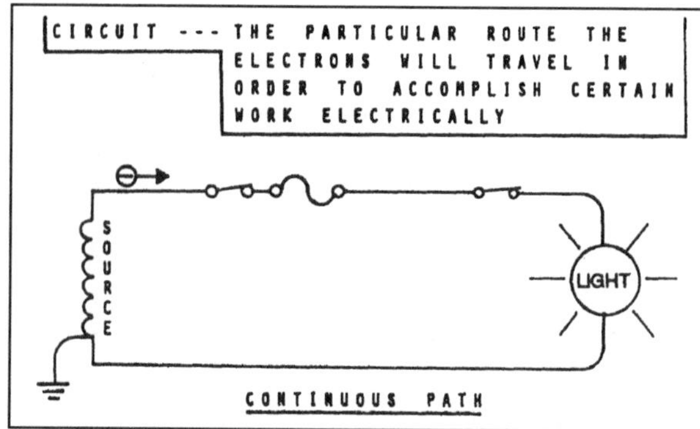

Fig. 10–5 Definition of *circuit*.

the source by way of the ground. In so doing, the electrons will seek the path of lowest impedance, but will take any and all paths.

The grounding system is the path the electrons travel onto the grounding electrode and into the ground. It is the electrons' circuit to ground. Therefore, the equipment grounding conductor should be installed with just as much care as the lighting or power circuit.

The definition of a circuit might be changed just a little to apply to grounding. The continuous path is an absolute necessity; that does not change. But the main part of the definition might read as follows:

"A circuit is the particular route the electrons will travel in order to reach ground and/or travel through the overcurrent protective device."

These are the two routes for which the controlled ground path is built.

EFFECTIVE GROUND PATH

Figure 10–6 illustrates effective grounding, as described in *Section 250-51, Effective Grounding Path.* According to the Code, a conducting path to ground shall meet the following criteria:

1. Continuity—It must be continuous. Continuity often depends on mechanical connections, as illustrated in figure 10–3 (page 122). Every mechanical connection is a splice in the equipment grounding conductor when a metal raceway is used.
2. Low impedance—Keep the opposition to the flow of current as low as possible.

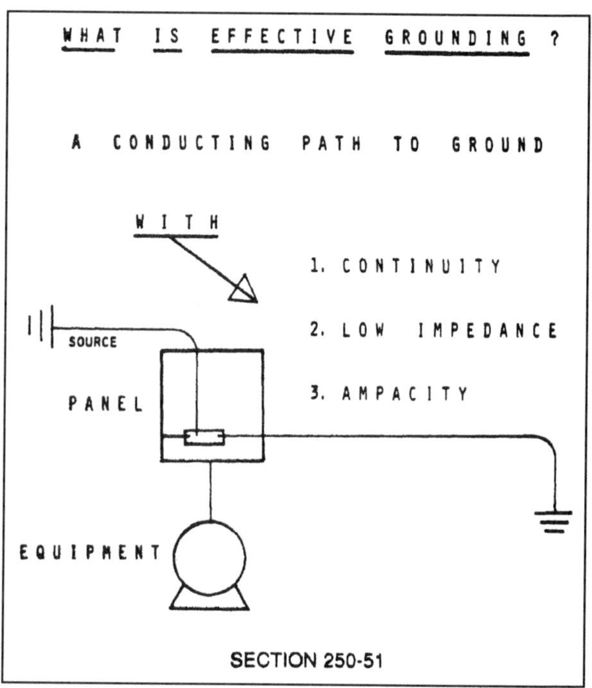

Fig. 10–6 Establishing an effective grounding path.

3. Ampacity—It must be of sufficient size to be able to carry the current the equipment may be required to carry under fault conditions.
4. The earth shall not be used as the sole equipment grounding conductor.

UNDER *FAULT* CONDITIONS, *GROUNDING* IS THE *ELECTRICAL CIRCUIT*. THE *GROUNDING CIRCUIT* IS *PLANNED* AND *PREPARED* FOR, JUST AS IF THE *FAULT* WERE REALLY GOING TO *HAPPEN*.

Engineers work at designing electrical installations with no faults. The electrician works at installing electrical circuits with no faults. But work at it as they may, no one has yet built the perfect electrical circuit, one without a possible fault. Electrical faults are like other accidents—it is not known when or where the accident is going to take place. We learn from past experiences and do the best we can to protect against electrical accidents in the future.

When there is a splice to be made in an electrical installation, as shown in figure 10–7 (page 125), it must be made with care to ensure proper electrical continuity for the electrical

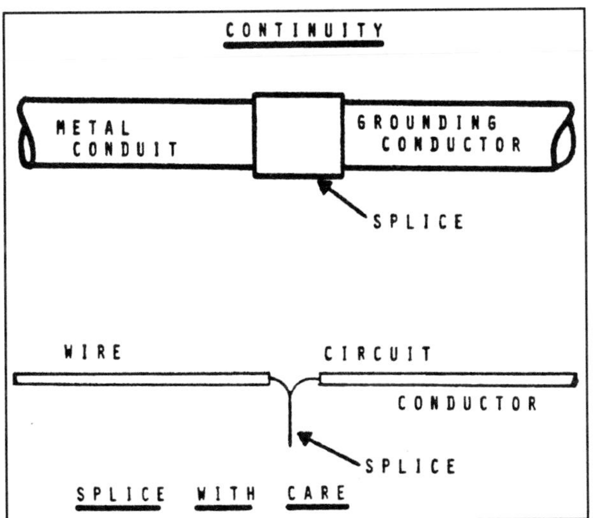

Fig. 10–7 Splicing with care to ensure continuity.

circuit. When a splice is made in a run of metal conduit, it must be made with the same care. The fitting in the metal conduit becomes an electrical splice in an electrical circuit when electrons travel on the equipment grounding conductor under fault conditions or to drain static electricity.

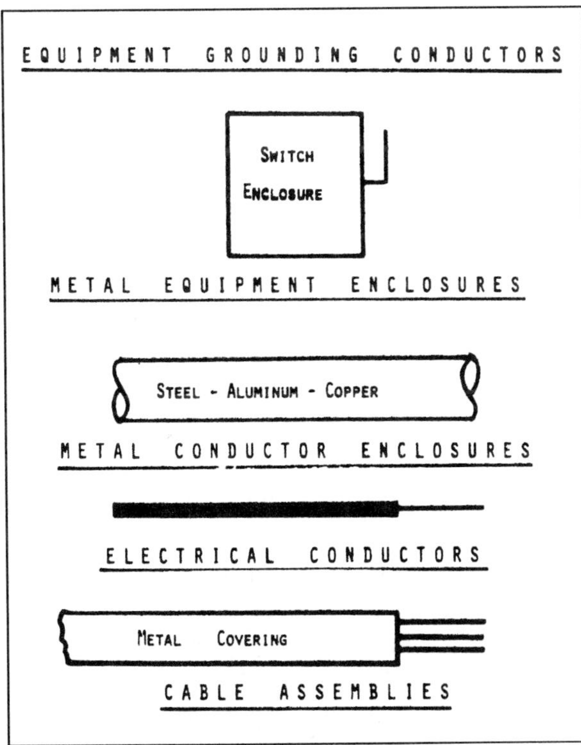

Fig. 10–8 Types of equipment grounding conductors.

Section 250-95, Exception 3, permits the use of metal raceway, armor, or sheath to be used for the equipment grounding conductor in lieu of the conductors listed in *Table 250-95*. However, it requires the raceway, armor, or sheath to fulfill the requirements of *Section 250-51*; the equipment grounding conductor, must be permanent and continuous, have capacity to conduct safely any fault current likely to be imposed, have sufficiently low impedance to limit the voltage to ground, and facilitate operation of circuit protective devices.

TYPES OF EQUIPMENT GROUNDING CONDUCTORS

The equipment grounding conductor may be a metal raceway, a metal enclosure, or an electrical conductor (as illustrated in figure 10–8) or a combination of metal raceway, enclosures, and conductors. More often than not, it is a combination of all of these. *Section 250-91(b)* lists the various types of equipment grounding conductors permitted.

WIRE USED FOR EQUIPMENT GROUNDING CONDUCTOR

When an electrical conductor is used, it can be either solid or stranded, insulated or bare. However, there are situations where the Code requires an insulated equipment grounding conductor, such as *Section 680-20(b)(1)* requires for swimming pools, illustrated in figure 10–9. Insulated equipment grounding conductors are used to protect the conductor from corrosion.

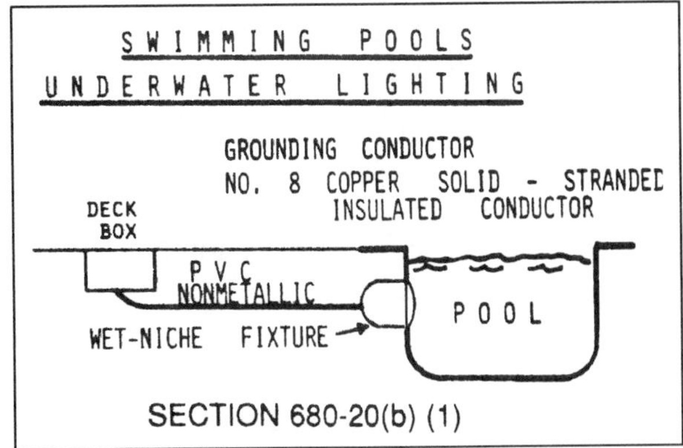

Fig. 10–9 An example that requires an insulated equipment grounding conductor.

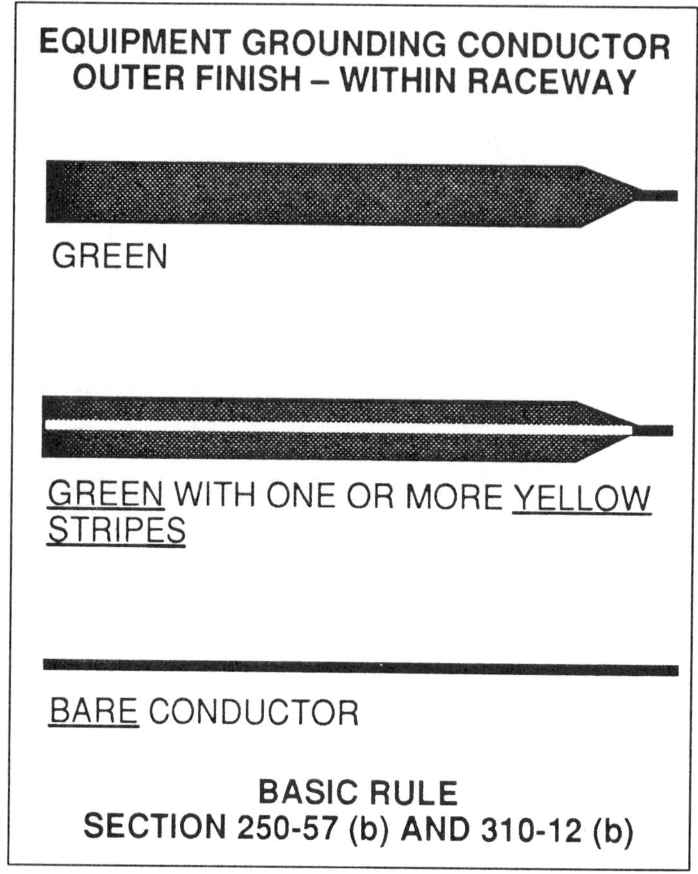

Fig. 10–10 Identifying the equipment grounding conductor.

IDENTIFICATION OF EQUIPMENT GROUNDING CONDUCTOR

Sections 250-57(b) and *310-12(b),* illustrated in figure 10–10, set down the basic rule for the color of the outer finish of the equipment grounding conductor when it is installed in a raceway, cable, or cord. The color green is reserved for the equipment grounding conductor. Green identifies the equipment grounding conductor. Green with one or more yellow stripes is also permitted to be used for an equipment grounding conductor. *Section 250-119(b)* specifies that the green color scheme also be used for the terminals of receptacles of the equipment grounding conductor.

Section 250-57(b), Exception No. 1, permits the use of an insulated conductor for the equipment grounding conductor installed in raceways to have an outer covering other than green (figure 10–11, page 127). The following is a breakdown of Exception No. 1 as it applies to a *single electrical conductor*, other than a green one, being installed for the equipment grounding conductor.

1. The conductor is larger than No. 6.
2. The conductor can be copper or aluminum.
3. The conductor must be permanently identified as the equipment grounding conductor.
4. The identification must be made at each termination and at every point the conductor is accessible. This includes pull and junction boxes.

Comment: This exception does not apply to a No. 6 conductor. Note the "larger than." The smallest conductor that could be used would be a No. 4 copper or No. 4 aluminum. It is unusual that the Code recognizes the same size copper or aluminum conductor for a particular installation. The identification must be made at all terminations and at all pull or junction boxes that the equipment grounding conductor passes through and where the conductor is accessible.

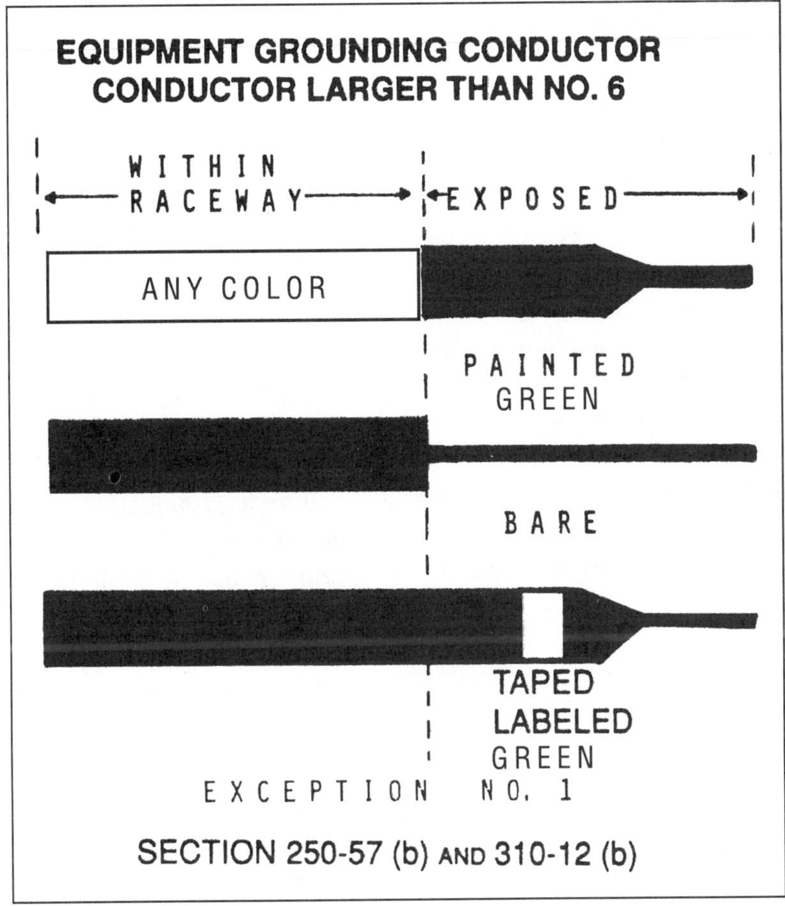

Fig. 10–11 Exception No. 1 to the basic rule for identifying the equipment grounding conductor.

5. The various ways to identify the conductor are as follows:
   a. Strip the insulation off the entire length of the exposed conductor at the termination or where it is accessible to make it look like a bare conductor.
   b. Color the insulation green by using green paint or green sleeving.
   c. Mark exposed insulation with green tape, labels, or some durable means of identification.

The following is a breakdown of Exception No. 4 as it applies to *multiconductor cable* using other than a green-colored conductor within the cable for the equipment grounding conductor.

Comment: The phrase "at the time of installation" puts the responsibility of marking the cable on the electrician who installs the cable. If the cable should be opened in a junction box or terminal box, the equipment grounding conductor will have to be identified.

1. The installation is restricted to areas where only qualified persons will service the installation.
2. The conductor shall be marked at each termination and at every point where the conductor is accessible.
3. The marking shall be permanent.
4. The marking and identification shall take place at the time of installation.
5. Methods permitted for identification include the following:
   a. Strip the insulation from the entire exposed length of the conductor.
   b. Color or paint the exposed insulation green.

c. Mark the insulation with green tape.
d. Use green-colored adhesive labels.

6. More than one conductor in a multiple conductor cable is permitted to be identified as an equipment grounding conductor.

Two equipment grounding conductors would be needed in a multiple conductor cable for the installation of an isolated grounded type receptacle in a metal box. One equipment grounding conductor would be needed to ground the metal box, and one equipment grounding conductor would be needed to ground the isolated receptacle.

Terminal identification to be used on the terminals of electrical devices is listed in *Section 250-119*. It contains the following requirements:

1. When a screw terminal is used it shall be

   green in color,
   not readily removable,
   and hexagonal in shape.

2. When a terminal nut is used it shall be

   green in color,
   not readily removable,
   and hexagonal in shape.

3. When a wire connection is used it shall be

   green in color
   and of the pressure type.

4. When an entrance hole for the equipment grounding conductor is not visible, the hole is required to be identified with any of the following markings:

   green,
   ground,
   letter "G,"
   letter "GR"
   ⏚

The various identification markings are permitted so as to harmonize the U.S. Electrical Code with the Canadian Electrical Code.

INSTALLATION OF EQUIPMENT GROUNDING CONDUCTOR

The equipment grounding conductor furnishes a low-impedance path to the service equipment. At the service equipment, it is connected to the grounding electrode conductor, which furnishes the path to the grounding electrode.

At Service Equipment

Sections 250-23(a) and *250-53(a)* require the equipment grounding conductor to be connected to the system grounded conductor, the main bonding jumper, and the grounding electrode conductor at the service equipment, as illustrated in figure 10–12 (page 129). *Section 250-54* requires the equipment grounding conductor to be connected to the common grounding electrode.

For a grounded system, a main bonding jumper is required to connect the system grounded conductor and the equipment grounding conductor within each service disconnect enclosure. This ensures continuity from the equipment grounding conductor to the system grounded conductor.

Using the Circuit Conductor Raceway

Section 250-57(b) requires the equipment grounding conductor to be installed in the same raceway or cable as the circuit conductors, as illustrated in figure 10–13 (page 129).

Reason: Under normal conditions there is no current flow in the equipment grounding conductor. When there is a fault, there is a current flow in the equipment grounding conductor. The current flow in the equipment grounding conductor is being fed to the fault by one of the circuit conductors and the equipment grounding conductor is acting as the return path. If the feed and return conductor are as close together as possible, the impedance caused by induction due to the alternating current will be held as low as possible.

Direct-Current System

Exception No. 2 of *Section 250-57(b)*, illustrated in figure 10–14 (page 129), permits the equipment grounding conductor installed with a direct-current circuit to be run separately from the circuit conductors.

Reason: There is no impedance due to inductance in a direct-current circuit, because there is no alternating magnetic field.

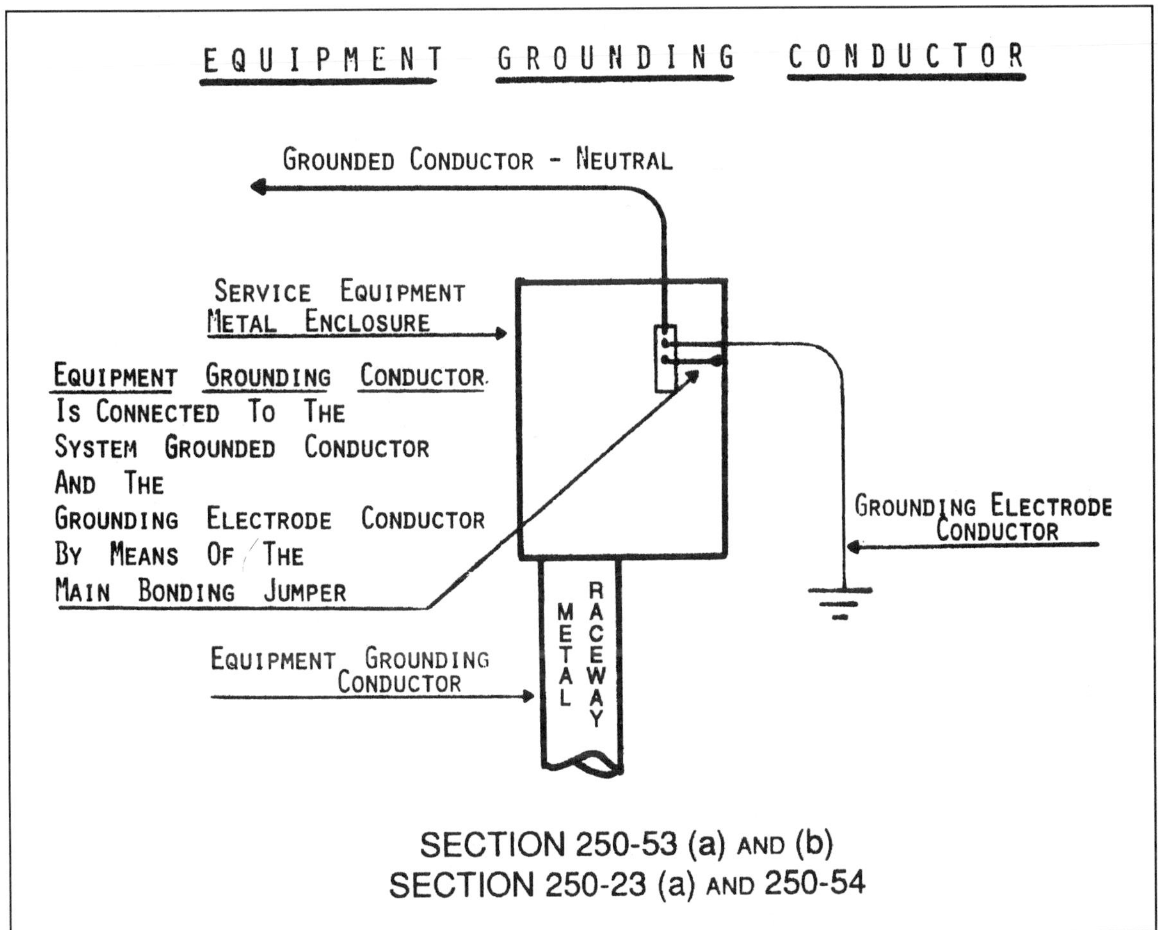

Fig. 10–12 Required connection of the equipment grounding conductor.

Raceways

The requirement for all conductors of the same circuit to be in the same raceway is repeated in *Section 300-3(b)* and is illustrated in figure 10–15 (page 130). Note the various conductors this section requires to be installed in the same raceway when a raceway is used. These are:

1. All phase conductors.
2. The neutral (the grounded) conductor, when used.
3. The equipment grounding conductor, when required.
4. When the circuit conductors are not installed in a raceway but in a trench as direct burial, the equipment grounding conductor is required to be in the same trench or close by.

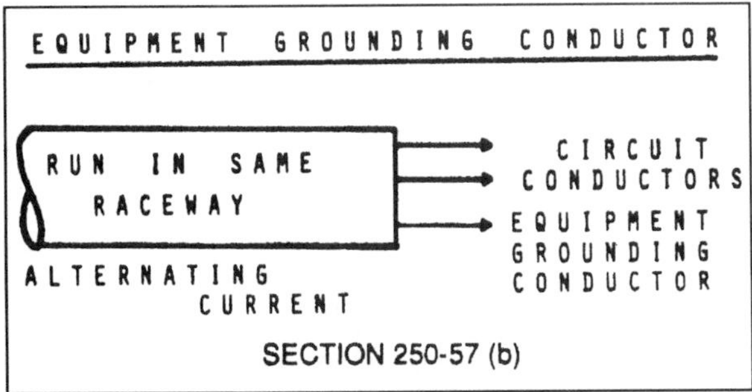

Fig. 10–13 The equipment grounding conductor installed in the same raceway as the AC circuit conductors.

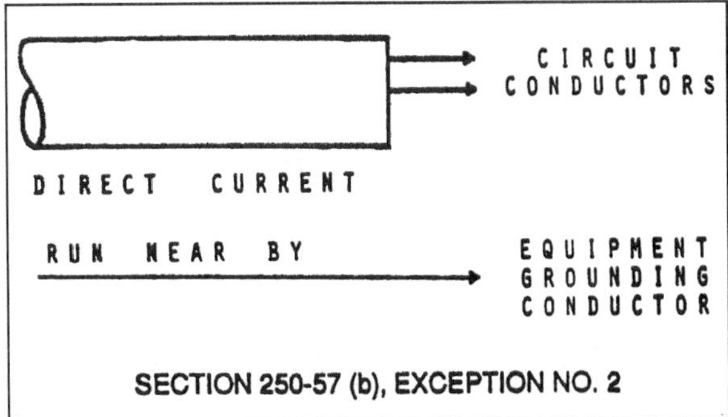

Fig. 10–14 The equipment grounding conductor installed close to the raceway with the DC conductors.

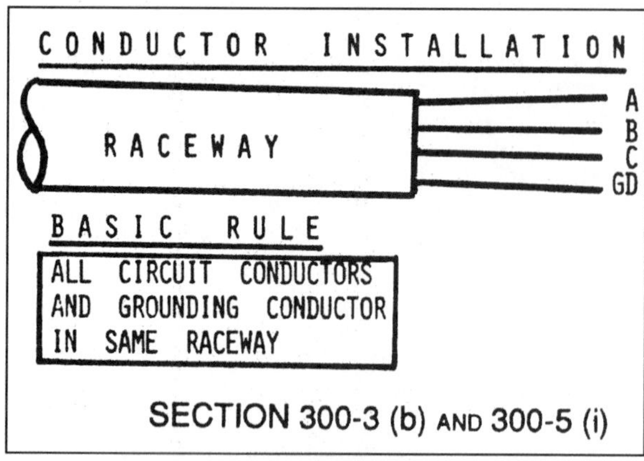

Fig. 10–15 Basic rule for installing the equipment grounding conductor in a raceway.

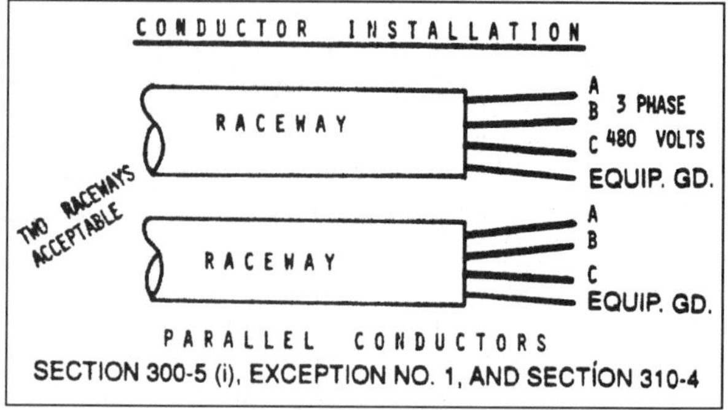

Fig. 10–17 Parallel feeder conductors installed in two raceways with an equipment grounding conductor in each raceway.

Comment: When the installation is made with a metal raceway and the raceway has continuity, the metal raceway is permitted to be the equipment grounding conductor and there would be no equipment grounding conductor installed in the conduit. However, if the raceway is nonmetallic, such as PVC, then an equipment grounding conductor is required and must be installed in the same raceway as the circuit conductors.

Figure 10–16 illustrates a violation of *Section 250-57(b)*. The equipment grounding conductor is not installed with the circuit conductors. This connection can be found on electrical installations. It will accomplish one thing: it will maintain the two pieces of equipment at the same potential. Its disadvantage is that it will provide a potential path for circulating ground currents and will contribute to creating "dirty electricity" for microelectronic or high-tech equipment.

Figure 10–17 illustrates the use of parallel conductors installed in two nonmetallic raceways, with one set of phase conductors (A, B, and C) in each raceway, as permitted by *Section 310-4*. The requirements of *Section 250-95* and Exception No. 1 of *Section 300-5(i)* are also included. When the raceway is not metal, for example if it is PVC, an equipment grounding conductor is required in each raceway.

Figure 10–18 illustrates the use of parallel conductors installed in nonmetallic raceway, with all phase A conductors in one raceway, all phase B conductors in one raceway, and all phase C conductors in one raceway, as permitted by *Section 310-4*. The requirements of *Section 250-95* and Exception No. 2 of *Section 300-5(i)*

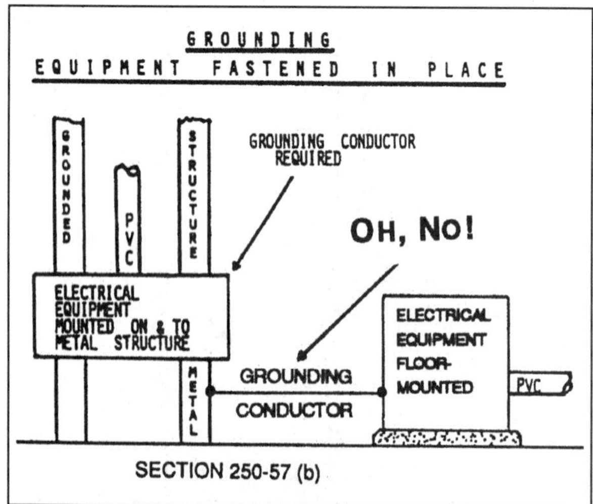

Fig. 10–16 Violation of the requirement for installing the equipment grounding conductor.

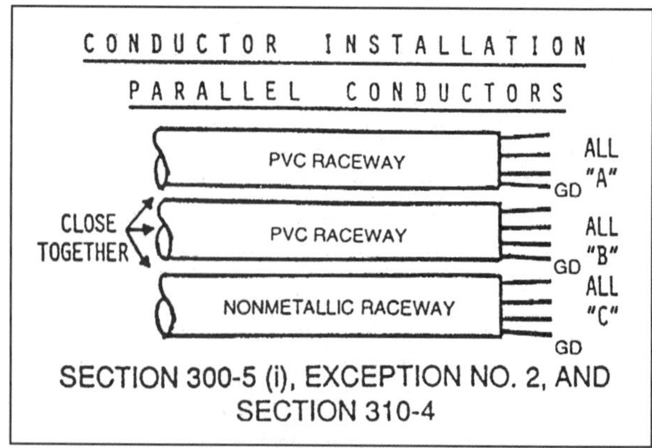

Fig. 10–18 Parallel feeder conductors installed in nonmetallic raceway with an equipment grounding conductor in each raceway.

are also included. This type of installation can only be made using a nonmetallic raceway. Therefore, an equipment grounding conductor is required to be installed in each raceway. When equipment grounding conductors are used with conductors in parallel, they shall comply with the requirements for conductors in parallel (*Section 310-4*), except that the equipment grounding conductor shall be sized in accordance with *Table 250-95*. This is an important exception. It is one of the few places in the Code where an exception is still part of the section. *Section 250-50(b)*, Exception, permits the equipment ground conductor to be run separately from the circuit conductors when replacing a nongrounded type receptacle with a grounded type receptacle. When replacing a two-wire nongrounded receptacle with a grounded receptacle, no equipment grounding conductor is available, therefore it is necessary to run the equipment grounding conductor separately from the circuit conductors. This exception recognizes such a situation. Not all nongrounded, two-wire receptacles are replaced by installing an equipment grounding conductor. *Section 210-7(d)* lists additional ways permitted to replace an ungrounded type receptacle. Connecting this equipment grounding conductor beyond the first 5 feet of water pipe entering the building is not permitted. (*Section 250–81*.)

When such an installation was made, it was common practice to run the equipment grounding conductor to the nearest water pipe and use that as the equipment grounding conductor. This is a violation of *Section 250-81*, figure 10–19. The metal water pipe may not be substituted for an equipment grounding conductor. The equipment grounding conductor must be installed to a permanent and effectively grounded point, which might be back to the service equipment or to any accessible point on the grounding electrode conductor.

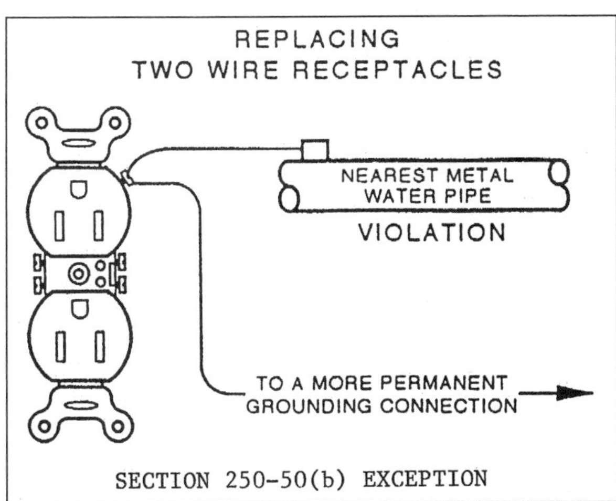

Fig. 10–19 Equipment grounding conductor installed separately from circuit conductors.

RACEWAYS AS EQUIPMENT GROUNDING CONDUCTORS

Section 250-91(b) contains a list of various types of equipment grounding conductors. The section also permits the equipment grounding conductor to be a metal raceway, a conductor, or a combination of any of the recognized types of equipment grounding conductors. The list in this section is rather long. It should also be noted that some of the recognized types of equipment grounding conductors listed have limitations placed on them, especially where flexible metal conduits are used. The following is a list of materials permitted to be used for equipment grounding conductors.

1. Copper or other corrosion-resistant conductor
    a. Aluminum or copper-clad aluminum
    b. Solid or stranded
    c. Insulated, covered, or bare
    d. A wire or bus bar of any shape
2. Rigid metal conduit (RMC)
3. Intermediate metal conduit (IMC)
4. Electrical metallic tubing (EMT)
5. Flexible metal conduit, to be used only when both the flex and the fittings are listed for grounding; commonly known as "greenfield"
6. Armor of Type AC cable (BX)
7. The copper sheath of mineral-insulated, metal-sheathed cable (MI cable)
8. A combination of the metal sheath and grounding conductors of Type MC cable
9. Cable tray; *Sections 318-3(c)* and *318-7* contain requirements for the use of cable tray as the equipment grounding conductor

10. The metal framework of cable bus enclosure as per *Section 365-2(a)*
11. The grandfather clause—other electrically continuous metal raceways listed for grounding

Metal Raceways

Figure 10–20 illustrates some of the metal raceways listed in *Section 250-91(b)* for use as the equipment grounding conductor. These steel raceways take the place of the conductor discussed previously. In order for this to be successful, all joints and connections of the metal raceway system must be mechanically secure to ensure a path for the current to flow that will have continuity and a low impedance.

Figure 10–21 (page 133) illustrates a definition of a *raceway*. Note the one phrase "with additional functions as permitted by the Code," in the definition of raceway. This phrase is inserted in the definition so that metal raceways can be used as equipment grounding conductors. Under the actual definition of a raceway there are a multitude of wiring methods listed, including the following:

rigid metal conduit
rigid nonmetallic conduit
intermediate metal conduit
liquidtight flexible conduit
flexible metallic tubing
flexible metal conduit
electrical nonmetallic tubing
underfloor raceway
cellular concrete floor raceway
cellular metal floor raceway
surface raceways
wireways
busways
and there can be others

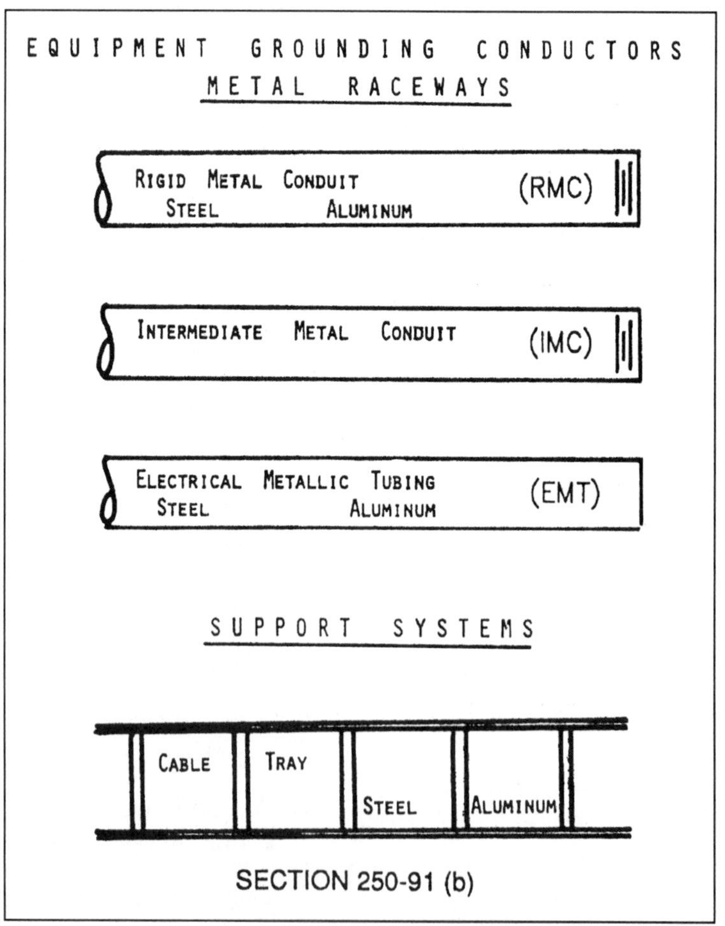

Fig. 10–20 Metal raceways that can be used as equipment grounding conductors.

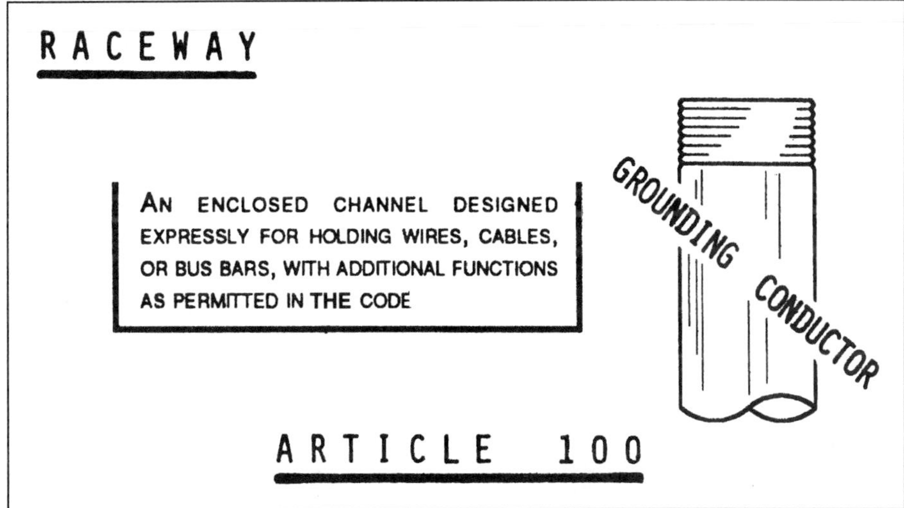

Fig. 10–21 Definition of *raceway*.

Question: How do the various metal raceways used for equipment grounding conductors compare with a copper conductor in their ability to conduct the electron flow?

Answer: An accurate comparison cannot be made because of the unknown length of the raceway, conductors enclosed, or the ambient temperature in which the raceway might be installed. Figure 10–22 uses approximate values for a simplified comparison illustration. It shows the resistance per 1000 feet of various metal conduit-type raceways and the copper wire size with a comparable resistance per 1000 feet. Aluminum is often used for an electrical circuit conductor. Note how the resistance of ½-inch aluminum conduit is approximately as low as the resistance of a No. 2/0 copper conductor.

The IMC has approximately 62 percent as much cross-sectional area as rigid steel conduit. EMT has approximately 22 percent of the cross-sectional area of rigid steel conduit. As the size of the conduit increases, the cross-sectional area of the metal in the conduit increases.

Reason: The resistance of a conductor is inversely proportional to its cross-sectional area. This means the resistance of the conductor will decrease as the cross-sectional area of the conductor increases.

Figure 10–23 illustrates some wire size comparisons for rigid steel conduit. IMC and EMT would be proportional in cross-sectional area, as they were in figure 10–22. A study made of steel raceways being used as the equipment grounding conductor provides some interesting and valu-

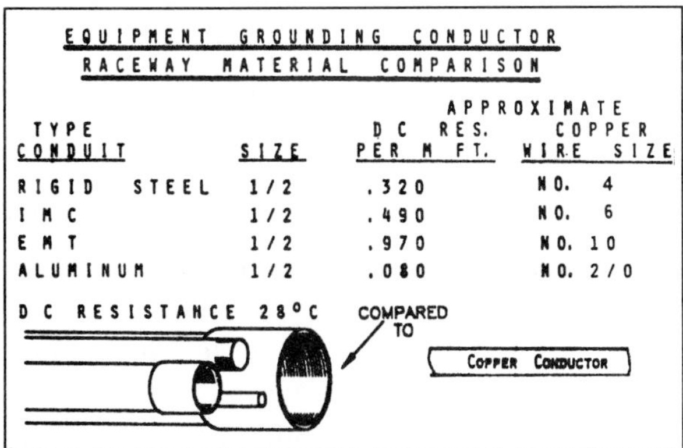

EQUIPMENT GROUNDING CONDUCTOR
RACEWAY MATERIAL COMPARISON

TYPE CONDUIT	SIZE	APPROXIMATE DC RES. PER M FT.	APPROXIMATE COPPER WIRE SIZE
RIGID STEEL	1/2	.320	NO. 4
IMC	1/2	.490	NO. 6
EMT	1/2	.970	NO. 10
ALUMINUM	1/2	.080	NO. 2/0

DC RESISTANCE 28°C

Fig. 10–22 Comparison of metal raceway's resistance to copper-conductor resistance.

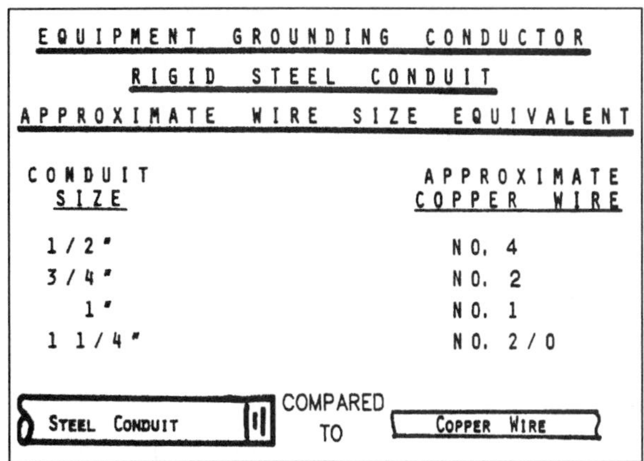

EQUIPMENT GROUNDING CONDUCTOR
RIGID STEEL CONDUIT
APPROXIMATE WIRE SIZE EQUIVALENT

CONDUIT SIZE	APPROXIMATE COPPER WIRE
1/2"	NO. 4
3/4"	NO. 2
1"	NO. 1
1 1/4"	NO. 2/0

Fig. 10–23 Comparison of steel-conduit sizes to copper-conductor size.

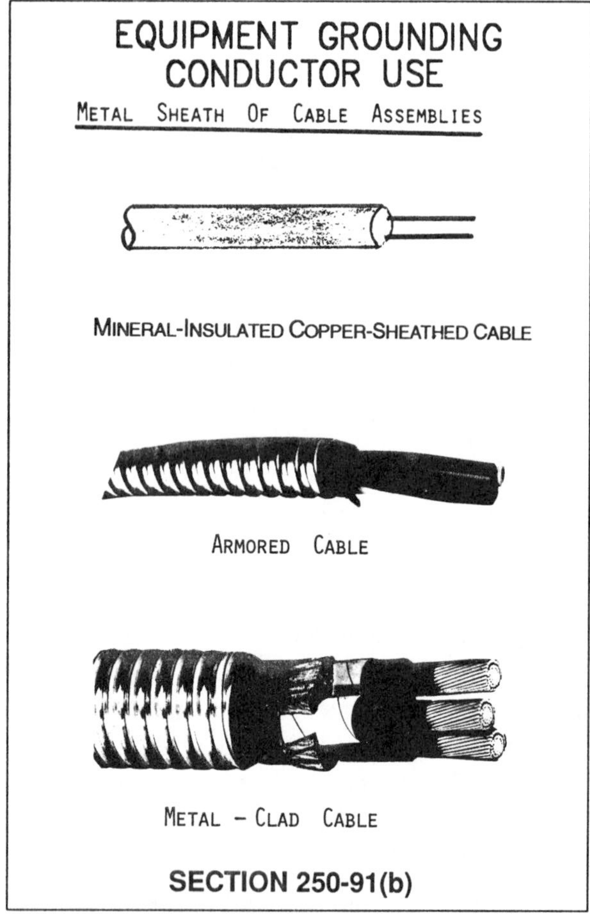

Fig. 10–24 Metal-sheathed cable assemblies permitted to be used as equipment grounding conductors.

able information. The study shows that comparable sizes of galvanized rigid steel conduit (GRC), intermediate steel conduit (IMC), and electrical metallic steel tubing (EMT), enclosing specific-sized electrical conductors and a given length, offer a lower impedance than the equipment grounding conductors required by *Table 250–95*. In turn, this allows a higher fault current to flow over the steel conduit. In an electrical conductor, the opposition to the flow of current is directly proportional to the length of the conductor. An unusual finding was that a given length of steel raceways tested decreased in impedance as the fault current increased. Tables for the maximum length of these raceways, when used as the equipment grounding conductor, are based on this study and are in the Appendix of this text.

Result: Steel conduit sizes required by the Code for the enclosure of various conductor sizes are of sufficiently low impedance to limit the voltage to ground and facilitate the operation of the circuit overcurrent protective devices for given lengths. Supplementary equipment grounding conductors in steel conduits are not needed when the steel conduits are properly installed with electrical continuity.

Metal-Covered Cable Assemblies

Figure 10–24 illustrates types of metal-covered cable assemblies with an outer metal covering, which is permitted by *Section 250-91(b)* to be used as the equipment grounding conductor.

Type MI (mineral-insulated) cable is manufactured with an outer sheath of copper or stainless steel. The copper sheath is required by *Section 330-22* to be adequate to serve as an equipment grounding conductor. Therefore, the outer copper sheath of MI cable is approved for use as the equipment grounding conductor. The stainless steel sheath is not acceptable as an equipment grounding conductor.

Section 333-19 requires Type AC Armored Cable (BX) to be manufactured with an internal bonding strip in intimate contact with the outer armor of the cable. The strip may be steel or aluminum. The outer sheath is required to be terminated in a fitting identified for the purpose, that purpose being to maintain continuity of the equipment grounding path.

The metal strip in armored cable is neither designed nor put there with the intent that it be used as an equipment grounding conductor. The primary purpose of the strip is to maintain continuity in case of an arcing fault across any opening that might occur from bending the armor. The outer flexible armor alone is depended on to have the necessary ampacity to conduct any fault current that might be imposed on it and to have sufficiently low impedance.

The trend to thinning the flexible outer armor amplifies concern for using flexible metal as an equipment grounding conductor.

The outer sheath of Type MC (metal-clad) cable can be steel, aluminum, bronze, or other suitable metal and is permitted to be smooth, welded, corrugated, or an interlocking metal tape. Unless the outer metal sheath is identified for use as the equipment grounding conductor, and most are not, the MC type cable will contain a green equipment grounding. The metal sheath of Type MC cable and the enclosed equipment grounding conductor can be connected together as the equipment grounding conductor.

Caution: If an insulated equipment grounding conductor is part of a Type AC or MC cable, and is installed for the purpose of establishing isolation, then it must be kept separate and insulated from the outer covering of the AC or MC cable.

Flexible Metal Raceways

Section 250–92(b) lists the different wiring methods permitted to be used as the equipment grounding conductor. Flexible metal conduit (greenfield) is permitted when listed fittings are used. However, the exceptions place limitations on the use of the flexible raceways as equipment grounding conductors.

Exception No. 1 permitted certain metal flexible raceways to be used as the equipment grounding conductor provided all of the conditions are fulfilled.

1. Wiring methods permitted are
   a. listed flexible metal conduit terminating in fittings listed for grounding,
   b. flexible metal conduit listed as a raceway but not listed for grounding and terminated in fittings listed for grounding,
   c. listed flexible metallic tubing terminating in fittings listed for grounding,
   d. listed liquidtight flexible metal conduit terminating in fitting listed for grounding.
2. The circuit conductors contained therein are protected at not over 20 amperes.
3. Raceway sizes range from $^3/_8$ inch through $1^1/_4$ inch trade sizes.
4. The total length of the ground return path when one type of raceway is used, or a combination of any of the three listed types of raceways are used, is limited to 6 feet.

Figure 10–25 illustrates the use of one 6-foot length of raceway used as the equipment grounding conductor. Because the raceway is smaller than $1^1/_4$ inch and the conductors contained therein are protected at 20 amperes or less, the raceway could be listed flexible metal conduit, flexible metal conduit listed as a raceway but not listed for grounding, listed flexible metallic tubing, or listed liquidtight flexible metal conduit.

There have been installations where, under fault conditions, the cross-sectional area of the flex is too small to carry the fault current without burning the flex in two and interrupting the ground path. Therefore, by limiting the branch circuit current overcurrent protection, the fault current on the flexible metal conduit is limited. Figure 10–25 illustrates flexible metal raceway installed for use as the equipment grounding conductor.

When the 20-amp limitation is placed on the branch circuit, it means that any circuit with overcurrent protection of more than 20 amps shall have an equipment grounding conductor installed inside or outside of the flexible metal conduit or flexible metallic tubing. Figure 10–26 (page 136) illustrates the use of a 40-amp, branch circuit, overcurrent protective device and a motor with 6 feet or less of flexible metal conduit.

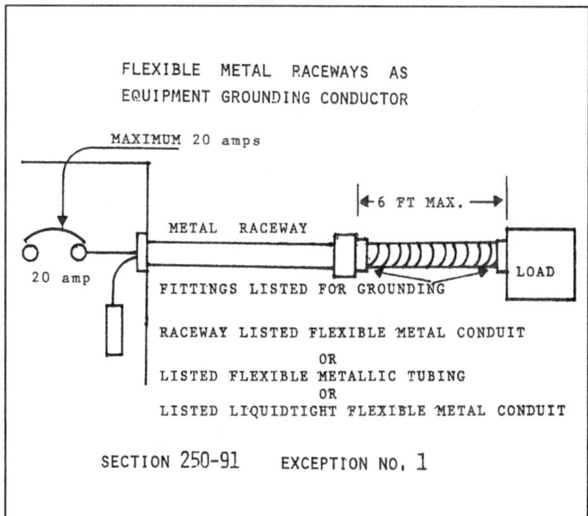

Fig. 10–25 An example of flexible metal raceways permitted to be used as the equipment grounding conductor.

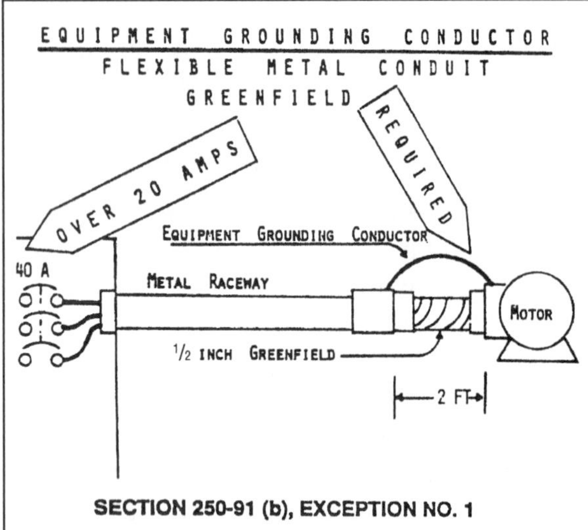

Fig. 10–26 Requirement for installing an equipment grounding conductor inside or outside a flexible metal conduit.

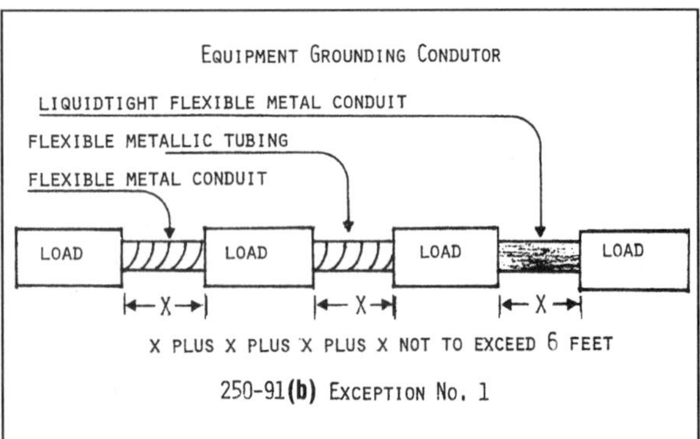

Fig. 10–27 Six-foot maximum length of flexible metal conduits in equipment grounding conductor path.

The equipment grounding conductor must follow the flex and cannot be wrapped around the flex. Should the equipment grounding conductor be wrapped around the metal flex, theoretically it would cause transformer action.

The length of the flex ground path is illustrated in figure 10–27. Three types of flex are available for use as the equipment grounding conductor. The 6-foot limitation placed on the ground path is the total length of ground path when all the individual sections of flex are added together, whether it be all the same type of flex or a combination of different types. Two 6-foot lengths of flex in the same equipment grounding path are not acceptable.

Liquidtight Flexible Metal Conduit

Figure 10–28 illustrates Exception No. 2 of *Section 250-91(b)*. This exception is directed at liquidtight flexible metal conduit. Liquidtight flexible metal conduit is recognized for use as the equipment grounding conductor when all of the following limitations are met:

1. The liquidtight flexible metal conduit is listed for use as an equipment grounding conductor.
2. The trade size is 1 1/4 inch or smaller.
3. The length of the ground return path does not exceed 6 feet.
4. The conduit is terminated in fittings listed for grounding.
5. For 3/8- and 1/2-inch trade sizes, the overcurrent protection is limited to 20 amps or less.
6. For 3/4-, 1-, and 1 1/4-inch trade sizes, the overcurrent protection is limited to 60 amps.

The 1 1/4-inch limitation also indicates that any time 1 1/2 inch or larger liquidtight flex is installed, an equipment grounding conductor shall be installed. Figure 10–29 (page 137) illustrates the proper installation of the equipment bonding jumper, when required, with flexible metal conduit or liquidtight flexible metal conduit.

A further restriction is placed on the use of flexible metal conduit by *Section 350-5*, Exception No. 1, as illustrated in figure 10–30 (a) (page 137).

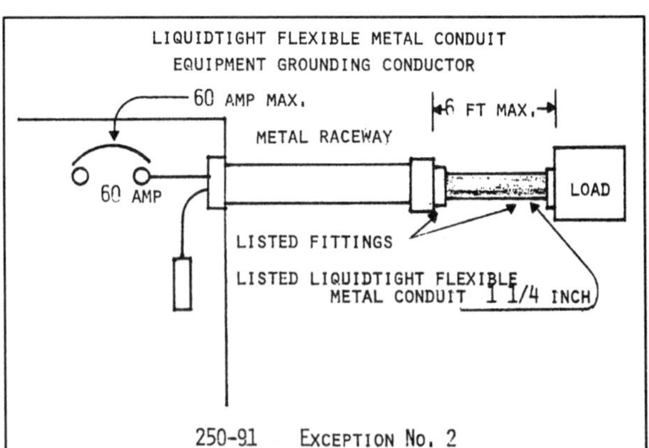

Fig. 10–28 Liquidtight flexible metal conduit as the equipment grounding conductor.

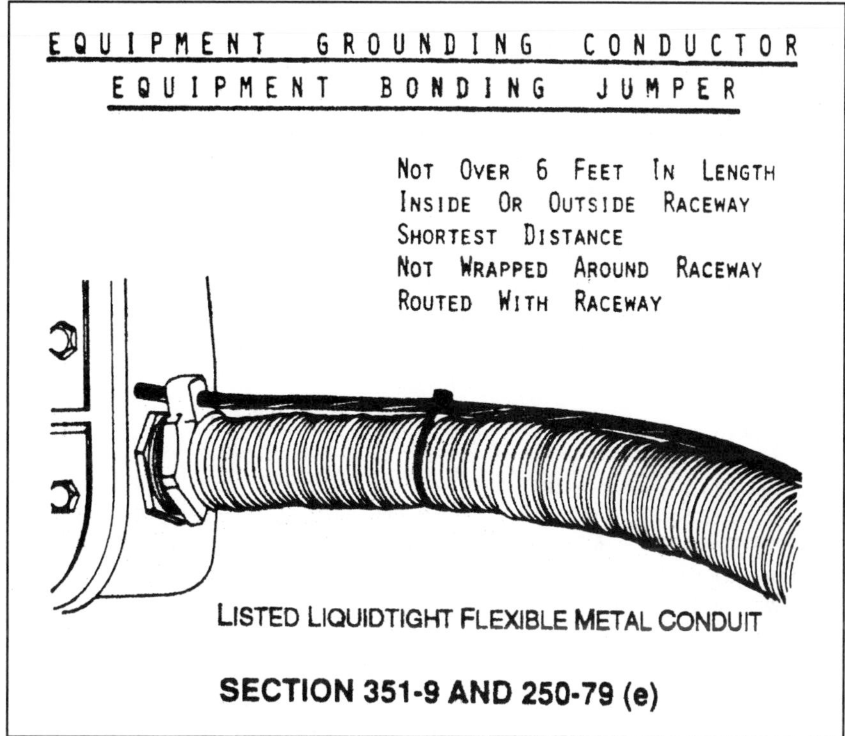

Fig. 10–29 An example of proper installation of an equipment grounding

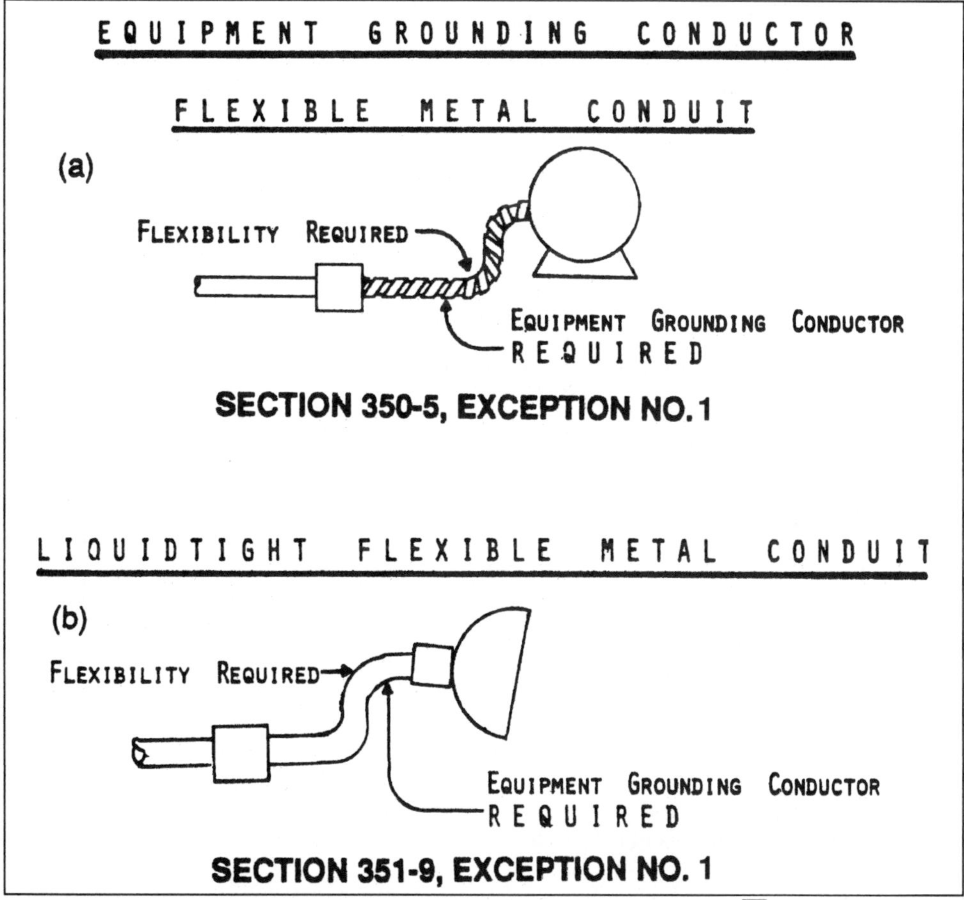

Fig. 10–30 (a) An example of where flexible metal conduit is not permitted to be used as the equipment grounding conductor; (b) an example of where liquidtight flexible metal conduit is not permitted to be used as the equipment grounding conductor.

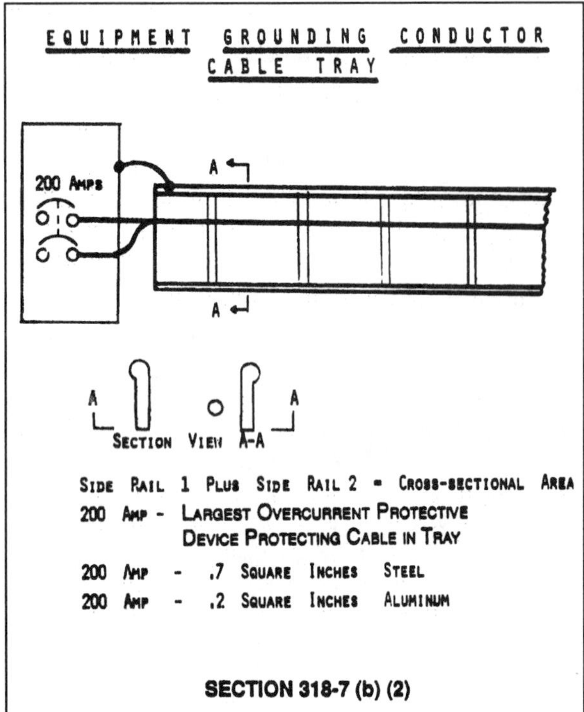

Fig. 10–31 Using cable tray as an equipment grounding conductor.

The exception requires that whenever equipment is installed requiring flexibility, and flexible metal conduit is used, an equipment grounding conductor is required to be installed. The same restriction is repeated for liquidtight flexible metal conduit in *Section 351-9,* Exception No. 1, as shown in figure 10–30 (b) (page 137).

Comment: The Code is putting less and less confidence in flexible metal conduits for use as an equipment grounding conductor. The Code does not require an equipment grounding conductor in every installation of flexible metal conduit or flexible metallic tubing, but for practical application, an equipment grounding conductor installed in all flex would create an extra margin of safety.

Cable Tray

Section 250-91(b)(9) permits cable tray to be used as an equipment grounding conductor with two conditions from *Table 318-7(b)(2)* taken into consideration. These are:

1. The cross-sectional area of the metal in the cable tray
2. Overcurrent protection of conductors in the cable tray
3. Assurance that only qualified persons will maintain the cable tray.
4. Sections and fittings are identified for grounding purposes.
5. All sections and fittings durably marked with cross-sectional area.

Table 318-7(b) (2).
Metal Area Requirements for Cable Trays Used as Equipment Grounding Conductors

Maximum Fuse Ampere Rating, Circuit Breaker Ampere Trip Setting, or Circuit Breaker Protective Relay Ampere Trip Setting for Ground-Fault Protection of any Cable Circuit in the Cable Tray System	Minimum Cross-Sectional Area of Metal* in Square Inches	
	Steel Cable Trays	Aluminum Cable Trays
60	0.20	0.20
100	0.40	0.20
200 →	0.70 →	0.20
400	1.00	0.40
600	1.50**	0.40
1000	—	0.60
1200	—	1.00
1600	—	1.50
2000	—	2.00**

Fig. 10–32 Using *Table 318-7(b)(2)* to determine the required metal cross-sectional area of cable trays to be used as equipment grounding conductors.*

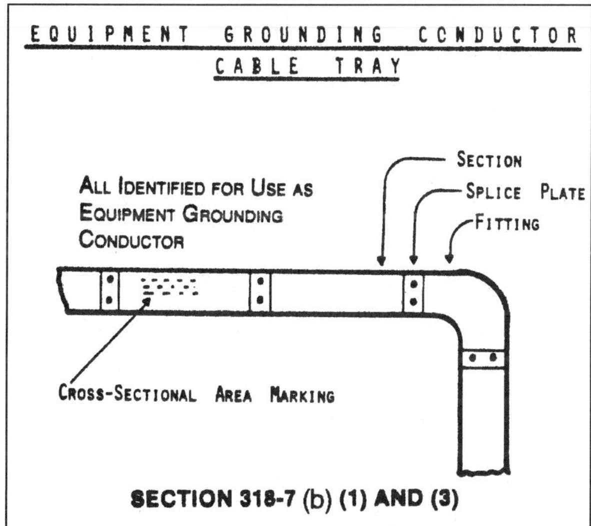

Fig. 10–33 Cable-tray fittings identified for use as equipment grounding conductors.

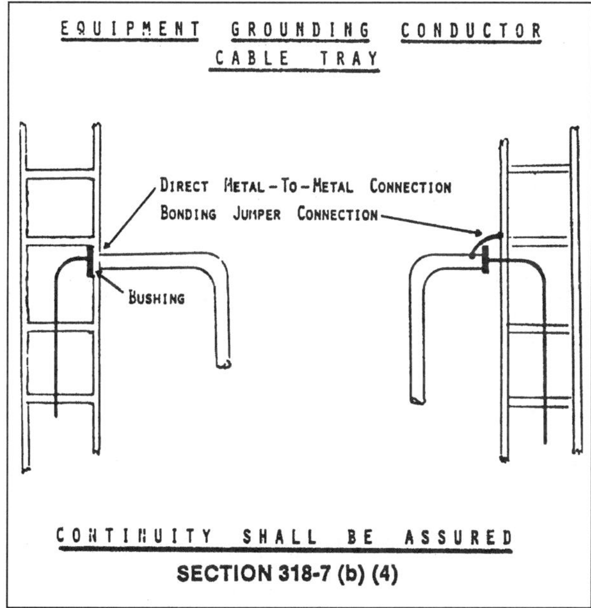

Fig. 10–34 Assuring cable-tray continuity.

6. All sectional and parts are bonded to insure continuity.

Figure 10–31 illustrates a cable tray, with a cable in the cable tray, protected by a 200-amp overcurrent protective device. The required cross-sectional area of the metal necessary for the cable tray to be an equipment grounding conductor is taken from *Table 318-7(b)(2)* (figure 10–32).

Cable trays used for equipment grounding conductors can be either steel or aluminum. The cross-sectional area of a ladder or trough-type cable tray is calculated by using the two side rails of the cable tray. Where solid cable tray is used, the total cross-sectional area of the metal is used. Steel or aluminum cable tray systems are permitted to be used as equipment grounding conductors when all the following conditions are met:

1. The cable tray sections are identified for grounding purposes (figure 10–33).
2. The cable tray fittings are identified for grounding purposes.
3. The minimum cross-sectional area of the cable tray shall be in accordance with *Table 318–7(b)(2)*.
4. Cable tray sections and fittings for channel-type cable trays and cable trays of one-piece construction shall be legibly and durably marked with the cross-sectional area.
5. Ladder or trough-type cable tray sections and fittings shall be legibly and durably marked with the cross-sectional area of the metal in the side rails.
6. Cable tray sections, fittings, and connected raceways shall be bonded according to *Section 250-75*.
7. Bonding is permitted to be accomplished by the use of bolted mechanical connectors or bonding jumpers (figure 10–33, page 139 illustrated cable tray bonding).
8. When bonding jumpers are used, they are installed and sized according to *Section 250-79* (figure 10–34).

Steel cable trays shall not be used as equipment grounding conductors for circuits with ground-fault protection above 600 amps. Aluminum cable trays shall not be used as equipment grounding conductors for circuits with ground-fault protection above 2000 amps. These two requirements are listed in the notes to *Table 318-7(b)(2)*.

EARTH AS AN EQUIPMENT GROUNDING CONDUCTOR

NO! Section 250-91(c) permits the use of other grounding electrodes to supplement the equipment grounding conductor. The supplemental electrode does not take the place of the equipment grounding conductor. As shown in

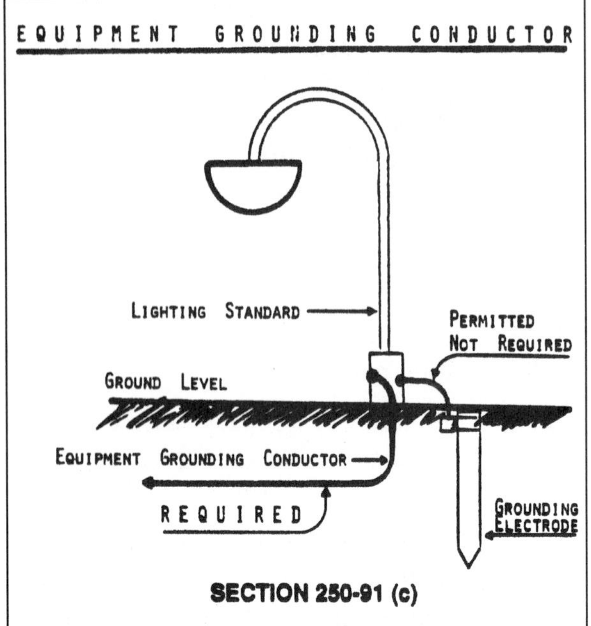

Fig. 10–35 A ground rod does not replace, but is permitted with, an equipment grounding conductor.

figure 10–35, if the equipment grounding conductor is not run to the lighting standard, the earth becomes the sole equipment grounding conductor. This is prohibited by *Sections 250-51* and *250-91(c)*.

EQUIPMENT GROUNDING CONDUCTOR CONNECTIONS

Figure 10–36 illustrates how all mechanical connections used to build a metallic raceway are depended upon to ensure continuity. *Section 250-92(c)(1)* sets down some regulations for making equipment grounding conductor connections when metal raceways or metal-sheathed cable is used as the equipment grounding conductor.

1. All joints and connections at fittings shall be madeup tight.
2. Suitable tools shall be used to makeup the fittings.
3. Paint, enamel, or similar coatings of nonconductive materials shall be removed at threads, contact points, and contact surfaces *(Section 250-75)*.
4. Fittings that are designed to make good electrical continuity without removal of the nonconductive material are permitted.

These regulations also hold true when the metal raceway is not depended upon as the equipment grounding conductor and a separate

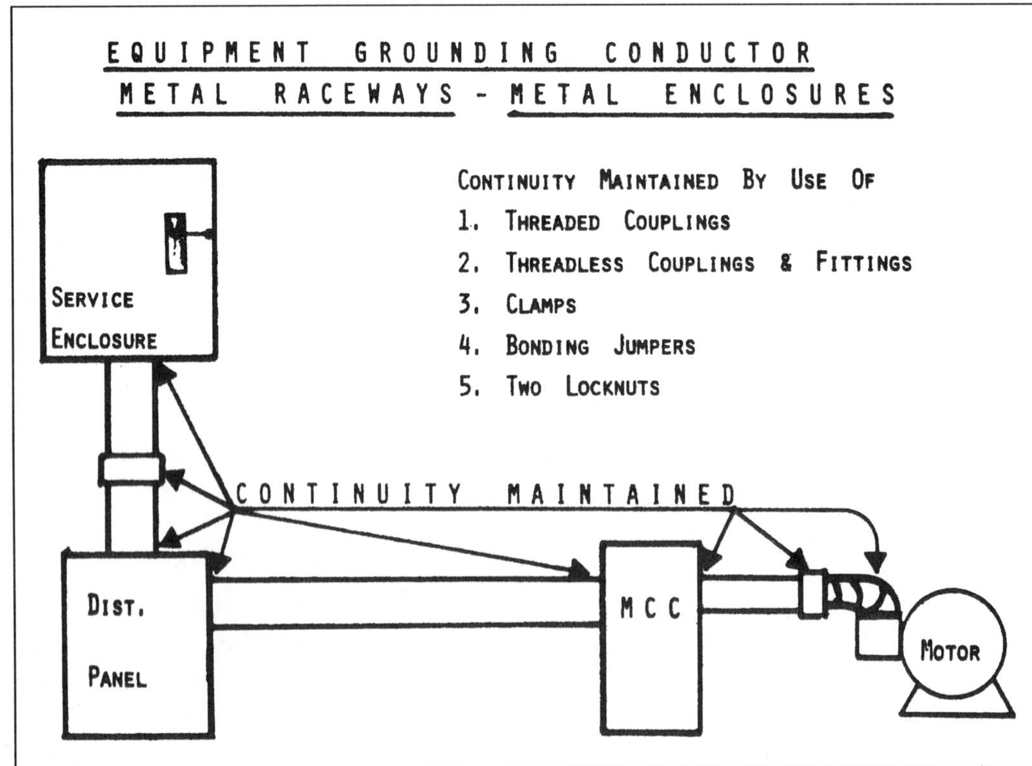

Fig. 10–36 Continuity of metal raceways and enclosures must be maintained.

equipment grounding conductor is installed in the metal raceway.

Section 250-113 requires the equipment grounding conductor connections to be

- Exothermic welding,
- Listed pressure connectors,
- Listed clamps, or
- Other listed means.
- No connections that depend solely on solder shall be used.

Section 250–113 specifically calls attention to the fact that sheet-metal screws are not permitted to be used to connect equipment grounding conductors to enclosures. Self-tapping machine screws are not considered sheet-metal screws. The thread on a sheet-metal screw makes very little contact while the self-tapping machine screw has more threaded contact.

EQUIPMENT GROUNDING CONDUCTOR CONTINUITY

The continuity of the equipment grounding conductor must be maintained and is required by *Section 250-99*. Particular attention is given to situations where the equipment grounding conductor is part of a disconnecting means. This does not mean a switch, but something such as cord- and plug-connected equipment or draw-out switchgear, such as that used with 480 and high-voltage switchgear. When these conditions exist, the equipment grounding contact shall be the first to make and the last to break. Check the prongs or blades on an attachment plug. Note how the grounding blade is longer than any of the others. The grounding blade is the first to make contact and the last to break contact. Exceptions are made for very special applications.

SIZING EQUIPMENT GROUNDING CONDUCTORS

The regulations for calculating the size of the equipment grounding conductor are covered in *Section 250-95*. These are:

1. *Table 250-95* shall be used to size the equipment grounding conductor.
2. When conductors are run in parallel in more than one raceway or cable, as permitted by *Section 310-4*, the equipment grounding conductor is run in parallel. Each of the paralleled equipment grounding conductors is sized according to the ampere rating of the overcurrent device protecting the conductors in the raceway or cable.
3. When conductors are adjusted in size to compensate for voltage drop, the equipment grounding conductor must be correspondingly adjusted in size.
4. Where more than one circuit is installed in a single raceway or cable, one equipment grounding conductor can be installed in the raceway or cable; it will be sized for the largest overcurrent device protecting conductors in the raceway or cable.
5. An equipment grounding conductor not smaller than No. 18 copper is permitted for flexible cords when the flexible cord is protected at or over 20 amps.
6. The equipment grounding conductor is never required to be larger than the circuit conductors.
7. Where the overcurrent protection is an instantaneous circuit breaker or a motor protector, the equipment grounding conductor is sized according to the size of the motor overload protective device.

Note how the title of *Table 250-95* applies to both raceways and equipment. The left-hand column gives the key to the table. It indicates that the size of the equipment grounding conductor is based on the overcurrent device next back on the line. The automatic overcurrent device can be either a set of fuses or a circuit breaker.

There is a warning note at the bottom of Table 250-95. it calls attention to the fact that the equipment grounding conductor sizes listed in Table 250-95 may not fulfil all the requirements of Section 250-51 and may need to be sized larger. Section 250-51 requires the equipment grounding conductor to have electrical continuity, low impedance, and "sufficient capacity to carry any ground fault current that might be imposed on it."

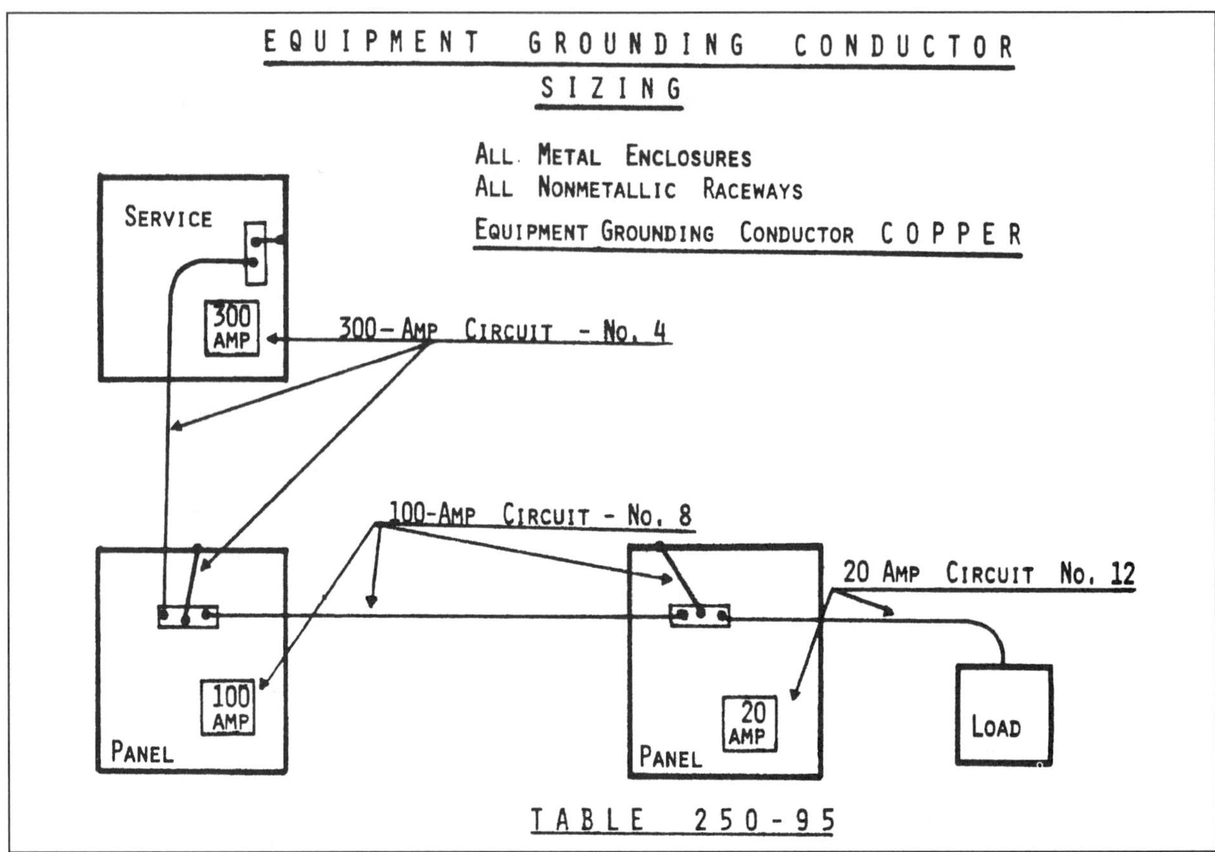

Fig. 10–37 Using *Table 250-95* to size equipment grounding conductors in nonmetallic raceway.

Table 250-95 lists the smallest equipment grounding conductors permitted. Larger equipment grounding conductors are permitted. When the fault-current for an electrical system or circuit is calculated, it could require a larger equipment grounding conductor than listed in Table 250-95.

Figure 10–37 illustrates a system installed in nonmetallic raceway requiring the installation of several equipment grounding conductors. A copper conductor is used. Each panel, other than the service panel, has an isolated equipment grounding bus. The size of each equipment grounding conductor is read directly from *Table 250-95*, as illustrated in figure 10–38 (page 143). All circuit breakers illustrated are other than the instantaneous type.

The feeder to the first panel is protected by a 300-amp breaker. Therefore, *Table 250-95* requires a No. 4 copper equipment grounding conductor.

Note the size of the equipment bonding jumper at the first panel. The 300-amp breaker at the service is the overcurrent protective device ahead of the equipment; therefore, its size is also read directly from *Table 250-95* and is No. 4 copper.

The second panel is protected by a 100-amp overcurrent protection device. *Table 250-95* shows that it requires a No. 8 copper conductor for the equipment grounding conductor and the bonding jumper in the second panel.

The branch circuit is protected by a 20-amp overcurrent device; therefore, *Table 250-95* requires a No. 12 copper conductor for the equipment grounding conductor.

Figure 10–39 (page 143) illustrates the use of a 400-amp circuit breaker of other than the instantaneous type, protecting a 400-amp feeder installed in nonmetallic raceway, which requires an equipment grounding conductor. An equipment grounding bus is illustrated in the panel with the panel bonded to the equipment grounding bus. It is not a neutral bus and is not bonded to the neutral bus. Either copper or aluminum can be used for the equipment grounding conductor. The size of the equipment grounding conductor is read directly from *Table 250-95* (figure 10–40, page 143). If copper is used, it will be a No. 3 copper conductor;

Table 250-95. Minimum Size Equipment Grounding Conductors for Grounding Raceway and Equipment

Rating or Setting of Automatic Overcurrent Device in Circuit Ahead of Equipment, Conduit, etc., Not Exceeding (Amperes)	Size	
	Copper Wire No.	Aluminum or Copper-Clad Aluminum Wire No.*
15	14	12
20	12	10
30	10	8
40	10	8
60	10	8
100	8	6
200	6	4
300	4	2
400	3	1
500	2	1/0
600	1	2/0
800	1/0	3/0
1000	2/0	4/0
1200	3/0	250 kcmil
1600	4/0	350 "
2000	250 kcmil	400 "
2500	350 "	600 "
3000	400 "	600 "
4000	500 "	800 "
5000	700 "	1200 "
6000	800 "	1200 "

Fig. 10–38 Reading the size of the equipment grounding conductor from *Table 250-95*.*

Table 250-95. Minimum Size Equipment Grounding Conductors for Grounding Raceway and Equipment

Rating or Setting of Automatic Overcurrent Device in Circuit Ahead of Equipment, Conduit, etc., Not Exceeding (Amperes)	Size	
	Copper Wire No.	Aluminum or Copper-Clad Aluminum Wire No.*
15	14	12
20	12	10
30	10	8
40	10	8
60	10	8
100	8	6
200	6	4
300	4	2
400	3	1
500	2	1/0
600	1	2/0
800	1/0	3/0
1000	2/0	4/0
1200	3/0	250 kcmil
1600	4/0	350 "
2000	250 kcmil	400 "
2500	350 "	600 "
3000	400 "	600 "
4000	500 "	800 "
5000	700 "	1200 "
6000	800 "	1200 "

Fig. 10–40 Sizing the equipment grounding conductor when a 400-amp circuit breaker (other than instantaneous) is used.*

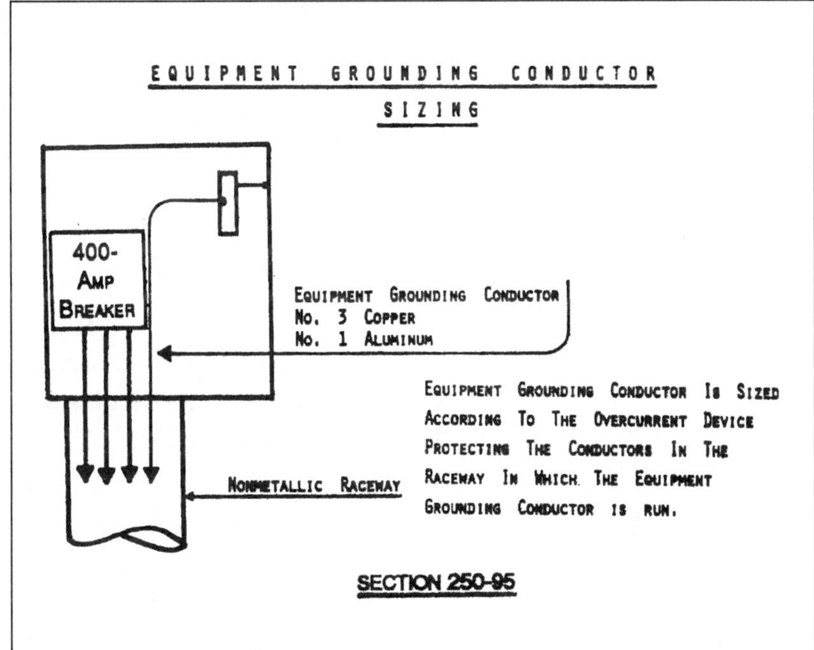
EQUIPMENT GROUNDING CONDUCTOR
SIZING
400-AMP BREAKER
EQUIPMENT GROUNDING CONDUCTOR
No. 3 COPPER
No. 1 ALUMINUM
EQUIPMENT GROUNDING CONDUCTOR IS SIZED ACCORDING TO THE OVERCURRENT DEVICE PROTECTING THE CONDUCTORS IN THE RACEWAY IN WHICH THE EQUIPMENT GROUNDING CONDUCTOR IS RUN.
NONMETALLIC RACEWAY
SECTION 250-95

Fig. 10–39 Using a 400-amp breaker and nonmetallic raceway, which requires an equipment grounding conductor.

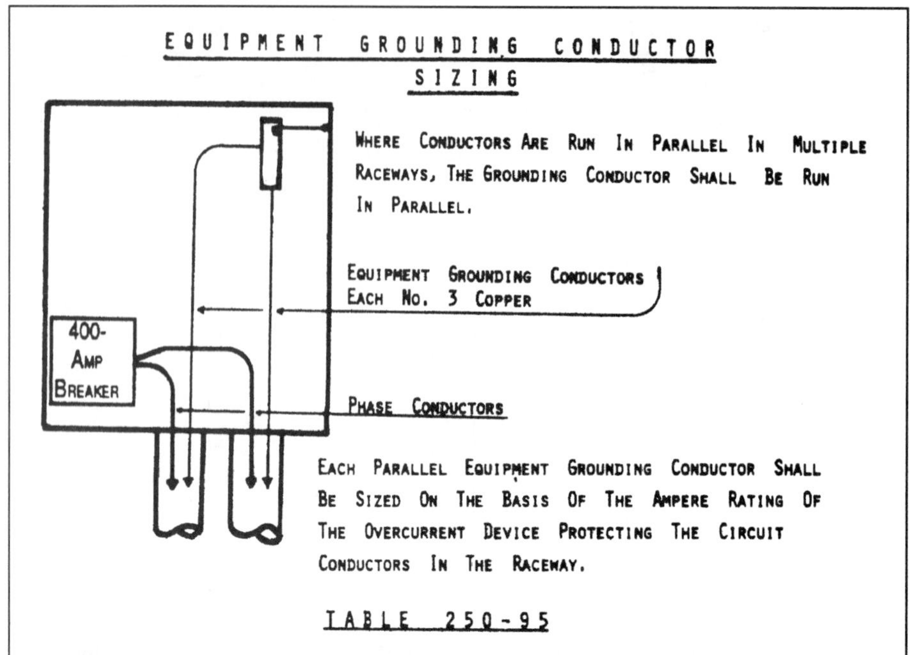

Fig. 10–41 Sizing the equipment grounding conductor when parallel feeder is installed in parallel nonmetallic conduits.

Table 250-95. Minimum Size Equipment Grounding Conductors for Grounding Raceway and Equipment

Rating or Setting of Automatic Overcurrent Device in Circuit Ahead of Equipment, Conduit, etc., Not Exceeding (Amperes)	Size	
	Copper Wire No.	Aluminum or Copper-Clad Aluminum Wire No.*
15	14	12
20	12	10
30	10	8
40	10	8
60	10	8
100	8	6
200	6	4
300	4	2
→ 400	→ 3	1
500	2	1/0
600	1	2/0
800	1/0	3/0
1000	2/0	4/0
1200	3/0	250 kcmil
1600	4/0	350 "
2000	250 kcmil	400 "
2500	350 "	600 "
3000	400 "	600 "
4000	500 "	800 "
5000	700 "	1200 "
6000	800 "	1200 "

Fig. 10–42 Using *Table 250-95* to select No. 3 copper as the equipment grounding conductor.*

if aluminum is used, it will be a No. 1 aluminum conductor.

Figure 10–41 is based on the second paragraph of *Section 250-95* for sizing the equipment grounding conductor when run with parallel conductors, as permitted by *Section 310-4*.

1. The equipment grounding conductor, when installed, shall be run in parallel.
2. The minimum size of the equipment grounding conductors is based on the overcurrent device protecting the circuit conductors in the raceways.
3. *Table 250-95* is used for sizing equipment grounding conductors.

Therefore, the size of the equipment grounding conductor, read directly from *Table 250-95* (figure 10–42), is No. 3 copper (other than the instantaneous type).

Table 250-95 requires a No. 3 copper conductor for a circuit backed up with a 400-amp breaker. The conductors in each conduit are backed up with a 400-amp breaker. Therefore, two No. 3 copper equipment grounding conductors are required, one in each raceway.

Figure 10–43 (page 145) illustrates the requirement in *Section 250-95* for voltage drop.

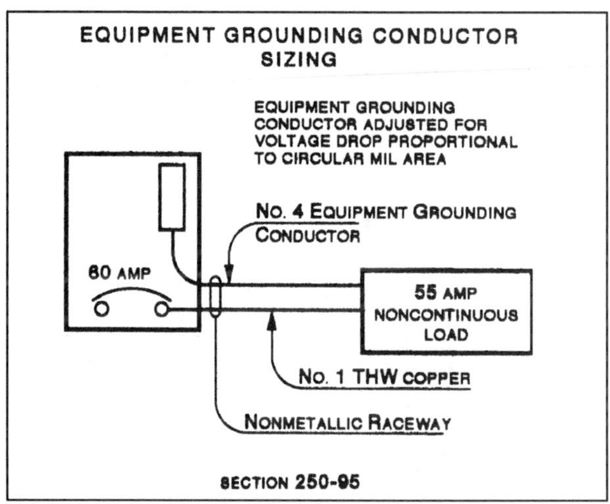

Fig. 10–43 Sizing equipment grounding conductor for voltage drop.

The reason a larger-size conductor is used to reduce voltage drop is that the larger conductor has a lower resistance. Therefore, when the size of the circuit conductors is increased for voltage drop, the size of the equipment grounding conductor is increased proportionally, thereby reducing the impedance of the ground fault path.

The size of the equipment grounding conductor increases proportionally to the increase in circular mil area of the circuit conductors. Figure 10–43 is based on the following calculations.

Basic THW copper conductor needed for 55-amp load: No. 6

No. 6 THW copper is rated 65 amps (*Table 310-16*)

60-amp breaker would be acceptable protection for a No. 6 THW copper conductor serving a 55 amp load.

No. 1 THW copper is used to compensate for voltage drop.

cmil area No. 6 copper 20,340 (*Table 8, Chapter 9*)

cmil area No. 1 copper 83,690 (*Table 8, Chapter 9*)

Proportional equation using circular mils

X = cmil area of equipment grounding conductor

$$\frac{X}{83{,}690} = \frac{10{,}380}{26{,}240}$$

X equipment grounding conductor = 33,106 cmils

33,106 cmil = No. 4 copper (*Table 8, Chapter 9*; figure 10–44)

Figure 10–45 (page 146) illustrates the use of one equipment grounding conductor with multiple circuits installed in the same raceway, as required by *Section 250-95*. It is not anticipated that a ground fault will happen simultaneously on all circuits in the raceway at the same time. Therefore, the equipment grounding conductor is sized according to the largest overcurrent device.

In the illustration, the 40-amp breaker is the largest overcurrent protective device protecting any conductor in the one raceway. Therefore, the size of the equipment grounding conductor is read directly from *Table 250-95* (figure 10–46, page 146). It would be No. 10 copper or No. 8 aluminum.

Table 8. Conductor Properties

Size AWG/kcmil	Area Cir. Mils	Conductors: Stranding Quantity	Stranding Diam. in.	Overall Diam. in.	Overall Area in.²	DC Resistance at 75°C (167°F): Copper Uncoated ohm/kFT	Copper Coated ohm/kFT	Aluminum ohm/kFT
18	1620	1	—	0.040	0.001	7.77	8.08	12.8
18	1620	7	0.015	0.046	0.002	7.95	8.45	13.1
16	2580	1	—	0.051	0.002	4.89	5.08	8.05
16	2580	7	0.019	0.058	0.003	4.99	5.29	8.21
14	4110	1	—	0.064	0.003	3.07	3.19	5.06
14	4110	7	0.024	0.073	0.004	3.14	3.26	5.17
12	6530	1	—	0.081	0.005	1.93	2.01	3.18
12	6530	7	0.030	0.092	0.006	1.98	2.05	3.25
10	10380	1	—	0.102	0.008	1.21	1.26	2.00
10	10380	7	0.038	0.116	0.011	1.24	1.29	2.04
8	16510	1	—	0.128	0.013	0.764	0.786	1.26
8	16510	7	0.049	0.146	0.017	0.778	0.809	1.28
6	26240	7	0.061	0.184	0.027	0.491	0.510	0.808
4	41740	7	0.077	0.232	0.042	0.308	0.321	0.508
3	52620	7	0.087	0.260	0.053	0.245	0.254	0.403
2	66360	7	0.097	0.292	0.067	0.194	0.201	0.319
1	83690	19	0.066	0.332	0.087	0.154	0.160	0.253
1/0	105600	19	0.074	0.372	0.109	0.122	0.127	0.201
2/0	133100	19	0.084	0.418	0.137	0.0976	0.101	0.159
3/0	167800	19	0.094	0.470	0.173	0.0766	0.0797	0.126
4/0	211600	19	0.106	0.528	0.219	0.0608	0.0626	0.100
250	—	37	0.082	0.575	0.260	0.0515	0.0535	0.0847
300	—	37	0.090	0.630	0.312	0.0429	0.0446	0.0707
350	—	37	0.097	0.681	0.364	0.0367	0.0382	0.0605
400	—	37	0.104	0.728	0.416	0.0321	0.0331	0.0529
500	—	37	0.116	0.813	0.519	0.0258	0.0265	0.0424
600	—	61	0.099	0.893	0.626	0.0214	0.0223	0.0353
700	—	61	0.107	0.964	0.730	0.0184	0.0189	0.0303
750	—	61	0.111	0.998	0.782	0.0171	0.0176	0.0282
800	—	61	0.114	1.030	0.834	0.0161	0.0166	0.0265
900	—	61	0.122	1.094	0.940	0.0143	0.0147	0.0235
1000	—	61	0.128	1.152	1.042	0.0129	0.0132	0.0212
1250	—	91	0.117	1.284	1.305	0.0103	0.0106	0.0169
1500	—	91	0.128	1.412	1.566	0.00858	0.00883	0.0141
1750	—	127	0.117	1.526	1.829	0.00735	0.00756	0.0121
2000	—	127	0.126	1.632	2.092	0.00643	0.00662	0.0106

Fig. 10–44 Using *Table 8* to select equipment grounding conductor size using circular mil area.*

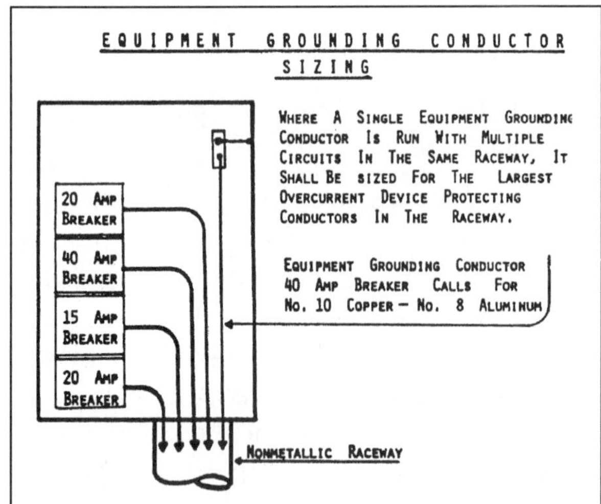

Fig. 10–45 More than one circuit in the same raceway requires sizing the equipment grounding conductor according to the largest overcurrent protective device.

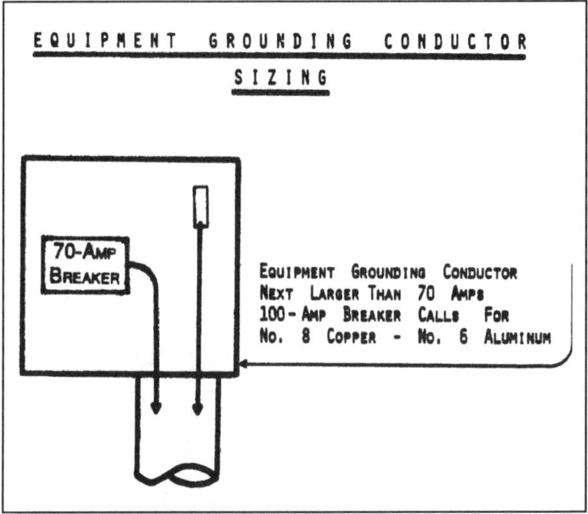

Fig. 10–47 Sizing an equipment grounding conductor protected by a 70-amp breaker. The next-larger-size equipment grounding conductor is required.

Figure 10–47 illustrates a circuit protected by a 70-amp, other-than-instantaneous-type circuit breaker, with a copper equipment grounding conductor. When checking *Table 250-95*, there is no 70-amp rating listed. Therefore, as indicated at the top of *Table 250-95* (figure 10–48, page 147), "Not Exceeding (Amperes)," the next larger size equipment grounding conductor is required—No. 8 copper.

Table 250-95. Minimum Size Equipment Grounding Conductors for Grounding Raceway and Equipment

Rating or Setting of Automatic Overcurrent Device in Circuit Ahead of Equipment, Conduit, etc., Not Exceeding (Amperes)	Size	
	Copper Wire No.	Aluminum or Copper-Clad Aluminum Wire No.*
15	14	12
20	12	10
30	10	8
40	10	8
60	10	8
100	8	6
200	6	4
300	4	2
400	3	1
500	2	1/0
600	1	2/0
800	1/0	3/0
1000	2/0	4/0
1200	3/0	250 kcmil
1600	4/0	350 "
2000	250 kcmil	400 "
2500	350 "	600 "
3000	400 "	600 "
4000	500 "	800 "
5000	700 "	1200 "
6000	800 "	1200 "

Fig. 10–46 Using *Table 250-95* to select No. 10 copper or No. 8 aluminum equipment grounding conductor.*

Figure 10–49 (page 147) illustrates a situation where *Table 250-95* would require a No. 10 copper or No. 6 aluminum conductor for the 50-amp time delay-type circuit breaker. But because the circuit's overcurrent protective device takes into consideration the starting current of the motor, the equipment grounding conductor need not be larger than the circuit conductor (No. 14).

When an "instantaneous trip-type circuit breaker" or a "motor short-circuit protector" is used as the motor branch circuit short circuit and ground-fault protection, *Section 250-95* permits the equipment grounding conductor to be sized according to the motor overload protection, as illustrated in figure 10–50 (page 148).

The motor full load current is 30 amps. The motor circuit conductors are No. 8 THW. *Section 430-52*(c)(3) Exception No. 1 permits the instantaneous circuit breaker for motor branch circuit short circuit protection on a design "E" motor to be as much as 1700 percent of motor full load current. The instantaneous-trip circuit breaker is rated 500 amps and the motor overload protection is 40 amps. The size of the

*Reprinted with permission from NFPA 70-1996, the National Electrical Code®, Copyright © 1995, National Fire Protection Association, Quincy, Massachusetts 02269. This reprinted material is not the complete and official position of the National Fire Protection Association, on the referenced subject, which is represented only by the standard in its entirety.

Table 250-95. Minimum Size Equipment Grounding Conductors for Grounding Raceway and Equipment

70 AMP
NEXT LARGER

Rating or Setting of Automatic Overcurrent Device in Circuit Ahead of Equipment, Conduit, etc., Not Exceeding (Amperes)	Size	
	Copper Wire No.	Aluminum or Copper-Clad Aluminum Wire No.*
15	14	12
20	12	10
30	10	8
40	10	8
60	10	8
100	8	6
200	6	4
300	4	2
400	3	1
500	2	1/0
600	1	2/0
800	1/0	3/0
1000	2/0	4/0
1200	3/0	250 kcmil
1600	4/0	350 "
2000	250 kcmil	400 "
2500	350 "	600 "
3000	400 "	600 "
4000	500 "	800 "
5000	700 "	1200 "
6000	800 "	1200 "

Fig. 10–48 Using *Table 250-95* to size equipment grounding conductor. The next larger size is a 100-amp breaker, which requires No. 8 copper or No. 6 aluminum.*

equipment grounding conductor is based on the 40 amps overload protection and not the 500-amp circuit breaker. Using *Table 250-95*, as illustrated in figure 10–51 (page 148), the equipment grounding conductor is No. 10 copper. Had the size of the equipment grounding conductor been based on the ampacity of the circuit breaker, it would have been larger than the branch circuit conductors.

Note the bonding jumper for the equipment grounding of the motor controller enclosure. The size of this bonding jumper will be the same as the equipment grounding conductor—a No. 10 copper.

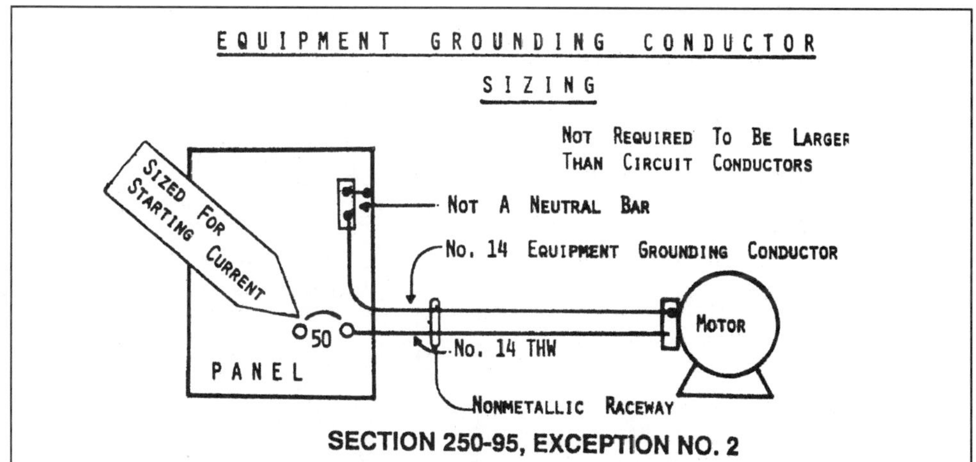

Fig. 10–49 An exception where the equipment grounding conductor is not required to be larger than the circuit conductors.

* Reprinted with permission from NFPA 70-1996, the National Electrical Code®, Copyright © 1995, National Fire Protection Association, Quincy, Massachusetts 02269. This reprinted material is not the complete and official position of the National Fire Protection Association, on the referenced subject, which is represented only by the standard in its entirety.

When an insulated conductor is installed for the equipment grounding conductor in a metal raceway (figure 10–52), or when it is part of a metal-covered cable assembly, all joints and fittings of the metal raceway, cable, and enclosure shall be madeup as if the raceway or enclosure is the primary equipment grounding conductor. This is specifically covered in the FPN to *Section 250-74* as a point of information.

The FPN also calls attention to the grounding of the box containing an isolated receptacle (figure 10–52). When a metal box is used in a run of nonmetallic conduit and an isolated receptacle is installed in the metal box, two equipment grounding conductors are required—one insulated equipment grounding conductor for the isolated grounded receptacle and one to ground the box.

Section 250-114 requires that two or more equipment grounding conductors be connected together when they are in the same box. This is not practical when an isolated grounded receptacle is installed (figure 10–53, page 149). Therefore the Exception to *250-114* permits the equipment grounding conductor for the isolated grounded receptacle to pass through the box without being connected to other equipment grounding conductors or to the box.

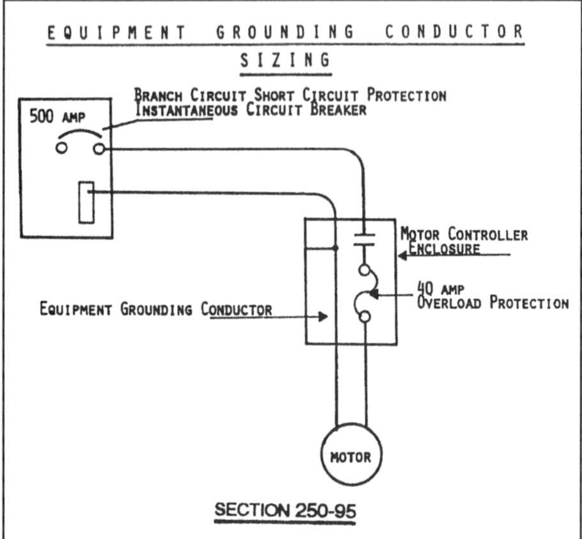

Fig. 10–50 Sizing the equipment grounding conductor where an instantaneous-type circuit breaker is used for branch-circuit short-circuit protection.

Table 250-95. Minimum Size Equipment Grounding Conductors for Grounding Raceway and Equipment

Rating or Setting of Automatic Overcurrent Device in Circuit Ahead of Equipment, Conduit, etc., Not Exceeding (Amperes)	Size: Copper Wire No.	Size: Aluminum or Copper-Clad Aluminum Wire No.*
15	14	12
20	12	10
30	10	8
40	10	8
60	10	8
100	8	6
200	6	4
300	4	2
400	3	1
500	2	1/0
600	1	2/0
800	1/0	3/0
1000	2/0	4/0
1200	3/0	250 kcmil
1600	4/0	350 "
2000	250 kcmil	400 "
2500	350 "	600 "
3000	400 "	600 "
4000	500 "	800 "
5000	700 "	1200 "
6000	800 "	1200 "

Fig. 10–51 Reading *Table 250-95* for equipment grounding conductor size for figure 10–50.*

EQUIPMENT GROUNDING CONDUCTOR IN BOXES

Section 250-114 pays special attention to equipment grounding conductors installed in metal boxes or nonmetallic boxes. The first part of this section covers both types of boxes. Then a special section is devoted to each type.

The uninterrupted continuity of the equipment grounding conductor is also protected by *Section 250-114* (figure 10–54). Often when a

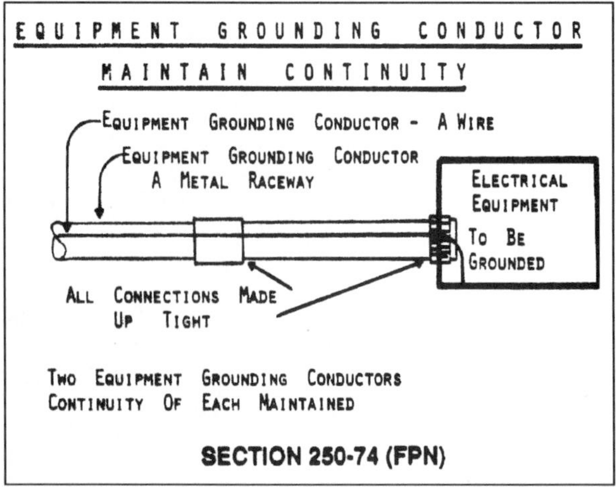

Fig. 10–52 Continuity of a metal raceway must still be maintained when a wire is installed for the equipment grounding conductor.

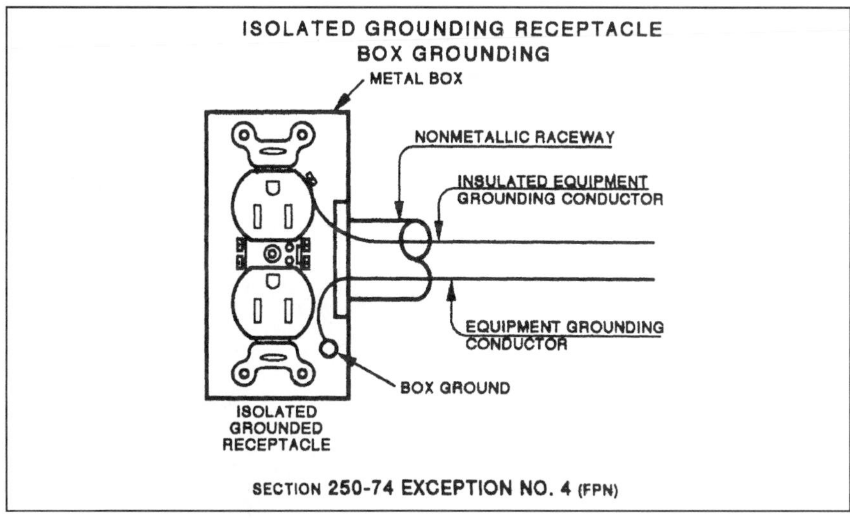

Fig. 10–53 Metal box used with isolated grounded receptacle is required to be grounded.

building is remodeled, receptacles, fixtures, or other devices are removed from the box that feeds them. Therefore, the arrangement of the equipment grounding conductor connections in the feed box shall be such that when one of these items is removed, the continuity of the equipment grounding conductor will not be interrupted.

Reason: If the splice is made on the receptacle or on the fixture and the receptacle or fixture is removed, an open circuit could result, interrupting the equipment grounding conductor path and creating a potential electrical hazard.

Metal Boxes

Section 250-114(a) is directed at equipment grounding conductors installed in metal boxes (figure 10–55). It contains the following information:

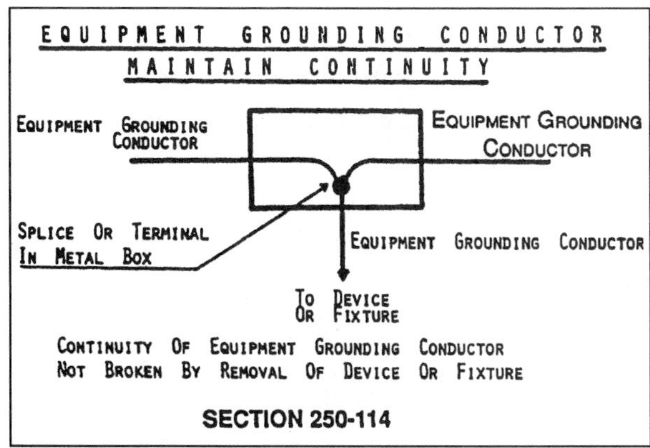

Fig. 10–54 Continuity must be maintained at pull or junction boxes.

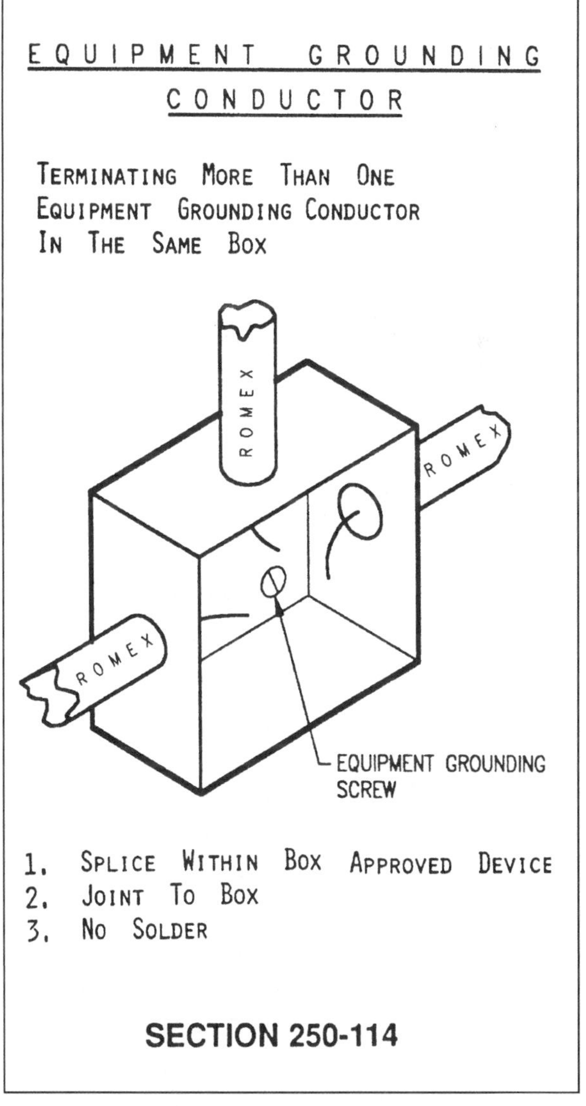

Fig. 10–55 A metal box is required to have a means of terminating and connecting equipment grounding conductor.

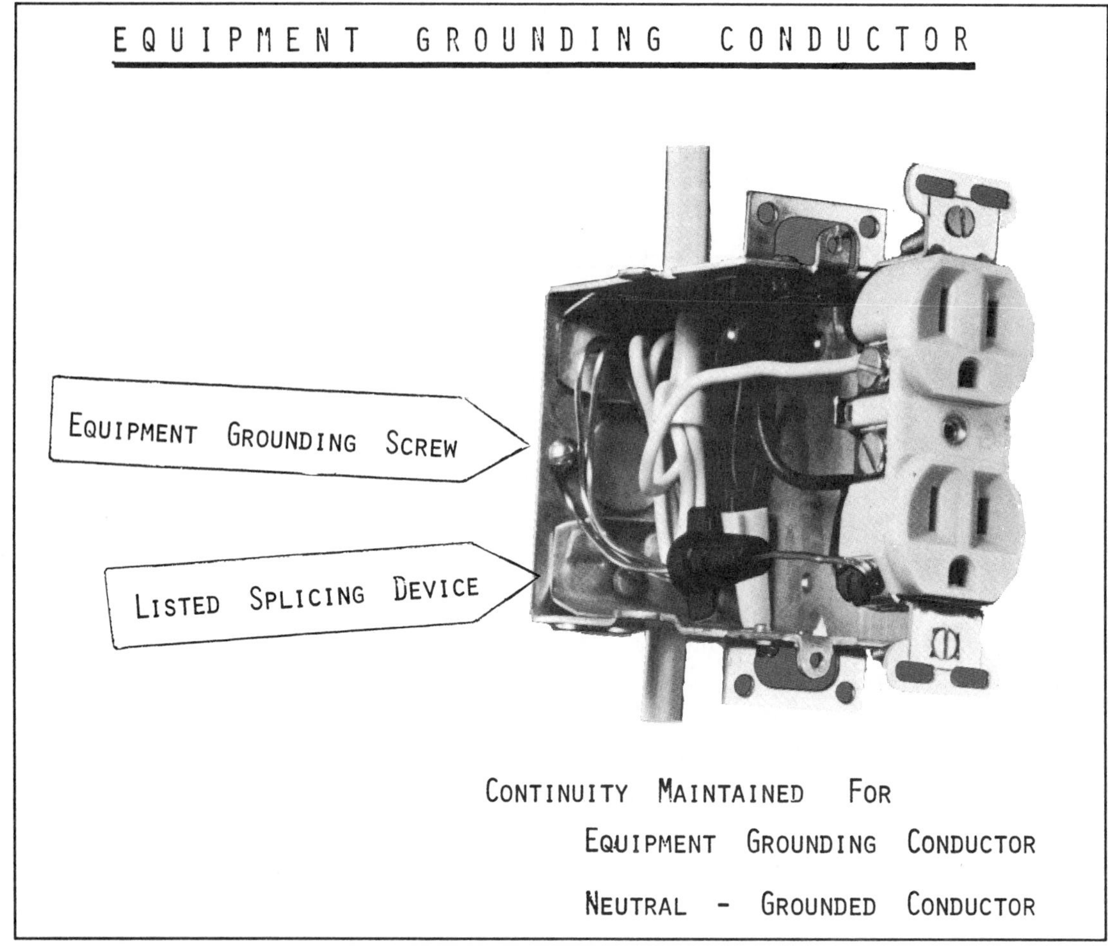

Fig. 10–56 Proper termination of an equipment grounding conductor and a grounded conductor in a device box.

1. A connection is required between the equipment grounding conductor and the box.
2. The connection can be made with
   a. a grounding screw, used for no other purpose,
   b. a listed grounding device, such as a connector.

Comment: This is backed up under construction specifications for boxes in *Article 370*. The equipment grounding screw is illustrated in figure 10–55.

Section 370-40(d) is also directed at metal boxes designed to be used with nonmetallic raceways and nonmetallic cable systems. It requires the box to have provisions manufactured into the box for connecting the equipment grounding conductor.

When the equipment grounding conductor is connected to the screw in the metal box, it serves two purposes. First, it makes a splice point for equipment grounding conductors passing through the box. Second, it provides a means to ground the box and maintains the metal box enclosing or serving the device or fixture at ground potential.

Section 250-114 permits splices to be made in the equipment grounding conductor in boxes, without the conductor being insulated.

CAUTION: Although a splice is permitted in the equipment grounding conductor without it being insulated, care must be used when making an installation in a box that is crowded. There are hot conductors in the box, such as the terminals on a receptacle, that could come in contact with the bare equipment grounding conductor and cause a fault.

Figure 10–56 (page 150) illustrates the proper installation with a metal box, nonmetallic sheathed cable, and an equipment grounding conductor in the metal box. The connections are made so the metal box is grounded, and the equipment grounding conductor's continuity and the grounded conductor's continuity would not be broken, should the receptacle be removed. A connection is made to the grounding screw provided in the box and a pigtail splice is made with a listed splicing device.

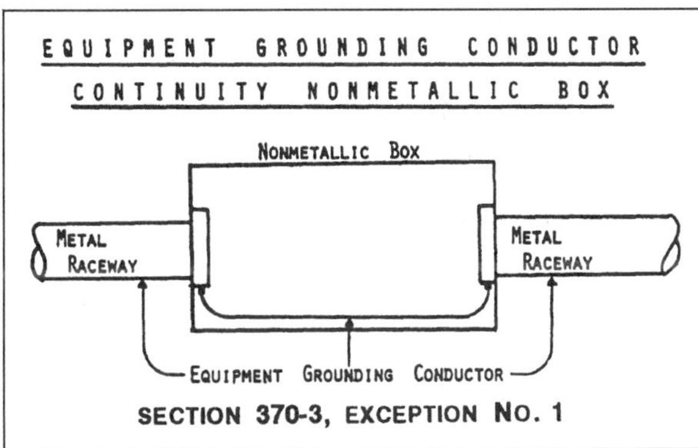

Fig. 10–57 Continuity must be maintained when using metal raceway with nonmetallic boxes.

Nonmetallic Boxes

Attention is also given to nonmetallic boxes. *Section 250-114(b)* requires the nonmetallic box to have conductor arrangements so that a connection can be made to any fitting or device in the box required to be grounded. *Section 370-3,* Exception No. 1, requires that when metal raceway or metal-sheathed cable is attached to a nonmetallic box by a threaded entry, bonding provisions shall be provided for the metal raceway or metal-sheathed cable.

Where the metal raceway is used as the equipment grounding conductor, the grounding path is interrupted and something must be done to maintain continuity when it passes through a nonmetallic box (figure 10–57).

Figure 10–58 illustrates the size of the bonding jumper to be used. The overcurrent device next back protecting the circuit conductors passing through the box is used to calculate the size of the equipment grounding conductor. In this case the conductors are protected with a 60-amp breaker. Therefore, the size of the bonding jumper is taken directly from *Table 250-95* and is No. 10 copper or No. 8 aluminum.

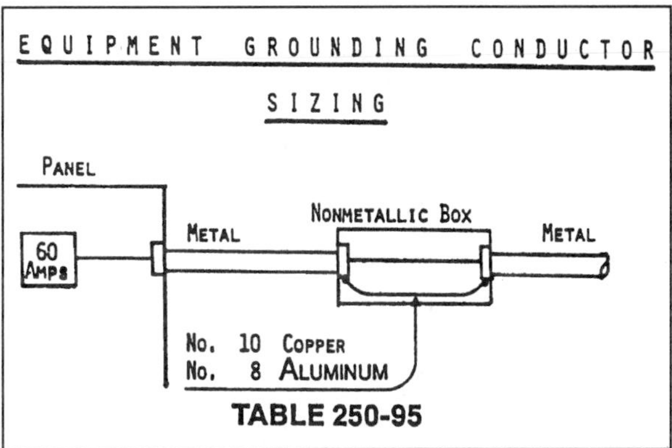

Fig. 10–58 Sizing the equipment grounding conductor through a nonmetallic box, based on circuit overcurrent protection.

AGRICULTURAL BUILDINGS

An agricultural building housing livestock is one place a copper equipment grounding conductor is required, as outlined in *Section 547-8(c)* (figure 10–59). Note that the equipment grounding conductor is installed in a metal raceway but an equipment grounding conductor is still installed. The metal raceway is not depended upon as the equipment grounding conductor; rather, it is a parallel equipment grounding conductor and is installed with proper continuity. When the equipment grounding conductor is installed overhead, it can be bare, insulated, or covered. When the equipment grounding conductor is installed underground, it is required to be covered or insulated. This is also required in part d of Exception No. 2, *Section 250-24*.

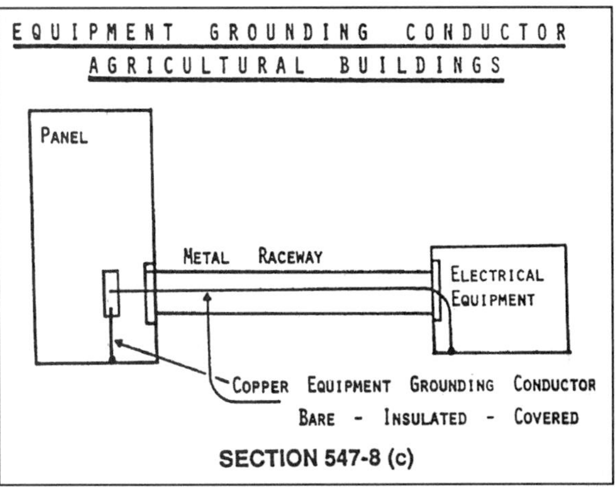

Fig. 10–59 Equipment grounding conductor requirements in agricultural buildings.

FOLLOW UP

Topics for self-study, discussion, or questioning.

1. Define the term *equipment grounding conductor.*
2. Define an *electrical system.*
3. Identify where the most faults occur in an electrical system.
4. Discuss what an "effective ground path" is.
5. Discuss the importance of maintaining continuity of the equipment grounding conductor.
6. Discuss the importance of making all points of connection in a metal raceway system, as if they were joints in a circuit conductor.
7. Discuss the types of equipment grounding conductors that may be used.
8. Discuss the use of an insulated conductor as the equipment grounding conductor.
9. Discuss the limitations placed on flexible metal raceways, when they are permitted to be used as equipment grounding conductors.
10. Discuss the different ways the equipment grounding conductor may be identified.
11. Discuss how devices and boxes are marked for the connection of the equipment grounding conductor.
12. Explain how to calculate the size of the equipment grounding conductor for a branch circuit installed in nonmetallic conduit and protected with a circuit breaker.
13. Explain how to calculate the size of the equipment grounding conductor when a parallel feeder is installed.
14. Explain how to calculate the size of the equipment grounding conductor when the circuit is adjusted for voltage drop.
15. Explain how to calculate the size of the equipment grounding conductor when more than one circuit is installed in the same conduit.
16. Explain how to calculate the size of the equipment grounding conductor for a motor circuit with an instantaneous circuit breaker and magnetic switch with overload relays.

CHAPTER 11

Equipment and Enclosure Bonding

OBJECTIVES

After completing this chapter, the student should be able to:

- define, and discuss the meaning of, the term *bonding*.
- explain the important part bonding plays in maintaining continuity of the equipment grounding path.
- identify the various places throughout the electrical system where bonding is required.
- explain when bonding is required and how it is accomplished on the supply side of the service disconnecting means.
- use *Table 250-94* to calculate the size of the bonding jumpers, when needed on the supply side of the service disconnecting means.
- use the $12^1/_2$ percent rule to calculate the size of the bonding jumpers, when needed on the supply side of the service disconnecting means.
- calculate the size of the equipment bonding jumpers, when needed on the supply side of the service disconnecting means, when parallel conduits are installed and parallel bonding jumpers are installed.
- calculate the size of the equipment bonding jumper required when a section of metal raceway is used for mechanical protection of the grounding electrode conductor.
- identify where bonding is required on the load side of the service equipment to maintain continuity of the equipment grounding conductor.
- use *Table 250-95* to calculate the size of the equipment bonding jumpers, when installed on the load side of the service.
- explain the safety hazard involved when multiple grounding electrodes are installed and are not bonded together.
- explain how an "equipotential plane" for equipment grounding is maintained in an agricultural building.

This chapter focuses on bonding as it functions in the grounding system. The equipment bonding jumpers maintain the equipment grounding conductor's continuity, so there is never an open circuit in the equipment grounding conductor's path. The main bonding jumper was covered in Chapter 9, and it has its particular purpose. Now the main focus of this chapter is

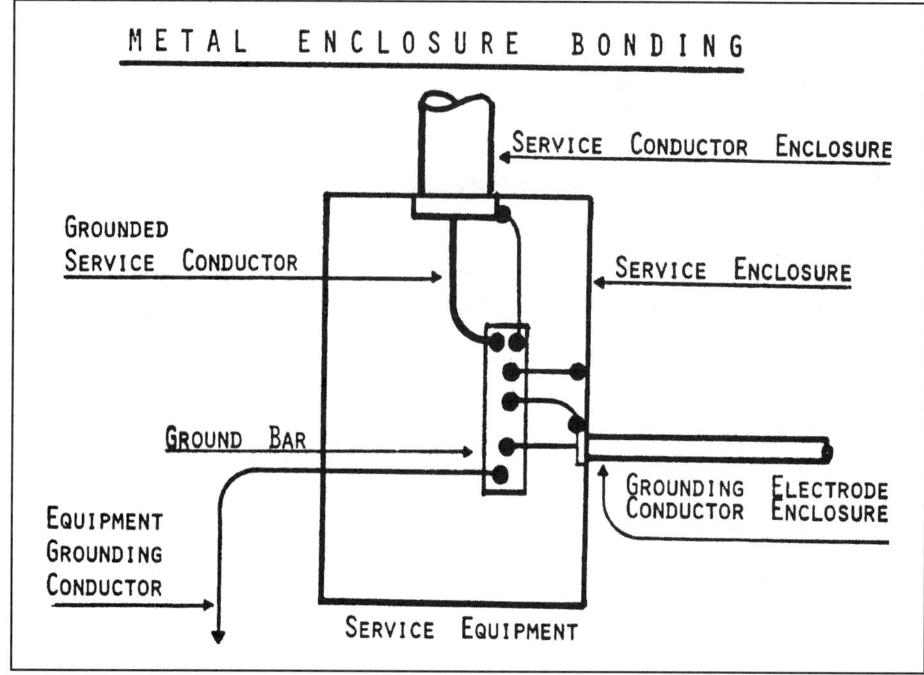

Fig. 11–1 Metal enclosure bonding—connections at service equipment.

on the equipment bonding jumper and the important part it plays in the overall grounding system (figure 11–1).

There are two identifying terms used with bonding, *line side of the service* and *load side of the service*. The division point between line and load is the service overcurrent protective device. Anything ahead of the service overcurrent device is line side. All service equipment enclosures, the grounding electrode conductors, and the main bonding jumper are considered to be on the line side. Anything after the overcurrent protection is load side. The only overcurrent protection anything on the line side has is whatever the utility company has next back on the line. The load side is protected by the service overcurrent device.

DEFINITIONS

Article 100 lists five definitions for "Bonding" and "Bonding Jumpers."

Bonding (figure 11–2), according to *Article 100,* is defined as follows:

Quote – "The permanent joining of metallic parts to form an electrically conductive path which will assure electrical continuity and the capacity to conduct safely any current likely to be imposed."*

Comment: This definition emphasizes three things. These are:

1. Permanent connection
2. Positive electrical continuity at all times
3. Ampacity to conduct fault current

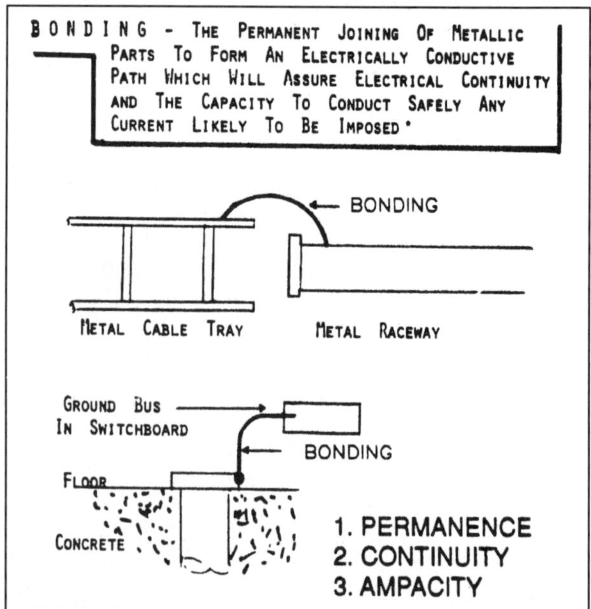

Fig. 11–2 Definition of *bonding*.

* Reprinted with permission from NFPA 70-1996, the National Electrical Code®, Copyright © 1995, National Fire Protection Association, Quincy, Massachusetts 02269. This reprinted material is not the complete and official position of the National Fire Protection Association, on the referenced subject, which is represented only by the standard in its entirety.

Bonding, as defined above, is accomplished by the use of a *Bonding Jumper*, also defined in *Article 100*.

Quote – "A reliable conductor to assure the required electrical conductivity between metal parts required to be electrically connected."*

The definitions of *bonding* and *bonding jumper* sound very much alike; the two things work together. The third definition is for the *Equipment Bonding Jumper*, also found in *Article 100* (figure 11–3).

Quote – "The connection between two or more portions of the equipment grounding conductor."*

A metal raceway may be used as the primary equipment grounding conductor, and equipment bonding jumpers are used to maintain the continuity and ampacity of the equipment grounding conductor.

Figure 11–3 illustrates two installations requiring the use of an equipment bonding jumper. Figure 11–3 (a) shows that without the equipment bonding jumper, there is no connection, no continuity, and no ampacity to carry fault current. There is an open circuit in the equipment grounding circuit. Therefore, the Code requires an equipment bonding jumper to be installed to maintain continuity of the grounding path.

With the use of metal flex, as shown in figure 11–3 (b), the circuit is closed, the continuity is there, but the cross-sectional area of the metal in the flex is not always large enough to carry the fault current. Therefore, an equipment bonding jumper is needed to assure ampacity for possible fault current.

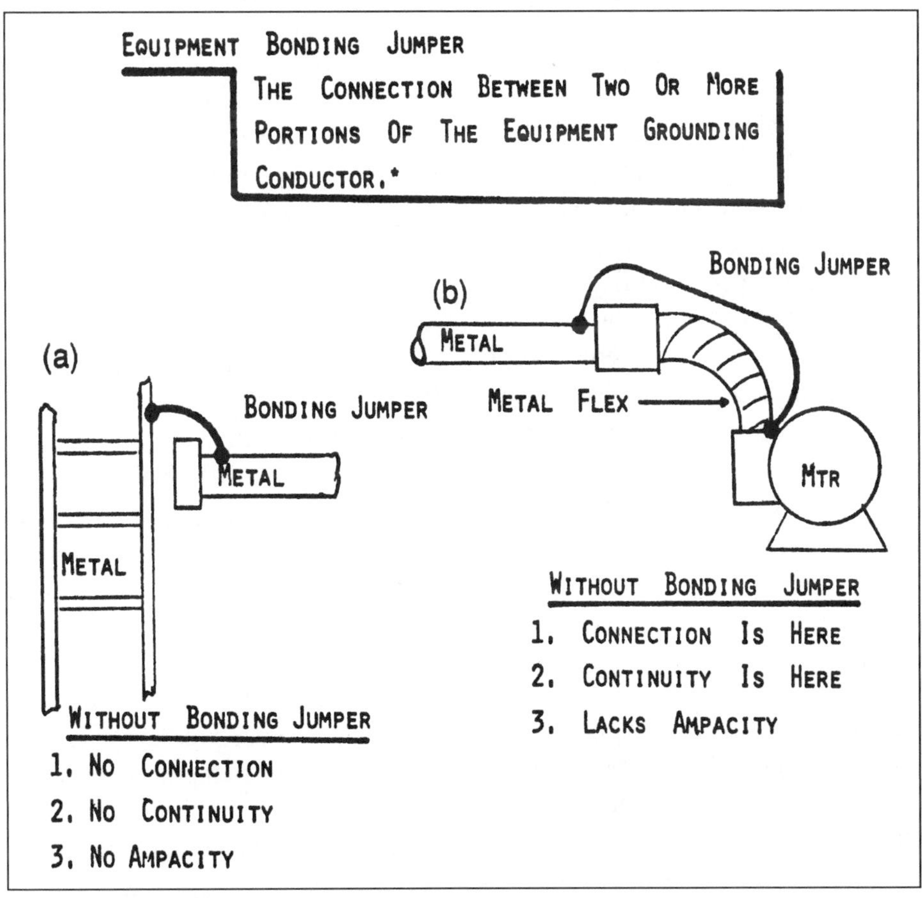

Fig. 11–3 Definition of *equipment bonding jumper*: (a) bonding jumper is sole connection between two metals to assure continuity; (b) bonding jumper is parallel connection with flex to assure continuity.

The equipment bonding jumpers in figure 11–3 (page 155) are insurance connections. For example, an individual may buy hospitalization insurance and have high hopes of never using it. The bonding jumper is also installed with high hopes that it will never have to be used. It helps create a healthy equipment grounding system called "safe." If the electrical installation always stays healthy and lucky, there might not be a need for equipment bonding jumpers and equipment grounding. But when an electrical installation is afflicted with an ailment such as a fault, or when it has an accident and is hit by lightning or a high current surge, the equipment bonding jumper insurance pays off.

Bonding is looked at in three different situations in this chapter. These are:

1. Service—equipment and enclosures
2. Other than service—equipment and enclosures
3. Multiple grounding electrode systems

MATERIALS

Section 250-79(a) permits the equipment bonding jumper to be copper or another corrosion-resistant material. Although this permits the use of other than copper conductors, there are specific places where a copper bonding jumper is required. Metal fittings listed for the purpose are permitted for use in place of equipment bonding jumpers in limited installations. *Section 250-91(b)* permits the equipment bonding jumper, which is part of the equipment grounding conductor, to be insulated, bare, stranded, or solid. However, the bare conductor cannot be used for all installations.

CONNECTIONS

All connection requirements for equipment grounding conductors apply to equipment bonding jumpers. Once again, *Section 250-92(c)(1)* comes into play. It requires all bonding jumper connections for joints and fittings to be madeup tight using suitable tools. *Section 250-75* requires the removal of nonconductive paint, enamel, or similar coatings. *Section 250-113* requires the equipment bonding jumper connection to be made by means of any of the following:

1. Exothermic welding
2. Listed pressure connectors
3. Listed clamps
4. Other listed means
5. Connections that depend solely on solder not permitted
6. Sheet metal screws shall not be used.

BONDING AT SERVICE EQUIPMENT

The requirements for equipment and enclosure bonding on the supply (line) side of the service equipment are more stringent than some of the requirements for bonding on the load side of the service equipment. For example, locknuts and bushings are not depended upon to assure continuity of the grounding system on the supply side of the service, but on the load side of the service equipment they are permitted under certain conditions.

There is good reason for this extra precaution. The only overcurrent protection for the service is the overcurrent protection on the primary side of the utility company transformer. This is to protect the utility company transformer and not the many services that will be connected to the secondary of the transformer. This overcurrent protection offers no protection for the service equipment or anything on the line side of the service equipment. Therefore, all grounding connections are made extra sure with the intent of trying to burn the fault clear before a more serious fault takes place.

Figure 11–4 (page 157) illustrates some of the various grounding conductors discussed up to this point. It also shows the location and identification of line side and load side equipment bonding jumpers.

Section 250-71(a)(2) requires the noncurrent-carrying metal parts of the service equipment to be effectively bonded together, as illustrated in figure 11–5 (page 157), and lists three specific parts of the service equipment where this shall occur. These are:

1. Conductor enclosure
2. Equipment enclosure
3. Grounding electrode conductor enclosure

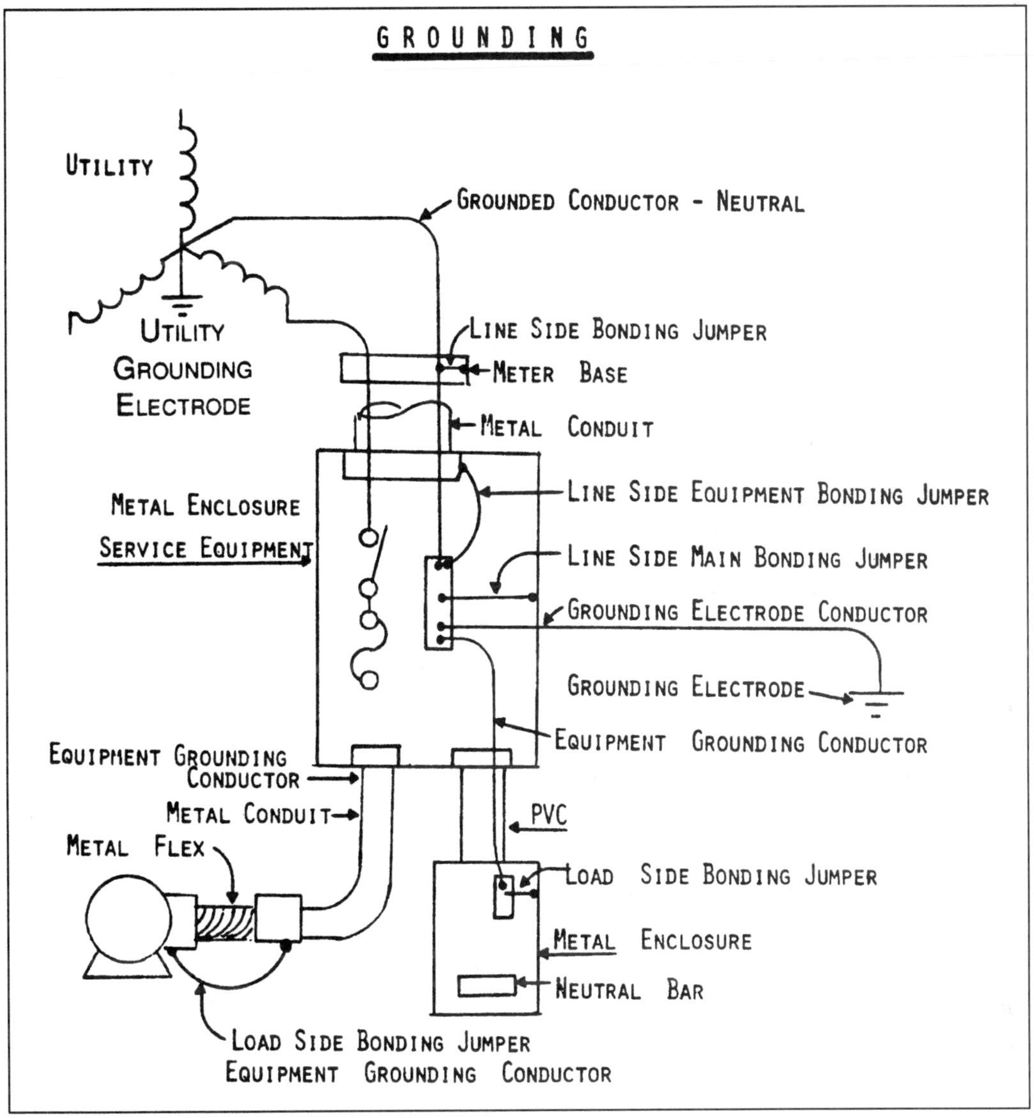

Fig. 11–4 Identification of equipment bonding jumpers on the line and load sides of service equipment.

Section 250-55 gives an exception to this requirement for underground service cable. This is a bit unusual for the exception not to be a separate part of the section. *Section 250-55* has to do with an underground installation of metal-clad cable and an underground system. This does not apply to metal-clad cable installed overhead in free air.

Cable tray is listed separately from metal raceways used for service-entrance conductors; its use as an equipment grounding conductor was covered in Chapter 10 of this text. However, in order to keep the continuity of cable tray as an equipment grounding conductor, equipment bonding jumpers are often needed. The metal service raceway for which equipment bonding

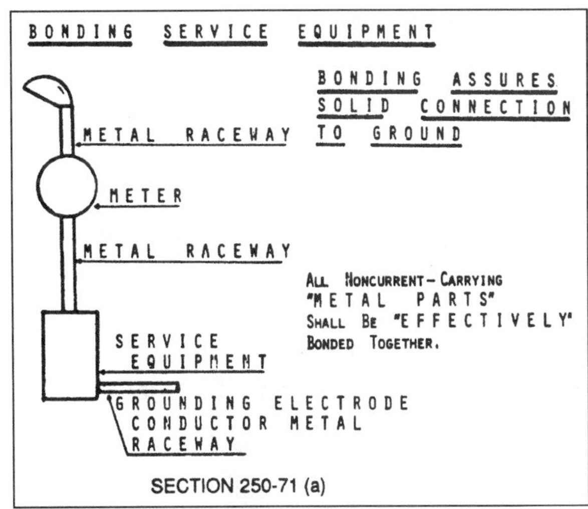

Fig. 11–5 Requirement for bonding together noncurrent-carrying metal parts of service equipment.

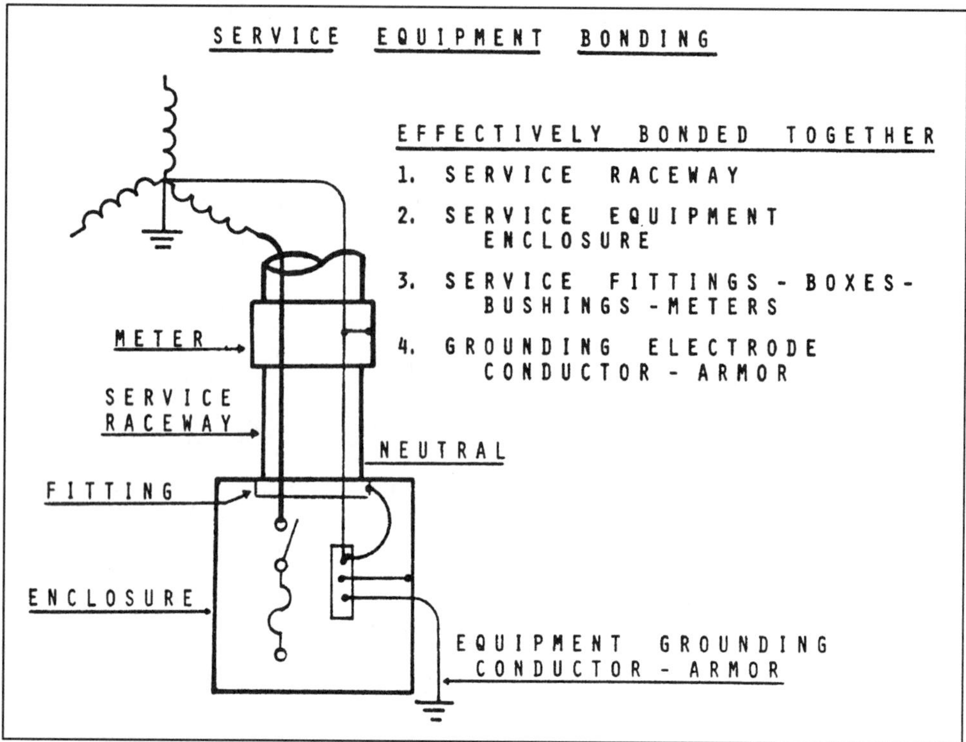

Fig. 11–6 Parts of service equipment effectively bonded together.

jumpers are required are those given in *Section 230-43*, which lists the wiring methods permitted to be used as support for the service-entrance conductor. Metal raceways permitted by *Section 230-43* are the following:

1. Rigid metal conduit (RMC)
2. Intermediate metal conduit (IMC)
3. Electrical metallic tubing (EMT)
4. Wireways
5. Busways
6. Auxiliary gutters
7. Cable bus
8. Flexible metal conduit or liquidtight flexible metal conduit not over 6 feet (and other limitations)

Certain cable assemblies with metal outer coverings are permitted by *Section 230-43* for use as service-entrance conductors. The metal covering must have continuity maintained with equipment bonding jumpers. Included are:

1. Type MC cable
2. Mineral-insulated, metal-sheathed cable
3. Type IGS cable

Figure 11–6 illustrates the bonding together of all service equipment enclosures, as required by *Section 250-71(a)*. These enclosures will include, but are not limited to, such things as the meter base; pull, junction, or terminal boxes; current transformer (CT) cans; service disconnecting means; service panel; service switchboard; or any metal enclosure that encloses anything ahead of the service disconnecting means.

The one bonding requirement often overlooked is stated in *Section 250-71(a)(3)*. This requires the bonding of the metallic raceway or armor enclosing the grounding electrode conductor at the service when it is installed in a metal raceway or armor. *Section 250-92(a)* permits the use of metal raceway, such as metal conduit, to be used to enclose the grounding electrode conductor. *Section 250-79(a)(3)* requires metal raceway or cable armor and all intervening raceways, boxes, and enclosures that enclose the grounding electrode conductor to be bonded to the grounding electrode conductor (figure 11–7, page 159). When the grounding electrode conductor is enclosed in a single raceway, the raceway is bonded at both ends. When individual sections of race-

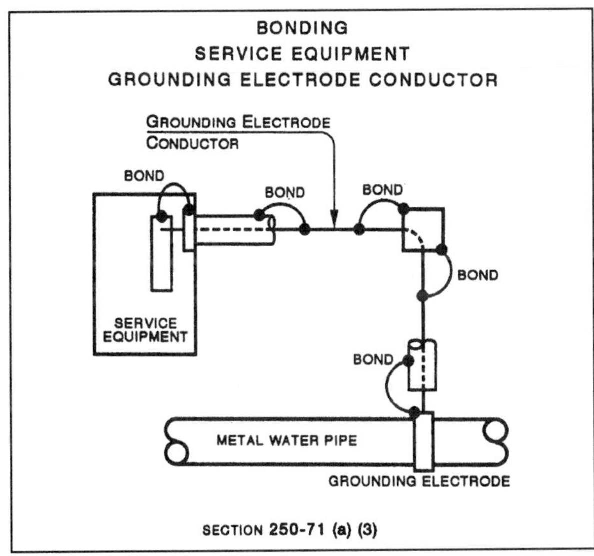

Fig. 11–7 Bonding grounding electrode conductor enclosures.

way and/or boxes are used, each individual section and/or box is required to be bonded to the grounding electrode conductor.

Methods of Bonding at Service

Methods of bonding, or the things listed for use to make the equipment bonding connections on the supply side of the service, are covered in *Section 250-72*. This section permits the grounded conductor (the neutral) to be used for bonding the service equipment on the LINE SIDE of the service equipment only (figure 11–8).

Threaded fittings and threadless fittings are permitted to be used for bonding the various service enclosures and equipment together; they are illustrated in figure 11–9 (page 160). *Section 250-72(b)* permits the use of these threaded fittings where rigid metal conduit or intermediate metal conduit is used, but requires them to be madeup wrenchtight. *Section 250-72(c)* permits the use of threadless couplings and connectors when made up tight, such as those used with rigid metal conduit, intermediate metal conduit, and EMT.

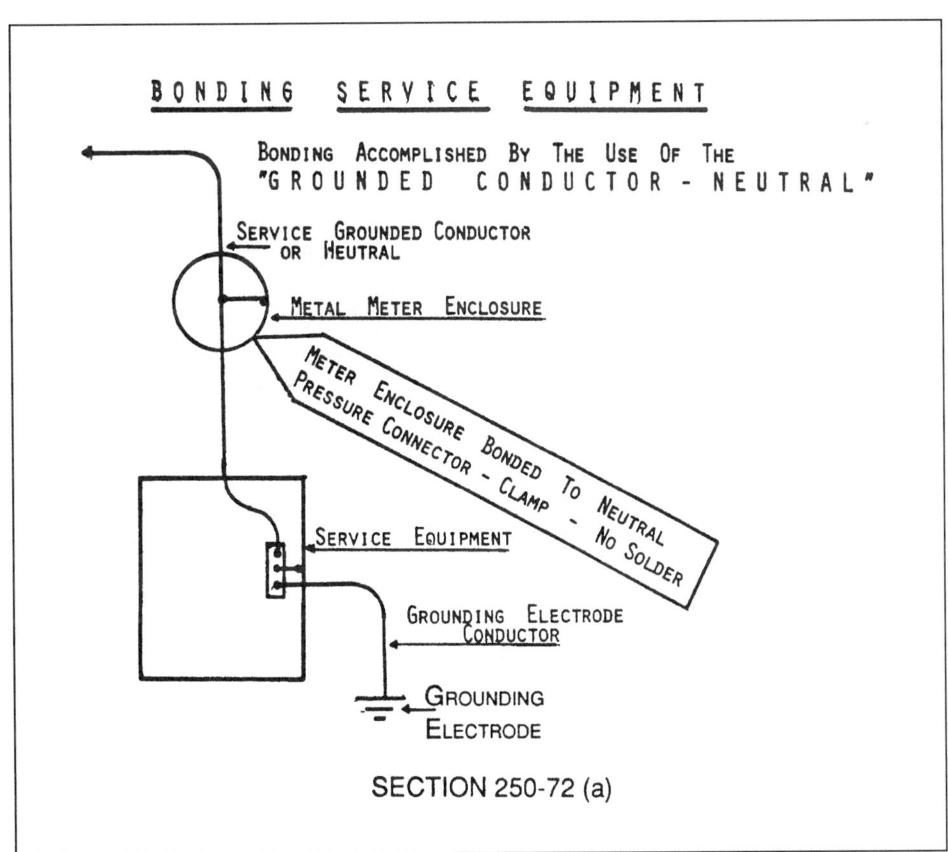

Fig. 11–8 Bonding service equipment using the neutral.

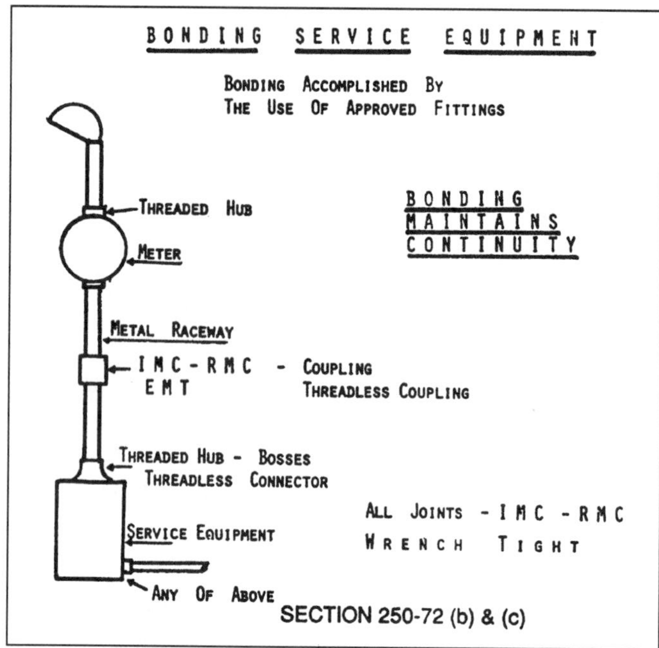

Fig. 11–9 Materials used to maintain continuity when bonding service equipment.

BONDING SERVICE EQUIPMENT

BONDING ACCOMPLISHED BY
THE USE OF "GROUNDING BUSHINGS"
OR "GROUNDING LOCKNUT"

METAL RACEWAY
THREADED HUB
METER
THREADED HUB
METAL RACEWAY
LOCKNUTS AND BUSHINGS
CLAMPS - PRESSURE CONNECTORS
OTHER APPROVED MEANS
"NO SOLDER"
GROUNDING ELECTRODE CONDUCTOR
METAL RACEWAY

SECTION 250-72 (e)

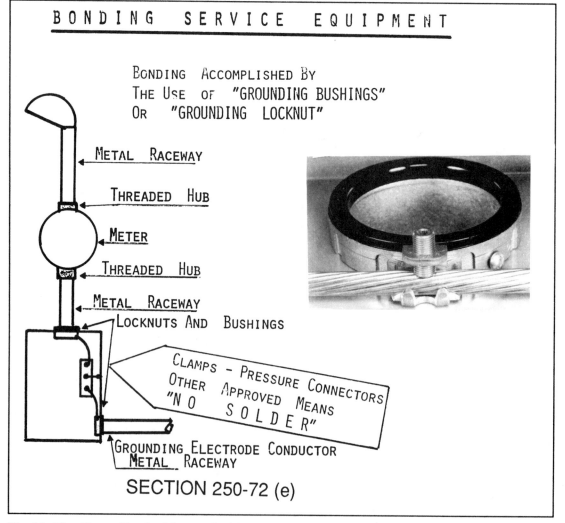

Fig. 11–10 Grounding bushing used with service equipment. Courtesy O.Z./Gedney Co.

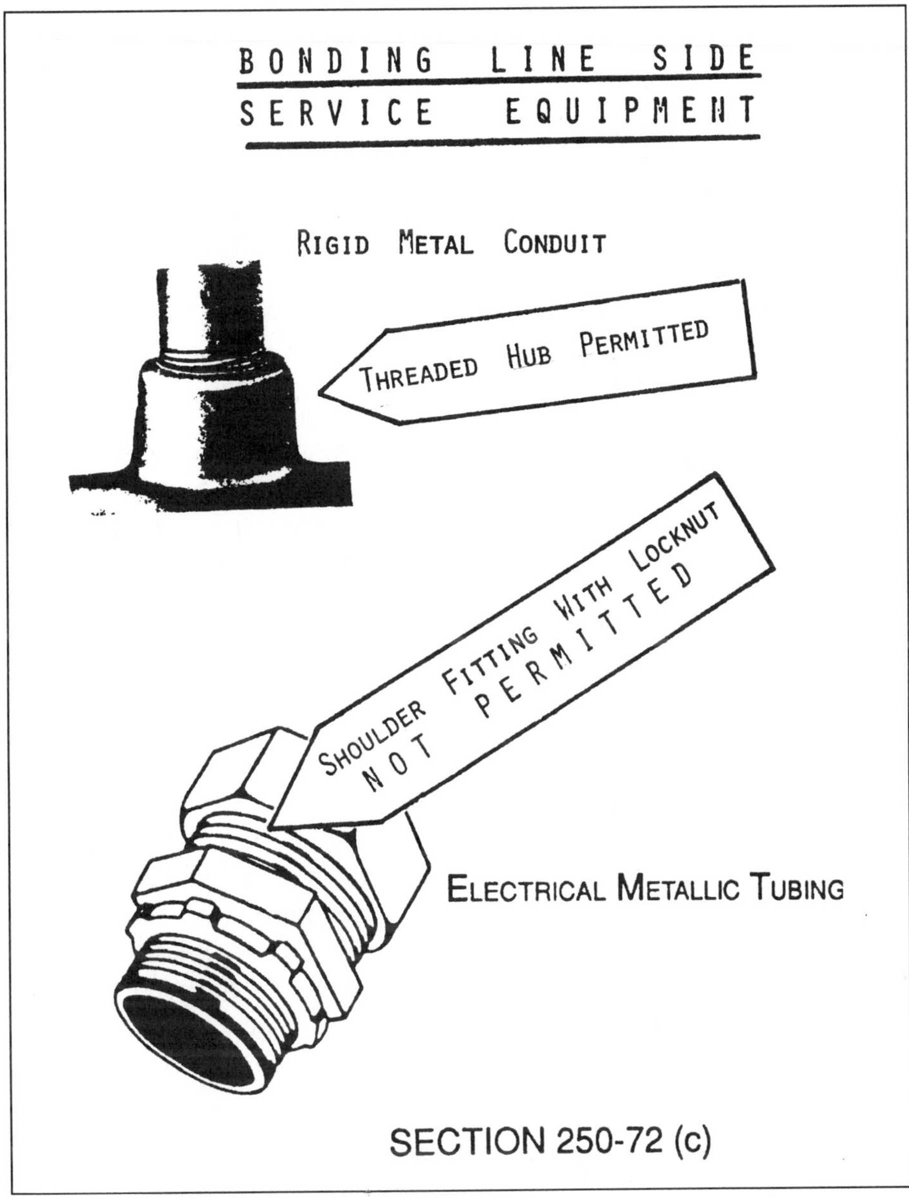

Fig. 11–11 A threaded hub is permitted; an EMT connector with standard locknut is not permitted. Courtesy Appleton Electric Co.

Standard locknuts or bushings shall not be used for bonding the service equipment. This requirement is followed up in *Section 250-72(e)*, which permits the use of the bonding-type locknuts and bonding-type bushings for bonding the service enclosures and equipment (figure 11–10).

Figure 11–11 illustrates a threaded connection or hub for metal conduit that is permitted for maintaining continuity on the line side of the service. The EMT connector, with its shoulder fit with standard locknut, is not permitted for maintaining the continuity on the line side of the service and must have an equipment bonding jumper installed, or a grounding locknut must be used.

Figure 11–12 (page 162) illustrates *Section 250-72(d)*, which requires a bonding jumper around knockouts in the service equipment when the maximum-size knockout (eccentric or concentric type) is not used. When the smaller knockout is removed, the process often weakens the knockouts left in the equipment; they do not make a good connection and cannot be depended upon to maintain continuity under fault conditions.

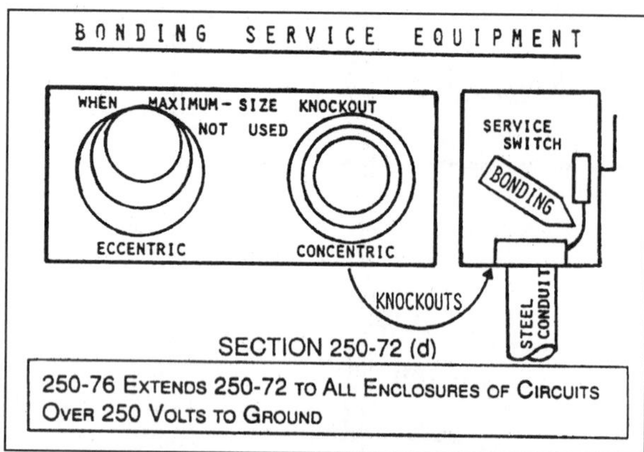

Fig. 11–12 Bonding service equipment when not all eccentric or concentric knockouts are used.

However, *Section 250-76 Exception* will permit the use of listed fittings without an equipment bonding jumper when oversized concentric or eccentric knockouts are encountered, but only if the enclosure is tested and is listed for such use.

When metal-clad cable is used for service-entrance cable (figure 11–13) with a bare conductor in contact with the outer armor or metal tape, it is considered grounded, according to *Section 250-73*.

SIZING BONDING JUMPERS ON SUPPLY SIDE OF SERVICE

Section 250-79(d) gives three methods for sizing the bonding jumpers on the supply side of the service. When doing so, the size of the service-entrance conductors and the material

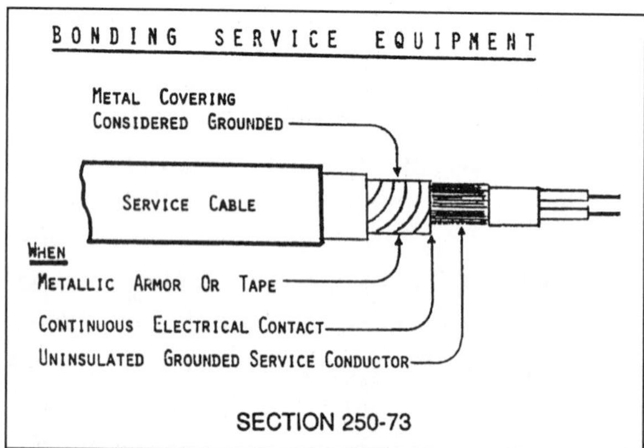

Fig. 11–13 The metal armor or tape of service-entrance cable is required to be bonded.

used for the bonding jumper are taken into consideration. This is the same method that was used for calculating the size of the main bonding jumper (Chapter 9 of this text).

Method Requirements

1. The bonding jumper shall not be smaller than the size given in *Table 250-94*. This is the same table used for sizing the grounding electrode conductor.
2. This is referred to as the $12^1/_2$ percent rule. Where the service-entrance phase conductors exceed the sizes listed in *Table 250-94*, which is 1100 kcmil for copper and 1700 kcmil for aluminum, the bonding jumper shall have an area not less than $12^1/_2$ percent of the area of the largest phase conductor or conductors, when parallel conductors are used.
3. Where the phase conductors and the bonding jumper are of different materials (copper or aluminum), the minimum size of the bonding jumper shall be based on the assumed use of phase conductors of the same material as the bonding jumper and with an ampacity equivalent to that of the installed phase conductors.

Table 250-94 is entitled "Grounding Electrode Conductor for AC Systems," but it is also used for sizing the equipment bonding jumpers on the line (supply) side of the service equipment.

Method 1 (figure 11–14, page 163) illustrates a service with 500 kcmil copper as the service-entrance conductors and the use of a copper equipment bonding jumper. The size of the equipment bonding jumper is read directly from *Table 250-94* (figure 11–15, page 163), which requires a No. 1/0 copper equipment bonding jumper.

Method 1 (figure 11–16, page 163) illustrates a service with 500 kcmil aluminum as service-entrance conductors and the use of an aluminum equipment bonding jumper. The size of the equipment bonding jumper is read directly from *Table 250-94* (figure 11–17, page 163) and is required to be No. 1/0 aluminum.

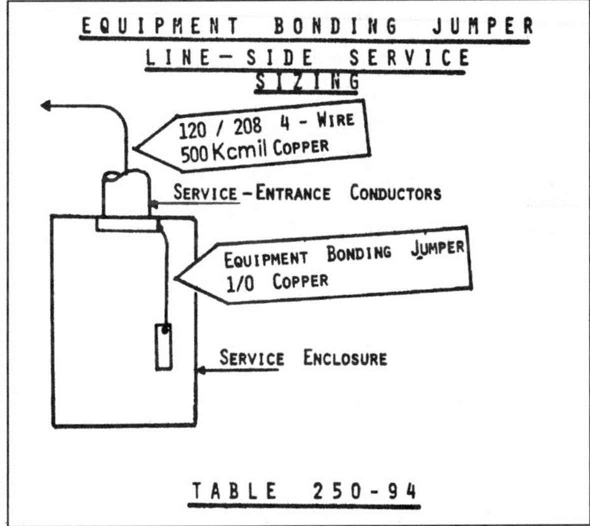

Fig. 11–14 Sizing an equipment bonding jumper on the line side of service using a copper conductor.

Method 2 (figure 11–18, page 164) illustrates a service with 750 kcmil copper, two conductors per phase, and the use of a copper equipment bonding jumper. The total cross-sectional area per phase of the service-entrance conductors is

$$2 \times 750 = 1500 \text{ kcmil}$$

which is greater than the 1100 kcmil copper listed in *Table 250-94*. Therefore, $12^1/_2$ percent of the total cross-sectional area of a phase conductor shall be used.

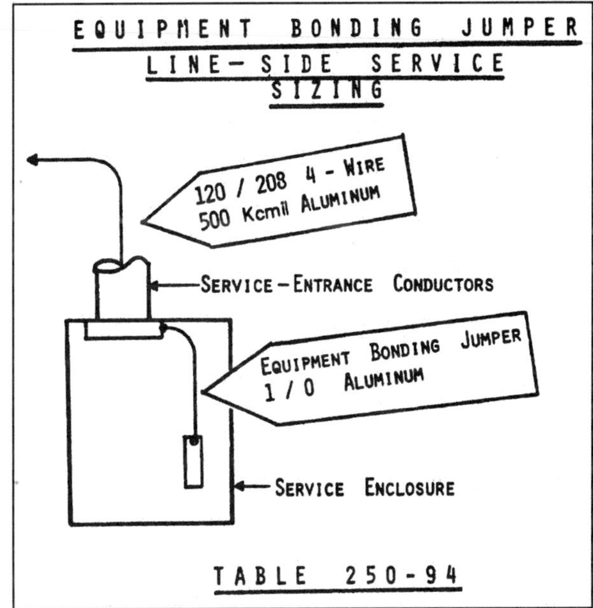

Fig. 11–16 Sizing the equipment bonding jumper on the line side of service when an aluminum conductor is used.

$$1{,}500{,}000 \times 12^1/_2\% = 187{,}500 \text{ circular mils}$$

Table 8, Chapter 9 of the Code (figure 11–19, page 164,) is used to establish a wire size for the equipment bonding jumper. This table shows that 187,500 is larger than No. 3/0 and smaller than No. 4/0; therefore, the larger size will be used and No. 4/0 will be the minimum size of

Size of Largest Service-Entrance Conductor or Equivalent Area for Parallel Conductors		Size of Grounding Electrode Conductor	
Copper	Aluminum or Copper-Clad Aluminum	Copper	*Aluminum or Copper-Clad Aluminum
2 or smaller	1/0 or smaller	8	6
1 or 1/0	2/0 or 3/0	6	4
2/0 or 3/0	4/0 or 250 kcmil	4	2
Over 3/0 thru 350 kcmil	Over 250 kcmil thru 500 kcmil	2	1/0
Over 350 kcmil thru 600 kcmil	Over 500 kcmil thru 900 kcmil	1/0	3/0
Over 600 kcmil thru 1100 kcmil	Over 900 kcmil thru 1750 kcmil	2/0	4/0
Over 1100 kcmil	Over 1750 kcmil	3/0	250 kcmil

Fig. 11–15 Reading *Table 250-94* to determine the size of the equipment bonding jumper shown in figure 11–14.*

Table 250-94.
Grounding Electrode Conductor for AC Systems

Size of Largest Service-Entrance Conductor or Equivalent Area for Parallel Conductors		Size of Grounding Electrode Conductor	
Copper	Aluminum or Copper-Clad Aluminum	Copper	*Aluminum or Copper-Clad Aluminum
2 or smaller	1/0 or smaller	8	6
1 or 1/0	2/0 or 3/0	6	4
2/0 or 3/0	4/0 or 250 kcmil	4	2
Over 3/0 thru 350 kcmil	Over 250 kcmil thru 500 kcmil	2	1/0
Over 350 kcmil thru 600 kcmil	Over 500 kcmil thru 900 kcmil	1/0	3/0
Over 600 kcmil thru 1100 kcmil	Over 900 kcmil thru 1750 kcmil	2/0	4/0
Over 1100 kcmil	Over 1750 kcmil	3/0	250 kcmil

Fig. 11–17 Reading *Table 250-94* to determine the size of the equipment bonding jumper shown in figure 11–16.*

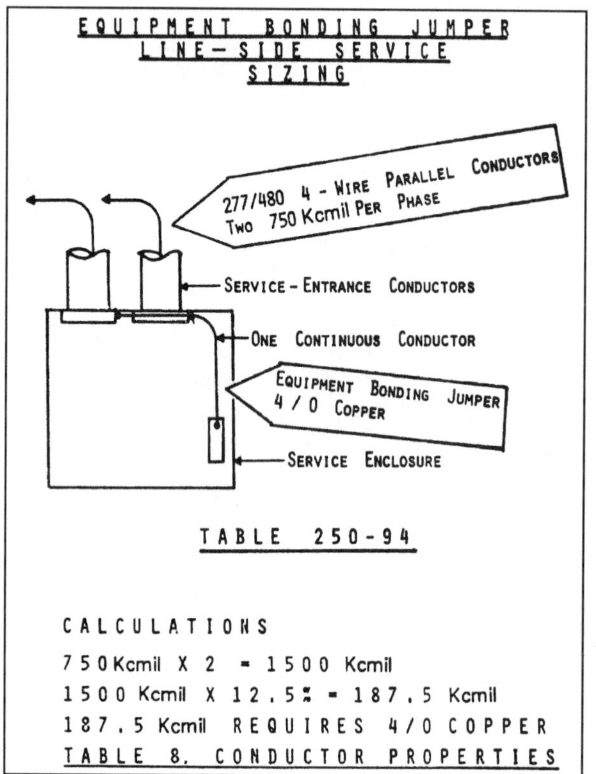

Fig. 11–18 Applying the 12½ percent rule to size the equipment bonding jumper when using copper.

the equipment bonding jumper. One continuous conductor, No. 4/0 copper, is used to bond the two raceways.

CAUTION: The equipment bonding jumper is not broken. It is one continuous wire when used to bond two or more raceways containing parallel service-entrance conductors.

Comment: The single bonding jumper, installed with parallel conduits as illustrated in figure 11–18, is often a point of discussion. Based on *Section 250-79(c)*, one interpretation is that *Section 250-79* requires two equipment bonding jumpers to be installed when there are parallel conduits.

The other interpretation is based on the wording of *Section 250-79* and the phrase "where routed with the raceways." When the conductors reach the switchgear, they are no longer in parallel raceways. Figures 11–20 (page 165) and 11–22 (page 166) illustrate the equipment bonding jumpers "routed with the raceways."

A very important point to consider here is that if a single unbroken equipment bonding

187,500 cmil

NEXT LARGER SIZE

Table 8. Conductor Properties

Size AWG/kcmil	Area Cir. Mils	Conductors: Stranding Quantity	Conductors: Stranding Diam. in.	Conductors: Overall Diam. in.	Conductors: Overall Area in.²	DC Resistance at 75°C (167°F) Copper Uncoated ohm/kFT	Copper Coated ohm/kFT	Aluminum ohm/kFT
18	1620	1	—	0.040	0.001	7.77	8.08	12.8
18	1620	7	0.015	0.046	0.002	7.95	8.45	13.1
16	2580	1	—	0.051	0.002	4.89	5.08	8.05
16	2580	7	0.019	0.058	0.003	4.99	5.29	8.21
14	4110	1	—	0.064	0.003	3.07	3.19	5.06
14	4110	7	0.024	0.073	0.004	3.14	3.26	5.17
12	6530	1	—	0.081	0.005	1.93	2.01	3.18
12	6530	7	0.030	0.092	0.006	1.98	2.05	3.25
10	10380	1	—	0.102	0.008	1.21	1.26	2.00
10	10380	7	0.038	0.116	0.011	1.24	1.29	2.04
8	16510	1	—	0.128	0.013	0.764	0.786	1.26
8	16510	7	0.049	0.146	0.017	0.778	0.809	1.28
6	26240	7	0.061	0.184	0.027	0.491	0.510	0.808
4	41740	7	0.077	0.232	0.042	0.308	0.321	0.508
3	52620	7	0.087	0.260	0.053	0.245	0.254	0.403
2	66360	7	0.097	0.292	0.067	0.194	0.201	0.319
1	83690	19	0.066	0.332	0.087	0.154	0.160	0.253
1/0	105600	19	0.074	0.372	0.109	0.122	0.127	0.201
2/0	133100	19	0.084	0.418	0.137	0.0976	0.101	0.159
3/0	167800	19	0.094	0.470	0.173	0.0766	0.0797	0.126
4/0	211600	19	0.106	0.528	0.219	0.0608	0.0626	0.100
250	—	37	0.082	0.575	0.260	0.0515	0.0535	0.0847
300	—	37	0.090	0.630	0.312	0.0429	0.0446	0.0707
350	—	37	0.097	0.681	0.364	0.0367	0.0382	0.0605
400	—	37	0.104	0.728	0.416	0.0321	0.0331	0.0529
500	—	37	0.116	0.813	0.519	0.0258	0.0265	0.0424
600	—	61	0.099	0.893	0.626	0.0214	0.0223	0.0353
700	—	61	0.107	0.964	0.730	0.0184	0.0189	0.0303
750	—	61	0.111	0.998	0.782	0.0171	0.0176	0.0282
800	—	61	0.114	1.030	0.834	0.0161	0.0166	0.0265
900	—	61	0.122	1.094	0.940	0.0143	0.0147	0.0235
1000	—	61	0.128	1.152	1.042	0.0129	0.0132	0.0212
1250	—	91	0.117	1.284	1.305	0.0103	0.0106	0.0169
1500	—	91	0.128	1.412	1.566	0.00858	0.00883	0.0141
1750	—	127	0.117	1.526	1.829	0.00735	0.00756	0.0121
2000	—	127	0.126	1.632	2.092	0.00643	0.00662	0.0106

Fig. 11–19 Using *Table 8* (Chapter 9) to convert to the next standard wire size.*

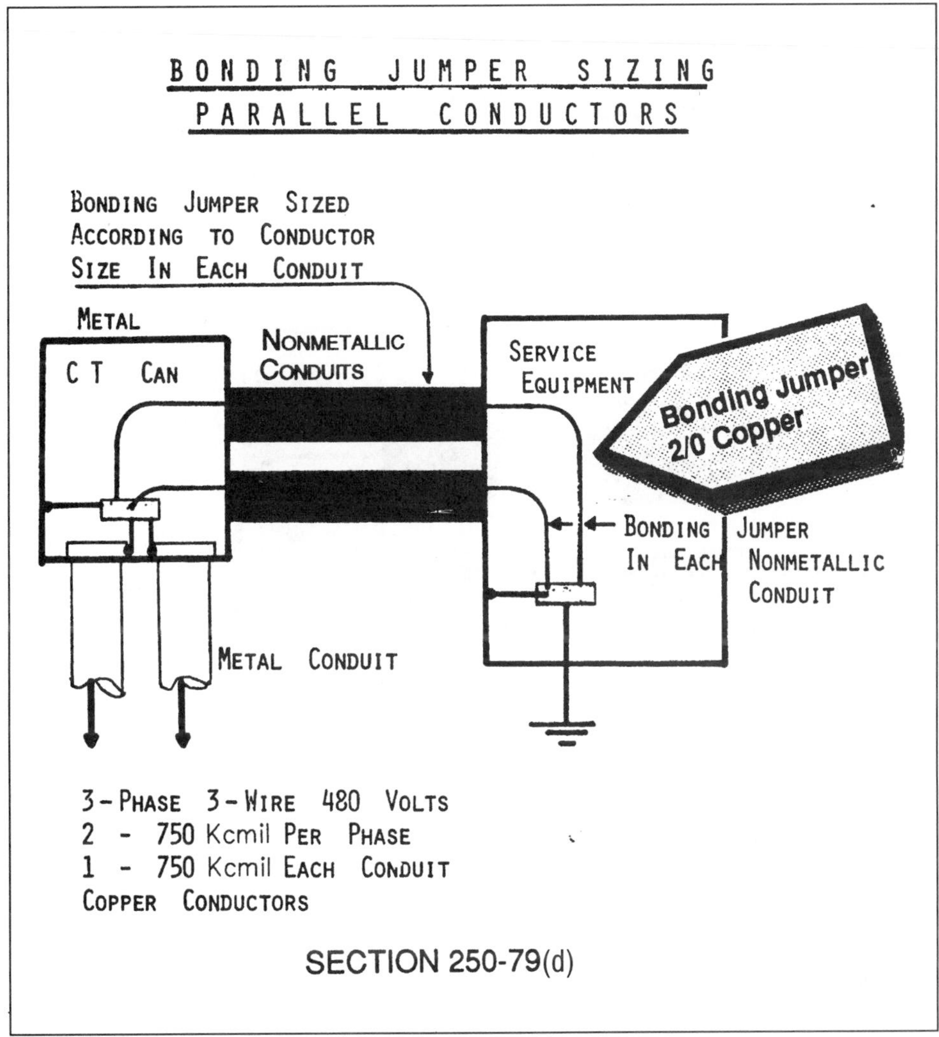

Fig. 11–20 Sizing the equipment bonding jumpers installed with 750 kcmil copper service-entrance conductors in parallel, nonmetallic raceways.

jumper is installed, the size of the equipment bonding jumper is calculated just as if all the conductors were in the same raceway, thereby offering an effective ground path.

Figure 11–20 illustrates service-entrance conductors in metal conduit. After passing through a CT box, they are in PVC, nonmetallic conduit. *Section 250-79(d)* requires that a separate equipment bonding jumper be run in each conduit and sized according to the service-entrance conductors in each conduit. Note also that the equipment bonding jumpers are routed with the parallel raceways as required by *Section 250-79(d)*. For 750 kcmil copper (figure 11–21), *Table 250-94* requires No. 2/0 copper. *Section 310-4* permits the paralleling of No. 2/0 conductors.

Table 250-94.
Grounding Electrode Conductor for AC Systems

Size of Largest Service-Entrance Conductor or Equivalent Area for Parallel Conductors		Size of Grounding Electrode Conductor	
Copper	Aluminum or Copper-Clad Aluminum	Copper	*Aluminum or Copper-Clad Aluminum
2 or smaller	1/0 or smaller	8	6
1 or 1/0	2/0 or 3/0	6	4
2/0 or 3/0	4/0 or 250 kcmil	4	2
Over 3/0 thru 350 kcmil	Over 250 kcmil thru 500 kcmil	2	1/0
Over 350 kcmil thru 600 kcmil	Over 500 kcmil thru 900 kcmil	1/0	3/0
Over 600 kcmil thru 1100 kcmil	Over 900 kcmil thru 1750 kcmil	2/0	4/0
Over 1100 kcmil	Over 1750 kcmil	3/0	250 kcmil

Fig. 11–21 Reading *Table 250-94* to determine the size of the copper equipment bonding jumper shown in figure 11–20.*

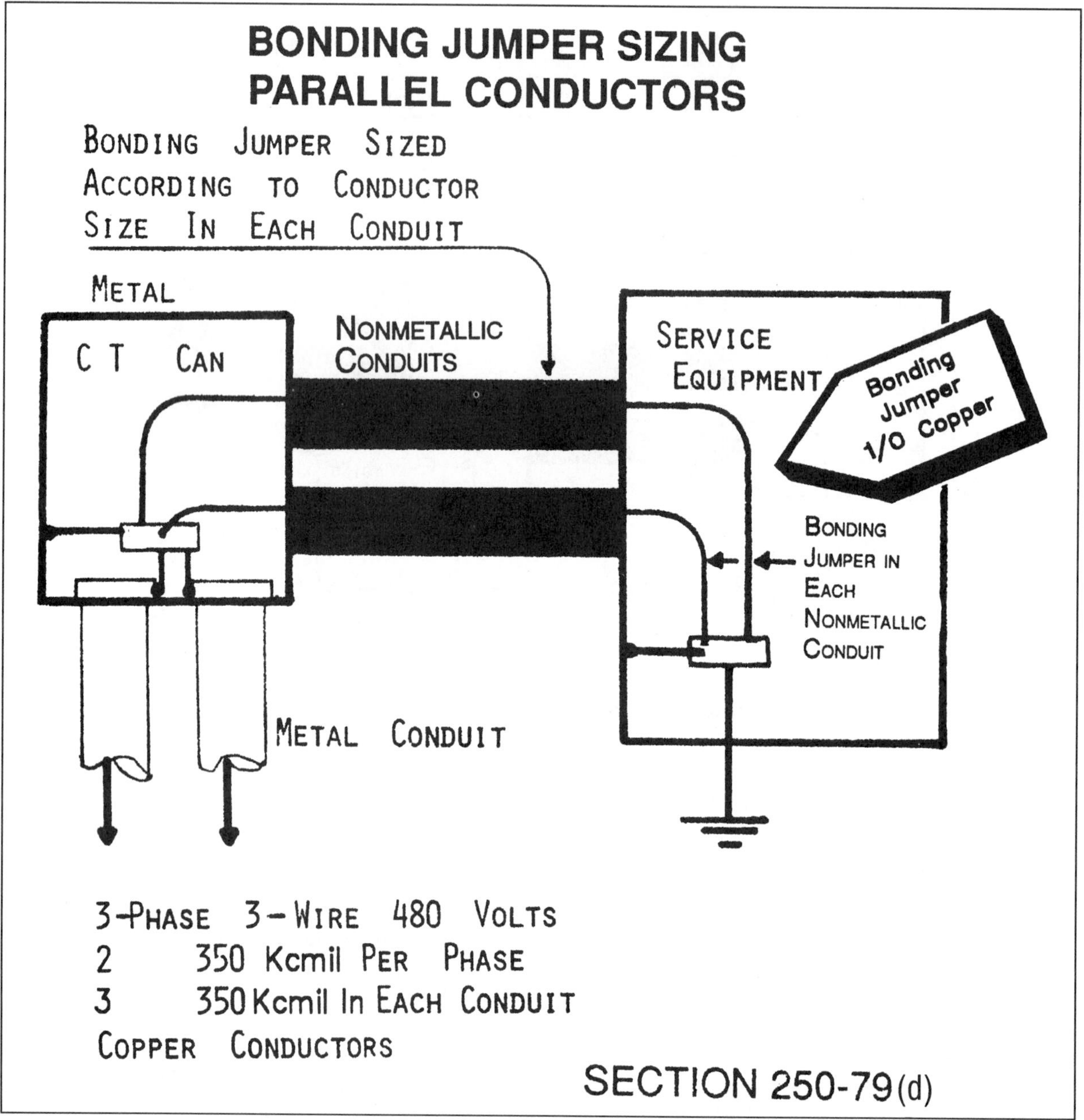

Fig. 11–22 Sizing the equipment bonding jumpers installed with 350 kcmil copper service-entrance conductors in parallel, nonmetallic raceways.

Should the service-entrance conductors be 350 kcmil copper, as in figure 11–22, *Table 250-94* requires a No. 2 copper equipment bonding jumper in each conduit. *Section 310-4* limits parallel conductors to No. 1/0 and larger, and the No. 2 copper equipment bonding jumper calculated here is smaller than No. 1/0. *Section 310-4* makes an exception when sizing the equipment grounding conductor according to *Table 250-95* but not when using *Table 250-94,* which is used to size this equipment bonding jumper. Therefore, the smallest parallel equipment grounding conductor that is permitted is the minimum size for parallel conductors—No. 1/0.

Another installation of the equipment bonding jumper with parallel conductors, when more than one metal raceway is used for service-entrance conductors, is illustrated in figure 11–23 (page 167). An individual equipment bonding

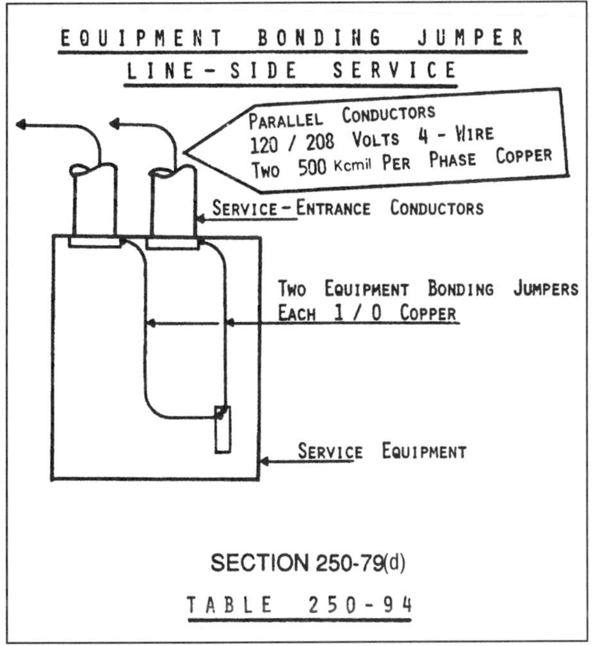

Fig. 11–23 Sizing the equipment bonding jumper for parallel service-entrance conduits using two equipment bonding jumpers.

jumper is run to each metal raceway and is sized according to the size of the service-entrance conductors in the raceway. Each metal conduit contains 500 kcmil copper conductors; therefore, the size of each of the equipment bonding jumpers is based on the 500 kcmil conductors in each conduit and is read directly from *Table 250-94*—No. 1/0 copper (figure 11–24).

Figure 11–25 illustrates the use of aluminum service-entrance conductors and a copper bonding jumper.

When the cross-sectional area of the service-entrance conductors does not exceed the

Table 250-94.
Grounding Electrode Conductor for AC Systems

Size of Largest Service-Entrance Conductor or Equivalent Area for Parallel Conductors		Size of Grounding Electrode Conductor	
Copper	Aluminum or Copper-Clad Aluminum	Copper	*Aluminum or Copper-Clad Aluminum
2 or smaller	1/0 or smaller	8	6
1 or 1/0	2/0 or 3/0	6	4
2/0 or 3/0	4/0 or 250 kcmil	4	2
Over 3/0 thru 350 kcmil	Over 250 kcmil thru 500 kcmil	2	1/0
Over 350 kcmil thru 600 kcmil	Over 500 kcmil thru 900 kcmil	1/0	3/0
Over 600 kcmil thru 1100 kcmil	Over 900 kcmil thru 1750 kcmil	2/0	4/0
Over 1100 kcmil	Over 1750 kcmil	3/0	250 kcmil

Fig. 11–24 Reading the size of the copper equipment bonding jumper shown in figure 11–23. One No. 1/0 required to each raceway.*

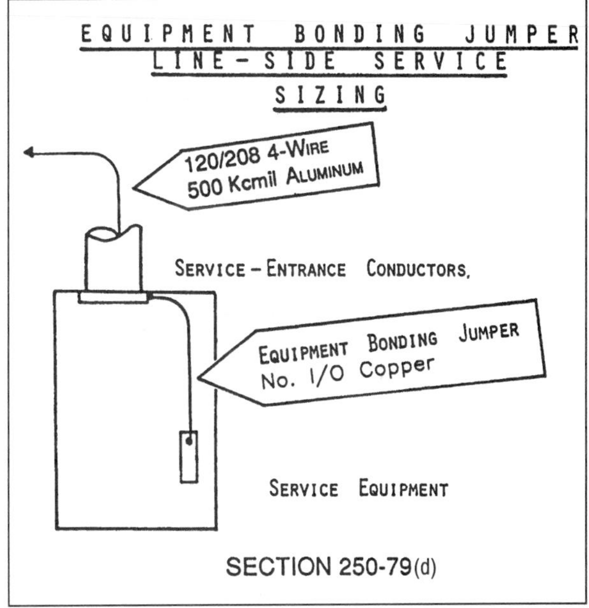

Fig. 11–25 Sizing the equipment bonding jumper for metal service-entrance raceway when aluminum service-entrance conductors are installed and a copper equipment bonding jumper is installed.

maximum listed in *Table 250-94*, the size of the bonding jumper is read directly from *Table 250-94* (figure 11–26). Read the 500 kcmil aluminum in the service-entrance conductor column and the 1/0 in the copper column for grounding electrode conductors.

Table 250-94.
Grounding Electrode Conductor for AC Systems

Size of Largest Service-Entrance Conductor or Equivalent Area for Parallel Conductors		Size of Grounding Electrode Conductor	
Copper	Aluminum or Copper-Clad Aluminum	Copper	*Aluminum or Copper-Clad Aluminum
2 or smaller	1/0 or smaller	8	6
1 or 1/0	2/0 or 3/0	6	4
2/0 or 3/0	4/0 or 250 kcmil	4	2
Over 3/0 thru 350 kcmil	Over 250 kcmil thru 500 kcmil	2	1/0
Over 350 kcmil thru 600 kcmil	Over 500 kcmil thru 900 kcmil	1/0	3/0
Over 600 kcmil thru 1100 kcmil	Over 900 kcmil thru 1750 kcmil	2/0	4/0
Over 1100 kcmil	Over 1750 kcmil	3/0	250 kcmil

Fig. 11–26 Reading the bonding jumper size directly from *Table 250-94* for service illustrated in figure 11–25.*

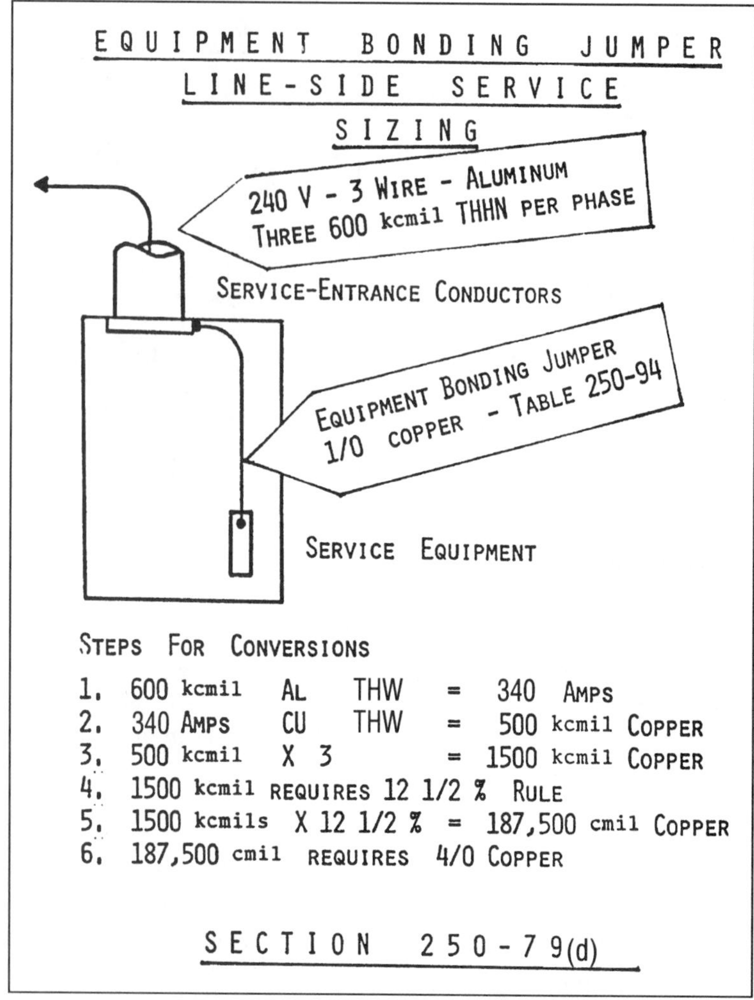

Fig. 11–27 Sizing the equipment bonding jumper for metal service-entrance raceway when aluminum service-entrance conductors are installed and a copper equipment bonding jumper is installed, using the 12½ percent rule.

Method 3 (figure 11–27) illustrates the use of a) 600 kcmil THHN aluminum with three conductors per phase connected in parallel as the service-entrance conductors, and b) a copper equipment bonding jumper. This figure illustrates the use of two different types of metal for conductors. Three times the 600 kcmil equals 1800 kcmil, which is greater than listed in *Table 250-94*.

When calculating the size of the equipment bonding jumper for this type of installation, the aluminum service-entrance conductors are assumed to be replaced with copper conductors of equal ampacity. This is accomplished in figure 11–28 (page 169) with the use of *Table 310–16*, which indicates it will require 500 kcmil THW copper to equal the ampacity of 600 kcmil THW aluminum.

The next step is to calculate the total cross-sectional area, which is 3 × 500 kcmil = 1500 kcmil. 1500 kcmil is greater than the largest conductor listed in *Table 250-94*; therefore, the 12½ percent rule applies.

$$1500 \text{ kcmil} \times 12\tfrac{1}{2}\% = 187{,}500 \text{ cmil}$$

Table 8 of Chapter 9 (figure 11–29, page 170) is used to select the next standard size conductor, which is 4/0 copper.

Figure 11–30 (page 170) illustrates a three-phase, 480-volt ungrounded service with one 750 kcmil copper conductor per phase. An

Table 310-16. Allowable Ampacities of Insulated Conductors Rated 0-2000 Volts, 60° to 90°C (140° to 194°F) Not More Than Three Current-Carrying Conductors in Raceway or Cable or Earth (Directly Buried), Based on Ambient Temperature of 30°C (86°F)

Size	Temperature Rating of Conductor. See Table 310-13.						Size
	60°C (140°F)	75°C (167°F)	90°C (194°F)	60°C (140°F)	75°C (167°F)	90°C (194°F)	
AWG kcmil	TYPES TW†, UF†	TYPES FEPW†, RH†, RHW†, THHW†, THW†, THWN†, XHHW† USE†, ZW†	TYPES TBS, SA SIS, FEP†, FEPB†, MI RHH†, RHW-2, THHN†, THHW†, THW-2†, THWN-2†, USE-2, XHH, XHHW†, XHHW-2, ZW-2	TYPES TW†, UF†	TYPES RH†, RHW†, THHW†, THW†, THWN†, XHHW†, USE†	TYPES TA, TBS, SA, SIS, THHN†, THHW†, THW-2 THWN-2, RHH†, RHW-2, USE-2 XHH, XHHW, XHHW-2, ZW-2	AWG kcmil
	COPPER			ALUMINUM COPPER-CLAD ALUMINUM			
18	....	....	14	....	....	....	....
16	....	....	18	....	....	....	....
14	20†	20†	25†	....	....	....	....
12	25†	25†	30†	20†	20†	25†	12
10	30	35†	40†	25	30†	35†	10
8	40	50	55	30	40	45	8
6	55	65	75	40	50	60	6
4	70	85	95	55	65	75	4
3	85	100	110	65	75	85	3
2	95	115	130	75	90	100	2
1	110	130	150	85	100	115	1
1/0	125	150	170	100	120	135	1/0
2/0	145	175	195	115	135	150	2/0
3/0	165	200	225	130	155	175	3/0
4/0	195	230	260	150	180	205	4/0
250	215	255	290	170	205	230	250
300	240	285	320	190	230	255	300
350	260	310	350	210	250	280	350
400	280	335	380	225	270	305	400
500	320	380	430	260	310	350	500
600	355	420	475	285	340	385	600
700	385	460	520	310	375	420	700
750	400	475	535	320	385	435	750
800	410	490	555	330	395	450	800
900	435	520	585	355	425	480	900
1000	455	545	615	375	445	500	1000
1250	495	590	665	405	485	545	1250
1500	520	625	705	435	520	585	1500
1750	545	650	735	455	545	615	1750
2000	560	665	750	470	560	630	2000

600 kcmil THW ALUMINUM 340 AMPS

340 AMPS THW COPPER 500 kcmil

Fig. 11–28 Using *Table 310-16* to select copper conductor of ampacity equal to aluminum conductor.*

equipment bonding jumper is required for ungrounded systems, the same as for grounded systems. An equipment bonding jumper is installed. The size of the equipment bonding jumper is calculated the same as any other equipment bonding jumper on the line side of the service equipment. Therefore, the size of the equipment bonding jumper in this illustration is based on the size of the service-entrance conductor and is read directly from *Table 250-94* (figure 11–31, page 170). It is required to be No. 2/0 copper.

It looks like a main bonding jumper has been installed in figure 11–30 (page 170). A point to remember about the main bonding jumper is that it is only used with a grounded system. This is an ungrounded installation. Therefore, it is an equipment bonding jumper on the line side of the service.

187,500 cmil

Table 8. Conductor Properties

Size AWG/kcmil	Area Cir. Mils	Conductors: Stranding Quantity	Conductors: Stranding Diam. in.	Conductors: Overall Diam. in.	Conductors: Overall Area in.²	DC Resistance at 75°C (167°F): Copper Uncoated ohm/kFT	DC Resistance at 75°C (167°F): Copper Coated ohm/kFT	DC Resistance at 75°C (167°F): Aluminum ohm/kFT
18	1620	1	—	0.040	0.001	7.77	8.08	12.8
18	1620	7	0.015	0.046	0.002	7.95	8.45	13.1
16	2580	1	—	0.051	0.002	4.89	5.08	8.05
16	2580	7	0.019	0.058	0.003	4.99	5.29	8.21
14	4110	1	—	0.064	0.003	3.07	3.19	5.06
14	4110	7	0.024	0.073	0.004	3.14	3.26	5.17
12	6530	1	—	0.081	0.005	1.93	2.01	3.18
12	6530	7	0.030	0.092	0.006	1.98	2.05	3.25
10	10380	1	—	0.102	0.008	1.21	1.26	2.00
10	10380	7	0.038	0.116	0.011	1.24	1.29	2.04
8	16510	1	—	0.128	0.013	0.764	0.786	1.26
8	16510	7	0.049	0.146	0.017	0.778	0.809	1.28
6	26240	7	0.061	0.184	0.027	0.491	0.510	0.808
4	41740	7	0.077	0.232	0.042	0.308	0.321	0.508
3	52620	7	0.087	0.260	0.053	0.245	0.254	0.403
2	66360	7	0.097	0.292	0.067	0.194	0.201	0.319
1	83690	19	0.066	0.332	0.087	0.154	0.160	0.253
1/0	105600	19	0.074	0.372	0.109	0.122	0.127	0.201
2/0	133100	19	0.084	0.418	0.137	0.0976	0.101	0.159
3/0	167800	19	0.094	0.470	0.173	0.0766	0.0797	0.126
4/0	211600	19	0.106	0.528	0.219	0.0608	0.0626	0.100
250	—	37	0.082	0.575	0.260	0.0515	0.0535	0.0847
300	—	37	0.090	0.630	0.312	0.0429	0.0446	0.0707
350	—	37	0.097	0.681	0.364	0.0367	0.0382	0.0605
400	—	37	0.104	0.728	0.416	0.0321	0.0331	0.0529
500	—	37	0.116	0.813	0.519	0.0258	0.0265	0.0424
600	—	61	0.099	0.893	0.626	0.0214	0.0223	0.0353
700	—	61	0.107	0.964	0.730	0.0184	0.0189	0.0303
750	—	61	0.111	0.998	0.782	0.0171	0.0176	0.0282
800	—	61	0.114	1.030	0.834	0.0161	0.0166	0.0265
900	—	61	0.122	1.094	0.940	0.0143	0.0147	0.0235
1000	—	61	0.128	1.152	1.042	0.0129	0.0132	0.0212
1250	—	91	0.117	1.284	1.305	0.0103	0.0106	0.0169
1500	—	91	0.128	1.412	1.566	0.00858	0.00883	0.0141
1750	—	127	0.117	1.526	1.829	0.00735	0.00756	0.0121
2000	—	127	0.126	1.632	2.092	0.00643	0.00662	0.0106

Fig. 11–29 Using *Table 8* to select standard wire size when cmil is calculated.*

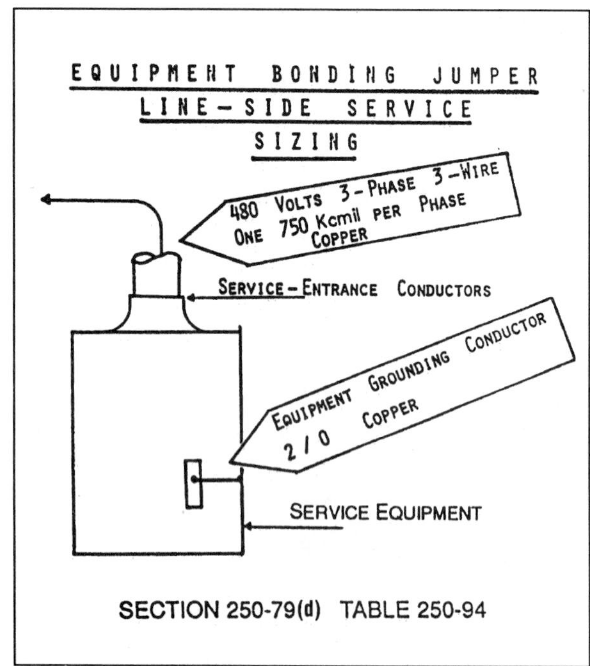

Fig. 11–30 Sizing the equipment bonding jumper for an ungrounded service.

Table 250-94. Grounding Electrode Conductor for AC Systems

Size of Largest Service-Entrance Conductor or Equivalent Area for Parallel Conductors: Copper	Size of Largest Service-Entrance Conductor or Equivalent Area for Parallel Conductors: Aluminum or Copper-Clad Aluminum	Size of Grounding Electrode Conductor: Copper	Size of Grounding Electrode Conductor: *Aluminum or Copper-Clad Aluminum
2 or smaller	1/0 or smaller	8	6
1 or 1/0	2/0 or 3/0	6	4
2/0 or 3/0	4/0 or 250 kcmil	4	2
Over 3/0 thru 350 kcmil	Over 250 kcmil thru 500 kcmil	2	1/0
Over 350 kcmil thru 600 kcmil	Over 500 kcmil thru 900 kcmil	1/0	3/0
Over 600 kcmil thru 1100 kcmil	Over 900 kcmil thru 1750 kcmil	2/0	4/0
Over 1100 kcmil	Over 1750 kcmil	3/0	250 kcmil

Fig. 11–31 Reading the size of the equipment bonding jumper shown in figure 11–30.*

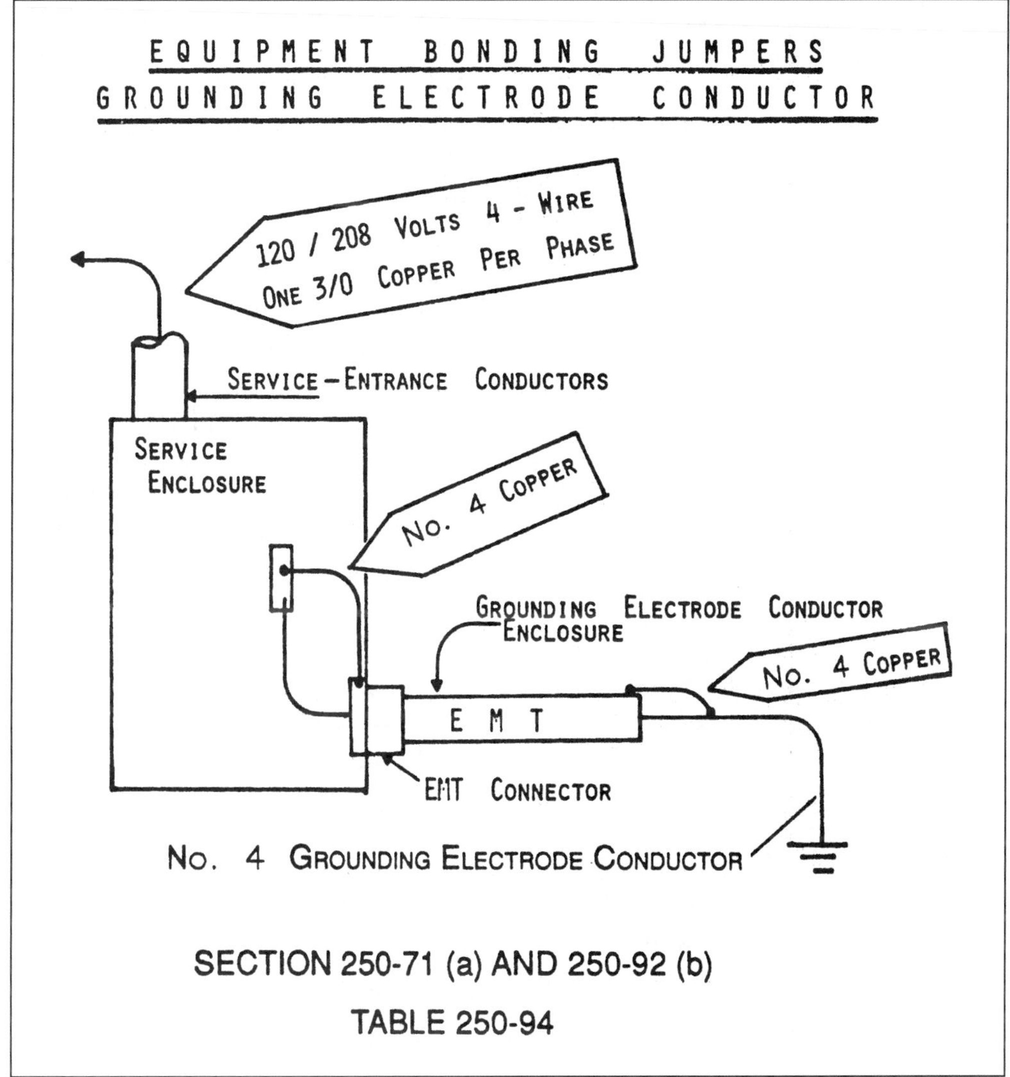

Fig. 11–32 Bonding when the grounding electrode conductor is partially protected by a metal raceway.

GROUNDING ELECTRODE CONDUCTOR ENCLOSURE BONDING

Figure 11–32 illustrates a grounding electrode conductor installed with EMT, which is used to protect part of the length of the grounding electrode conductor. The EMT is connected to the service enclosure with a shoulder-type connector with a standard locknut, which is not acceptable for maintaining continuity at the service equipment according to *Section 250-71(a)*. Therefore, the metal raceway shall be bonded at the service with an equipment bonding jumper. Figure 11–32 shows that where the metal raceway ends, the raceway is to be bonded to the grounding electrode conductor according to *Section 250-92(b)*.

Section 250-79(d) covers the sizing of the equipment bonding jumper for bonding the metal raceway enclosing the grounding electrode conductor to the grounding electrode conductor. The equipment bonding jumper is required to be equal to or larger than the enclosed grounding electrode conductor, as illustrated in figure 11–32. The grounding electrode conductor and all bonding jumpers used with the grounding electrode conductor are considered to be on the line side of the service disconnecting means.

Using *Table 250-94*, 3/0 copper service-entrance conductors are required to have a No. 4 copper grounding electrode conductor. The equipment bonding jumpers used with the equipment grounding conductor are the same size as

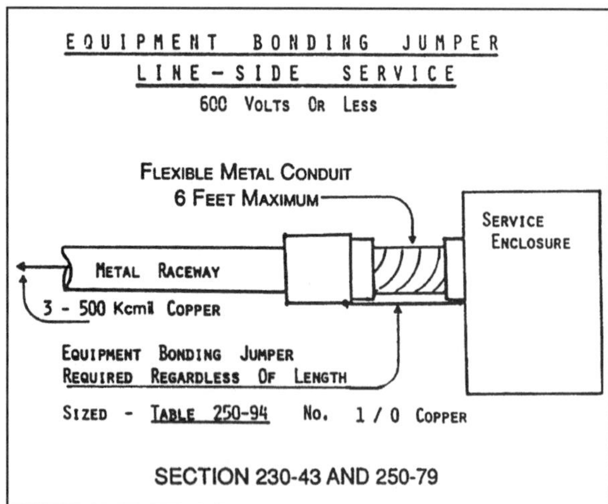

Fig. 11–33 Any length of flexible metal conduit is required to be bonded when it is part of the service-entrance raceway.

the grounding electrode conductor, or the equipment bonding jumper may be larger.

FLEXIBLE METAL CONDUIT IN SERVICE-ENTRANCE RACEWAY

Figure 11–33 illustrates the use of flexible metal conduit installed as part of the metal raceway for the service-entrance conductors. The same illustration could be used for the installation of liquidtight flexible metal conduit. *Section 230-43* permits the use of flexible metal conduit and liquidtight flexible metal conduit between the service-entrance raceway and the service equipment or in any part of the service raceway, provided it has an equipment bonding jumper installed with it. *Section 250-79* lists other installation and sizing requirements. The following are the restrictions on the installation of either of these flexible metal conduits:

1. Regardless of the length of flexible metal conduit when it is installed as part of the service equipment or raceway, there shall be a bonding jumper installed around it (*Section 230-43*).
2. It cannot be over 6 feet in length when installed between raceways.
3. It cannot be over 6 feet in length when installed between raceway and service equipment.

Comment: The maximum length of the flexible metal conduit allowed is 6 feet. Should a 4-foot length of flexible metal conduit be used, an equipment bonding jumper would also have to be installed. When flexible metal conduit is used as any part of the service-entrance conductor's raceway, it shall have an equipment bonding jumper installed with it. It can be installed inside or outside the raceway.

The size of the equipment bonding jumper is calculated according to the size of the service-entrance conductors. In this case the raceway contains a 500 kcmil copper conductor; therefore, the size of the equipment bonding jumper is read directly from *Table 250-94* and is required to be No. 1/0 copper.

BONDING OTHER THAN AT SERVICE

Section 250-75 is almost a summary of other sections of the Code. It applies to maintaining continuity of the equipment grounding conductor. The following is an outline of *Section 250-75* and the many things it covers, especially when any of the following items are used as the equipment bonding jumper, with or without the use of a supplementary equipment grounding conductor.

1. They shall be effectively bonded together.
2. They shall assure electrical continuity.
3. They shall have the ampacity to conduct safely any fault current that might be imposed on them.
4. They shall make a good electrical contact by having the contact surface free of any nonconductive paint or similar coatings. Unless the fittings used are so designed, it makes it unnecessary to remove the nonconductive material.

Those items used as an equipment bonding jumper are:

1. Metal raceways
2. Metal cable trays
3. Armored cable
4. Metal-sheathed cable
5. Metal enclosures
6. Metal frames

7. Metal fittings
8. Other noncurrent-carrying parts that serve as equipment grounding conductors

Bonding Prepunched Knockouts

When knockouts are prepunched in a box or equipment enclosure and all the knockouts are not used, there is concern about continuity and the amount of cross-sectional area of the punched metal remaining. Bonding around concentric and eccentric knockouts in enclosures downstream from the service is required due to the higher voltage; it is also required in hazardous locations because a greater hazard is posed by the possibility of poor continuity. The Code addresses these concerns at three points. These are:

1. At the service, as illustrated in figure 11–12 (page 162), locknuts and bushings are not depended on for continuity; an equipment bonding jumper is required regardless of system voltage.
2. *Section 250-76* addresses prepunched knockout bonding, other than at the service, when all knockouts are not used. When the system is over 250 volts to ground, locknuts and bushings are not to be depended upon for grounding continuity. A bonding jumper is required to assure continuity of the ground path. When the enclosure or box with the concentric or eccentric knockouts is tested and listed for use without bonding, the exception permits it to be used without bonding.

   Examples of common distribution systems where the voltage exceeds 250 volts to ground and equipment bonding jumpers are required to be installed are:

   - Three-phase, four-wire, wye, 277/480 volts
   - Three-phase, three-wire, delta, 480 volts
3. This is not listed as such, but for other than at the service for system and circuits of less than 240 volts to ground, locknuts and bushings are permitted for equipment bonding of metal raceway enclosures to the equipment enclosures.

Examples of common distribution systems where the voltage does not exceed 250 volts to ground and locknuts and bushings are permitted for continuity of the equipment grounding conductor are:

- Single phase, 120/240 volts
- Three-phase, four-wire, wye, 120/208 volts
- Three-phase, four-wire, delta, 120/240 volts
- Three-phase, four-wire, wye, 220/380 volts
- Three-phase, three-wire, delta, 240 volts
- Three-phase, three-wire, wye, 208 volts

Where prepunched knockouts are completely removed (figure 11–34) or there are no prepunched knockouts and knockouts are made by some other means, the voltage is not mentioned and the equipment bonding is permitted by *Section 250-72* to be accomplished by the use of the following:

1. Threadless couplings
2. Cable connectors with metal-sheathed cable
3. Two locknuts—one inside and one outside the enclosure for rigid metal conduit or intermediate metal conduit
4. Fittings that seat firmly against the enclosure such as electrical metallic tubing connectors and cable connectors (this basic rule illustrated in figure 11–35, page 174)

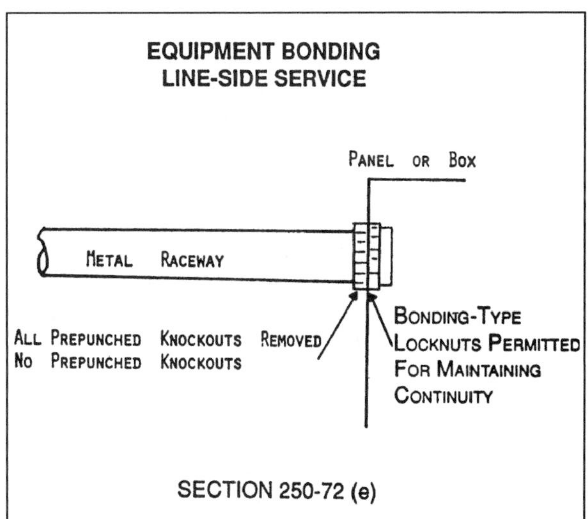

Fig. 11–34 A bonding-type locknut is permitted for line-side service continuity.

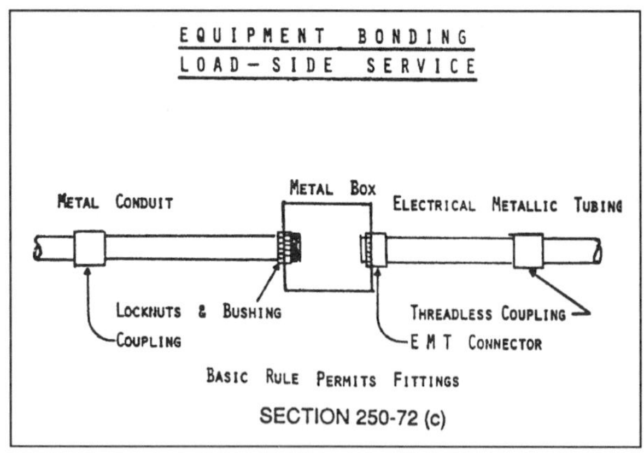

Fig. 11–35 On the load side of the service equipment, the basic rule permits the use of listed fittings for grounding continuity.

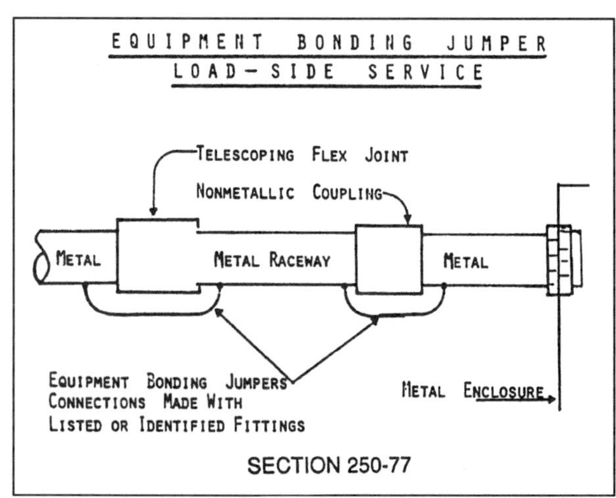

Fig. 11–36 An equipment bonding jumper is required when there are loose fittings in a metal raceway.

Bonding Loose-Fitting Sections

At any point where there is not a firm metal-to-metal contact between the two parts of a metal raceway system, an equipment bonding jumper shall be installed (figure 11–36) as required by *Section 250-77.* The equipment bonding jumper may be installed inside or outside a raceway or an enclosure (figure 11–37). When the equipment bonding jumper is installed

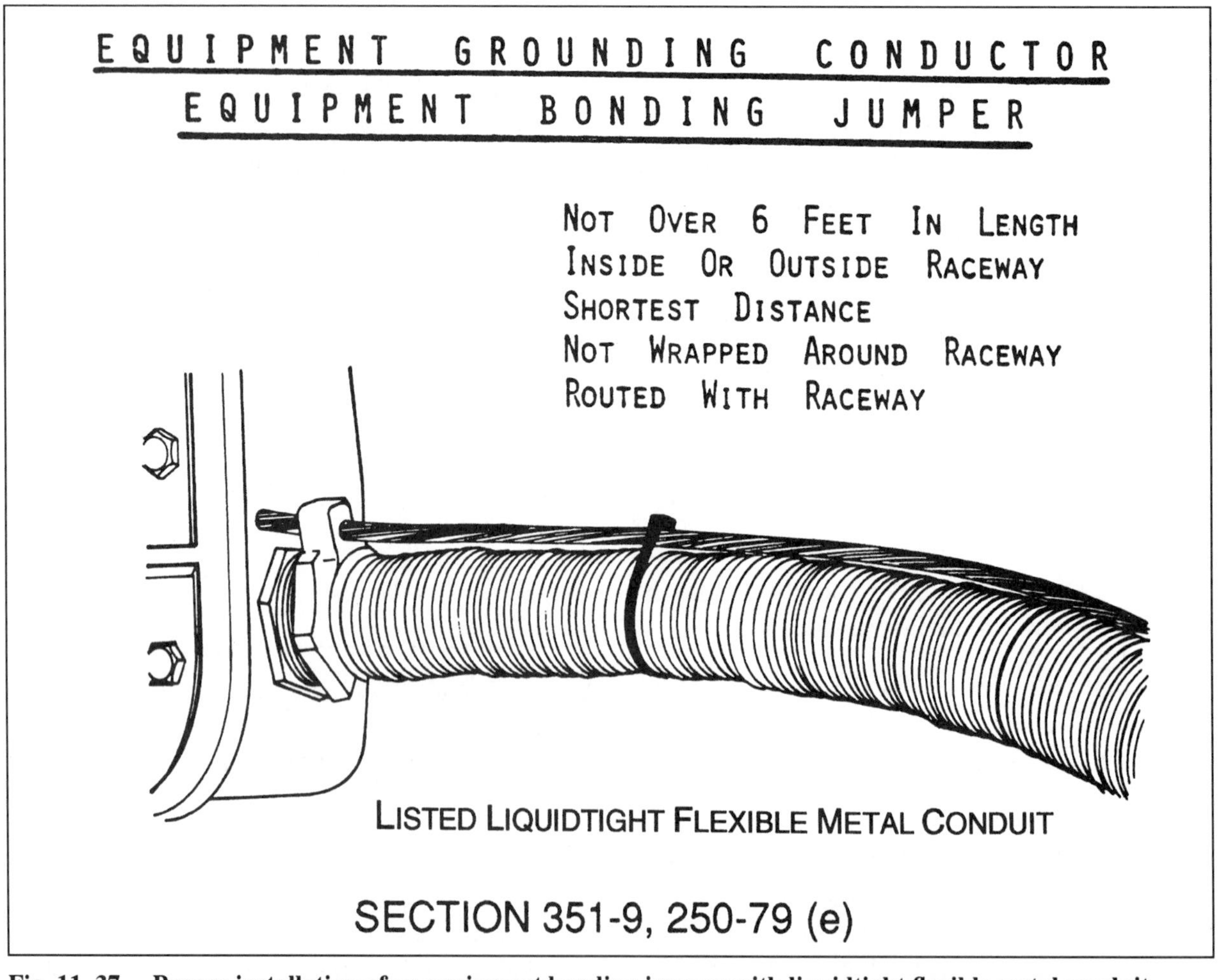

EQUIPMENT GROUNDING CONDUCTOR
EQUIPMENT BONDING JUMPER

NOT OVER 6 FEET IN LENGTH
INSIDE OR OUTSIDE RACEWAY
SHORTEST DISTANCE
NOT WRAPPED AROUND RACEWAY
ROUTED WITH RACEWAY

LISTED LIQUIDTIGHT FLEXIBLE METAL CONDUIT

SECTION 351-9, 250-79 (e)

Fig. 11–37 Proper installation of an equipment bonding jumper with liquidtight flexible metal conduit.

outside the enclosure, the equipment bonding jumper shall:

1. not exceed 6 feet and
2. be routed with the raceway or enclosure.

Bonding Metal Piping Systems

Interior metal water piping systems are always required to be bonded to the service equipment (figure 11–38). In buildings of multiple occupancy (figure 11–39) where the water piping is part metal and part plastic, the exception to *Section 250-80(a)* DOES permit metallic sections of the water piping to be bonded to an enclosure that is grounded.

Piping other than the water piping that might become energized is required by *Section 250-80(b)* to be bonded to something that is effectively grounded. The section permits any of these piping systems to be bonded to:

1. the service equipment enclosure,
2. the grounded conductor at the service,
3. the grounding electrode conductor,
4. to one or more of the grounding electrodes used.

All of the installation requirements of *Section 250-92(a)* and *(b)* for the installation of an equipment grounding conductor are applicable to the installation of this bonding jumper. These include the protection and support of the conductor, as well as proper continuity and bonding of the metal raceway when it is used to protect the conductor.

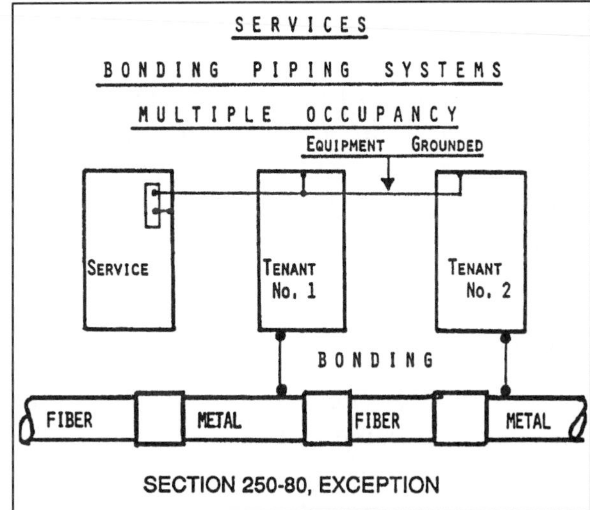

Fig. 11–39 An exception to the basic rule for bonding piping systems to service in multifamily dwellings with metal and nonmetal water piping.

Question: Does this include the gas piping?

Answer: By the use of the phrase "which may become energized" in *Section 250-80(b)*, yes. It could include the gas piping. If it might become energized, it should be grounded. If there is a remote possibility the gas piping will become energized, it need not be grounded.

Figure 11–40 illustrates a gas furnace with electrical controls. It is now possible for the gas line to the furnace to become energized by way of the electrical controls. The metal furnace would have to be grounded because it contains electrical equipment. In the process of grounding the furnace, the gas line is grounded. *Section 250-80(b)* permits this to be used as a grounding method. The same application would hold true

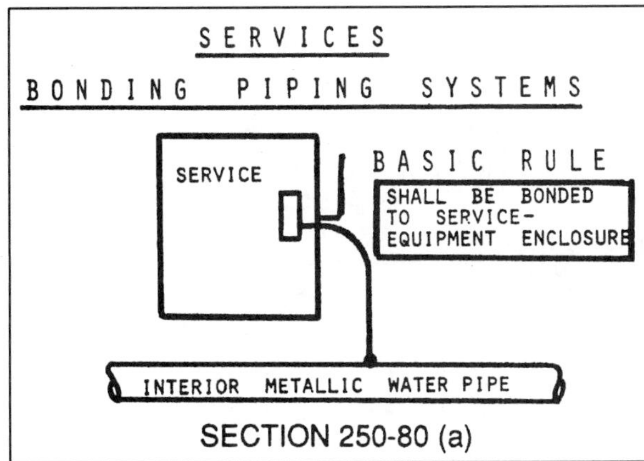

Fig. 11–38 Basic rule for bonding piping systems to service.

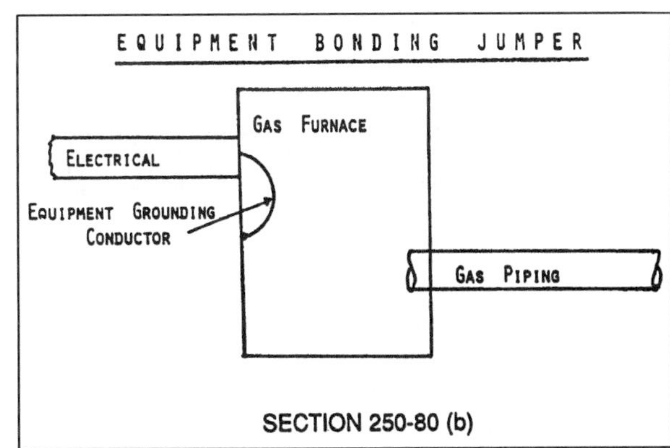

Fig. 11–40 Gas piping system is grounded through the metal continuity of the furnace and an equipment grounding conductor.

for a gas dryer with an electric motor, a gas range with an electric light, and/or a receptacle or a gas heater with an electric blower. However, the FPN to *Section 250-80(b)* contains a good suggestion. It recommends bonding all piping and metal air ducts within the premises for additional safety.

STRUCTURAL BONDING STEEL

Exposed, interior, interconnected structural steel building frame that is not intentionally grounded and may become energized is required to be bonded to ground by *Section 250-80(c)*. The bond may be made to the service equipment enclosure, the grounded conductor at the service, the grounding electrode conductor, or the grounding electrode. The bonding jumper is sized according to *Table 250-94*. This bonding jumper is sized as being on the load side of the service disconnect means. Figure 11-41 illustrates a service with 4/0 copper conductors and a No. 2 bonding jumper.

This requirement is directed at a structure, built on a concrete slab, with an interconnected steel framework that will not be grounded unless it is intentionally grounded. A single steel beam supported on wood posts in a dwelling unit is not considered interconnected structural steel and is not required to be bonded to ground. Beams in churches and like buildings that are not part of the interconnected structural steel forming the building frame are not considered likely to become energized, and are not required to be bonded to ground.

SIZING LOAD SIDE OF SERVICE BONDING JUMPERS

On the load side of the service, the equipment bonding jumpers are also part of the equipment grounding conductor. Therefore, they are sized the same way the equipment grounding conductor is sized. *Section 250-79(d)* requires this, according to *Table 250-95*.

Figure 11–42 illustrates a metal conduit being used for a feeder. The conduit enters the distribution switchgear through a concrete floor. The metal conduit is an equipment grounding conductor and needs to be bonded to the equipment ground bar in the switchboard. The necessary equipment bonding jumper is sized according to the overcurrent protective device protecting conductors in that conduit. *Table 250-95* (figure 11–43, page 177) shows that a 200-amp overcurrent protective device requires a No. 6 copper or No. 4 aluminum equipment bonding jumper.

Figure 11–44 (page 177) illustrates parallel conductors installed in two separate conduits. The copper equipment bonding jumper is one continuous conductor connected to each metal conduit. The size is read directly from *Table 250-95* (figure 11–45, page 177). An 800-amp overcurrent protective device requires a No. 1/0 copper equipment bonding jumper.

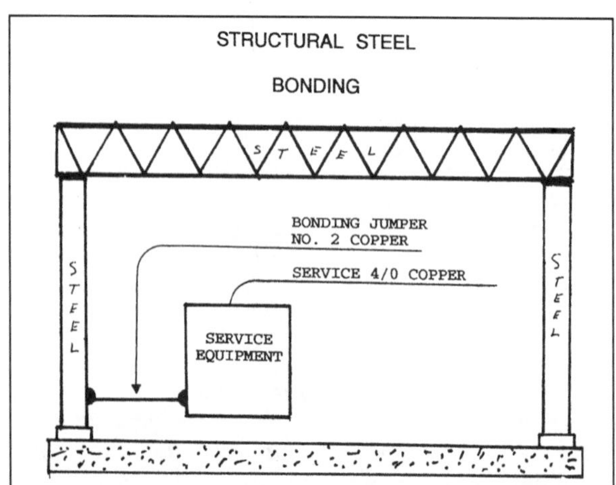

Fig. 11–41 Structural steel bonding.

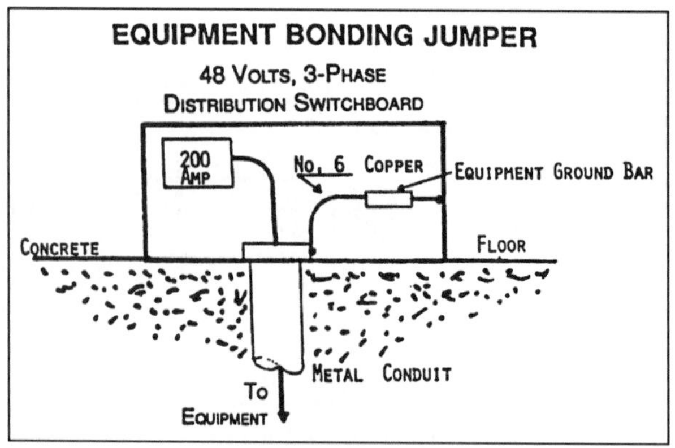

Fig. 11–42 Sizing the equipment bonding jumper for a feeder conduit used as an equipment grounding conductor.

Table 250-95. Minimum Size Equipment Grounding Conductors for Grounding Raceway and Equipment

Rating or Setting of Automatic Overcurrent Device in Circuit Ahead of Equipment, Conduit, etc., Not Exceeding (Amperes)	Size	
	Copper Wire No.	Aluminum or Copper-Clad Aluminum Wire No.*
15	14	12
20	12	10
30	10	8
40	10	8
60	10	8
100	8	6
200	6	4
300	4	2
400	3	1
500	2	1/0
600	1	2/0
800	1/0	3/0
1000	2/0	4/0
1200	3/0	250 kcmil
1600	4/0	350 "
2000	250 kcmil	400 "
2500	350 "	600 "
3000	400 "	600 "
4000	500 "	800 "
5000	700 "	1200 "
6000	800 "	1200 "

Fig. 11–43 Reading *Table 250-95* for the size of the equipment grounding conductor shown in figure 11–42.*

Table 250-95. Minimum Size Equipment Grounding Conductors for Grounding Raceway and Equipment

Rating or Setting of Automatic Overcurrent Device in Circuit Ahead of Equipment, Conduit, etc., Not Exceeding (Amperes)	Size	
	Copper Wire No.	Aluminum or Copper-Clad Aluminum Wire No.*
15	14	12
20	12	10
30	10	8
40	10	8
60	10	8
100	8	6
200	6	4
300	4	2
400	3	1
500	2	1/0
600	1	2/0
800	1/0	3/0
1000	2/0	4/0
1200	3/0	250 kcmil
1600	4/0	350 "
2000	250 kcmil	400 "
2500	350 "	600 "
3000	400 "	600 "
4000	500 "	800 "
5000	700 "	1200 "
6000	800 "	1200 "

* See installation restrictions in Section 250-92(a).

Fig. 11–45 Reading the size of the bonding jumper shown in figure 11–44.*

A similar situation is illustrated in figure 11–46. Two separate copper equipment bonding jumpers, one from each metal conduit, are installed. The conductors in each conduit are backed up by an 800-amp breaker; therefore, each must be protected with a No. 1/0 copper equipment bonding jumper. Either installation, that shown in figure 11–44 or the one shown in figure 11–46, is permitted.

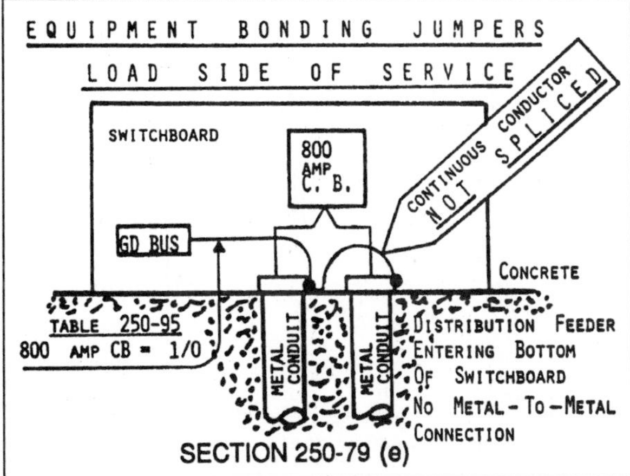

Fig. 11–44 Sizing a single equipment bonding jumper used for bonding two metal enclosures containing a parallel feeder.

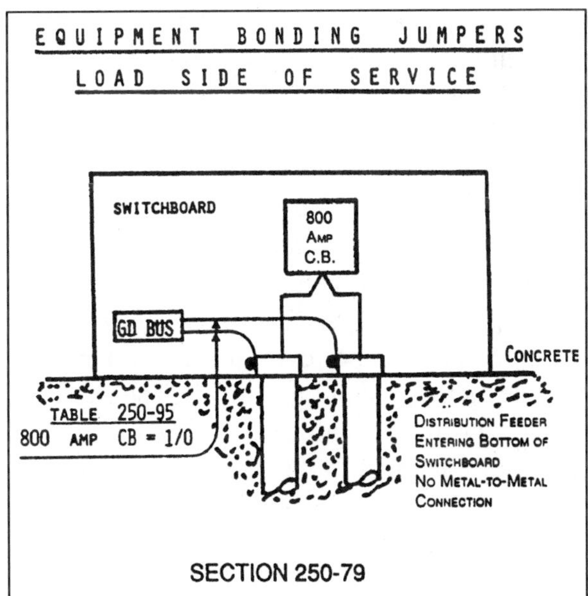

Fig. 11–46 Sizing two equipment bonding jumpers used for bonding two metal enclosures containing a parallel feeder.

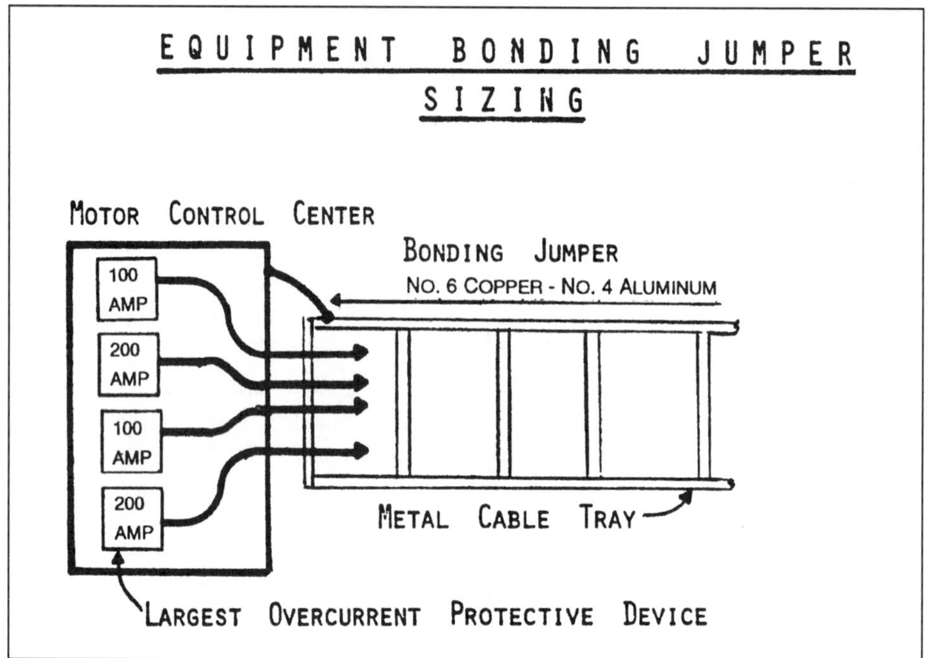

Fig. 11–47 Cable tray bonding to a metal enclosure is sized according to the largest overcurrent protective device protecting conductors installed in the cable tray.

Figure 11–47 illustrates a copper equipment bonding jumper installed to maintain continuity between a cable tray and a switchboard. The equipment bonding jumper is sized according to the largest overcurrent device protecting any cable in the cable tray. In this case the largest overcurrent protective device is a 200-amp breaker. The size of the equipment bonding jumper is read directly from *Table 250-95* and is No. 6 copper or No. 4 aluminum (figure 11–48).

Figure 11–49 (page 179) illustrates an equipment bonding jumper used in conjunction with flexible metal conduit (greenfield). The circuit is protected with a 60-amp overcurrent device. The size of the equipment grounding conductor is read directly from *Table 250-95* (figure 11–50, page 179), and is No. 10 copper or No. 8 aluminum.

Table 250-95. Minimum Size Equipment Grounding Conductors for Grounding Raceway and Equipment

Rating or Setting of Automatic Overcurrent Device in Circuit Ahead of Equipment, Conduit, etc., Not Exceeding (Amperes)	Size	
	Copper Wire No.	Aluminum or Copper-Clad Aluminum Wire No.*
15	14	12
20	12	10
30	10	8
40	10	8
60	10	8
100	8	6
200	6	4
300	4	2
400	3	1
500	2	1/0
600	1	2/0
800	1/0	3/0
1000	2/0	4/0
1200	3/0	250 kcmil
1600	4/0	350 "
2000	250 kcmil	400 "
2500	350 "	600 "
3000	400 "	600 "
4000	500 "	800 "
5000	700 "	1200 "
6000	800 "	1200 "

* See installation restrictions in Section 250-92(a).

Fig. 11–48 Reading the size of the equipment bonding jumper shown in figure 11–47.*

BONDING GROUNDING ELECTRODE SYSTEMS

The telephone company, the cable TV company, and the computer companies often feel they should have an isolated grounding electrode. However, this is not permitted by the Code.

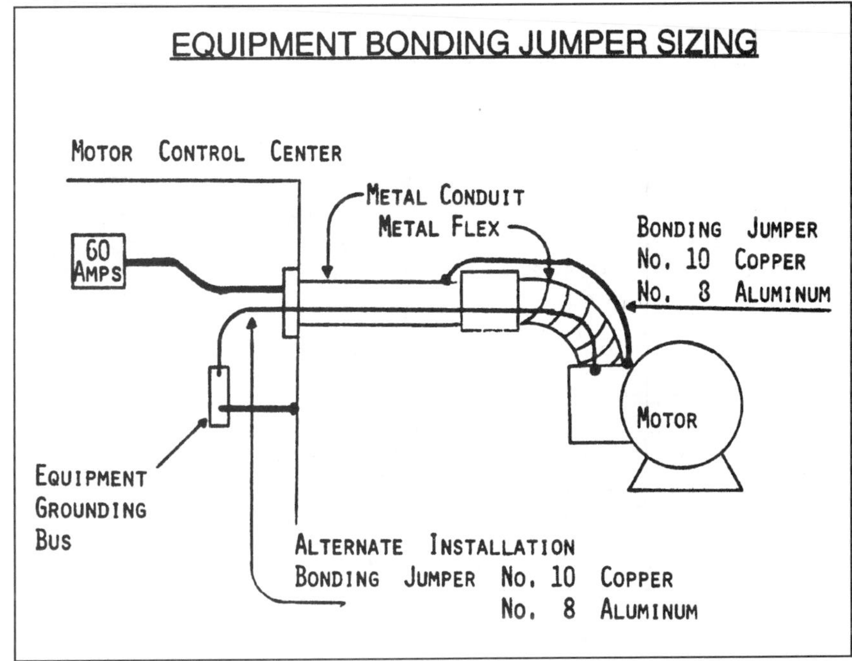

Fig. 11–49 Sizing an equipment bonding jumper used with flexible metal conduit.

More often than not, the telephone company seeks out the existing grounding electrode system and bonds to it. The cable TV company very often drives a ground rod of their own and establishes a separate grounding electrode system. Their reason is that the neutral feeds back into their system. This is possible but there is equipment that can be installed that will prevent a neutral feedback.

The computer people want to establish their own isolated grounding electrode system and not be connected to the premises grounding electrode system. Their reason is that the power system's electricity is too dirty and too noisy.

The Code permits these entities to establish their own grounding electrode system, but no matter how many grounding electrode systems are established, they shall all be bonded together.

Figure 11–51 (page 180) illustrates three separate grounding electrodes established. There is a potential difference between each of the electrodes and there is an impedance between each of the electrodes when there is potential difference. There is a hazard and there is current flow.

Table 250-95. Minimum Size Equipment Grounding Conductors for Grounding Raceway and Equipment

Rating or Setting of Automatic Overcurrent Device in Circuit Ahead of Equipment, Conduit, etc., Not Exceeding (Amperes)	Size	
	Copper Wire No.	Aluminum or Copper-Clad Aluminum Wire No.*
15	14	12
20	12	10
30	10	8
40	10	8
60	10	8
100	8	6
200	6	4
300	4	2
400	3	1
500	2	1/0
600	1	2/0
800	1/0	3/0
1000	2/0	4/0
1200	3/0	250 kcmil
1600	4/0	350 "
2000	250 kcmil	400 "
2500	350 "	600 "
3000	400 "	600 "
4000	500 "	800 "
5000	700 "	1200 "
6000	800 "	1200 "

Fig. 11–50 Reading the size of the equipment bonding jumper shown in figure 11–49.*

*Reprinted with permission from NFPA 70-1996, the National Electrical Code®, Copyright © 1995, National Fire Protection Association, Quincy, Massachusetts 02269. This reprinted material is not the complete and official position of the National Fire Protection Association, on the referenced subject, which is represented only by the standard in its entirety.

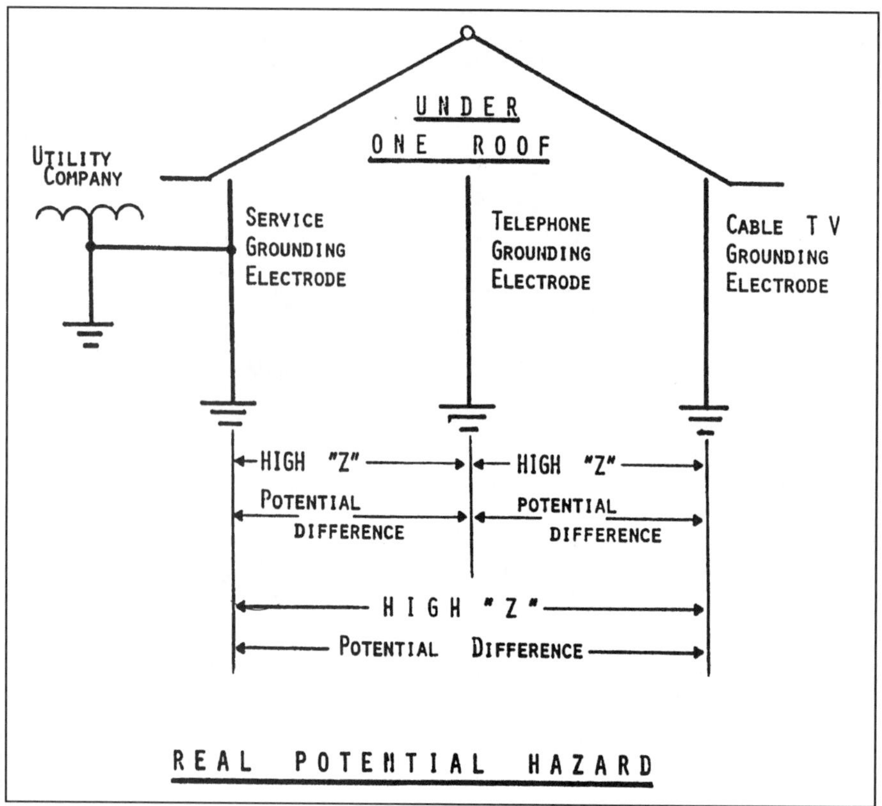

Fig. 11–51 Bonding grounding electrodes when more than one is installed.

A simple Ohm's law calculation might be:

The impedance between two of the electrodes is 200 ohms.

There is a half-amp trickle of current flow.

Ohm's law E = I Z
E = .5 × 200
E = 100 volts

Under fault, lightning, or surge conditions, the current value could increase, Ohm's law would still hold true, and the voltage could be extremely high. When the separate grounding electrodes are not connected together, a very dangerous and hazardous condition is built into the system.

When more than one electrode system is installed, *Section 250-81* requires all grounding electrodes to be bonded together. *Section 250-71(b)* (figure 11–52) requires that a means of bonding be made available. *Section 250-71(b)* sets the requirements for bonding to other systems.

1. The purpose is to maintain zero potential between all metal equipment enclosures.
2. The availability of a grounding means for intersystem grounding is required for all installations, including mobile homes.

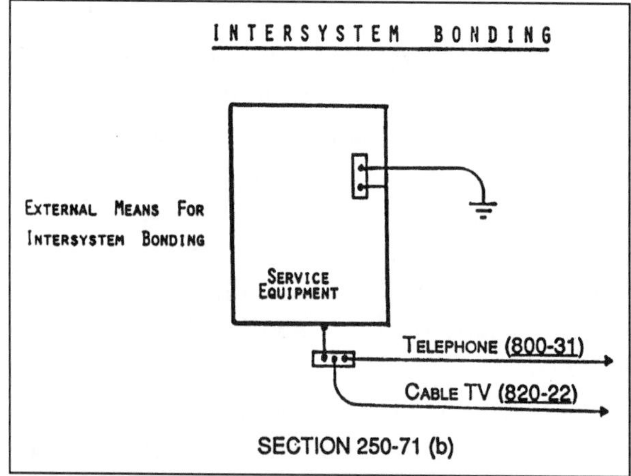

Fig. 11–52 An external means is provided for intersystem bonding.

3. The means provided shall be external to the enclosure. The means shall be accessible.
4. It shall be provided by one of the following means:
   a. Exposed metallic service raceway,
   b. Exposed grounding electrode conductor,
   c. Approved means for external connection of a bonding or grounding conductor to the service raceway or equipment.

The FPN No. 1 to *Section 250-71(b)* (figure 11–53) suggests that the bonding connection be:

1. No. 6 copper or other corrosion resistant material
2. At least 6 inches long
3. Bonded to the service raceway or equipment at one end
4. Accessible on the outside of the wall of the building

BONDING RECEPTACLES

Figure 11–54 illustrates the basic rule in *Section 250-74* for bonding the equipment grounding connection to the grounded metal box. It requires the use of an equipment bonding jumper to bond the receptacle grounding terminal to the metal box.

Figure 11–55 illustrates Exception No. 1 to the basic rule. The exception allows the metal yoke of the receptacle to be used as part of the equipment grounding conductor. Note that the yoke must be listed or identified for that purpose and the box is surface mounted. Exception No. 2 permits a yoke designed and listed for the purpose and the supporting screws to establish continuity for equipment grounding between the yoke and flush type boxes..

Figure 11–56 (page 182) illustrates the exception contained within Exception No. 1. This exception prohibits the use of a cover-mounted receptacle unless the box and cover combination

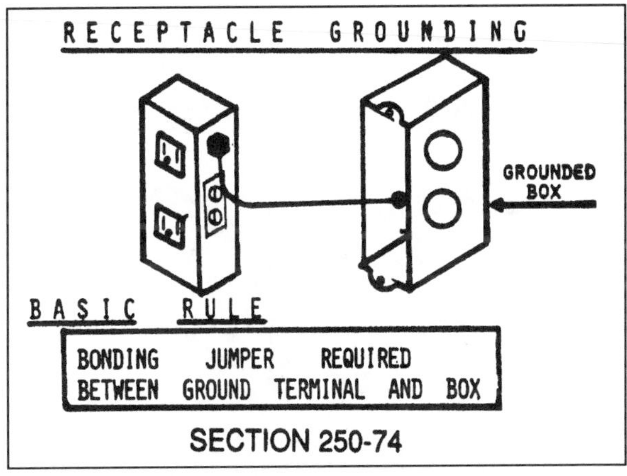

Fig. 11–54 Basic rule for bonding the equipment grounding connection to a receptacle.

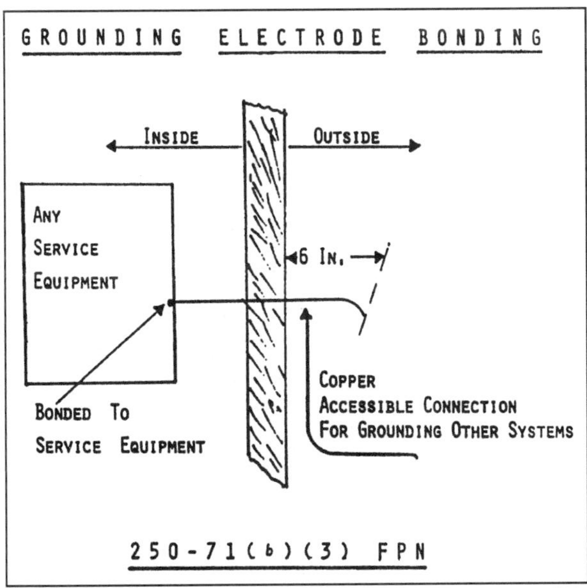

Fig. 11–53 Suggested accessible connection for intersystem grounding.

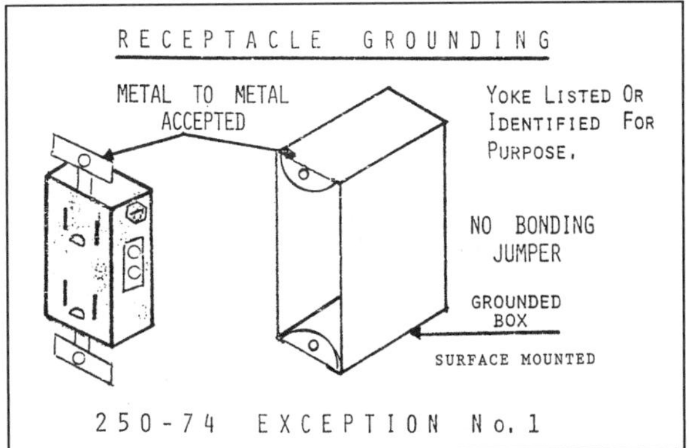

Fig. 11–55 Exception No. 1 to the basic rule for bonding the equipment grounding connection to a receptacle.

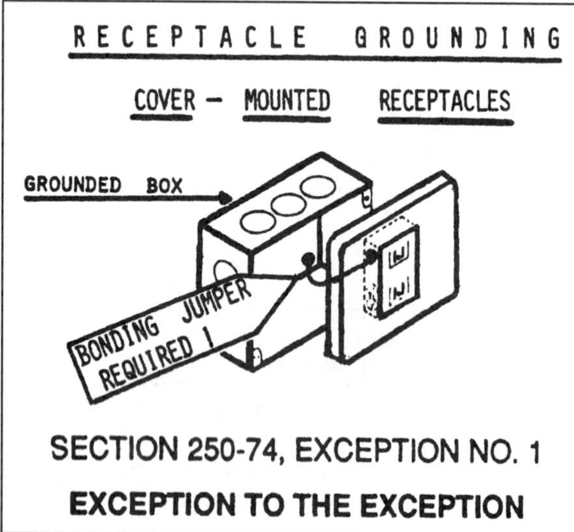

Fig. 11–56 An exception to the exception to the basic rule for bonding the equipment grounding connection to a receptacle.

are listed as providing satisfactory ground continuity between the box and the receptacle.

BONDING LIGHTNING ROD CONDUCTORS AND ELECTRODES

Section 250-46 requires electrical equipment to be kept clear of lightning rod conductors (figure 11–57). When metal raceways, equipment enclosures, metal frames of electrical equipment, or other noncurrent-carrying parts of electrical equipment have less than 6 feet of clearance between them and any lightning rod conductors, the equipment and the lightning rod conductor shall be bonded together. The bonding jumper is required by *Section 250-46* to be installed at the point the metal raceway or enclosure and the lightning rod conductor are 6 feet or closer together.

Reason: This prevents a flashover (arcing contact) between the lightning rod conductor and the metal enclosing current-carrying equipment. A lightning strike carries with it extremely high voltage and builds up an extremely high voltage between metal and the lightning rod conductors. This high voltage can cause a flashover and result in considerable damage.

Figure 11–58 illustrates electrical equipment installed less than 6 feet from a lightning rod conductor and shows that an equipment bonding jumper is required. It would be sized as an equipment bonding jumper. In the illustration, the panel close to the lightning rod conductor is protected by a 400-amp breaker. *Table*

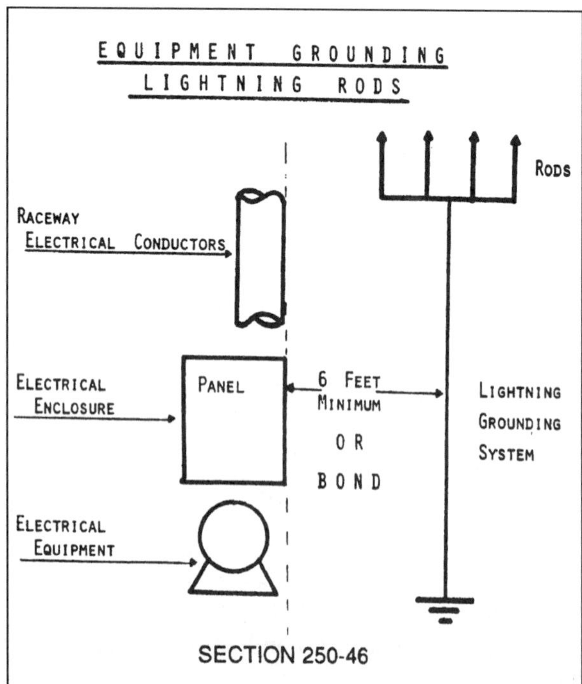

Fig. 11–57 Electrical equipment must be kept clear of lightning rod conductors.

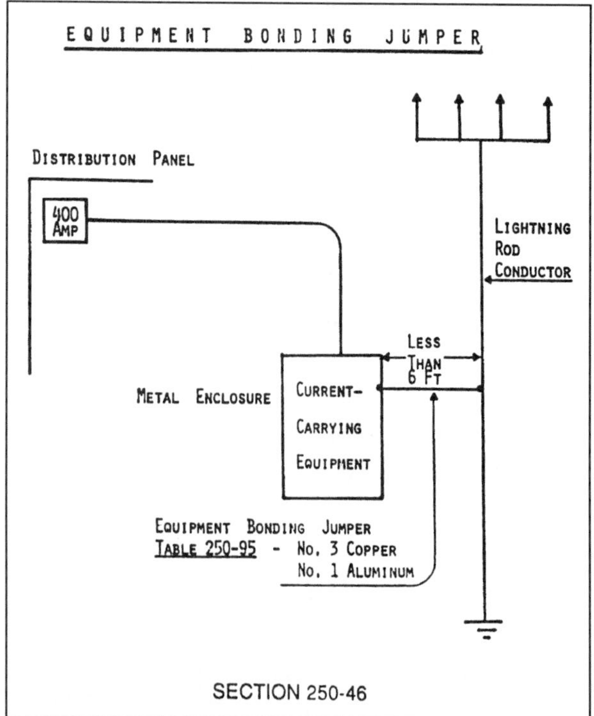

Fig. 11–58 An equipment bonding jumper is required when the metal enclosure for electrical equipment is installed within 6 feet or less of a lightning rod conductor.

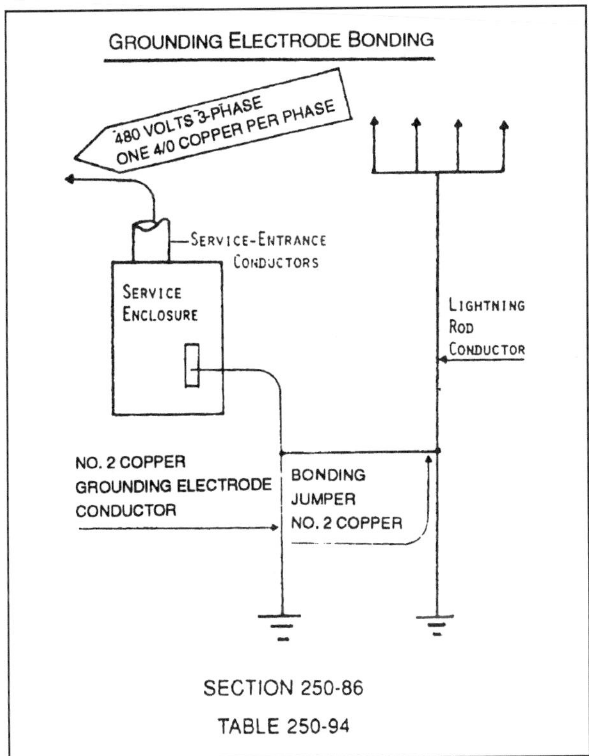

Fig. 11–59 Bonding the service grounding electrode and the lightning grounding electrode together is permitted.

250-95 requires a No. 3 copper or No. 1 aluminum equipment bonding jumper.

Figure 11–59 illustrates the service grounding electrode and the lightning grounding electrode being connected together with a bonding jumper. This bonding jumper is part of the grounding electrode conductor and is the same size as the grounding electrode conductor.

Establishing an Equipotential Plane in an Agricultural Building

Figure 11–60 illustrates the problem that occurs in agricultural buildings used for housing livestock. When wire mesh or other metal conducting materials are buried in the concrete, a potential difference can be detected between metal items in the vicinity. The illustration uses voltmeters to indicate that a potential difference can exist. When cattle stand on the concrete and brush against or come in contact with any metal surface, they feel a "tingle voltage," which is actually a low-voltage electric shock and could alter animal behavior or productivity. To combat the "tingle voltage," an "equipotential plane" is created by bonding all conductive materials in the building together. A definition of *equipotential plane* is given in *Section 547-8(b)*.

Quote – "An equipotential plane is an area where a wire mesh or other conductive elements are embedded in concrete, bonded to all adjacent conductive equipment,

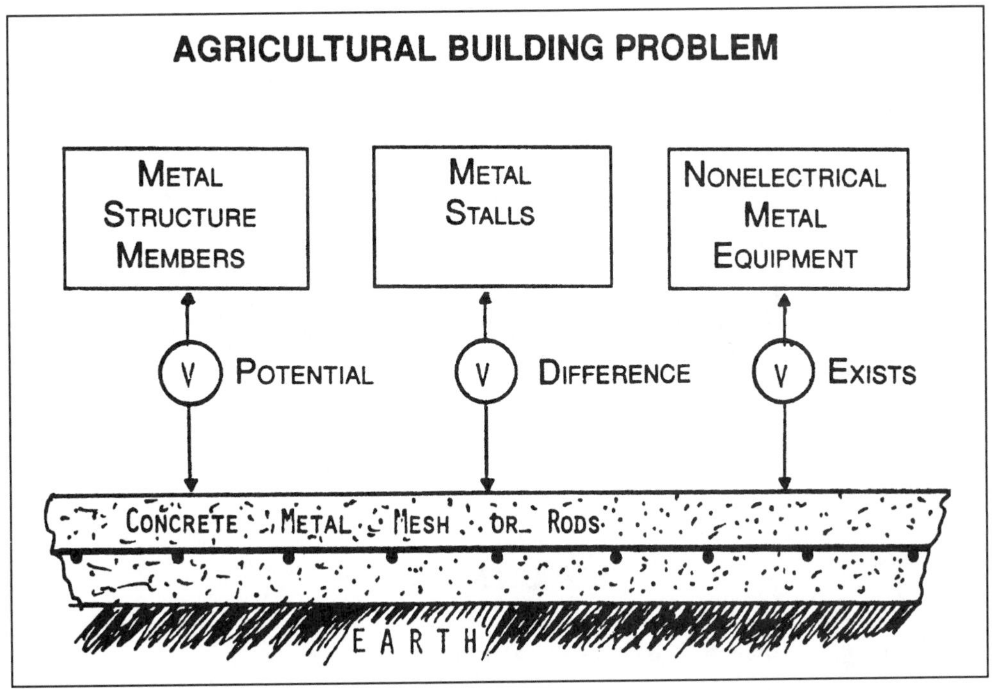

Fig. 11–60 A problem with potential difference in agricultural buildings.

structures, or surfaces and connected to the electrical grounding system to prevent a difference in voltage from developing within the plane."*

Figure 11–61 illustrates the equipotential plane with the following points, as required by *Section 547-8(b):*

1. All metal surfaces bonded to metal mesh or rods in concrete
2. No. 8 copper bonding conductor
3. Insulated, covered, or bare conductor
4. Bonded to building grounding electrode system
5. Connections made by means of pressure connectors or clamps of brass, copper, copper alloy, or equally substantial approved means

SWIMMING POOL BONDING GRID

The purpose of the bonding grid is explained in *Section 680-22* (FPN) and is illustrated in figure 11–62 (page 185). The FPN makes two very important points:

1. The purpose is to eliminate voltage gradients in the pool area.
2. The grid is not required to be connected back to an equipment grounding conductor or a grounding electrode.

Items required by *Section 680-22(a)* to be bonded together are:

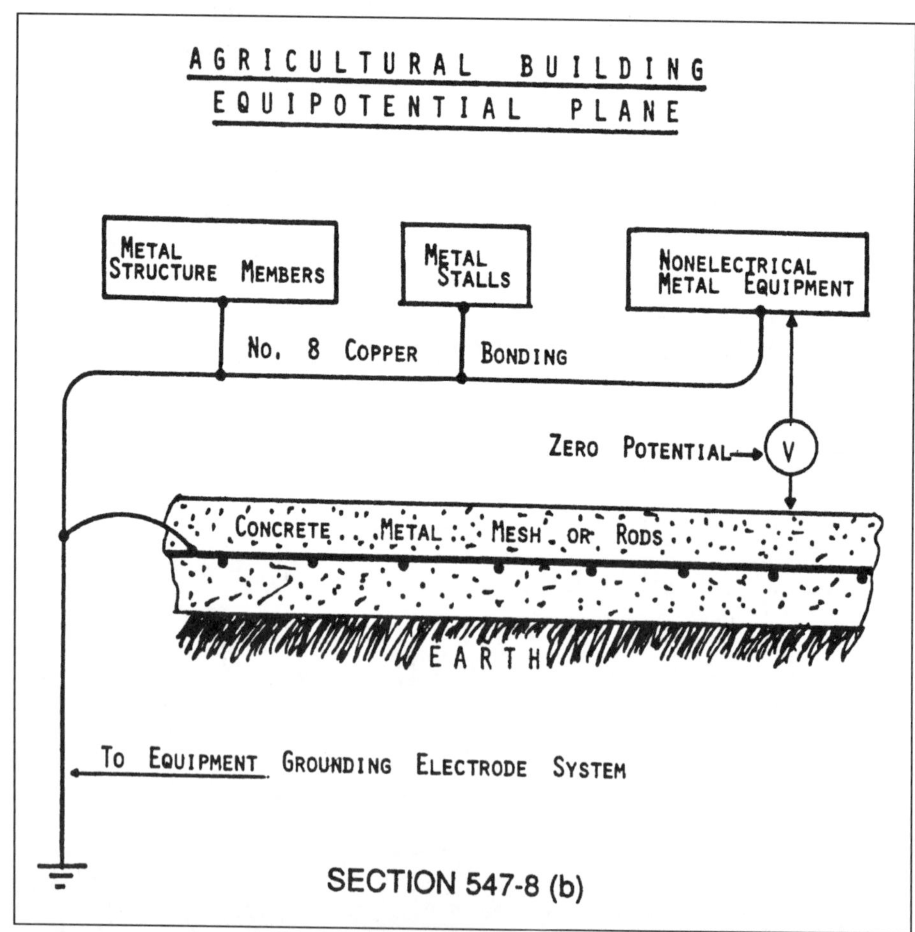

Fig. 11–61 Equipotential plane in agricultural buildings.

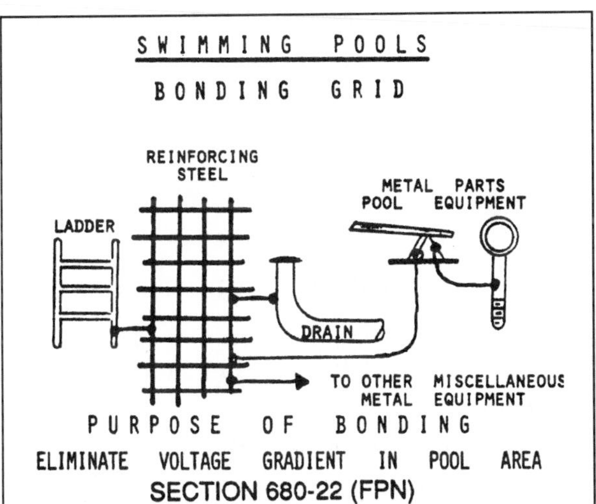

Fig. 11–62 Purpose of the bonding grid in swimming pools.

1. All metal parts of the pool structure, including reinforcing metal of the pool shell, coping stones, and deck.
2. All forming shells and mounting brackets of no-niche fixtures.
3. All metal fittings within or attached to the pool structure. Not included are isolated parts that are not over 4 inches in any dimension and do not penetrate into the pool structure more than 1 inch.
4. Metal parts of pump motors and other pool equipment.
5. Metal parts of motors and equipment associated with pool covers.
6. Metal-sheathed cable, raceways, piping, and other fixed metal parts located within:
   - 5 feet horizontally of the inside walls of the pool or
   - 12 feet above the maximum water level of the pool.
7. Also included, unless separated by a barrier, are any observation stands, towers, platforms, and diving structures.

Section 680-22(b) permits the common bonding grid to be any of the following:

1. Structural reinforcing steel of concrete pools with tie wire permitted to be used as the bonding means between the reinforcing rods
2. Wall of bolted or welded pools
3. Solid copper conductor not smaller than No. 8; insulated, covered, or bare

When stranded conductors are used in the smaller sizes, there is a possibility that one or more strands of the conductor may break off for a variety of reasons, such as corrosion; this reduces the size, and consequently the ampacity, of the conductor. Therefore, a solid conductor is required to protect against any loss of conductor cross-sectional area.

Figure 11–63 illustrates the reinforcing steel being used as the common grounding grid with all metal bonded to the grid with No. 8 solid copper.

SUMMARY

Using equipment bonding jumpers in the equipment grounding conductor circuit is good insurance against open circuits in the equipment grounding conductor path. They are a good investment for the protection of people and equipment.

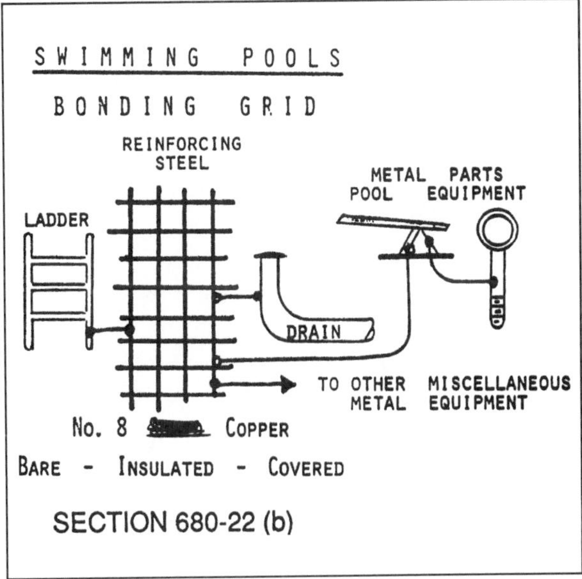

Fig. 11–63 Bonding grid requirements in swimming pools.

FOLLOW UP

Topics for self-study, discussion, or questioning.

1. Discuss the definition of bonding.
2. Discuss the purpose of bonding.
3. Discuss bonding on the line side of the service disconnecting means and the service equipment.
4. Explain, using *Table 250*, how to calculate the size of the bonding jumper installed on the line side of the service disconnecting means.
5. Explain how to use the 12½ percent rule to calculate the size of the bonding jumper installed on the line side of the service disconnecting means.
6. Explain how to calculate the size of the bonding jumper installed on the line side of the service when the bonding jumpers are installed in parallel conduits.
7. Explain how to calculate the size of the bonding jumper required to bond the grounding electrode conductor to a section of metal raceway enclosing it.
8. Discuss where equipment bonding jumpers are required on the load side of the service equipment.
9. Explain, using *Table 250-95*, how to calculate the size of the equipment bonding jumper on the load side of the service.
10. Discuss the hazard created when multiple grounding electrodes are installed and not bonded together.
11. Discuss the term "equipotential plane."
12. Identify the line and load side of the service.

CHAPTER 12

Equipment and Enclosure Grounding

OBJECTIVES

After completing this chapter, the student should be able to:

- explain why metal enclosures and equipment are grounded.
- identify some of the exceptions to the basic rule requiring all metal raceways and enclosures to be grounded.
- identify the specific equipment, when fastened in place or connected by permanent wiring, that is specifically identified to be grounded.
- identify where and when double insulation is permitted to be used in lieu of equipment grounding.
- identify cord- and plug-connected equipment that is specifically identified to be grounded.
- identify the nonelectrical equipment that is specifically identified to be grounded.
- explain the methods permitted for grounding enclosures and equipment.
- explain the use of a separate neutral bus and a separate equipment grounding bus in an enclosure.
- explain the hazard involved when the neutral bus and the equipment grounding bus are not kept separate in distribution panels.
- explain the purpose and installation of an isolated grounding receptacle.
- locate equipment grounding requirements in other than *Article 250* of the Code.

When an enclosure or a raceway is grounded, as the definition of *grounded* states, the enclosure or raceway is connected to earth in some way. When effectively connected to earth, it becomes part of the overall grounding system and the metal enclosure will have zero potential to ground as long as it remains effectively connected to ground (figure 12–1, page 188).

WHY GROUND METAL ENCLOSURES AND EQUIPMENT?

Once again the question is asked, Why ground conductive materials and enclosures of electrical equipment? The answer is illustrated in figure 12–2 (page 188).

Electrical equipment enclosures are grounded to

- limit the voltage to ground,

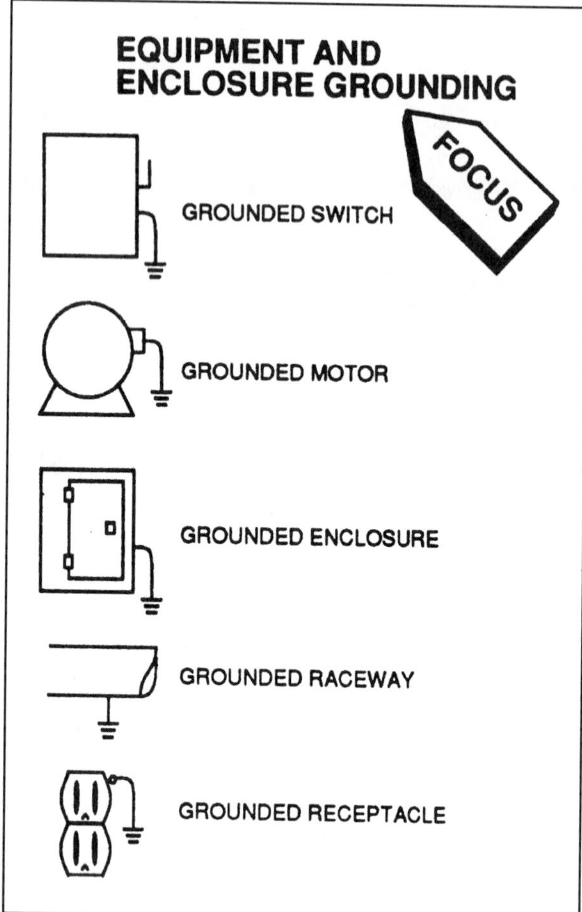

Fig. 12–1 Equipment and enclosure grounding.

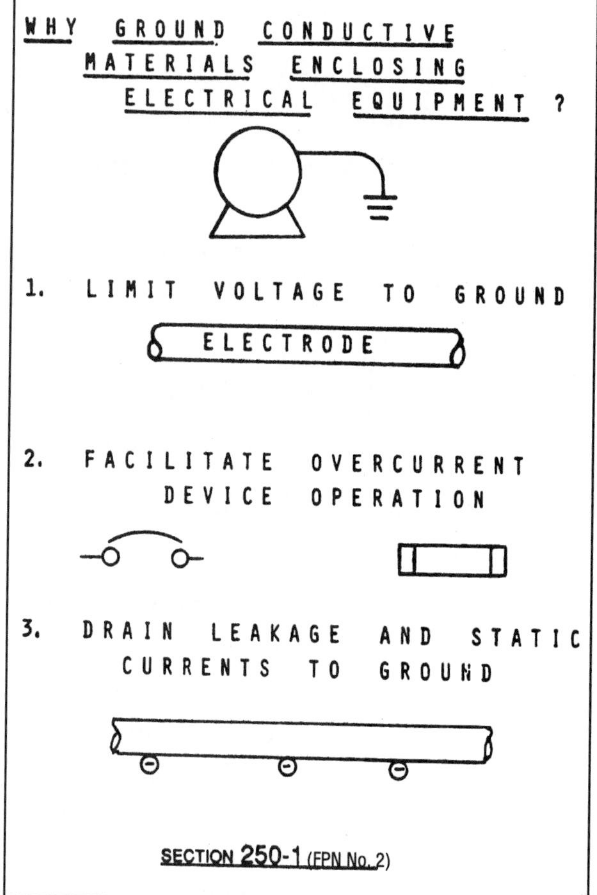

Fig. 12–2 Reasons for grounding conductive materials enclosing electrical equipment.

- facilitate sufficient current flow for the operation of the overcurrent protective device,
- drain leakage or static currents to ground.

Part of the reason for grounding has to do with *voltage*. Part of the reason for grounding has to do with *current*. Electrical equipment and enclosure grounding takes into consideration both voltage and current because these two working together pose the greatest danger to individuals and equipment.

Section 300-9, Chapter 3, under *General Provisions* for wiring methods, is another good example of how the Code continually coordinates grounding. *Section 300-9* requires the following metal enclosures to be grounded, according to *Article 250:*

1. Metal raceways
2. Metal boxes
3. Metal cabinets
4. Cable armor
5. Metal fittings

ENCLOSURE AND RACEWAY GROUNDING

Part D of *Article 250* (Enclosure and Raceway Grounding) consists of only two sections and each section contains only one sentence. But the two sentences cover all enclosures and raceways for the entire electrical installation.

Quote – "Section 250-32, Service Raceways and Enclosures. Metal enclosures for service conductors and equipment shall be grounded."*

*Reprinted with permission from NFPA 70-1996, the National Electrical Code®, Copyright © 1995, National Fire Protection Association, Quincy, MA 02269. This reprinted material is not the complete and official position of the National Fire Protection Association, on the referenced subject, which is represented only by the standard in its entirety.

Comment: This section takes care of all metal enclosures pertaining to the service.

The one exception to *250-32* permits the installation of metal elbows in a service raceway run of nonmetallic conduit without being grounded, provided the elbow is isolated from possible contact by a minimum burial cover of 18 inches over any part of the elbow (figure 12-3). Normally these are the elbows installed underground in a horizontal position. However, the same holds true for a vertical metal elbow. It is not required to be grounded when the uppermost part of the elbow is buried 18 inches. A pull rope or cable can cut through nonmetallic conduits much more easily than through steel. Therefore, steel elbows are installed for pulling purposes. When the elbows are buried according to the depth chart, *Table 300-5*, no one is likely to touch them and no electrical hazard is involved. An exception is also made to *Section 230-33* permitting the same installation in other than service raceways.

Quote – "Section 250-33, Other Conductor Enclosures and Raceways. Metal enclosures for other than service conductors shall be grounded."*

Comment: This takes care of all metal enclosures used for other than service conductors.

Section 250-33 lists four exceptions. Exception No. 1 is illustrated in figure 12–4 (page 190). This applies mainly where the metal enclosure is used more for mechanical protection of the cable. As an example, apply this exception to a change of wiring methods. An existing installation of nonmetallic sheathed cable (Romex) is being changed to a type of metal raceway wiring. In order for this installation to be made with an ungrounded metal wiring method, there are four requirements. These are:

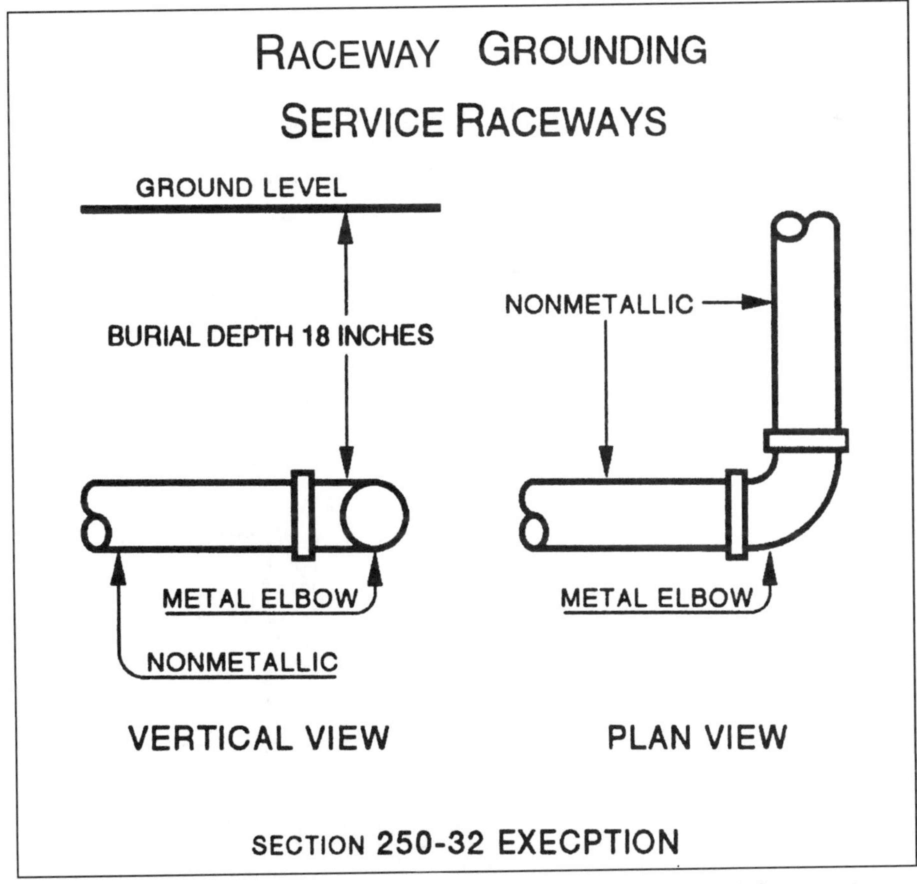

Fig. 12–3 Steel elbows in underground runs of nonmetallic conduit are not required to be grounded.

1. It must be an addition to an existing installation of knob and tube or nonmetallic sheathed cable.
2. It must be less than 25 feet long.
3. It must be free from probable contact with any grounded surface, such as metal lath.
4. It must be guarded against contact by persons.

Figure 12–5 (page 191) illustrates Exception No. 2, where a metal enclosure is used to protect cable assemblies. Such cable assemblies would include nonmetallic sheathed cable, service-entrance cable, underground feeder, and branch circuit cable.

Example: The protection illustrated is the same protection required by *Section 336-10(b)* for nonmetallic sheathed cable. It requires the cable to be protected a minimum of 6 inches above the floor.

Exception No. 3 permits the enclosure for equipment supplied by Class 1, Class 2, or Class 3 remote-control, signaling, and fire protection signaling circuits to be ungrounded unless required by *Article 250. Article 250* requires systems operating at less than 50 volts to be grounded:

1. When the transformer supply system exceeds 150 volts to ground.
2. When the transformer supply system is ungrounded.
3. Where installed as overhead conductors outside a building.

Example: A transformer with a 120-volt primary and a 24-volt secondary is used for a remote-control or signaling circuit. The enclosure for the 24-volt secondary equipment is not required to be grounded because it is less than 150 volts to ground.

Exception No. 4 is the same for other than service conductors, as illustrated for service conductors in figure 12–3 (page 189).

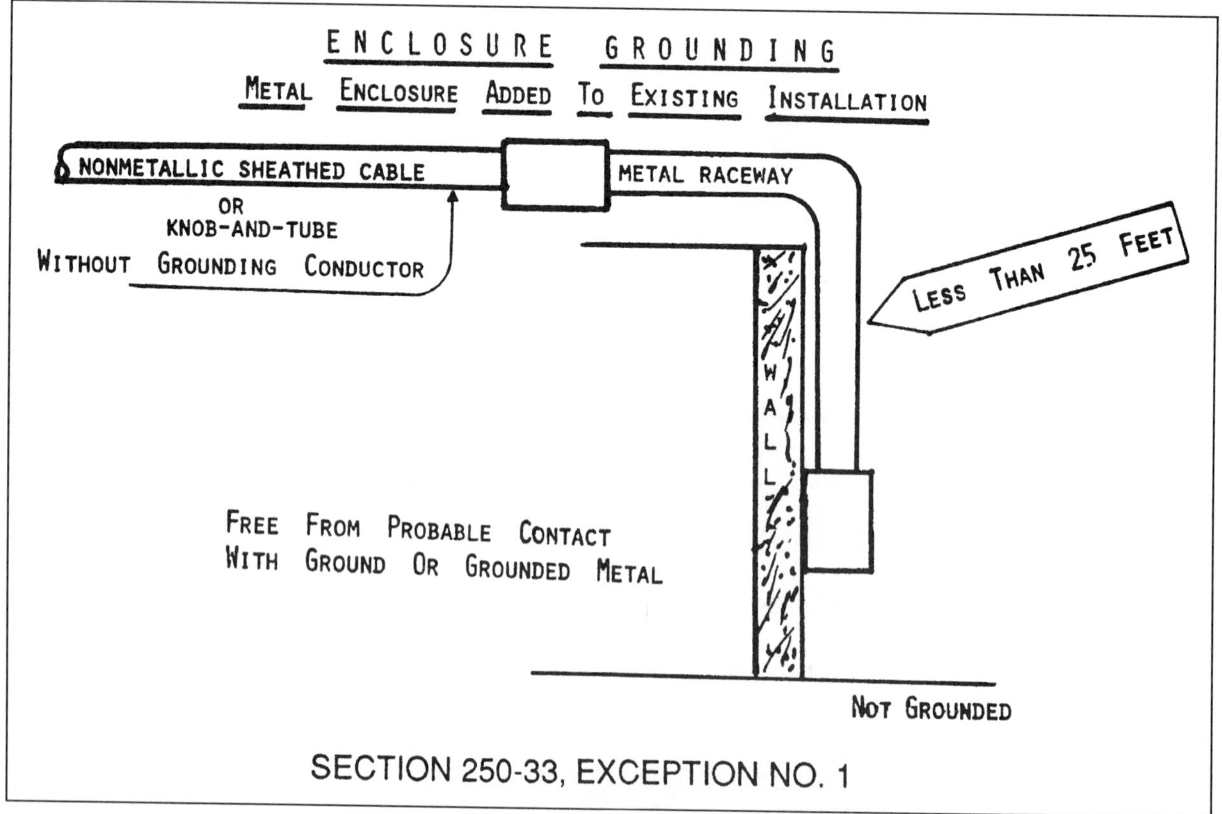

Fig. 12–4 Exception No. 1 to the requirement for metal enclosure and raceway grounding.

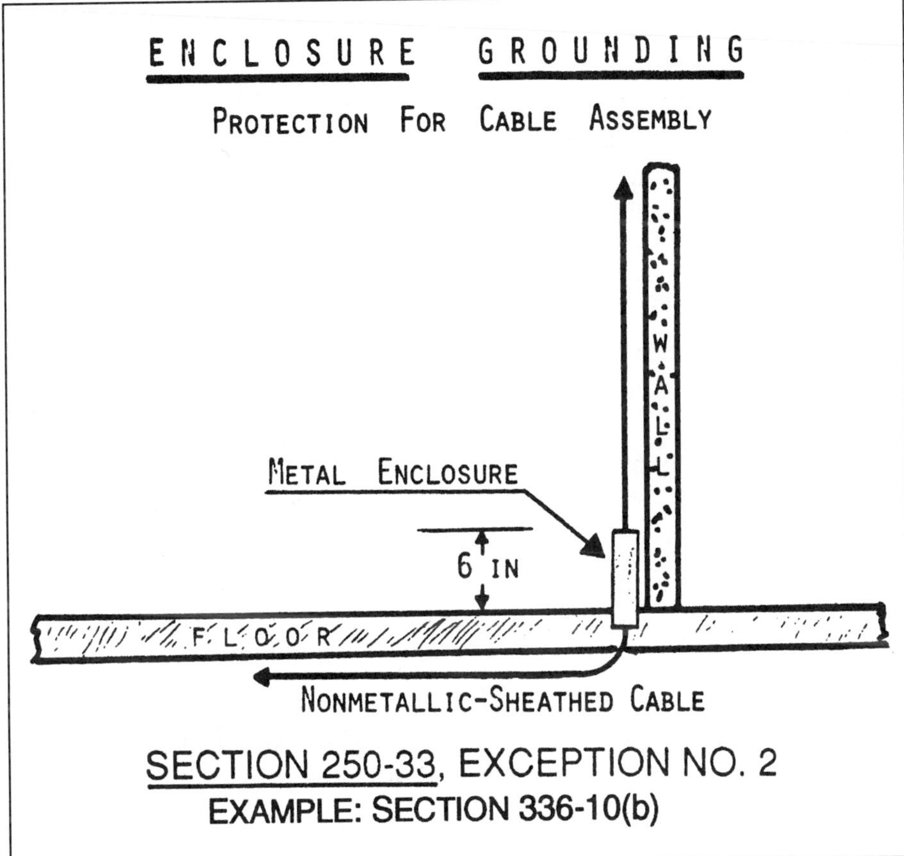

Fig. 12–5 Exception No. 2 to the requirement for metal enclosure grounding.

EQUIPMENT GROUNDING

Here the Code is talking about the electrical equipment used in the workplace or in the home. New electrical equipment is being designed every day to make an individual's job easier, to help that individual do the job faster or better. The equipment must be made safe. One part of safety is the effective grounding of electrical equipment no matter how small or how large the equipment.

There are many sections of the Code that interlock with *Article 250*. Figure 12–6 illustrates some of these interlocking sections. For example:

1. Under *Services* in *Section 230-63*, the grounding of service equipment is interlocked with *Article 250*.
2. Under *Switches* in *Section 380-12*, the grounding of switches is interlocked with *Article 250* and includes the grounding of metal faceplates installed on nonmetallic boxes.
3. Under *Switchboards and Panelboards* in *Sections 384-11, 384-3(c),* and *384–20*, the grounding of switchboards and panelboards is interlocked with *Article 250*.

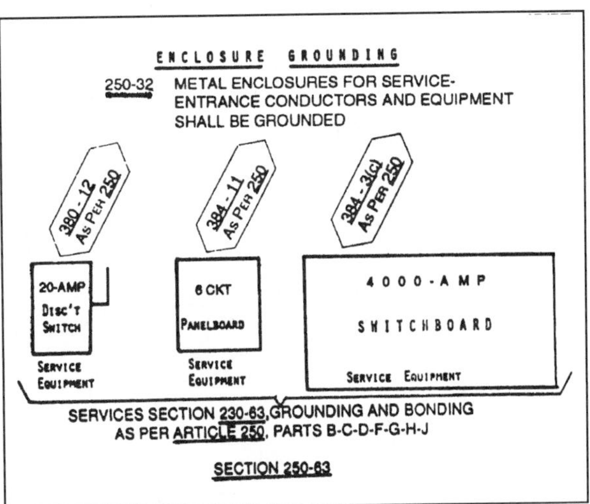

Fig. 12–6 Metal enclosure grounding is coordinated with other parts of the Code.

Part E. Equipment Grounding

Part E, Equipment Grounding, of *Article 250* sets down the regulations for grounding exposed noncurrent-carrying metal parts of electrical and nonelectrical equipment. The following is a brief but interesting outline of Part E.

1. Equipment fastened in place
   a. Applies to all exposed noncurrent-carrying parts of electrical equipment fastened in place.
   b. Connected by a permanent wiring method
   c. Information on location
   d. Information on environment
   e. Information on voltage
   f. Conditions of installation
2. Equipment fastened in place (specific list)
   a. Connected by a permanent wiring method
   b. Identifies a specific list of fixed equipment fastened in place so there is no mistaking the particular piece of electrical equipment to be grounded
3. Nonelectrical equipment—Lists specific nonelectrical equipment that is required to have its noncurrent-carrying metal parts grounded
4. Equipment connected by plug and cord
   a. Hazardous locations
   b. Over 150 volts to ground
   c. In residential occupancies
   d. In other than residential occupancies

Section 250-42 requires those exposed noncurrent-carrying metal parts of fixed electrical equipment likely to become energized to be grounded under the conditions listed. The listed conditions cover location, environment, and operating voltage.

Guarding and Isolating Electrical Equipment

The exceptions in Part E of *Article 250* permitting equipment to be installed without

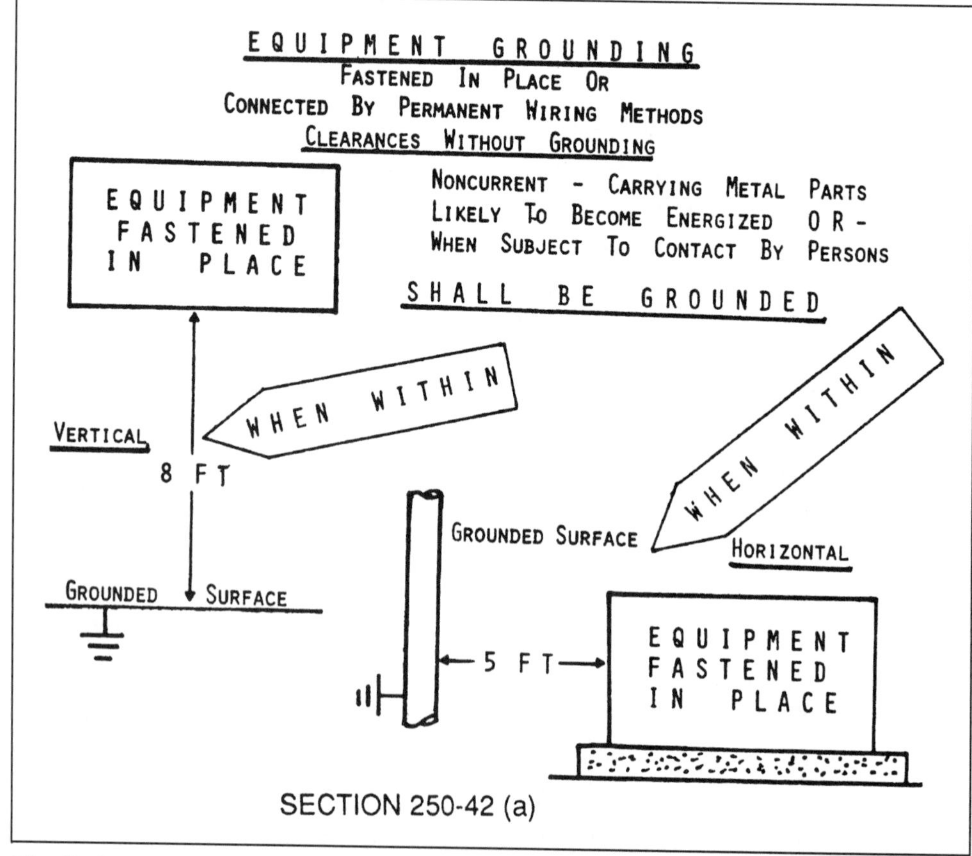

Fig. 12–7 Clearances for electrical equipment installations without grounding.

being grounded are taking into consideration one or more of the following points:

1. Specific piece of equipment
2. Double insulation
3. Guarded equipment
4. Isolated equipment

Equipment Required to Be Grounded

Figure 12–7 (page 192) illustrates the 8-foot vertical and 5-foot horizontal distances electrical equipment must be from ground or a grounded surface before it can be installed ungrounded. When the equipment is installed with less than these distances to ground, the equipment shall be grounded.

When electrical equipment is located in a wet or damp location, it shall be grounded. Figure 12–8 shows an example of this, where an outdoor air conditioning unit is installed at ground level. Anyone could walk up and touch it while standing on earth that may or may not be damp or wet.

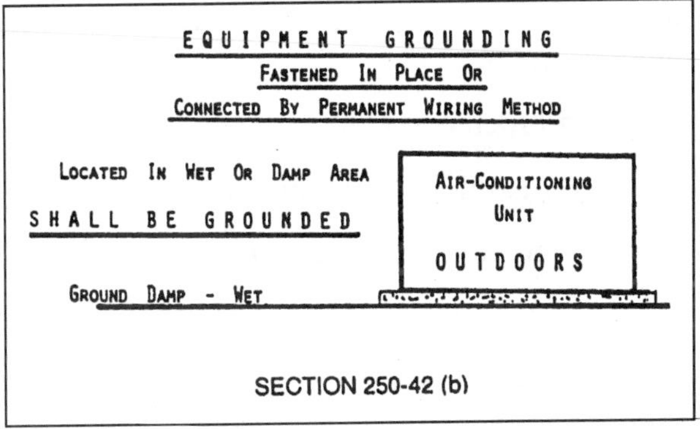

Fig. 12–8 Electrical equipment installed in a damp or wet location shall be grounded.

Figure 12–9 illustrates *Section 250-42(c),* where an enclosure for electrical equipment is in contact with metal that could possibly become energized through a fault in the enclosure. In this case, it shall be grounded. For grounding in hazardous locations or health care facilities, *Article 250* refers to *Articles 500* and *517.*

Equipment Connected by Permanent Wiring

When the equipment is supplied by any of the metallic wiring methods listed in Chapter 3, *Wiring Methods and Materials,* it shall be

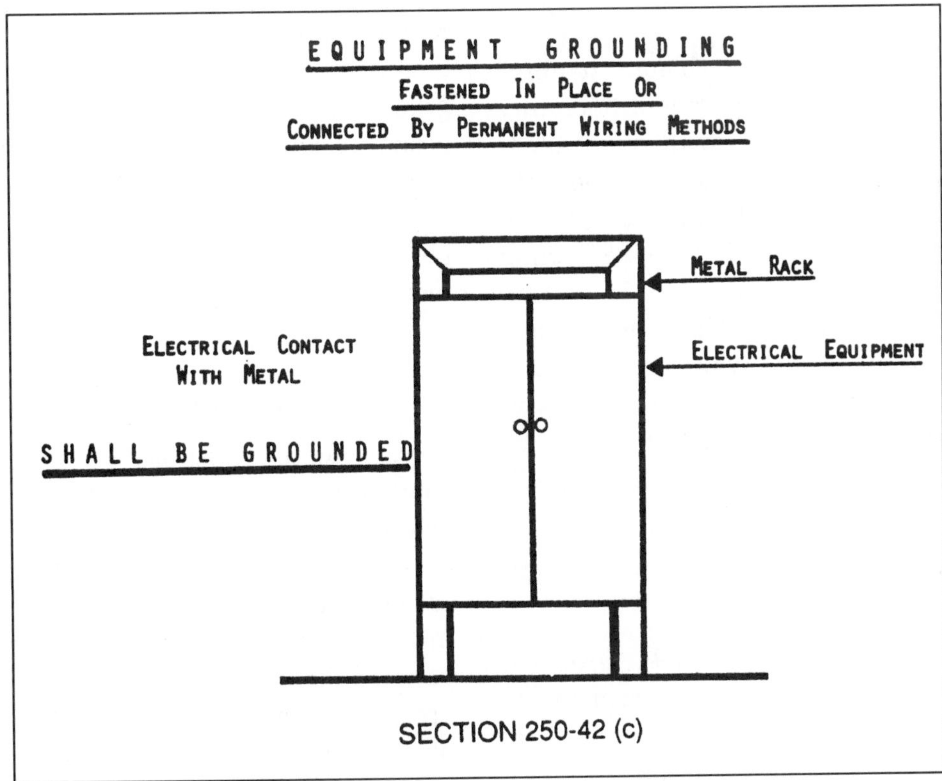

Fig. 12–9 Nonelectrical equipment in metal contact with electrical equipment shall be grounded.

grounded. Such conductor-enclosure wiring methods include:

- Rigid metal conduit
- Intermediate metal conduit
- Electrical metallic tubing
- Flexible metal conduit
- Flexible metallic tubing
- Surface metal raceway
- Metal wireway
- Metal underfloor duct
- Metal bus duct
- Any wiring method with a metal covering

When the equipment is supplied by any of the metal-covered cable assemblies listed in Chapter 3 of the Code, the metal covering shall be grounded. Such cable assemblies include:

1. Type AC armored cable
2. Type MC metal-clad cable
3. Type MI mineral-insulated cable
4. Any other cable assembly with a metal covering

Section 250-42(f) gives a blanket requirement for grounding all equipment operating over 150 volts to ground, with four exceptions. Figure 12–10 illustrates *Section 250-42(f)*, Exception No. 3, where the equipment is mounted more than 8 feet above ground level.

Figure 12–11 (page 195) illustrates *Section 250-42(f)*, Exception No. 4, which permits equipment to be ungrounded when manufactured with a double insulation, such as the illustrated office equipment. There are three important points to note here.

1. The title of *Section 240-42(f)* is "Over 150 Volts to Ground."
2. The equipment must be double-insulated equipment or have the equivalent of double insulation.
3. The equipment is distinctively marked.

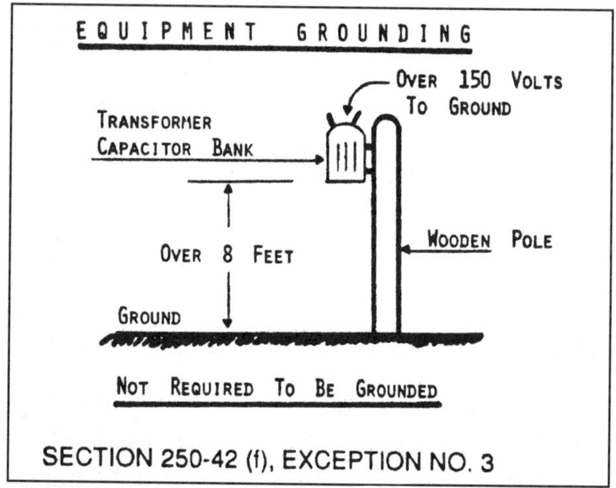

Fig. 12–10 Exception No. 3 to the requirement for grounding all equipment operating over 150 volts to ground.

Note that this is under the heading of "Over 150 Volts to Ground." Therefore, it does not apply to equipment operating at 120 volts to ground. It is applicable to enclosures for equipment operating at 220 and 277 volts to ground.

Section 250-43 contains a list (figure 12–12, page 195) of specific equipment that is fastened in place and shall be grounded, *regardless of voltage*. There are few exceptions.

When any Class 1, Class 2, and Class 3 remote control and signaling circuit, or fire alarm circuit, is supplied by a system required to be grounded, the equipment is then required to be grounded as well. Such systems are described in Chapter 7.

Section 250-43(k) requires motor-operated pumps to be grounded; this includes the submersible type pump.

Grounding Nonelectrical Equipment

There are situations that can arise when some piece of electrical equipment is mounted on nonelectrical equipment, which could possibly cause the entire metal parts of the nonelectrical equipment to become energized. In these installations, the noncurrent-carrying metal parts of the nonelectrical equipment shall be grounded. Figure 12–13 (page 195) shows the nonelectrical equipment, as listed in *Section 250-44*, that shall be grounded.

EQUIPMENT GROUNDING

OFFICE EQUIPMENT

PERMITTED TO BE UNGROUNDED WHEN

1 - OVER 150 VOLTS TO GROUND
2 - DOUBLY INSULATED
3 - LISTED EQUIPMENT
4 - DISTINCTIVELY MARKED

SECTION 250-42 (f), EXCEPTION NO. 4

Fig. 12–11 Exception No. 4 to requirement for grounding office equipment over 150 volts to ground. Courtesy International Business Machines Corporation.

EQUIPMENT GROUNDING

FASTENED IN PLACE OR
CONNECTED BY PERMANENT WIRING METHOD

SPECIFICS

SWITCHBOARD FRAMES AND STRUCTURES
PIPE ORGAN
MOTOR FRAMES
ENCLOSURES FOR MOTOR CONTROLLERS
ELEVATORS AND CRANES
COMMERCIAL GARAGES
THEATERS AND MOTION PICTURE STUDIOS
ELECTRIC SIGNS
MOTION PICTURE PROJECTOR EQUIPMENT
REMOTE-CONTROL CLASS I, CLASS II, & CLASS III
FIRE SIGNALING
LIGHTING FIXTURES
SUBMERSIBLE MOTOR-OPERATED WATER PUMP
METAL WELL CASING

SHALL BE GROUNDED

SECTION 250-43

Fig. 12–12 A list of equipment, fastened in place or connected by permanent wiring, that is required to be grounded.

EQUIPMENT GROUNDING

NONELECTRIC EQUIPMENT

CRANES
ELEVATOR CARS
ELECTRIC ELEVATORS
METAL PARTITIONS
MOBILE HOMES AND RECREATIONAL VEHICLES

SHALL BE GROUNDED

SECTION 250-44

Fig. 12–13 Nonelectrical equipment that shall be grounded.

Cord- and Plug-connected Equipment—Residential

Where cord- and plug-connected equipment is used and the exposed noncurrent-carrying metal parts might become energized, the equipment shall be grounded. There are two locations in which the cord- and plug-connected equipment is used: one is in the home or residential occupancy and the other is in the workplace or in other than a residential occupancy.

Damp or wet locations tend to set up hazardous conditions. The Code does not intend for tools and/or appliances to be used in damp or wet locations, whether it is a residential or other location. The use of double insulated tools in damp or wet locations is not the intent of the Code, and some of these tools bear just such labels. The electrical hazards in wet or damp locations still exist even with the use of double insulated tools.

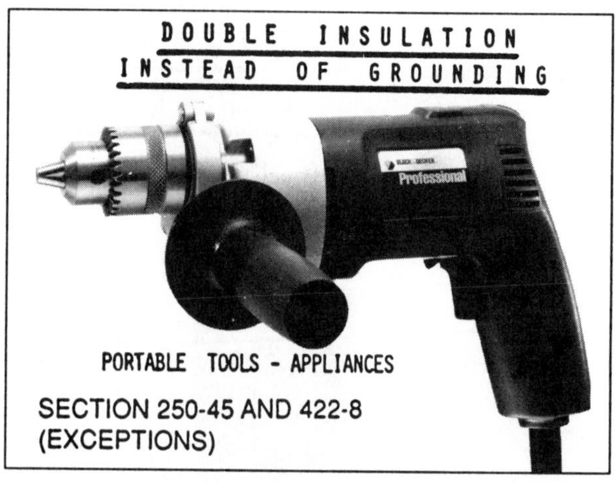

Fig. 12–15 Exceptions that allow the use of double insulation on listed tools and appliances. Courtesy Black & Decker.

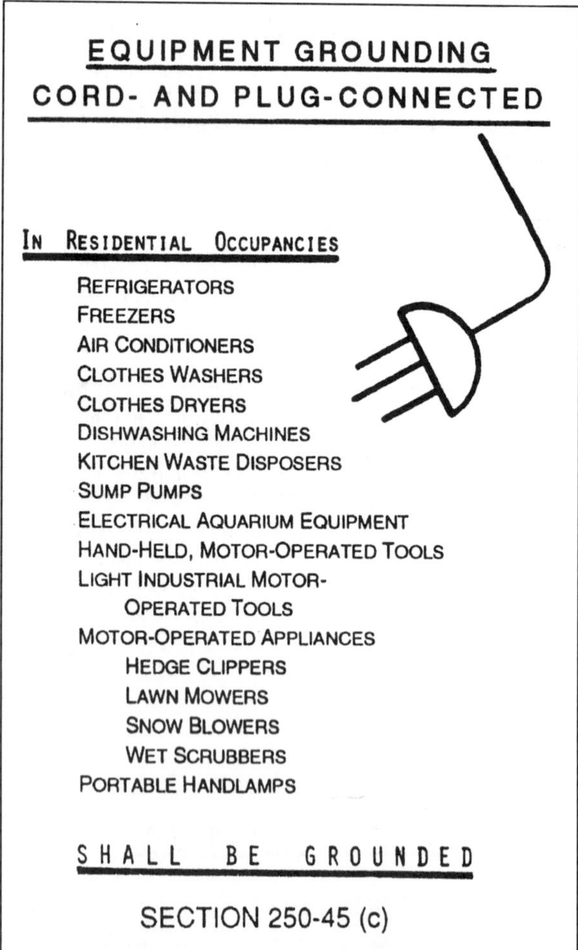

Fig. 12–14 Cord- and plug-connected equipment that shall be grounded when located in a residential area.

Figure 12–14 is a list of cord- and plug-connected equipment that shall be grounded, as required by *Section 250-45(c)*, when this equipment is located in a *residential occupancy*. Figure 12–15 illustrates the exception to *Section 250-45(c)*, which allows the use of double insulation on listed tools and appliances. When such double insulation is used, it shall be distinctively marked. This exception is also repeated in *Section 422-8(d)* for kitchen waste disposers, trash compactors, and dishwashers.

Cord- and Plug-connected Equipment—Other Than Residential

Figure 12–16 (page 197) is a list of items taken from *Section 250-45(d)* that shall be grounded when they are located *in other than residential occupancies*. The list repeats almost everything listed on the residential list plus several more items. There are two exceptions here, one recognizing the double-insulated tool or appliance and one the use of an isolation transformer, as illustrated in figure 12–17 (page 197). An example of this exception would be the use of an isolation transformer for low-voltage lighting used for temporary lighting inside a large metal tank.

CAUTION: The list given for residential occupancies and for other than residential occupancies is not an all-inclusive list of everything that shall be grounded.

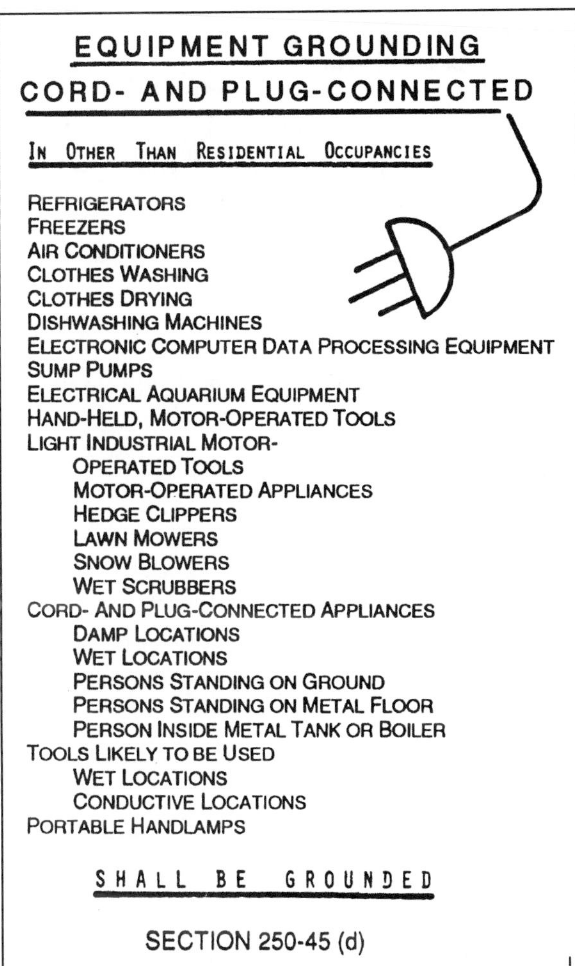

Fig. 12–16 Cord- and plug-connected equipment that shall be grounded when located in other than residential occupancies.

Example: Section 310-6, illustrated in figure 12–18, requires the metal shield of conductors operating at over 2000 volts to be grounded.

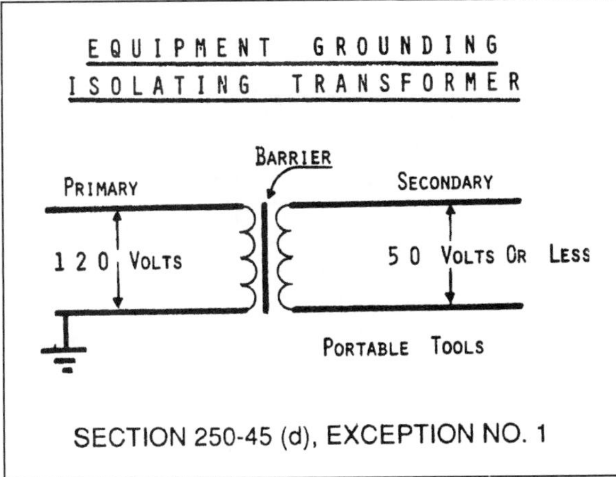

Fig. 12–17 An isolation transformer is permitted with an ungrounded secondary.

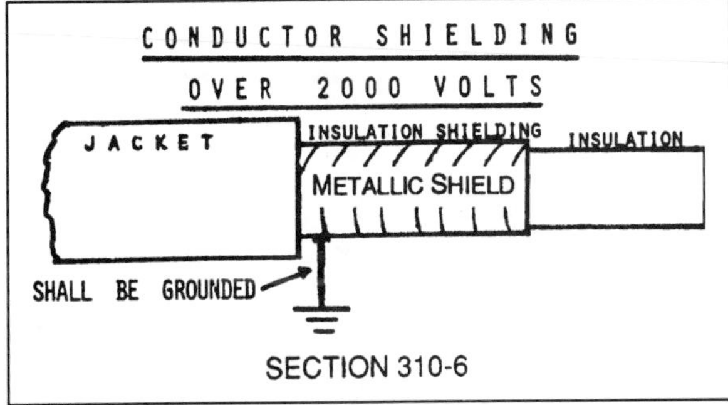

Fig. 12–18 Requirement for grounding metal conductor shielding operating over 2000 volts.

METHODS OF GROUNDING ENCLOSURES AND EQUIPMENT

Section 250-57 lists the ways that cord- and plug-connected equipment is permitted to be grounded. These are:

1. By the use of metal enclosures and/or metal raceways, or the use of metal covering of some cable assemblies and fittings listed for the purpose. The raceway or cable must contain the circuit conductors serving the equipment.
2. By the use of an equipment grounding conductor contained within the same raceway, cable, or cord.
3. *Section 250-59(c)* permits grounding cord- and plug-connected equipment by the following means:
   a. Separate flexible wire
   b. Separate flexible strap
   c. Wire or strap—permitted to be insulated or bare
   d. Wire or strap—shall be protected, as well as is practical, against physical damage.

GROUNDING PANELBOARDS

Section 384-20 (figure 12-19, page 198) requires a ground bar for the neutral conductor connections and an equipment grounding bar for the equipment grounding conductor connections in distribution panels where nonmetallic raceway is used. There are several points covered by *Section 384-20* for an installation using nonmetallic raceway, when wire is used for equipment grounding conductors. These are:

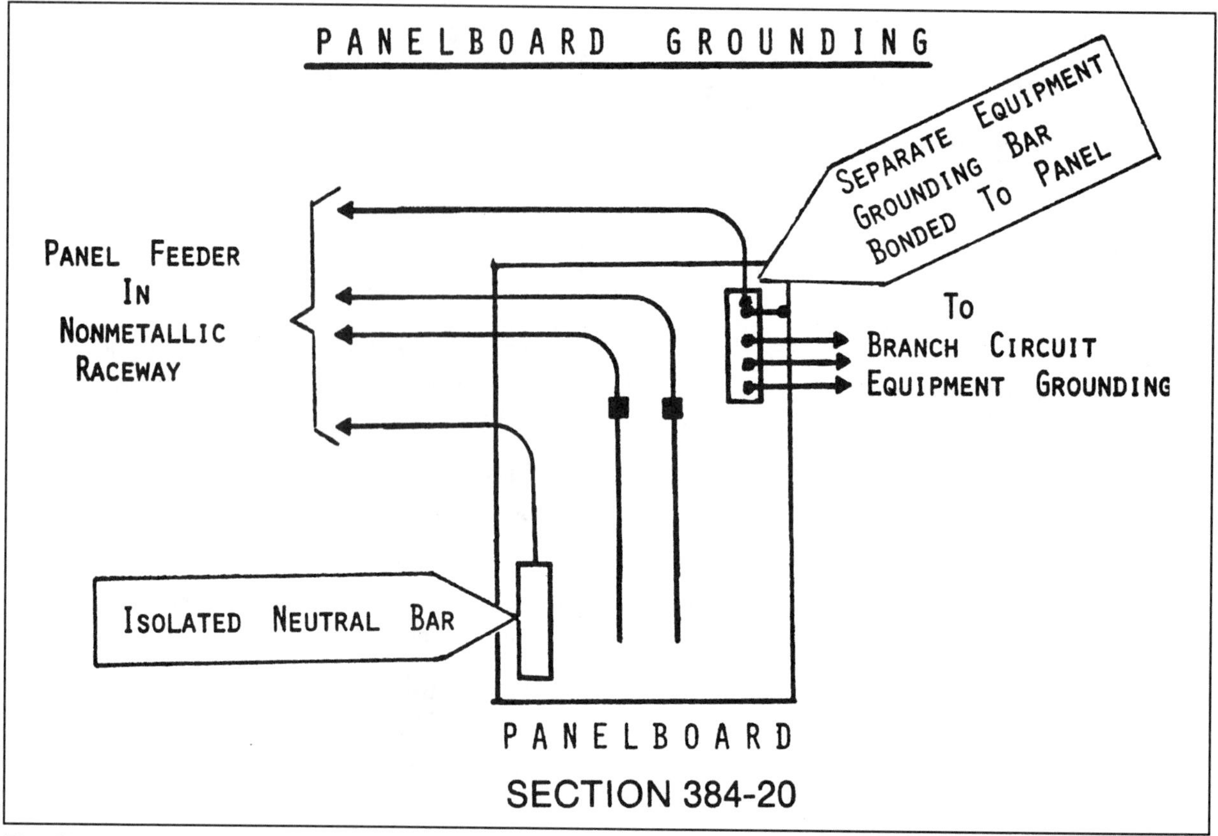

Fig. 12–19 Equipment grounding in panelboards.

1. Metal cabinets and metal frames shall be in direct contact and maintain continuity.
2. An approved terminal bar shall be used.
3. The terminal bar shall be secured inside the cabinet.
4. The terminal bar shall be specifically for the connection of equipment grounding conductors.
5. The equipment grounding conductors can be for feeders or for branch circuits.
6. The equipment grounding terminal bar shall be bonded to the cabinet or panelboard frame.
7. For a separately derived system, the equipment grounding terminal bar shall be located at the first system disconnecting means or overcurrent device.
8. The equipment grounding bar shall not be connected to the neutral bar in any panel other than the service equipment.
9. Sheet-metal screws are not permitted for the connecting of the grounding conductor to an enclosure (*Section 250-113*). The self tapping machine screw is not considered a sheet metal screw and is permitted to be used.

Figure 12–20 illustrates the installation of a separate ground bar in a cabinet for the neutrals

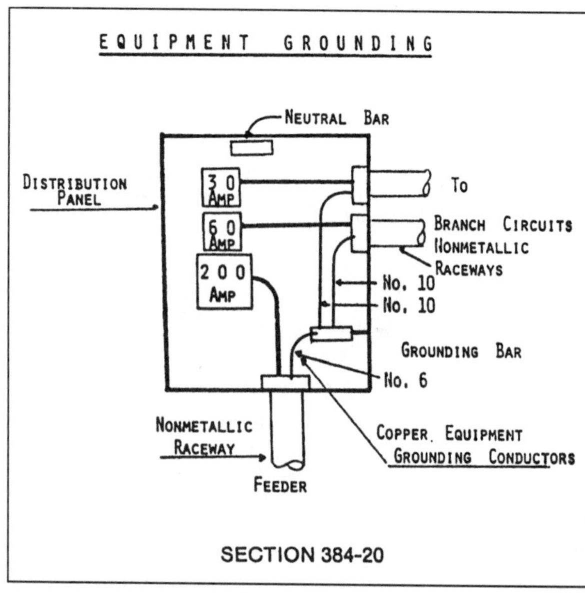

Fig. 12–20 Use of a separate neutral bar and a separate equipment grounding bar in panels.

and a separate ground bar for the equipment grounding conductors.

Reason: By having two separate bars—one for the neutral and one for the equipment grounding—the current flow (the electron flow) is controlled, as illustrated in figure 12–21. There is only one path for the current to flow on, even though the grounded conductor (the neutral) does furnish the return path for the current flow.

Figure 12–22 (page 200) illustrates a series circuit that ends in many parallel paths. When the neutral conductor is bonded to panels other than the service equipment, many paths are created and the electrons will take each and every path offered. There no longer is control over the electron flow (figure 12–23, page 200). The electrons now have a multitude of paths for return to the source, paths for circulating ground currents are established, and this is just another way to install "dirty, noisy" electricity.

ISOLATED EQUIPMENT GROUNDING RECEPTACLES

The exception to *Section 384-20* speaks of an isolated equipment grounding conductor. The isolated equipment grounding conductor is used in conjunction with an isolated grounding receptacle (figure 12–24, page 201). Isolated equipment grounding receptacles are used in hospitals. They are also used in conjunction with computers and data processing equipment. When the isolated grounding receptacle is used, an insulated equipment grounding conductor is permitted to be run all the way back to the grounding electrode conductor connection at the service, as illustrated in figure 12–25 (page 201). Isolated

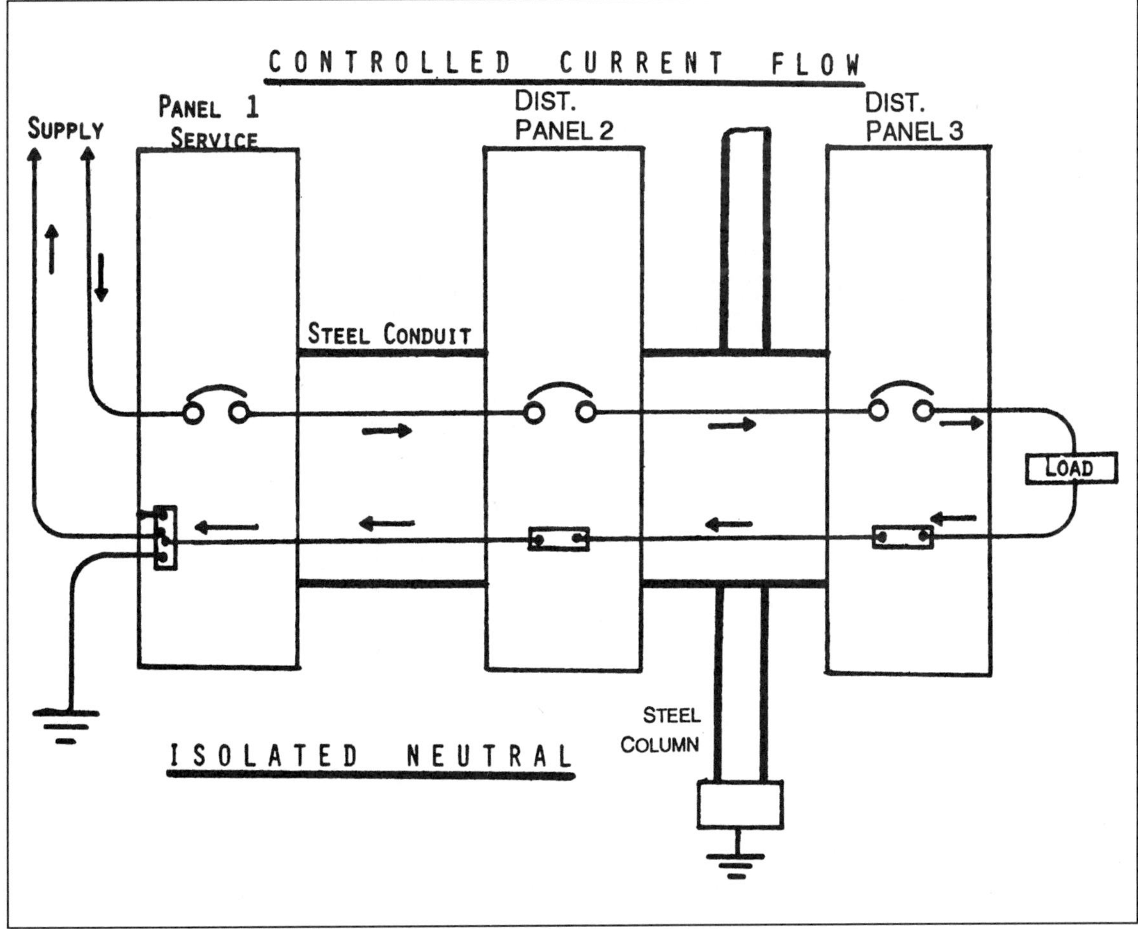

Fig. 12–21 Controlled current flow when the neutral bar is connected to the service enclosure only.

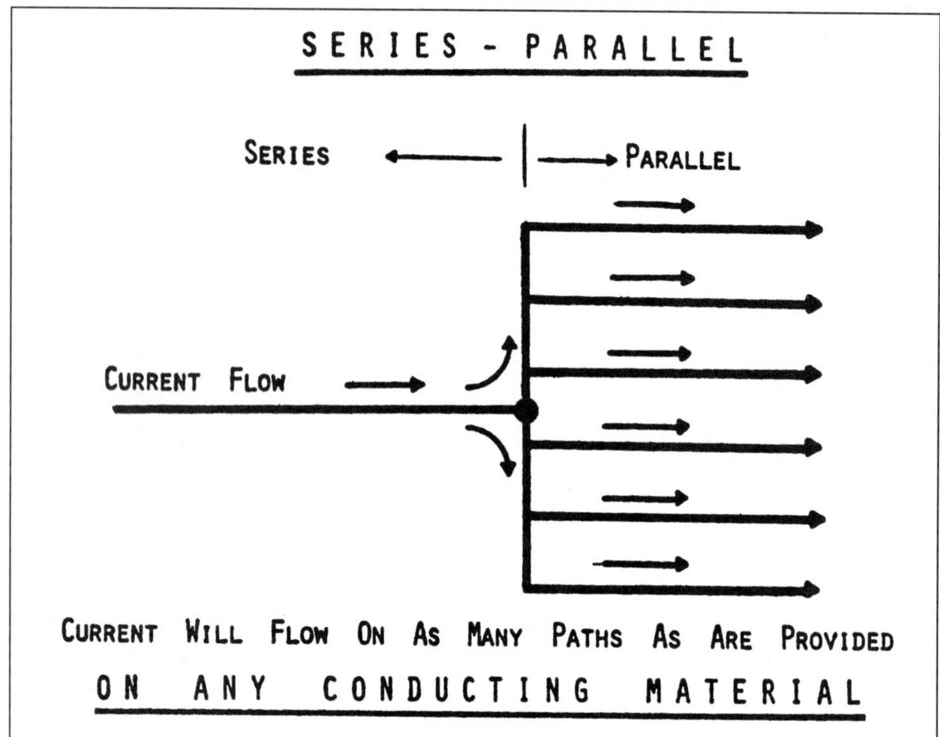

Fig. 12–22 Current flow in a series parallel circuit.

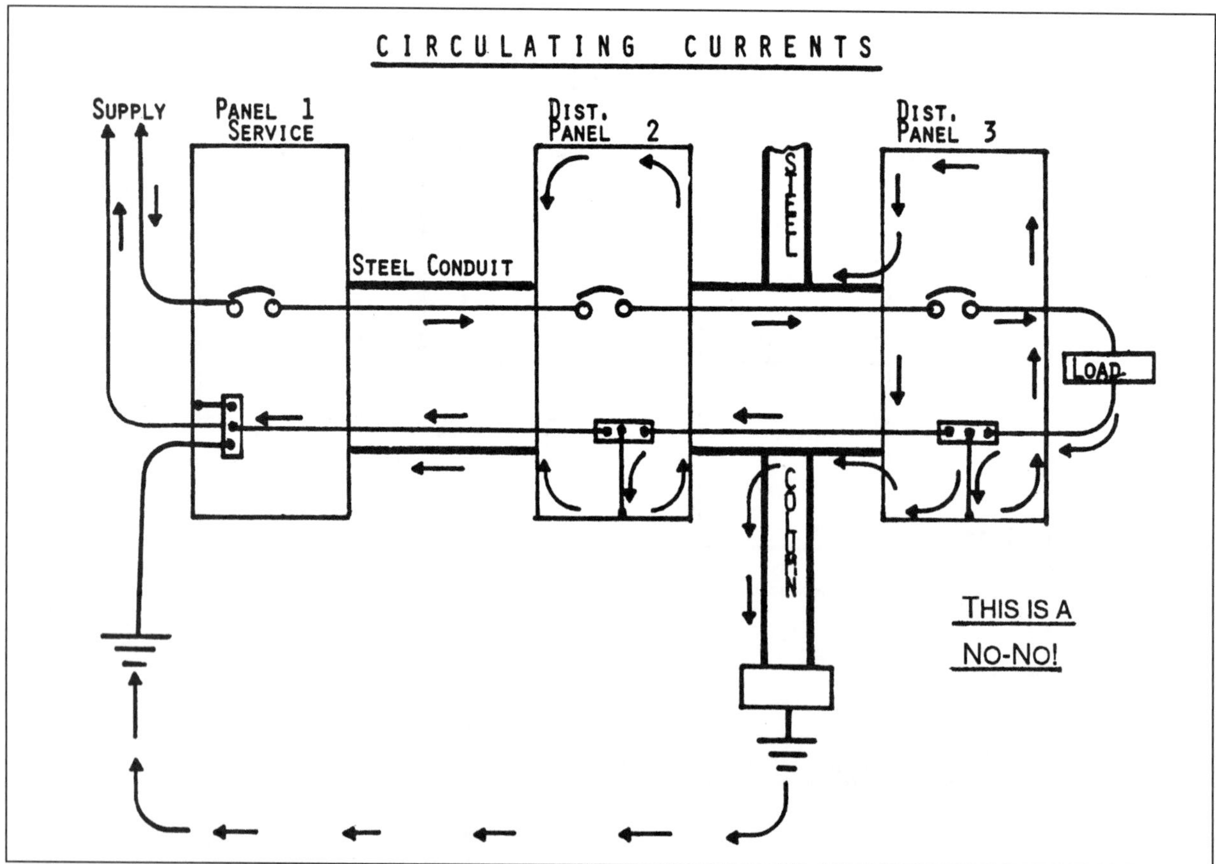

Fig. 12–23 Uncontrolled current flow when neutral is bonded to each enclosure. Many paths for circulating currents are created.

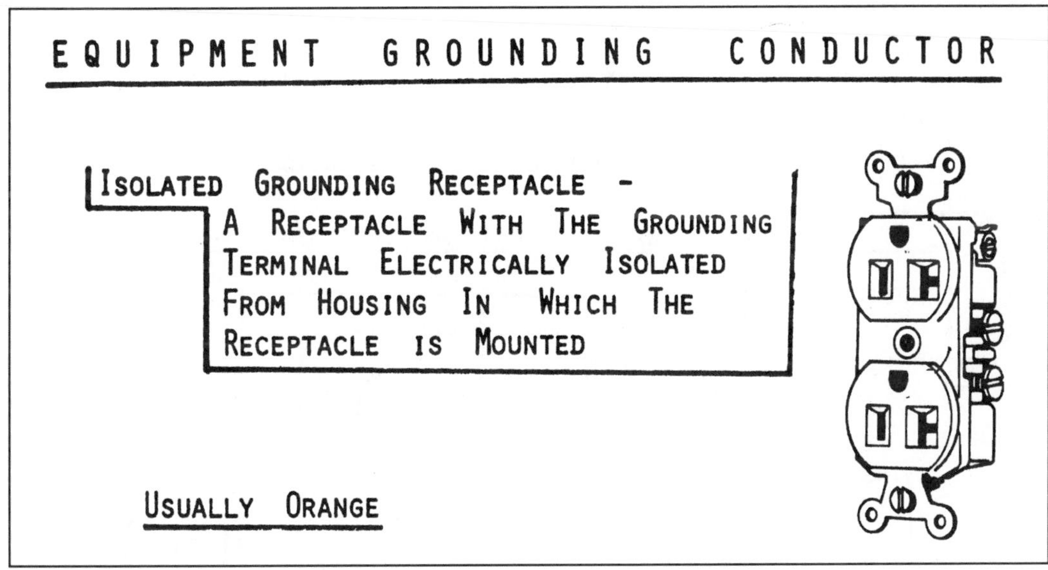

Fig. 12–24 Definition of isolated grounding receptacle.

receptacles are identified by an orange color or an orange triangle on the receptacle.

There are really two equipment grounding conductors involved here. One is the isolated, insulated equipment grounding conductor connected to the green terminal on the isolated grounding receptacle and carried all the way back to the supply with a green insulated equipment grounding conductor.

The metal box (the enclosure) housing the isolated grounding receptacle must also be grounded, but not to the receptacle. When the receptacle is fed with effectively grounded metal conduit, the conduit becomes the second equipment grounding conductor.

Figure 12–26 (page 202) illustrates how an isolated grounding receptacle could be installed, when a separately derived system is the source of supply. An insulated equipment grounding conductor is installed from the grounding terminal of the receptacle back to the source of supply. It is installed in the same metal raceway with the feeder and branch circuit conductors. The metal raceway is then used as the equipment grounding conductor for things other than the isolated grounded receptacle. In this particular illustration (the source of supply being a separately derived system) there is more than one way that the source of supply could be installed. For example:

1. It can be connected through a ground bar back to the point of connection of the grounding electrode conductor.
2. It can be carried directly back to the point of connection of the equipment grounding conductor.

Reason: The isolated grounding receptacle and the isolated equipment grounding conductor help to get rid of some of that dirty electricity that causes problems for computers and other microelectronic equipment.

When an installation is made using all nonmetallic conduit, two grounding conductors will

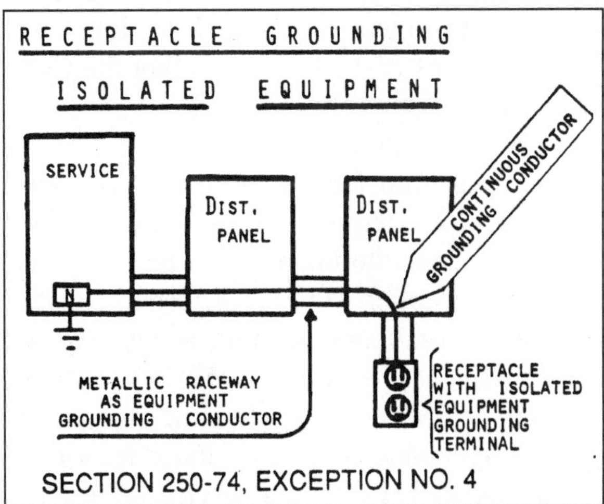

Fig. 12–25 Installation of an isolated grounding receptacle.

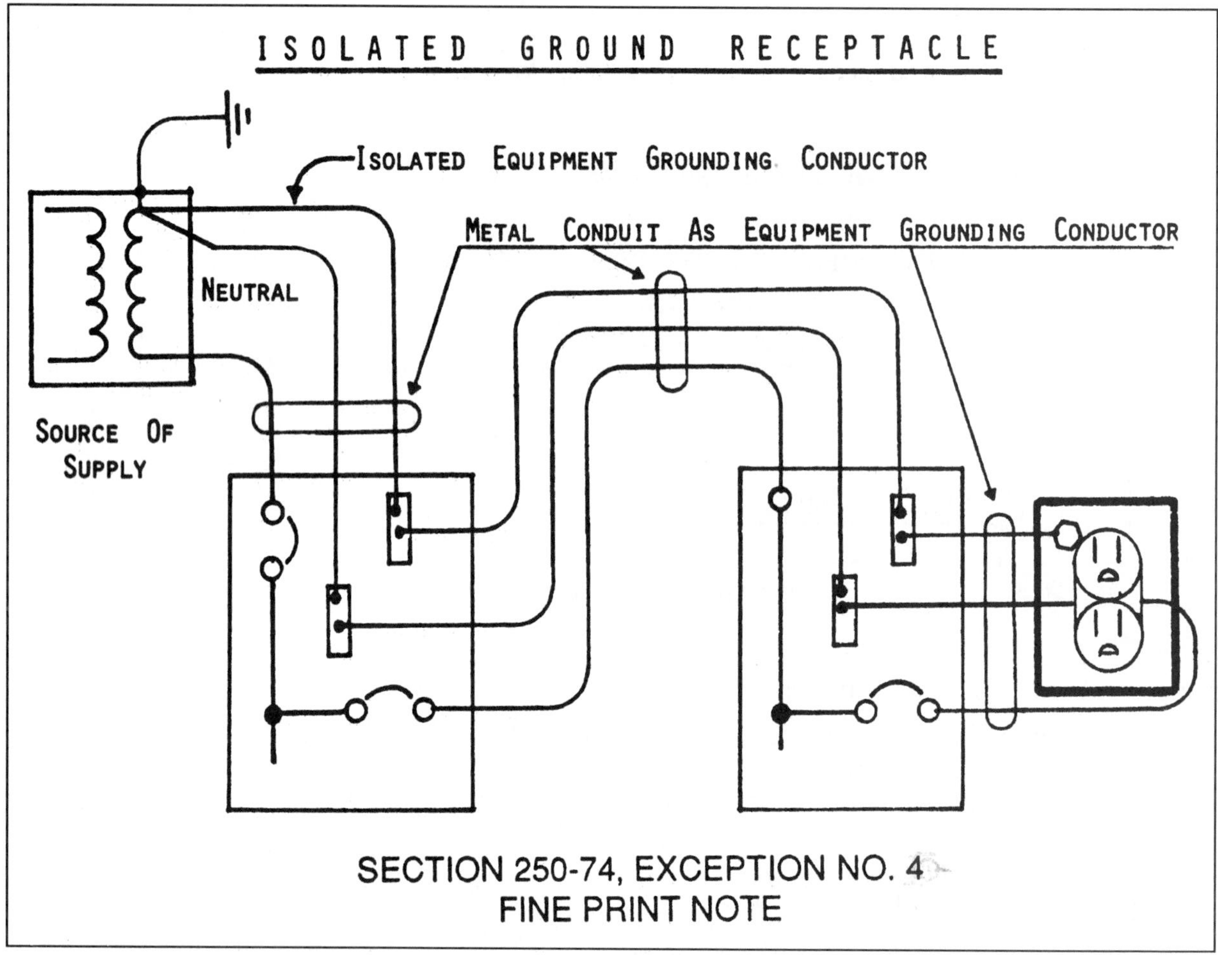

Fig. 12–26 Insulated equipment grounding conductor installed from isolated grounded receptacle back to source of supply.

be required, one for the isolated grounding receptacle and one for other equipment grounding.

When a metal box is installed in a nonmetallic raceway and an isolated receptacle is installed in the metal box, the FPN following Exception 4 of *250-74* indicates that the Code intends for the box to be grounded. This requires two equipment grounding conductors, one for the box and one for the isolated receptacle. *Section 250-114* requires all equipment grounding conductors entering a box to be connected together. Exception 4 to *250-74* permits isolated receptacle installation without connecting the two equipment grounding conductors together.

The basic rule required the equipment grounding conductor for an isolated receptacle to be carried back to the service. When the service is in one building and the isolated receptacle is in the second building, the equipment grounding conductor for the isolated receptacle is not required to be installed back to the service in the first building (figure 12–27, page 203). The equipment grounding conductor is only required to be installed back to the source of supply entering the second building.

Section 380-12 requires metal face plates for snap switches to be effectively grounded where installed in a nonmetallic enclosure and used with a wiring method that includes or provides an equipment ground. Metal face plates do not come with a means for grounding. Therefore, this regulation indicates metal face plates are not to be used with switches in nonmetallic boxes.

TOWER GROUNDING

When a tower is connected by any electrical conductors, as a TV tower might be con-

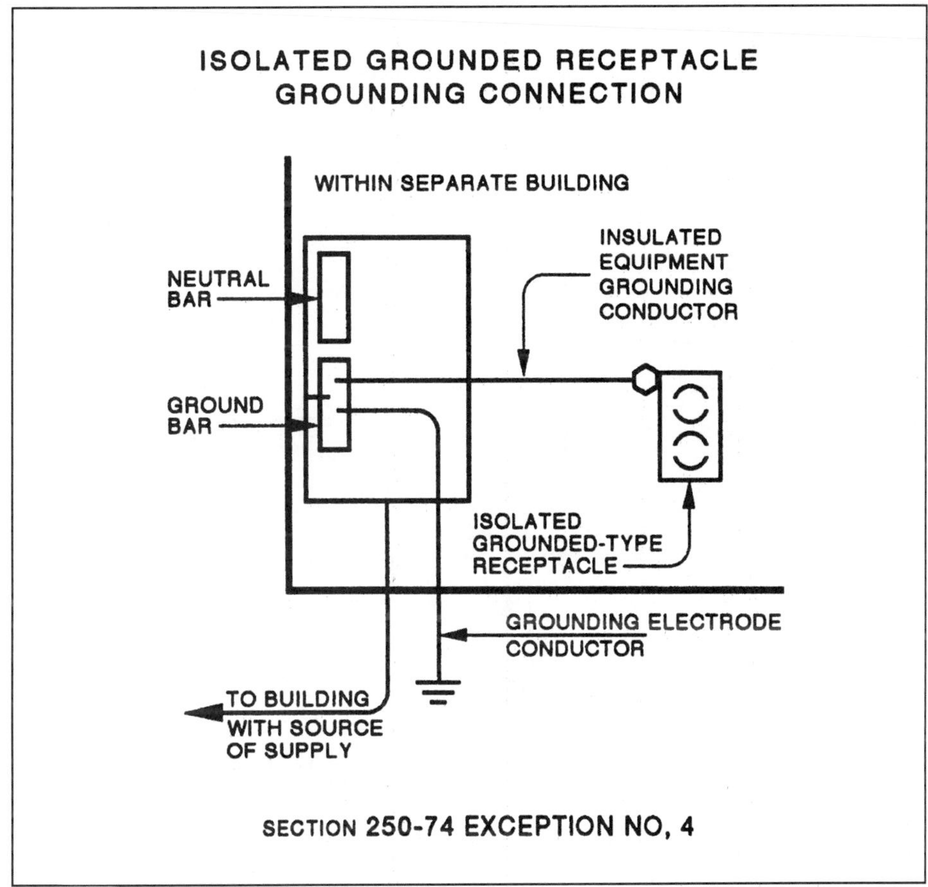

Fig. 12–27 Connections for equipment grounding conductor in separate building.

nected at a residence, the equipment grounding conductor shall be run to the tower and connected to the tower, as shown in figure 12–28 (page 204). The figure illustrates a fault that could take place between the tower and the aerial lead back to the TV set. Without the equipment grounding conductor, a serious hazard could be created.

The tower is permitted to be grounded to a grounding electrode, but the grounding electrode does not take the place of the equipment grounding conductor. *Section 250-51* prohibits the use of the earth as the sole equipment grounding conductor.

COMPUTER GROUNDING

As stated in *Section 90-1(c)*, the Code is not intended as a design specification manual. The purpose of the Code is to protect people and property from hazards arising from the use of electricity *(Section 90-1(a))*. However, to accomplish the purpose of the Code and have an effectively grounded system, Code regulations for grounding must be incorporated into the design of any electrical installation or computer system. The Code gives the minimum requirements. There is nothing in the Code that prohibits making an installation better. In the case of computers, the installation almost has to be better than the minimum Code requirements.

Section 250-21, "Objectionable currents over grounding conductors," lists some things that can be done to interrupt the ground path. *Section 250-21(b)(1)* lists one method as "discontinue one or more such grounding connections." However, the Code is careful here to add this statement: "but not all grounding connections." The objectionable currents referred to are those currents, possibly leakage currents, that might be traveling back to the source by way of the equipment grounding conductor rather than the neutral conductor. However, in *250-21(d)*, "Limitations to permissible alterations," the Code does not recognize currents that cause noise or

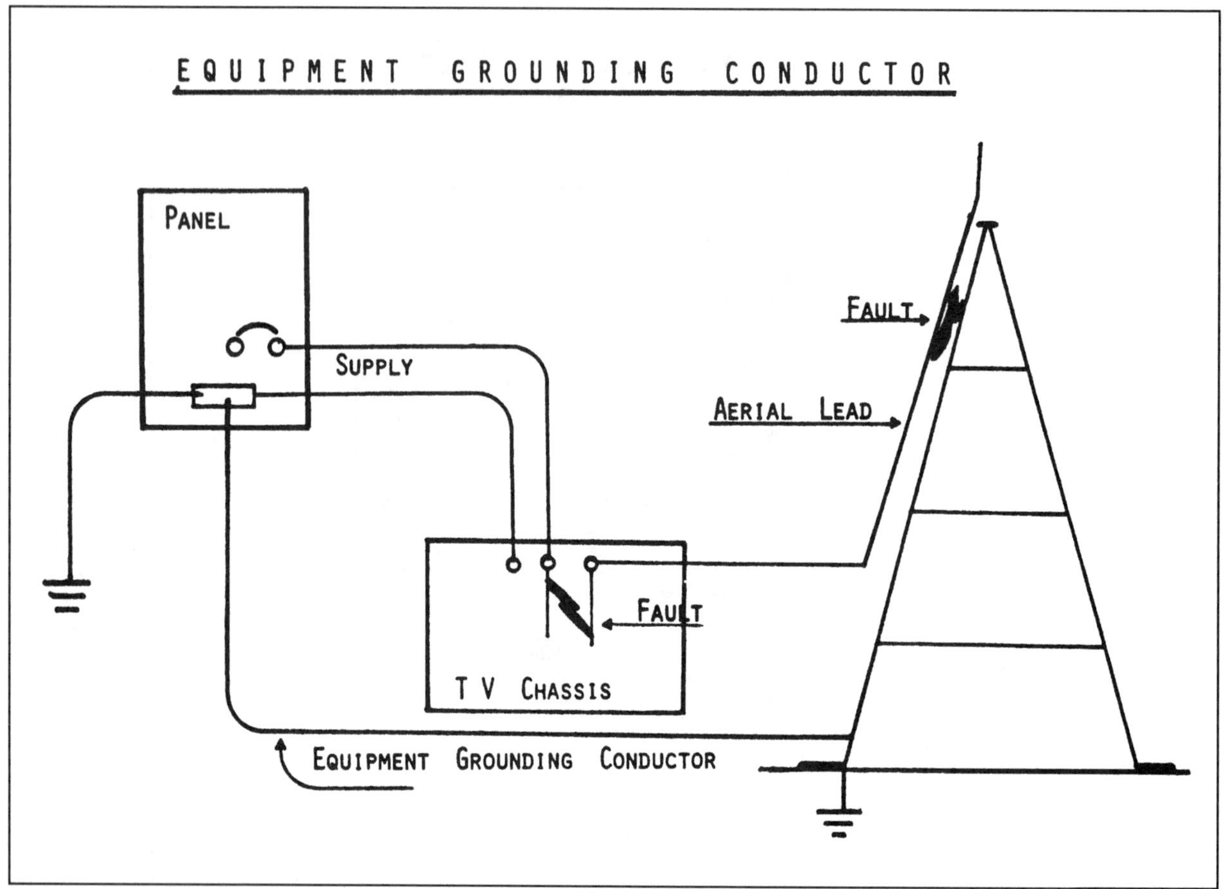

Fig. 12–28 Tower grounding with an equipment grounding conductor.

data errors in electronic equipment as the objectionable currents addressed in *Section 250-21*. The electronic equipment includes computers, data processing equipment, and similar equipment. As illustrated in figure 12–29, the exception to *Section 250-75* permits the continuity between a metal raceway and a metal enclosure to be interrupted when there is a problem with electrical noise (electromagnetic interference) provided:

1. The equipment enclosure is supplied by a branch circuit.
2. The branch circuit does not extend beyond the equipment enclosure.
3. The insulating fitting is a listed fitting.
4. The equipment enclosure is grounded by means of an equipment grounding conductor.

The exception permits isolating the equipment enclosed by means of a nonmetallic spacer or fitting, installed at the point of attachment. This spacer or fitting would be an insulating material. The insulating fitting is required to be a listed fitting. The Code does not mean the fitting has to

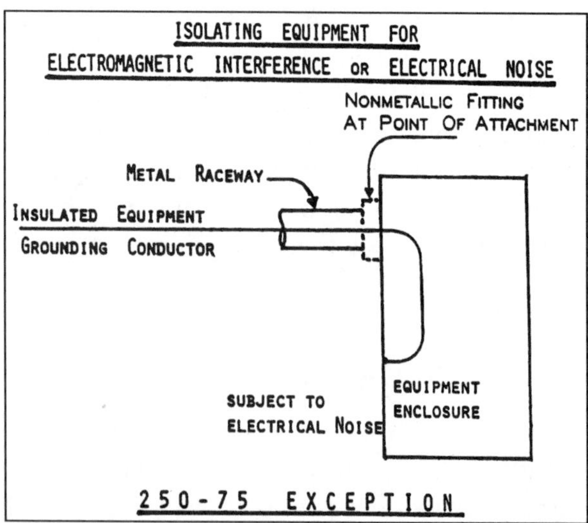

Fig. 12–29 Insulating equipment to protect against transmission of electrical noise via metal raceways (electromagnetic interference).

be listed for this specific use; it can be any listed electrical fitting that will accomplish the purpose. A homemade fitting is not permitted.

When the continuity of the raceway is broken with the nonmetallic fitting, it also breaks up any circulating current paths the metal raceway might establish. This does not mean, however, that the enclosure is not grounded; the exception also requires that an insulated grounding conductor be installed to ground the enclosure. An example of such an installation would be when a cash register or a computer terminal is hard wired rather than cord- and plug-connected.

The FPN following *Section 250-75* calls attention to the fact that when the Code permits an isolated receptacle or electrical equipment to be isolated, and that equipment is enclosed in a metal enclosure, it does not eliminate the requirement for grounding the metal enclosure.

An entire book could be written on computer grounding alone, and this text is not intended to include all the information on the subject. The relationship between computer grounding and the requirements of the *National Electrical Code®* will be covered here, especially some of the things the Code requires and some of the things the Code permits. Successful computer grounding can be accomplished and can be compatible with the Code regulations. For example, the Code requires the following:

1. All grounding shall be installed in accordance with *Article 250*, including:
   a. Grounding electrode
   b. Grounded conductor
   c. Main bonding jumpers
   d. Grounding conductor
   e. Equipment and enclosure bonding and grounding
2. All noncurrent-carrying metal parts of equipment and enclosures shall be grounded so there is no potential difference between a piece of equipment and ground.
3. All grounding electrodes shall be bonded together (*Section 250-81*).
4. Where a separately derived system is used, it shall comply with separately derived system installations.

The Code permits the following:

1. An isolated grounding system is permitted (*Section 250-74*, Exception No. 4 and *Section 384-20*, Exception No. 1).
2. Equipment protected by a double insulation or an equivalent shall not be required to be grounded (*Section 250-42*, Exception No. 4).
3. When the power source and the computer source are common, a separate grounding electrode is permitted to be established, but it shall be bonded to the service equipment grounding electrode *(Section 250-91(c))*.
4. An entirely separately derived system, dedicated to computer equipment with a separate grounding electrode and equipment grounding, is permitted (*Section 250-26*).

Figure 12–30 (page 206) illustrates how a computer system could have its own isolated equipment grounding system, common with the power source grounding electrode. All equipment grounding conductors used are insulated copper conductors, run the shortest distance possible. All collect at the special grounding bar in the power distribution panel and all return to the grounding electrode by means of an insulated, unbroken, equipment grounding conductor. Where a computer floor is used and is set on metal floor pedestals, the pedestals are permitted to be bonded and connected to the special ground bar in the power panel (figure 12–31, page 206).

Figure 12–32 (page 207) illustrates the use of a No. 4/0 insulated copper conductor installed as a grounding electrode conductor riser for computer grounding. The riser is used to establish a common grounding electrode for separately derived systems on the various floors. It is connected to a separate grounding electrode or to the power source grounding electrode. When connected to a separate grounding electrode, it is bonded to the power source grounding elec-

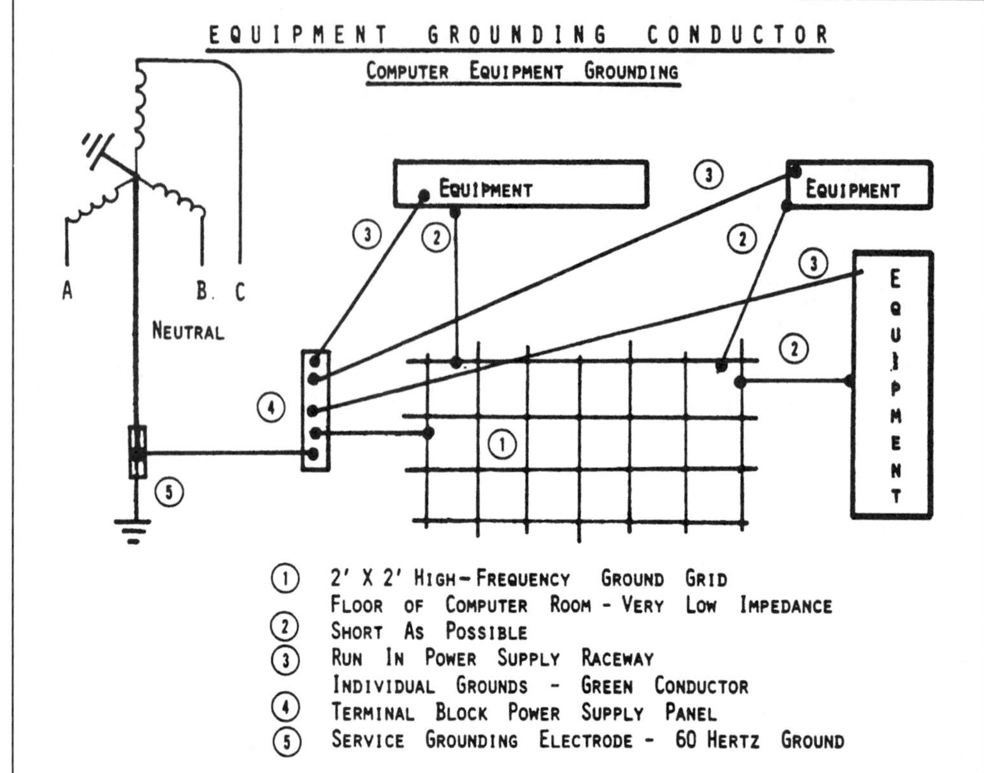

Fig. 12–30 One method of computer room grounding.

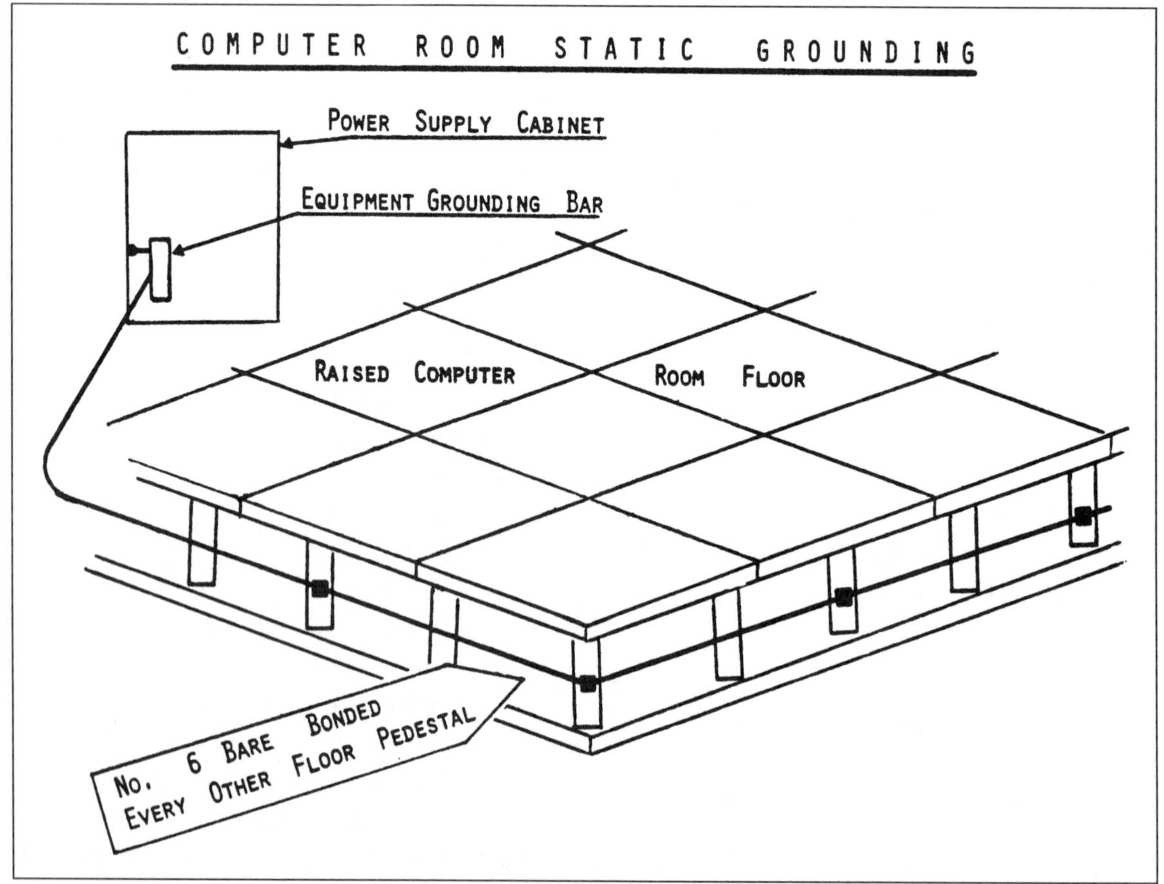

Fig. 12–31 One method of grounding a computer room floor.

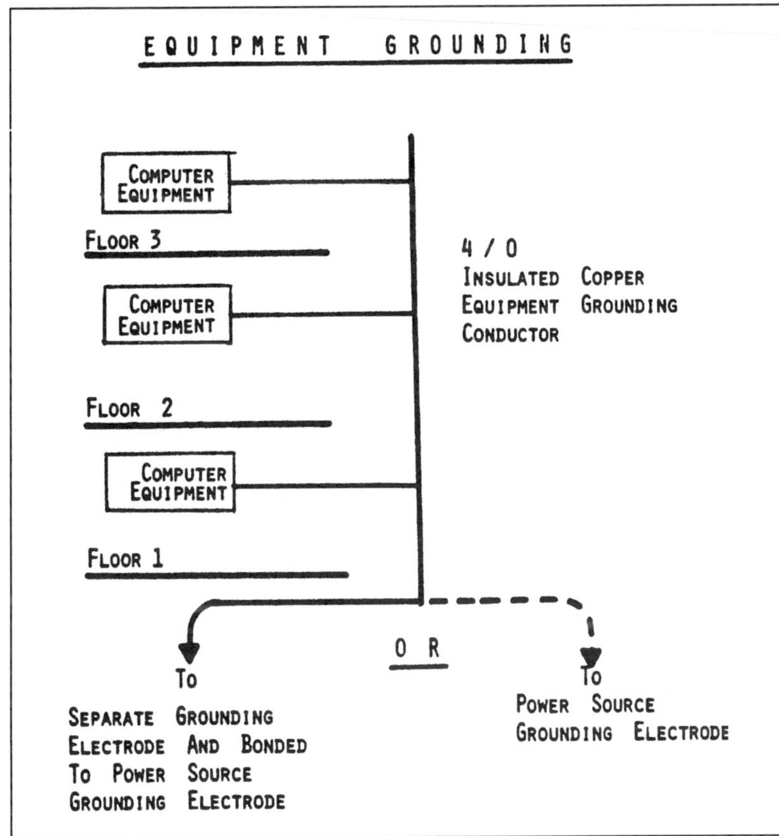

Fig. 12–32 A separate No. 4/0 copper conductor riser used for computer grounding.

trode. Where computer equipment is interconnected on different floors, the same reference point to ground is established on all floors. It is used in place of building steel on one floor and the metal water piping on another floor for a separately derived system.

FOLLOW UP

Topics for self-study, discussion, or questioning.

1. Why are metal enclosures and equipment grounded?
2. Discuss how *Sections 250-32* and *250-33* cover the grounding of all metal enclosures installed in the electrical system.
3. Discuss guarding and isolating by distance and elevation.
4. Discuss the electrical equipment fastened in place or installed with a permanent wiring method that is specifically identified to be grounded.
5. Discuss cord- and plug-connected electrical equipment that the Code specifically identifies to be grounded.
6. Discuss where the use of double insulation is permitted in place of equipment grounding.
7. Discuss the use of the isolated transformer.

8. Explain the purpose of using separate bus bars for the neutral conductor and for the equipment grounding conductor in an enclosure.
9. Define an *isolated grounding receptacle.*
10. Explain the installation of an isolated grounding receptacle.
11. Discuss tower grounding.
12. Discuss computer grounding.
13. Discuss how electrical equipment is permitted to be insulated from the supplying raceway to protect against electrical noise.

CHAPTER 13

Grounded Circuit Conductor for Grounding Equipment

OBJECTIVES

After completing this chapter, the student should be able to:

- identify where the grounded circuit conductor (neutral) may be used as the equipment grounding conductor on the line side of the service.
- identify where the grounded circuit conductor (neutral) may be used as the equipment grounding conductor on the line side of the disconnecting means for the service to a second building.
- identify where the grounded circuit conductor (neutral) may be used as the equipment grounding conductor on the load side of the service.
- identify where the grounded circuit conductor (neutral) may be used as the equipment grounding conductor on the load side of the disconnecting means for a separately derived system.
- explain the requirements for the use of the grounded circuit conductor (neutral) as the equipment grounding conductor for grounding appliances on the load side of the service equipment.

Section 250-61 looks at two locations for using the grounded conductor (neutral) as the equipment grounding conductor. These are:

1. Supply side of service equipment
2. Load side of service equipment

Figure 13–1 shows the overcurrent protection devices as the point of division. Anything on the utility side is line or supply, and any equipment enclosures after the overcurrent protection are considered the load side.

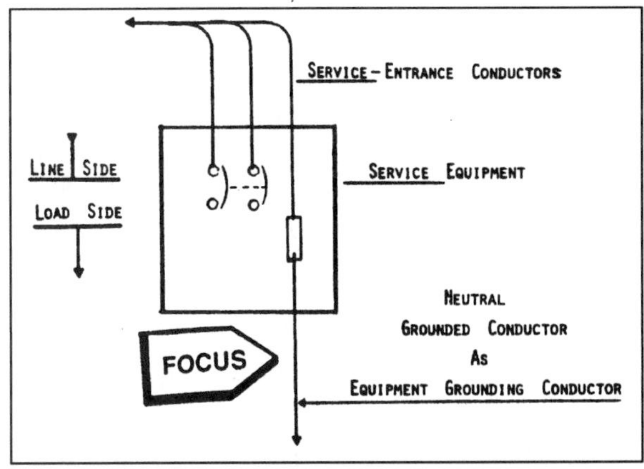

Fig. 13–1 Equipment grounding conductor—line and load side.

Section 250-61 is quickly followed by exceptions, which are the same as those listed in

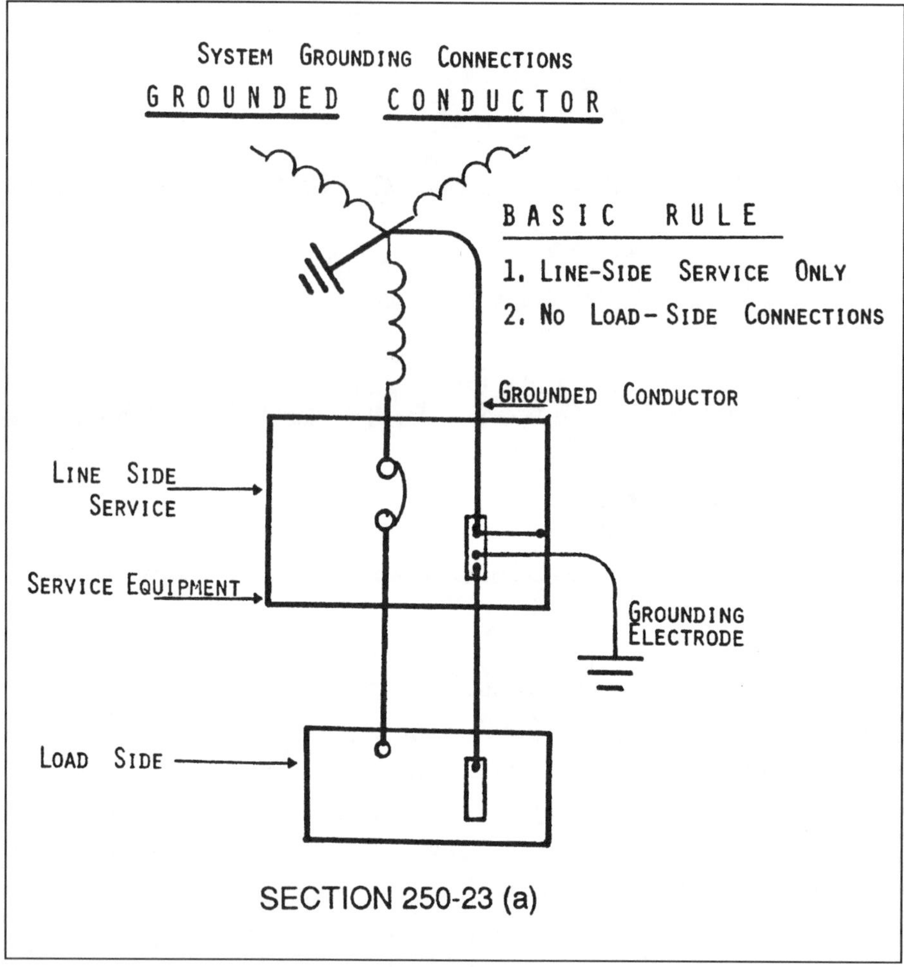

Fig. 13–2 The basic rule for use of neutral as the equipment grounding conductor.

Section 250-23. Each of these divisions and the exceptions will be looked at individually in this chapter.

The use of the grounded circuit conductor (the neutral) for the equipment grounding conductor is almost unlimited on the line side of the service disconnecting means but is very limited on the load side of the service disconnecting means. (For a review of the line and load sides of the service disconnecting means, check figure 11–4 (page 157), in the previous chapter.) This limitation is stated several times in *Article 250*, starting with *Section 250-23* (figure 13–2).

THE BASIC RULE

The basic rule in *Section 250-23* prohibits using the grounded conductor as the equipment grounding conductor on the load side of the service disconnecting means. This rule is followed by an exception permitting limited use of the neutral as the equipment grounding conductor on the load side of the service.

SUPPLY-SIDE USE

The Code uses the term *supply side*, and the field term generally used is *line side*; they mean the same thing. *Section 250-61(a)* permits using the grounded conductor for grounding equipment on the supply or line side of the service disconnecting means. This permits grounding the following items by using the grounded (neutral) conductor:

1. Noncurrent-carrying metal parts of service equipment
2. Metal service raceways

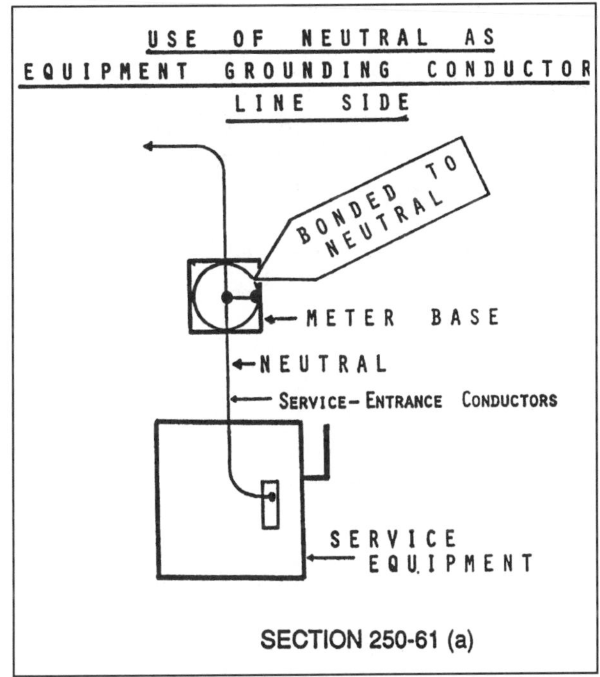

Fig. 13–3 Neutral used to ground meter base on line side of service.

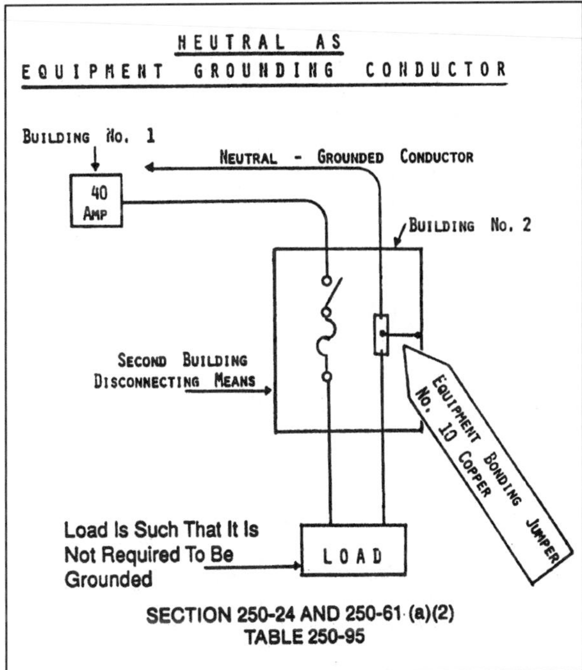

Fig. 13–4 Neutral used as an equipment grounding conductor to a second building.

3. Current transformer (CT) can
4. Meter base
5. Other service equipment metal enclosures

This actually puts very little limitation on the use of the neutral for grounding metal enclosures for current-carrying equipment on the supply side. Some of the enclosures used in conjunction with service equipment, for which the neutral can be used to ground, are the meter base, weather head, CT can, auxiliary gutter, wireway, or any section of metal enclosure for the service-entrance conductors (figure 13–3).

SECOND BUILDING

Section 250-61(a)(2) permits metal enclosures and/or equipment on the supply side of the service disconnecting means for the second building to be grounded by use of the neutral, as illustrated in figure 13–4. The conductor that bonds the second building service enclosure to the neutral is really an equipment bonding jumper. Therefore, it is sized according to the size of the overcurrent protective device protecting the feeder going to the second building, and *Table 250-95* is used.

SEPARATELY DERIVED SYSTEM

Section 250-26(b) permits the grounding electrode conductor for a separately derived system to be connected at the source of supply or at the first system disconnecting means or overcurrent protection. When a separately derived system has a grounded conductor (neutral), *Section 250-61(a)(3)* sets down the regulations for using the neutral for grounding equipment and enclosures on the line side. In this regulation, the key is the point of connection of the grounded conductor (neutral) to the grounding electrode conductor.

Figure 13–5 (page 212) illustrates the use of a two winding transformer as a separately derived source of supply. The point of connection of the grounding electrode conductor is at the transformer. Therefore, nothing can be grounded to the neutral after it leaves the transformer. The result of this is that the equipment grounding conductor for the metal enclosed disconnecting means and overcurrent protection must be run back to the point of connection of the grounding electrode conductor at the transformer.

Figure 13–6 (page 212) illustrates the use of a two winding transformer as a separately derived source of supply with the point of connection of the grounding electrode conductor at

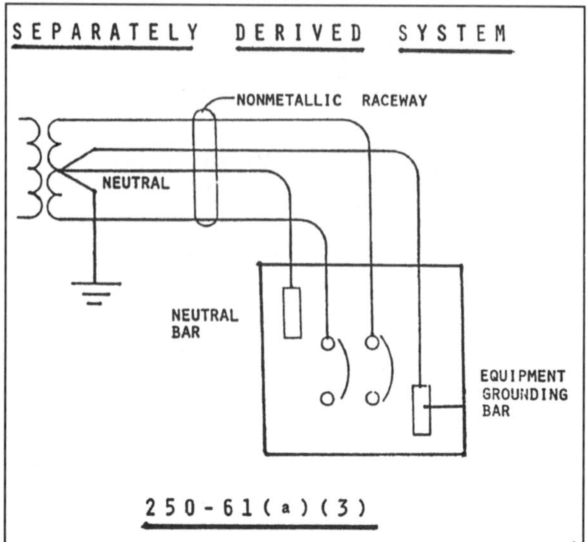

Fig. 13–5 The grounded conductor (neutral) used for equipment grounding on the supply side of a separately derived system.

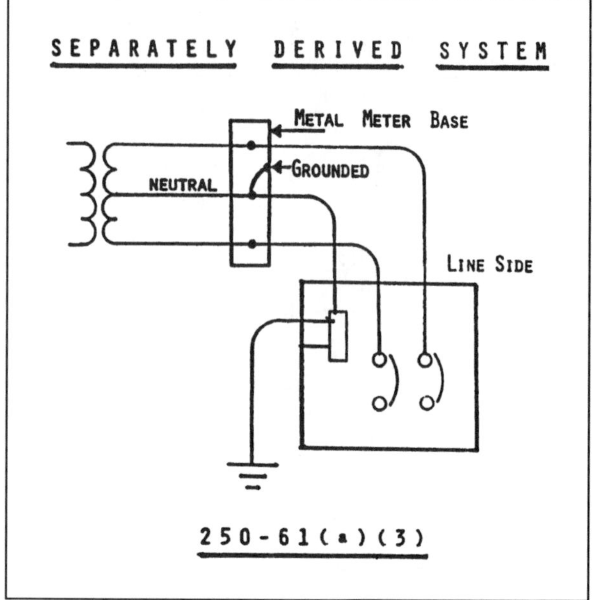

Fig. 13–6 Grounded conductor (neutral) used for equipment grounding on the supply side of a separately derived system.

the first disconnecting means or overcurrent protection for the system. Metal enclosures on the line side of the disconnecting means can be grounded to the grounded conductor. Also, the disconnecting means enclosure can be grounded to the neutral. However, the neutral cannot be used for grounding equipment on the load side of the disconnecting means.

LOAD-SIDE USE

The use of the grounded conductor for equipment grounding on the load side of the service disconnecting means is limited. The basic rule in *Section 250-61(b)* prohibits using the grounded conductor (neutral) for grounding equipment on the *load side* of the following locations:

1. The service disconnecting switch
2. The disconnecting switch for a separately derived system
3. The main disconnecting means for a separate building

This regulation prohibits using the grounded conductor as a means of equipment grounding. Should the neutral be used promiscuously for equipment grounding, there could be a multitude of unintentional paths set up for electrons to travel on, resulting in circulating ground currents. By regulating the use of the neutral as an equipment grounding conductor, there is more control exercised over the path the electrons will travel.

Exception No. 3 in *Section 250-23(a)* and Exception No. 1 in *Section 250-61(b)* both refer to *Section 250-60*, which permits using the grounded conductor (the neutral) as the equipment grounding conductor for existing branch circuits only (figure 13-7, page 213).

The wording in *Section 250-60* and the *Section 250-61(b)* Exception No. 1 means that when new installations are made, the neutral of the branch circuit conductors can no longer be used as the equipment grounding conductor. If a dwelling is remodeled, and the branch circuit is existing and the appliances are changed out with no installation of a new branch circuit, the exception would be permitted, and the existing neutral could be used as the equipment grounding conductor.

Section 250-60(a) is specific about the supply circuit when the neutral is used to ground an electric range or clothes dryer. Actually, only two circuits are permitted. These are:

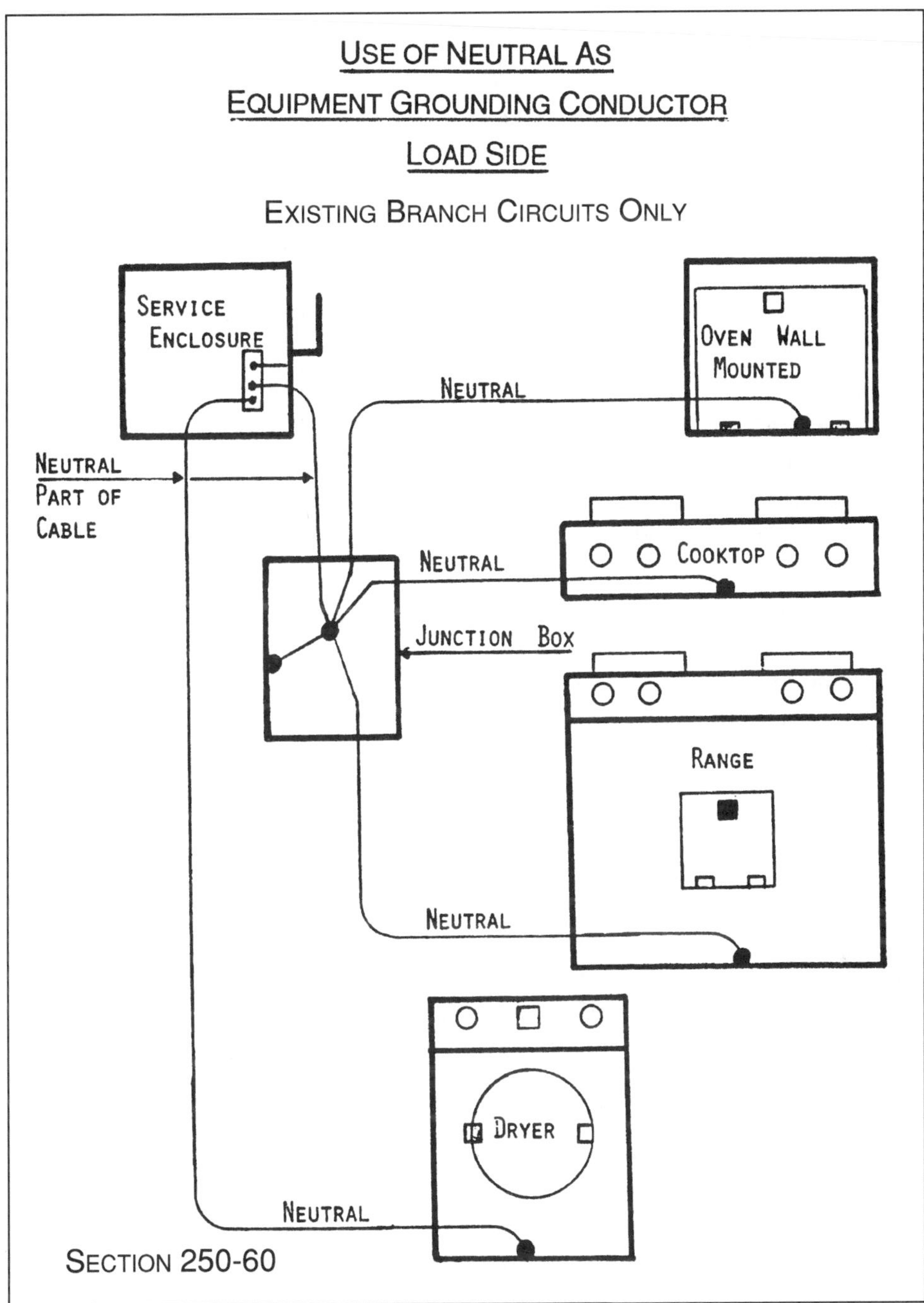

Fig. 13–7 Neutral used as equipment grounding conductor for grounding electrical cooking equipment and dryer on existing branch circuits only.

1. 120/240-volt, single-phase, three-wire circuit
2. 120/208-volt, single-phase, three-wire circuit derived from a three-phase, four-wire system

The requirement of single phase and the lower voltage almost limits the use of this exception to residential installation. In addition to the circuit requirement, all the following conditions must be met before the neutral can be used as the equipment grounding conductor.

1. The use of the neutral as the equipment grounding conductor is limited to existing branch circuits only.
2. The grounded conductor is not smaller than No. 10 copper or No. 8 aluminum.
3. The grounded conductor is insulated unless part of Type SE service-entrance cable.

4. The circuit originates at the service equipment.
5. Grounding contacts of receptacles furnished as part of the equipment are bonded to the equipment.

Looking at *Table 250-95*, No. 10 copper or No. 8 aluminum is permitted when the overcurrent protective device is not over 60 amps. This is applicable to the majority of electric ranges or cooking equipment installed in residential occupancies. Once again, note in point 3 above how there is an indication of the use being limited to residential occupancies. This occurs by the use of an insulated conductor or a conductor that is covered in a service-entrance cable. The ground path for the electrons to travel on is also controlled. When point 4 above requires the circuit to originate in the service equipment, it eliminates any situations where the equipment is fed from a distribution panel. An example of point 5 is an electric range with built-in receptacles. The grounded contact of the receptacle must be bonded to the range before the range can be grounded with the neutral conductor.

There is encouragement here to use cord- and plug-connected appliances with an equipment grounding means built into the cord, so that when a nonqualified person moves the equipment from house to house, there is no hard wiring to be done. The installation of an equipment grounding conductor is not left to an unqualified person.

Section 250-61, Exception No. 3 is illustrated in figure 13–8. It permits the grounded conductor to be used as the equipment grounding conductor on the load side of the service equipment to ground meter socket enclosures on the load side of the service disconnect, when all the following conditions are met:

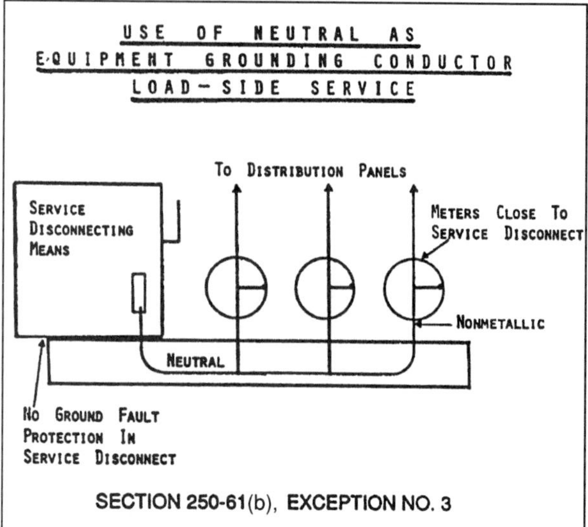

Fig. 13–8 Neutral used to ground meter socket enclosure located on load side and close to service disconnecting means.

1. No service ground-fault protection is installed.
2. All meter socket enclosures are located near the service disconnect.
3. The grounded circuit conductor (neutral) is sized according to *Table 250-95* for equipment grounding conductors.

Such an installation could be used for a multifamily dwelling with each unit individually metered, or for a small building with each unit individually metered.

SUMMARY

This chapter has shown the mixed use of a grounded conductor, intentionally grounded and installed as a current-carrying circuit conductor. Under certain conditions this grounded conductor serves a twofold purpose. It is the grounded, current-carrying circuit conductor and the equipment grounding conductor.

FOLLOW UP

Topics for self-study, discussion, or questioning.

1. Discuss the basic rule set down for the use of the grounded conductor's use as an equipment grounding conductor.
2. Identify the line and load sides of the service.

3. Discuss the use of the grounded conductor (neutral) as the equipment grounding conductor on the line side of the service.
4. What appliances are permitted to be grounded on the load side of the service by means of the grounded conductor (neutral)?
5. Discuss the requirements that must be met in order to use the grounded conductor (neutral) as the equipment grounding conductor on the load side of the service to ground appliances.
6. Discuss the use of the grounded conductor (neutral) on the load side of the service to ground meter bases.

CHAPTER 14

Ground-Fault Protective Equipment

OBJECTIVES

After completing this chapter, the student should be able to:

- explain what the term "ground-fault protection for equipment" means.
- identify when ground-fault protection of equipment is required at the service.
- identify when ground-fault protection of equipment is permitted when not required.
- identify when ground-fault protection is required on feeders.
- explain the operation of a "ground-fault circuit interrupter" (GFCI).
- identify specific locations where GFCI receptacles must be installed.
- identify specific installations, other than receptacles, where GFCI protection is required.
- explain how a two-wire receptacle is permitted to be replaced with a GFCI receptacle.

This chapter focuses on the two pieces of ground-fault equipment required by the Code to protect equipment and personnel from the hazards arising from ground faults (figure 14–1). These are:

1. Ground-fault protection device for equipment protection
2. Ground-fault circuit interrupter for personnel protection

Although the purpose of these two pieces of equipment is different, there are three things they have in common. These are:

1. Their operation depends on a ground fault.
2. They open the circuit with the ground fault.
3. There is a certain time frame within which the equipment must open the circuit.

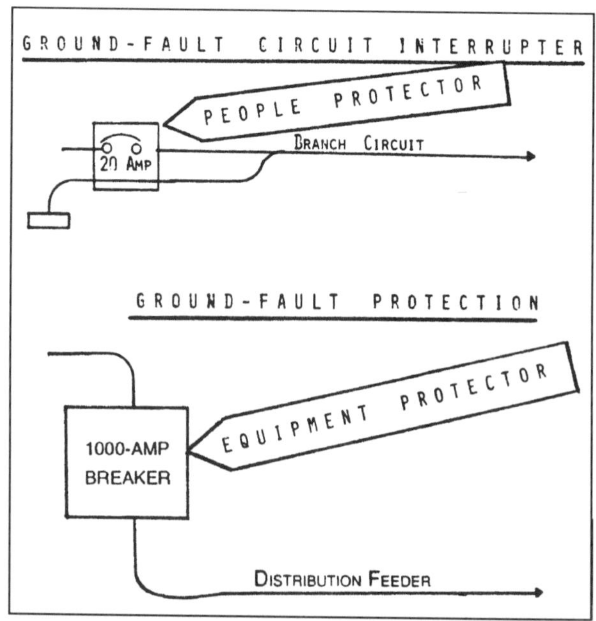

Fig. 14–1 Ground-fault protection for people and equipment.

Ground faults are arcing faults; arcing creates heat, heat creates fire, and heat will attack and destroy the conductor insulation.

GROUND-FAULT PROTECTION OF EQUIPMENT

Figure 14–2 illustrates the definition of *Ground-Fault Protection of Equipment.* The following lists some important points in the definition.

1. Protects equipment

   Comment: There is no mention of personnel because the fault current trip setting of a ground-fault protector is of such magnitude that it could be fatal to a person.

2. Operates on line-to-ground fault current

   Comment: The ground-fault protector gives no phase-to-phase fault protection. That is the responsibility of the overcurrent protective device.

3. Opens the disconnecting means

   Comment: There are no ringing bells, there are no flashing lights, there is no warning, but the circuit is opened, whether it is a service, feeder, or branch circuit. The disconnecting means can be a switch or a circuit breaker with proper current and voltage ratings that can be automatically operated. It is hoped that the overcurrent device nearest the ground fault will open the faulted circuit and disconnect only that part of the circuit before the ground-fault protection operates.

4. Operates at a current level less than the circuit overcurrent device is set for

   Comment: A ground fault can draw current and still not trip the circuit overcurrent

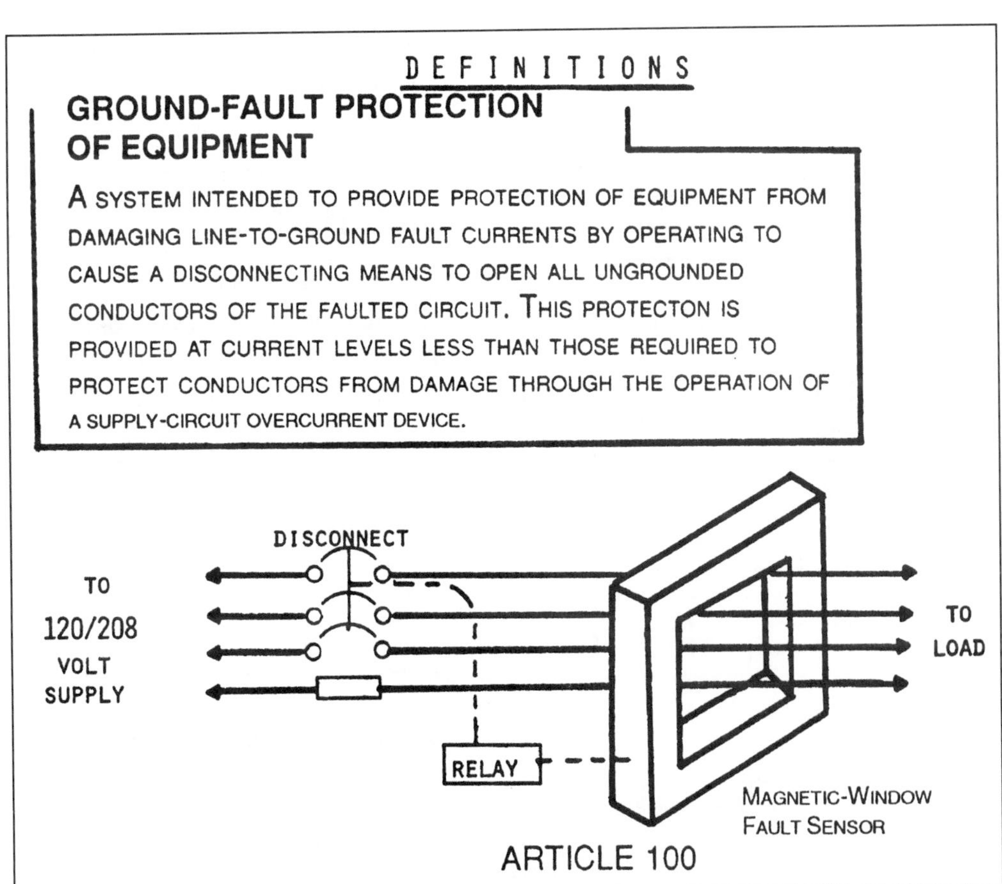

Fig. 14–2 Definition of *ground-fault protection of equipment.**

protective device. For example, a 1200-amp overcurrent device has an 800-amp load working and there is a 200-amp ground fault. The breaker sees the total current needed as 1000 amps and continues to furnish 1000 amps. The overcurrent device does not operate.

GROUND-FAULT PROTECTION EQUIPMENT REQUIRED AT SERVICE

Section 230-95 (figure 14–3) sets the basic rules for equipment ground-fault protection. All of the following conditions must be met before ground-fault protection of equipment is required:

1. Solidly grounded
2. Wye connected service
3. More than 150 volts to ground
4. Not exceeding 600 volts between phases
5. Disconnecting means rated for 1000 amps or more
6. All ungrounded conductors opened by service disconnecting means
7. Maximum setting of overcurrent device: 1200 amps
8. Maximum time delay for opening service disconnecting means: 1 second for ground-fault currents 3000 amps or larger
9. Equipment ground-fault protection permitted on distribution feeders
10. Equipment ground-fault protection permitted on disconnecting means rated at less than 1000 amps

An exception to the basic rule permits an installation to be made without ground-fault protection in a continuous industrial process plant where a nonorderly shutdown would introduce a hazard to personnel and/or equipment.

Pinpointing the wye connection eliminates the delta or delta-with-a-grounded-leg connection. The limitations of over 150 volts to ground and under 600 volts between phases almost

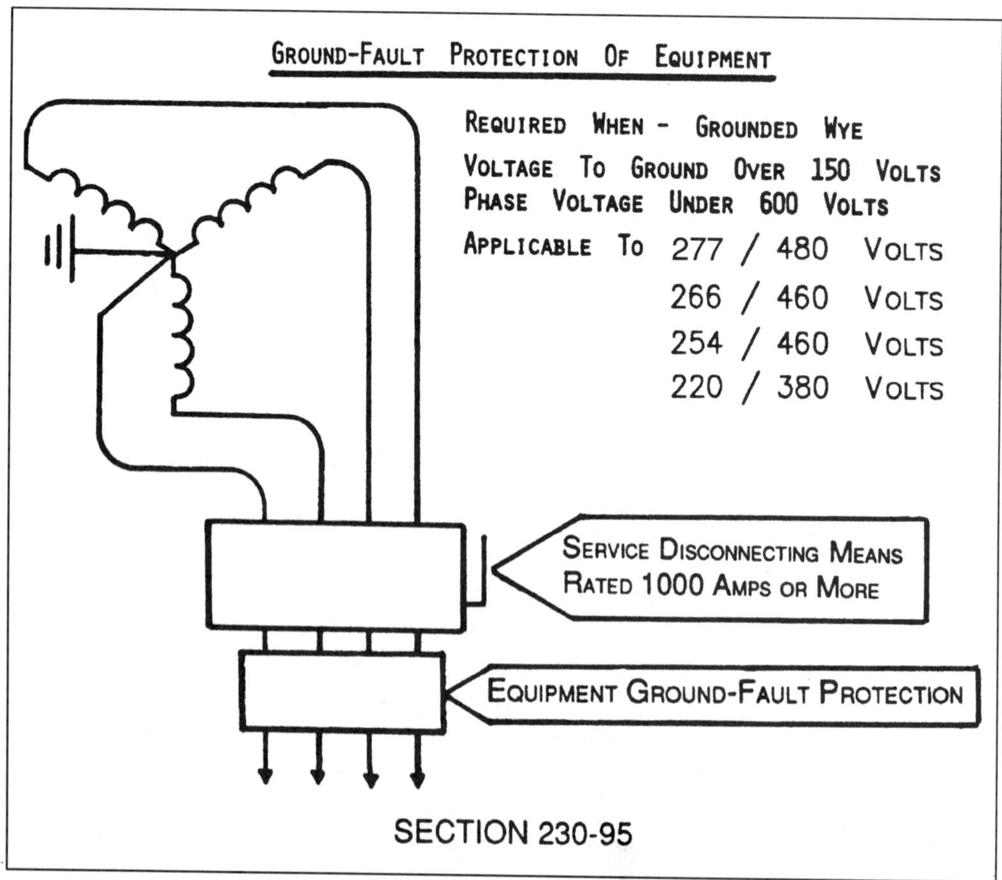

Fig. 14–3 Ground-fault protection of equipment is required by *Section 230-95*.

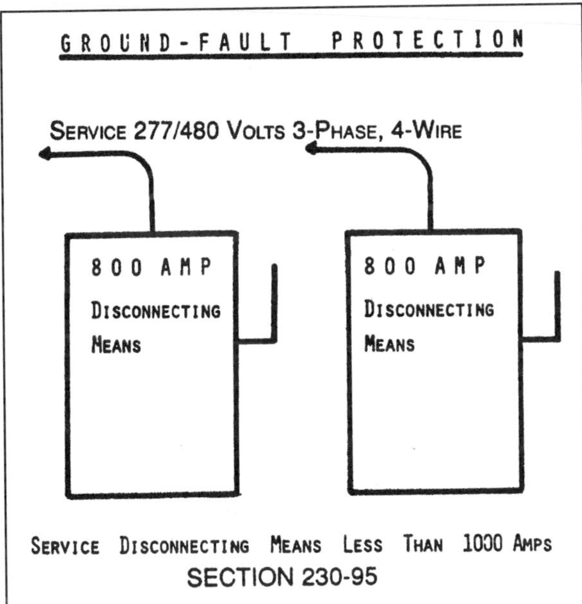

Fig. 14–4 Ground-fault protection is permitted but not required when using two 800-amp service disconnecting switches.

pinpoints the 277/480, nominal voltage, wye connection. The 120/208-volt wye connection is less than 150 volts to ground.

Figure 14–4 illustrates the use of two service disconnecting means, each rated at 800 amps. Although the total is 1600 amps, the service is not required to have ground-fault protection. However, ground-fault protection is permitted on 277/480-volt, wye connected systems with less than a 1000-amp service disconnecting means.

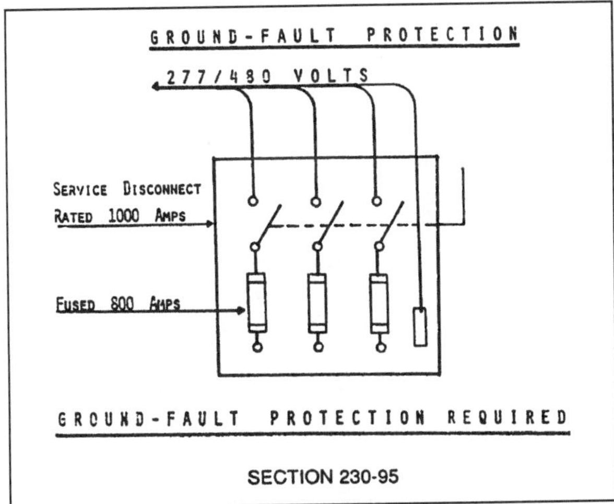

Fig. 14–5 Ground-fault protection is required at the service when using a 1000-amp switch with 800-amp fuses.

Figure 14–5 illustrates the use of a 1000-amp switch with 800-amp fuses in it. This is classified as a 1000-amp disconnect, and ground-fault protection is required. The FPN to *Section 250-95* identifies the service disconnecting means rating when fuses are used or a circuit breaker is used for the overcurrent protection.

1. The rating of the disconnecting means is determined by the largest fuse that can be installed in the disconnecting switch.
2. The rating of the disconnecting means is determined by the higher trip setting for which the actual overcurrent device installed in a circuit breaker is rated or can be adjusted.

There are two exceptions where the ground-fault protection is not required, should the situation qualify for exemption. These are:

1. An industrial process where an orderly shutdown is needed
2. A supply to a fire pump where there is need for the pump motor to keep running under any and all conditions

Figure 14–6 illustrates a 277/480, three-phase, four-wire service with a 600-amp discon-

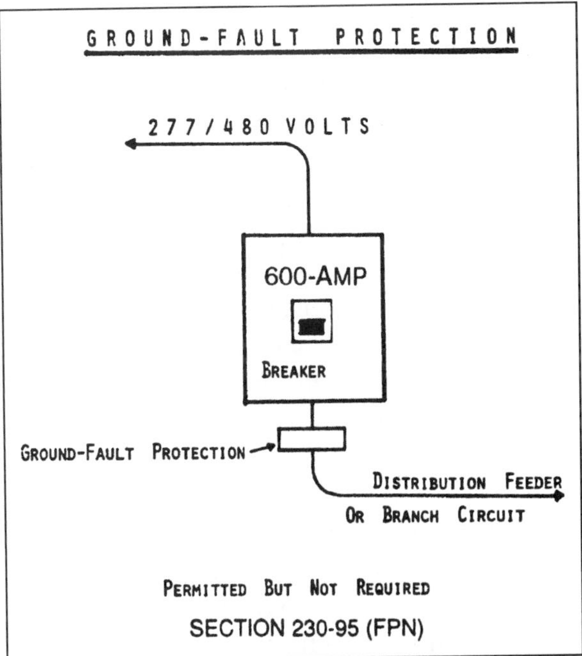

Fig. 14–6 When the service switch is rated at less than 1000 amps, ground-fault protection is not required.

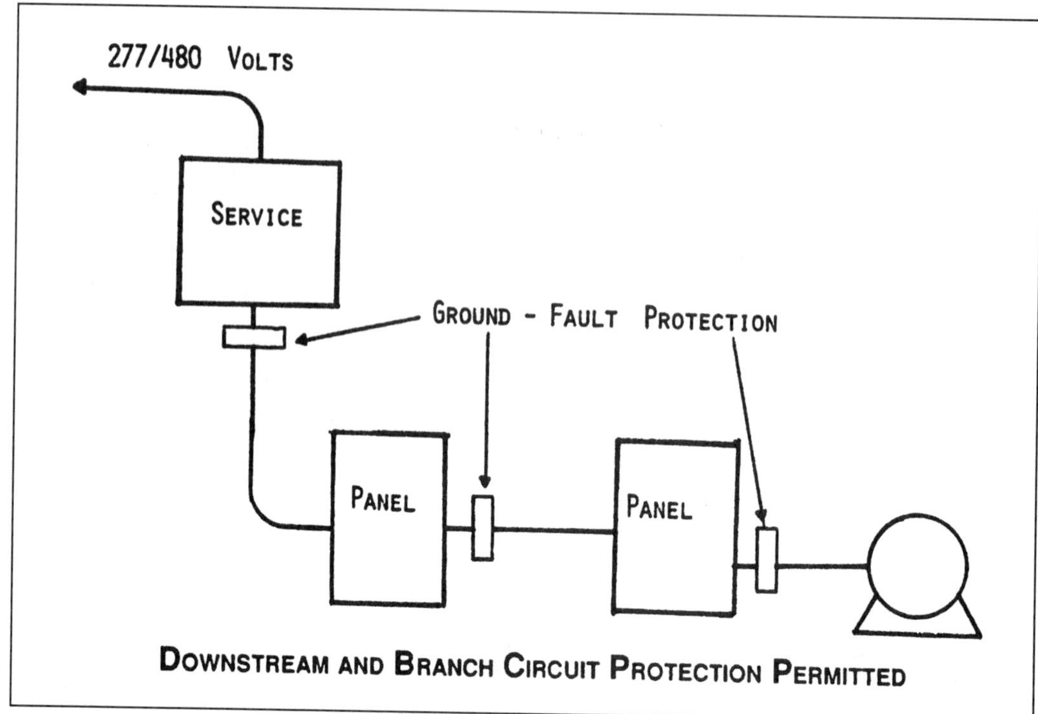

Fig. 14–7 Downstream ground-fault protection is not required but is permitted.

necting means. This installation is not required to have ground-fault protection but it is permitted to have ground-fault protection. The requirement in *Section 230-95* is only for the service, but an FPN indicates it would be advantageous to also have ground-fault protection downstream (figure 14–7).

The principle of operation of the magnetic-window type ground-fault protector (figure 14–2, page 217) has all the phase conductors and the neutral passing through an iron ring. When there is more current going out on the circuit than is coming back, the sensing device will cause the disconnecting means to open, taking the service off the line. Just an unbalanced current situation between the phase conductors and the neutral will not trigger the sensing device.

A second type of ground-fault protection used to protect services is illustrated in figure 14–8. A current transformer monitors the current flow on the equipment grounding conductor. When a predetermined current flows on the equipment grounding conductor, the secondary of the current transformer will activate a relay. This, in turn, will cause the disconnecting means to operate. The relay can also be connected so it will sound an alarm instead of tripping the breaker. Note in figure 14–8 how any current in the equipment grounding conductor must flow through the current transformer before reaching the grounding electrode conductor or the grounded conductor.

Section 230-95(c) requires testing of the service ground-fault protection when first installed on site. The manufacturer is required to

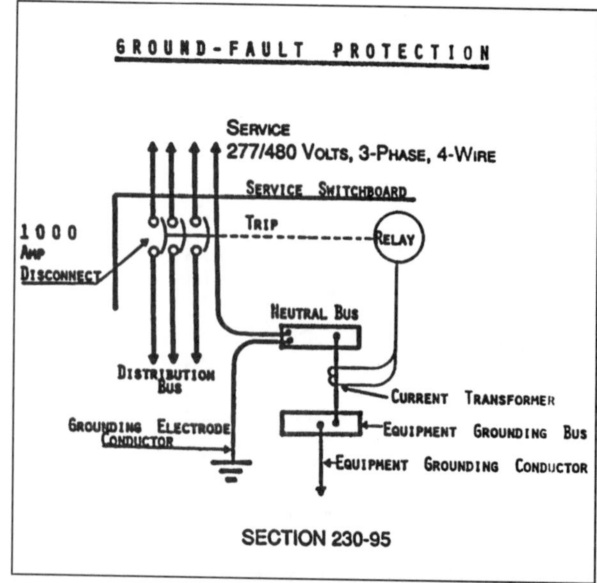

Fig. 14–8 Using a current transformer for ground-fault protection.

furnish the specifications and details for this test and the test is to be performed according to the manufacturer's specifications.

GROUND-FAULT PROTECTION EQUIPMENT REQUIRED—FEEDER

Up to this point, ground-fault protection has been considered only for the service. There are situations, however, where a feeder is so much like a service that it must also have the same protection. *Section 215-10* extends the ground-fault protection of equipment to feeders when the feeder looks very much like the service conductors. In this situation, feeders are to have the same protection required for services in *Section 230-95*. The basic requirements for the feeder are much the same as for the service. The disconnecting means is

1. for a solidly grounded wye system
2. rated at 1000 amperes or greater
3. a wye connected system
4. greater than 150 volts to ground
5. not over 600 volts phase-to-phase

An exception is made to cover the situation where ground-fault protection has been already installed upstream on the supply to the feeder. However this does not prohibit the use of ground-fault protection on feeders.

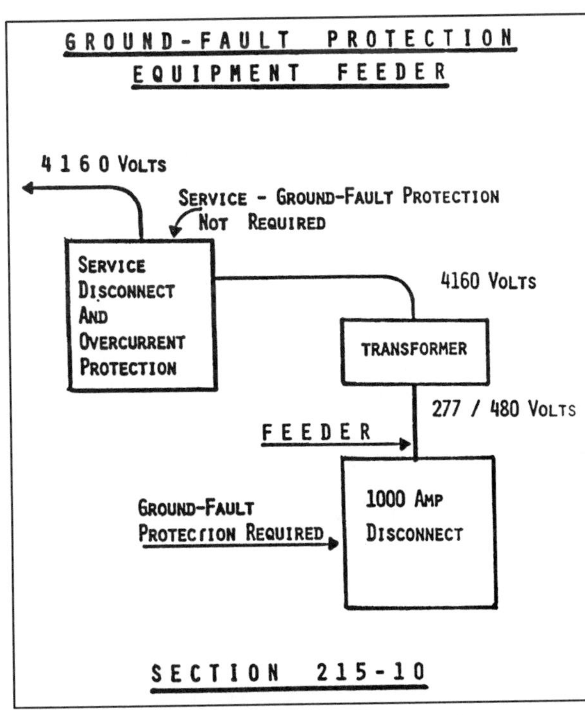

Fig. 14–9 Feeder ground-fault protection.

Figure 14–9 illustrates a separately derived system where the secondary of the transformer is treated very much like a service; technically, however, the secondary of the transformer is a feeder and ground-fault protection is required.

DEFINITION OF *GROUND-FAULT CIRCUIT INTERRUPTER*

Figure 14–10 (page 222) illustrates the definition of *Ground-Fault Circuit Interrupter*, usually referred to as a *GFCI*. The following lists some important points in the definition:

1. Intended to protect personnel
2. Functions to de-energize a circuit or a portion thereof

Comment: The GFCI can be a circuit breaker that will clear the entire circuit or a device that will protect only one outlet or a number of outlets on a circuit.

3. Operates within an established period of time

Comment: This time can vary with the manufacturer, but is usually considered to be 30 milliseconds (30/1000 of one second) to comply with Underwriters Laboratories standards.

4. The predetermined current setting of the GFCI will allow it to operate at less than the rating of the branch circuit overcurrent protective device.

Comment: To comply with Underwriters Laboratories, the predetermined value here is 4 to 6 milliamps. The branch circuit overcurrent protective device might be a 20-amp breaker and will protect the branch circuit at 20 amps, but the GFCI will function at 4 to 6 milliamps to protect personnel.

Theory of Operation

Figure 14–11 (page 222) illustrates a breakdown of a ground-fault circuit interrupter. A breaker is illustrated, but the principle of opera-

A DEVICE
INTENDED FOR THE PROTECTION OF PERSONNEL
THAT FUNCTIONS TO DE-ENERGIZE A CIRCUIT
OR PORTION THEREOF
WITHIN AN ESTABLISHED PERIOD OF TIME
WHEN A CURRENT TO GROUND
EXCEEDS SOME PREDETERMINED VALUE
THAT IS LESS THAN THAT REQUIRED
TO OPERATE THE OVERCURRENT PROTECTIVE DEVICE
OF THE SUPPLY CIRCUIT

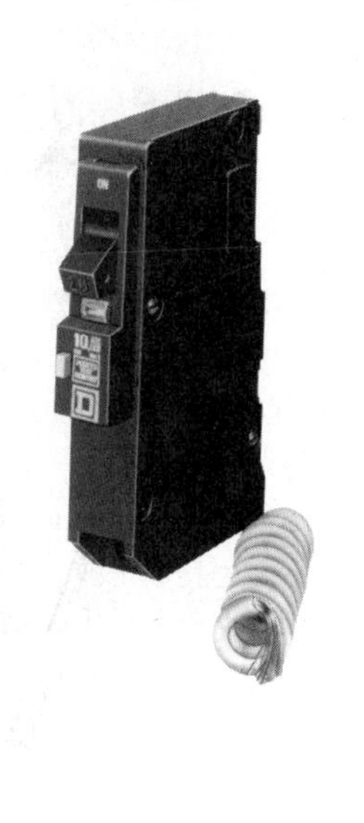

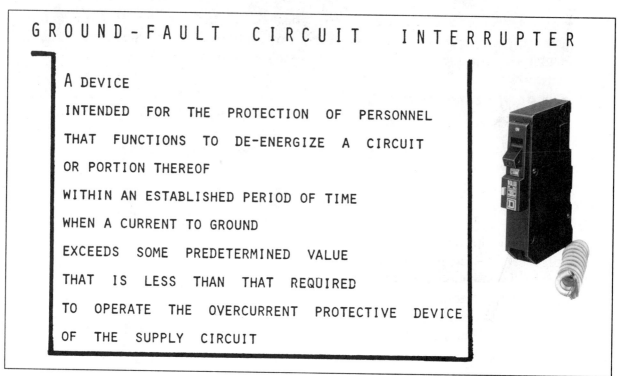

Fig. 14–10 Definition of *ground-fault circuit interrupter*.*

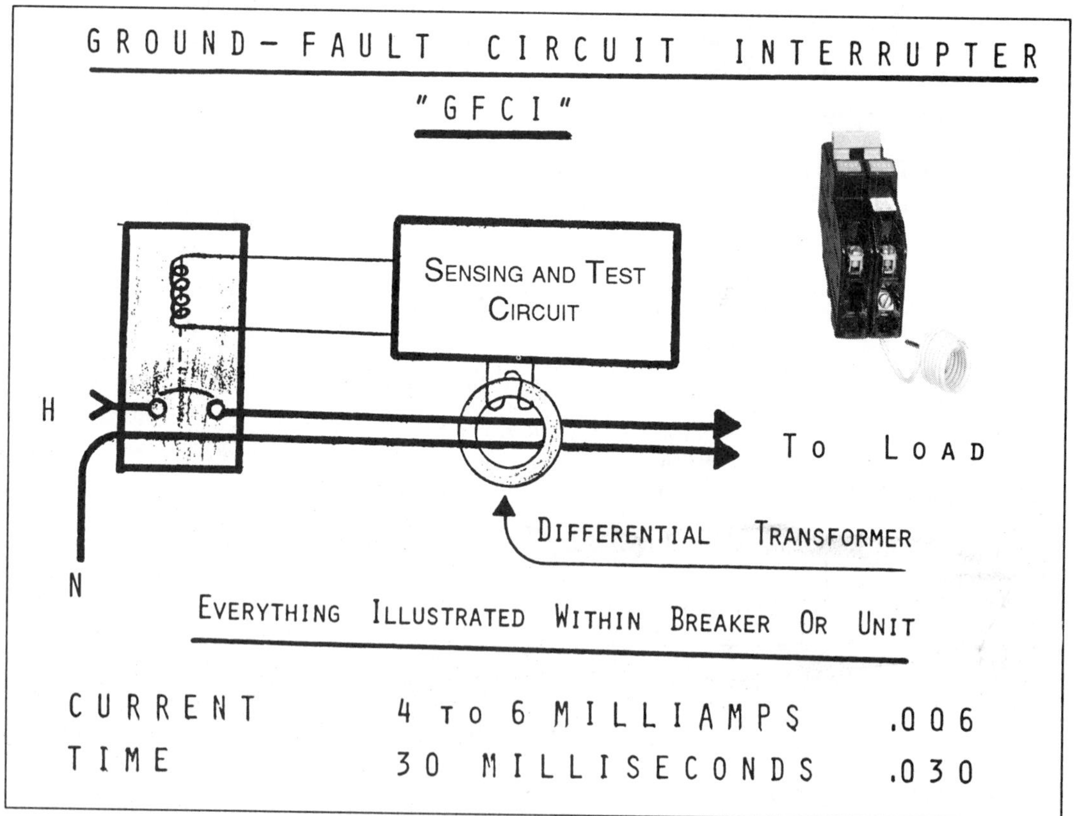

Fig. 14–11 GFCI theory of operation. Courtesy Eaton Corporation "Cutler-Hammer" Products.

* Reprinted with permission from NFPA 70-1996, the National Electrical Code®, Copyright © 1995, National Fire Protection Association, Quincy, Massachusetts 02269. This reprinted material is not the complete and official position of the National Fire Protection Association, on the referenced subject, which is represented only by the standard in its entirety.

tion is the same for an individual GFCI. The hot conductor and the neutral conductor must be installed together as they pass through a differential transformer. The transformer uses a magnetic field to measure the amount of current going to the load against the current returning from the load. The strength of a magnetic field is directly proportional to the current flowing in the conductor. When the amount of current going to the load does not equal the current returning from the load, the induction in the secondary of the differential transformer causes the sensing unit to operate. The sensing unit causes the circuit breaker or the device to trip and open the circuit.

Circuits protected by a GFCI breaker require two conductors to the circuit. There are no three-phase, four-wire circuits for GFCIs for personnel protection.

The GFCI does not protect someone against receiving a shock, but it does limit the time the hazard exists (figure 14–12). The danger still exists, even when there is a GFCI in the circuit. And when an individual receives a shock, the surprise of the shock may cause an injury. For example, an individual might be outside on a metal ladder working with an electric tool and receive an electric shock through the defective tool. Before the GFCI could operate, the surprise shock could cause the individual to fall from the ladder.

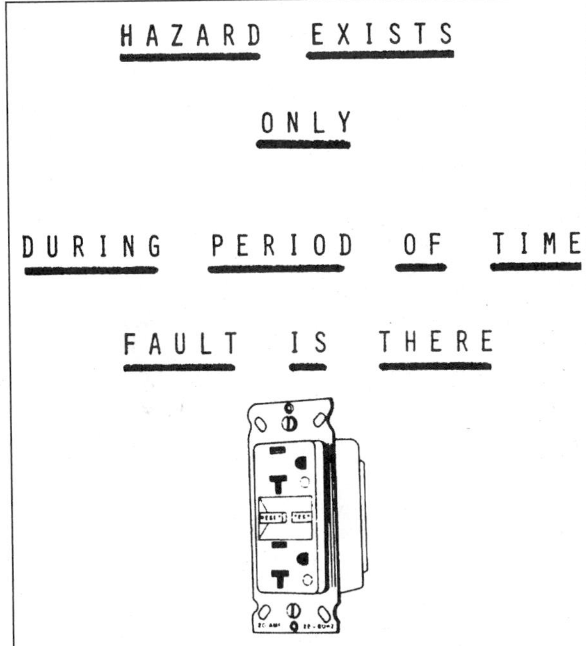

Fig. 14–12 Electric shock hazard exists only during the period of time that the fault is there.

RECEPTACLES REQUIRING GFCI PROTECTION

There are a multitude of receptacle locations for which the Code requires GFCI protection. The requirement can be fulfilled if the branch circuit has a GFCI breaker or if an individual GFCI is installed at the particular location. The following list shows how the use of the GFCI receptacle continues to grow.

125 Volts—15 and 20 amps

Dwelling Units

210-8(a)(1)	Bath area
210-8(a)(2)	Garage and unfinished buildings
210-8(a)(3)	Outdoors
210-8(a)(4)	Crawl spaces
210-8(a)(5)	Unfinished basements
210-8(a)(6)	Serving kitchen counter top
210-8(a)(7)	Within 6 feet wet bar sink
210-52(d)	Two wash bowls in bath
210-52(g)	Detached garage, when power available

Commercial and Industrial Locations

210-8(b)(1)	Bathrooms
210-8(b)(1)	Roof tops
305-6(a)	All temporary power for new or remodel construction
422-8(d)(3)	Portable high-pressure spray washing machines
511-10	Commercial garages, diagnostic equipment, electric hand tools, portable lighting devices
517-20(1)	Health care facilities, wet locations
620-86	Elevator machine rooms, pits, and car tops
625-22	Vehicle Charging

Swimming Pools

680-5(b)	Branch circuit supplying transformer for underwater lighting
680-6(a)(3)	Within 20 feet of inside wall of swimming pool
680-41(a)	Within 10 feet of spa or hot tub
680-41(a)(3)	Receptacles supplying spas or hot tubs
680-62(a)	All therapeutic pool equipment
680-70	Within 5 feet of hydromassage bathtub

Mobile Homes

550-8(b)	Outdoors
550-8(b)	Bathroom
550-8(b)	Within 6 feet of any lavatory or sink

Recreation Vehicle

551-41(c)(1)	Adjacent to bathroom lavatory
551-41(c)(2)	Within 6 feet of any lavatory or sink
551-41(c)(3)	Area of toilet, shower, tub, or combination thereof
551-41(c)(4)	On exterior of vehicle
571-71	Recreation-vehicle parks, outdoors

Marinas and Boatyards

555-3	Marines and boatyards, other than shore power

Section 680-42 requires spas, hot tubs, and associated electrical equipment to be protected by GFCI. This GFCI may be 240 volts and may be rated greater than 20 amps. The principle of operation of the 240-volt GFCI is similar to that of the 125-volt GFCI.

Replacing Nongrounded Type Receptacles

The basic rule requires 120-volt, 15 and 20 ampere receptacles to be the grounded type. When a two-wire nongrounded type receptacle is replaced, *Section 210-7(d)* recognizes several methods of replacement.

Replacement No. 1 Section 210-7(d)(3)a:

> A two-wire, nongrounded type receptacle may be replaced with a two-wire nongrounded type receptacle.

This gives permission to replace a two-wire ungrounded type receptacle with a two-wire ungrounded type receptacle where these type receptacles exist in older installations.

Replacement No. 2 (Section 210-7(d)(1):

> When there is an equipment grounding conductor present, the nongrounded type receptacle is replaced with a grounded type receptacle.

An example of this would be an installation made with a metal raceway identified for use as an equipment grounding conductor with two electrical conductors installed. In this case, the metal raceway is the existing equipment grounding conductor.

Replacement No. 3 (Section 210-7(d)(1) & 250-50(b) Exception):

> A grounded type receptacle is permitted to replace a nongrounded type receptacle with no marking, when an equipment grounding conductor is installed and connected to any accessible point on the grounding electrode system or the grounding electrode conductor.

The identification of the locations for the connection of the equipment grounding conductor continues to evade the use of the metal water pipe as an equipment grounding conductor. Notice how the "grounding electrode system" and the "grounding electrode conductor" are listed separately. This means that if an equipment grounding conductor is installed for a receptacle replacement, it is not permitted to be connected to the first five feet of water pipe entering the building.

Replacement No. 4 Section 210-7(d)(3)b:

> When there is no grounding means available, a nongrounded type receptacle is permitted to be replaced with a GFCI type receptacle, and the receptacle is marked "NO EQUIPMENT GROUND," figure 14-13.

A grounded type receptacle is readily identifiable. When a person sees a grounded type receptacle, it tells that person this receptacle has an equipment grounding conductor connection.

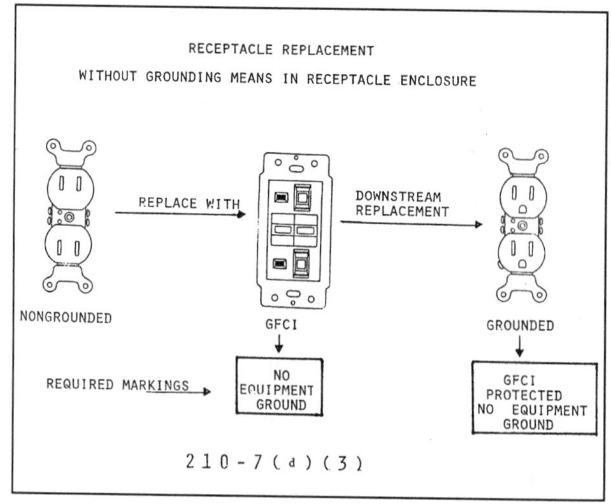

Fig. 14–13 Replacing nongrounded type receptacles.

This is the reason for the marking, "NO EQUIPMENT GROUND."

When a grounded type receptacle is installed in place of a nongrounded type receptacle, and there is no equipment grounding conductor present and an appliance with a three conductor cord is connected to it, there is no equipment grounding conductor connected to the appliance. The normal fault current path via the equipment grounding conductor is not there. If the receptacle is a GFCI type receptacle without an equipment ground, there is ground-fault protection for personnel, but no path for fault current over an equipment grounding conductor back to the overcurrent device.

Replacement No. 5 Section 210-7(d)(3)c:

> Grounded type receptacles are permitted to replace nongrounded type receptacles downstream from the location of a ground-fault type receptacle installation without an equipment grounding conductor, and it is required to be marked "GFCI PROTECTED NO EQUIPMENT GROUND," figure 14-13 (page 224). When this installation is made, there is no equipment grounding conductor permitted to be installed between the GFCI and the downstream grounded type receptacle,

The grounded receptacle downstream must be fed through the GFCI receptacle. When properly installed, this means that when one two-wire ungrounded receptacle is replaced downstream from a GFCI receptacle, both receptacles are GFCI protected.

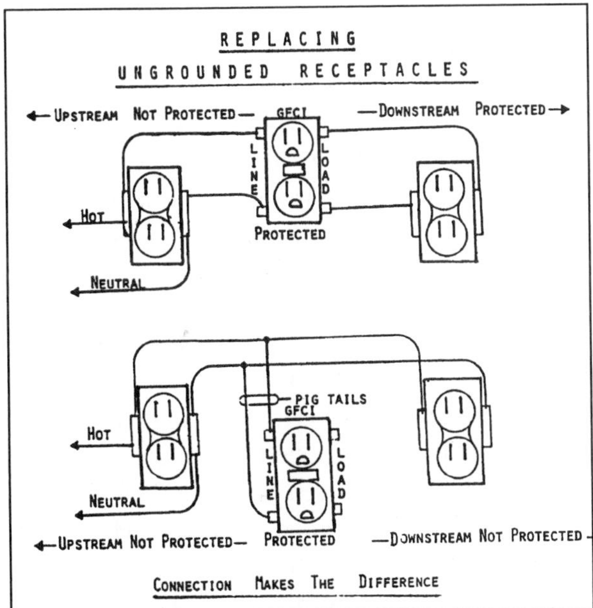

Fig. 14–14 Connection for using a GFCI receptacle to replace an ungrounded type of receptacle.

CAUTION: The downstream receptacle must be fed through the GFCI receptacle in order to be protected. A pigtailed GFCI will not provide downstream protection, figure 14-14. In order for the GFCI to protect the receptacles downstream, the current flow to the downstream receptacles must pass through the current-sensing device in the GFCI. If it is bypassed by the use of the pigtail connections, the downstream current does not pass through the GFCI sensing device: therefore, the downstream receptacles are not protected.

The GFCI receptacle should not be considered as a replacement for ground-fault protection. Rather, a GFCI installation without an equipment grounding conductor offers a margin of safety over nothing at all.

Replacement No. 6 Section 210-7(d)(2):

> When a grounded type receptacle or a nongrounded type receptacle is replaced in a location that a GFCI receptacle is called for by the Code, a GFCI receptacle is required to be installed.

This means that in an older dwelling unit when a receptacle serving a kitchen counter top is replaced, it must now be replaced with a GFCI receptacle.

Section 210-8 lists several locations that GFCIs are required to be installed. Each of the installations starts out with one specific requirement in common:

> all 125-volt,
> single-phase,
> 15- and 20-ampere receptacles

and ends with the same statement:

> protection for personnel.

Figure 14–15 (page 226) illustrates a receptacle installed in a bathroom of a dwelling unit. The Code requires one GFCI receptacle to be installed near the washbowl in each bathroom.

The definition of a bathroom is found in *Article 100, Definitions,* and refers to the bathroom as an area. This includes the bathroom area in a

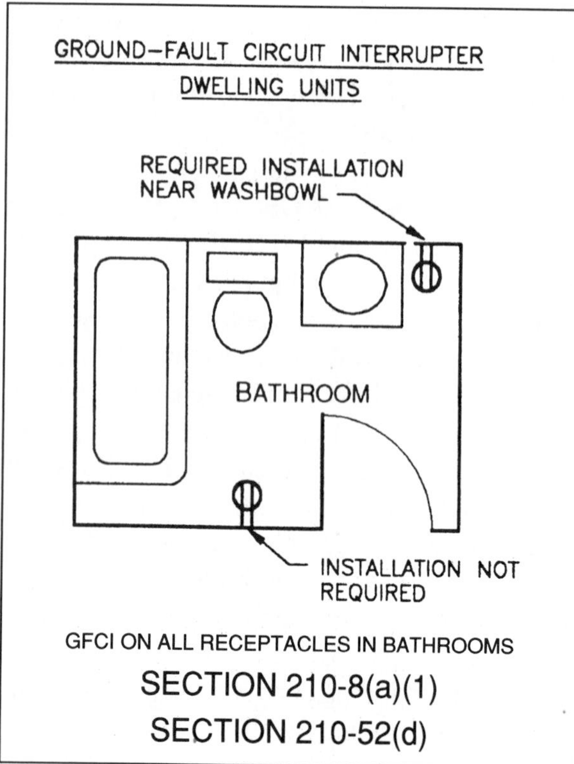

Fig. 14–15 GFCI-protected receptacles are required in bathrooms of dwelling units.

motel where the toilet is separate from the wash bowl or like installations. The first thing necessary to have a bathroom is a basin. However, a room with a basin only is not a bathroom. When a toilet, a shower, or a tub is installed in the same room with a basin, it becomes a bathroom. When more than the one required receptacle is installed in a bathroom, *Section 210-8(a)(1)* requires all receptacles installed in a bathroom to be GFCI protected.

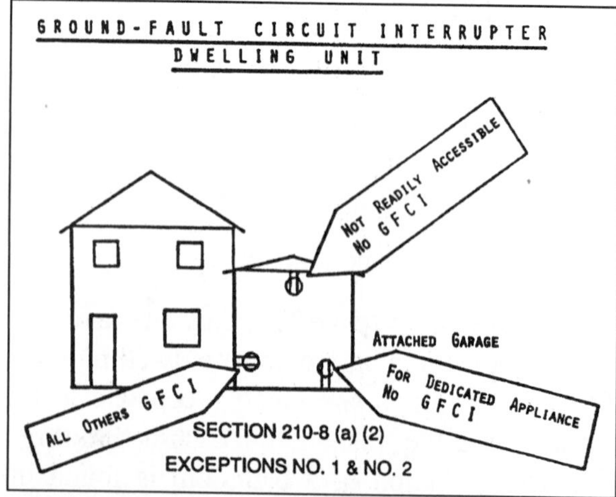

Fig. 14–16 GFCI-protected receptacles are required in attached garages of dwelling units.

Section 210-8(a)(2) (figure 14–16) requires all receptacles installed in attached garages of a dwelling unit to have GFCI protection. Exception No. 1 to *Section 210-8(a)(2)* refers to receptacles that are not readily accessible. The term "readily accessible" means close approach is easily accomplished. No ladders, locked doors, or such are in the way or need to be used to reach the equipment. The phrase "not readily accessible" permits installing a receptacle without GFCI protection in the ceiling of a garage for an overhead-door operator, or any other receptacles that are installed and are not readily accessible. Exception No. 2 allows cord- and plug-connected equipment occupying dedicated space to be installed without GFCI protection when the cord and plug connection is used for changing or repairing the equipment or preventing transmission of vibration or noise. However, the non-GFCI receptacle installed in the dedicated space, without GFCI protection, is required to be a single receptacle when there is a single appliance.

Reason: The appliance would be plugged into only one-half of the receptacle and would leave the second half of the receptacle available for appliances, tools, extension cords, etc.

Where there are two dedicated spaces side by side, an exception permits the use of a duplex receptacle. It is anticipated that both dedicated appliances will remain plugged in at all times. An example of such an installation would be a washing machine and a gas dryer with an electrical motor installed side by side. When there is more than one receptacle installed in an attached garage not covered by Exception No. 1 or No. 2, all must be GFCI protected.

Figure 14–17 (page 227) illustrates a detached garage for a dwelling unit with a ground-fault receptacle installed in the garage. If there is no electrical power carried to the detached garage, there is no requirement for a receptacle to be installed in the detached garage. However, when power is carried to the detached garage, such as for the installation of a light, a receptacle shall be installed, and it shall be GFCI protected. Any additional receptacles installed in the de-

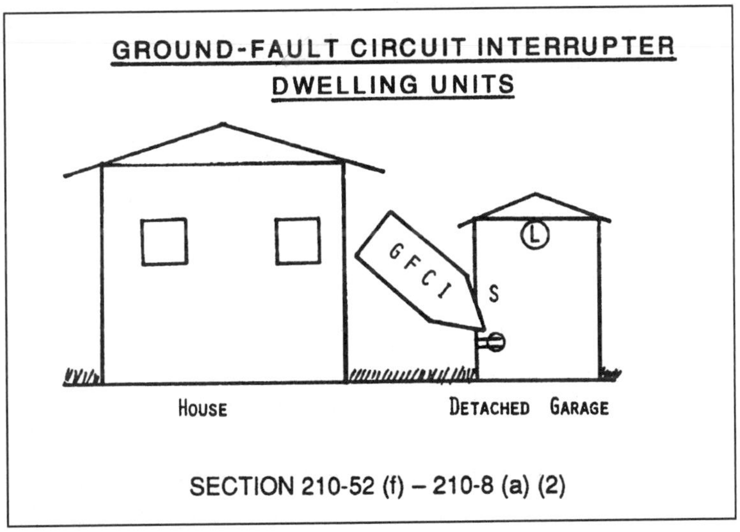

GROUND-FAULT CIRCUIT INTERRUPTER
DWELLING UNITS

GFCI

S

L

HOUSE

DETACHED GARAGE

SECTION 210-52 (f) – 210-8 (a) (2)

Fig. 14–17 GFCI-protected receptacles are required in a detached garage of a dwelling unit when power is brought to the garage.

tached garage would be affected by the requirements of *Section 210-8(a)(2)* and its exceptions, as illustrated in figure 14–16 (page 226). *Section 210-52(g)* requires a receptacle to be installed in a residential garage. *Section 210-8(a)(2)* requires receptacles installed in residential garages and unfinished accessory buildings used for storage or work area to have GFCI protection, figure 14–18. Receptacles are not required in these buildings but when they are installed in them, the receptacle shall be GFCI protected.

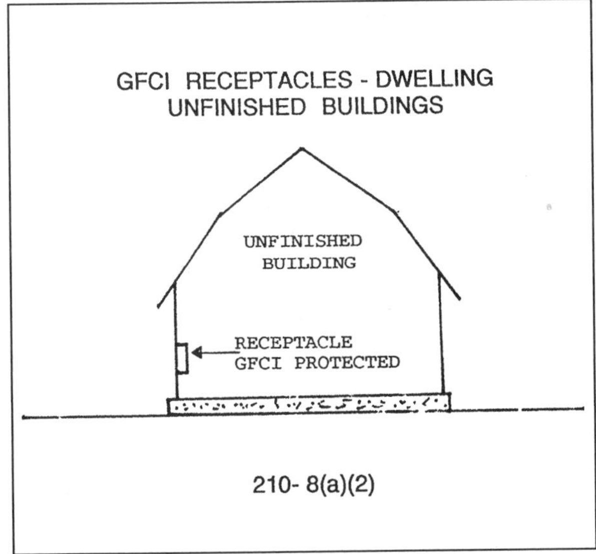

Fig. 14–18 Ground level area receptacles in unfinished buildings are GFCI protected.

Prefabricated buildings are often installed unfinished on a dwelling premises with a dirt, wood, or concrete slab as the floor. These are often used as storage sheds or workshops. There are no electrical outlets required in them, but should receptacles be installed at ground level area inside the building they are required to be GFCI protected. If the building is finished off as office space, the requirement does not apply.

Reasons: It is too easy to plug an extension cord into an outlet in a garage or unfinished building and use an electric tool or appliance in a hazardous situation outside of the garage. The concrete floor of a garage is considered a grounded surface. Defective electric tools can be a real hazard when making automobile repairs in a garage.

Figure 14-19 (page 228) illustrates the installation of GFCI receptacles outdoors for dwelling units, as required by *Section 210-8(a)(3)*. All dwelling units' outdoor receptacles are required to be GFCI protected. This includes grade level access receptacles, receptacles above outside decks, and receptacles on balconies of multistory, multifamily dwellings.

A receptacle may be installed outdoor above a readily accessible area on a dedicated branch circuit for snow-melting and deicing equipment. *Section 210-8(a)(3)* Exception exempts this receptacle from being GFCI protected. However,

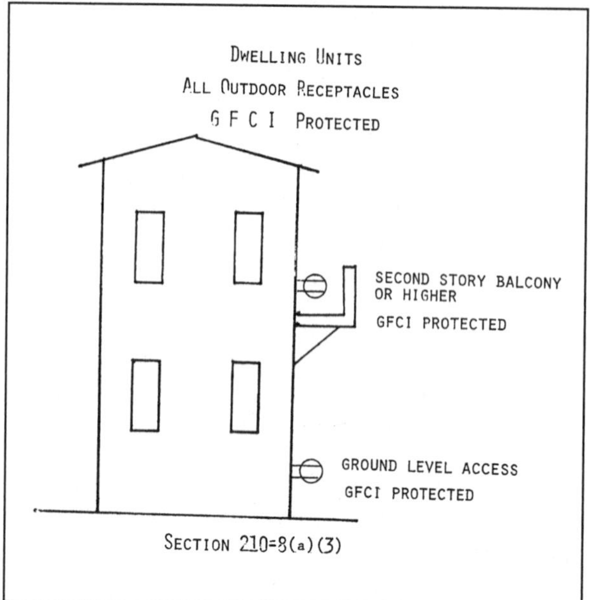

Fig. 14–19 All outdoor receptacles for dwelling units are required to have GFCI protection.

Section 426-28 requires the branch circuit supplying the receptacle to have GFPE (ground-fault protection for equipment) protection. A receptacle installed under the eaves on a general purpose branch circuit and used for decorative lighting would be required to have GFCI protection.

Section 215-9 refers to *Section 210-8,* as illustrated in figure 14–20 that receptacle GFCI protection required by *Section 210-8* need not be installed when the feeder has GFCI protection.

Section 210-8(a)(4) requires receptacles installed in crawl spaces, at or below grade level to have GFCI Protection. An example of such an installation would be where a house is built on the side of a hill, and part of the area under the house is used as storage area, and has a receptacle installed. The receptacle is not required but when installed, it must have GFCI protection.

Figure 14-21 illustrates the installation of GFCI receptacles in an unfinished basement of a dwelling unit. *Section 210-8(a)(5)* requires all receptacles installed in unfinished basements to have GFCI protection. As far as the Code is concerned, an unfinished basement is portions or areas of a basement not intended as habitable rooms. The area is used for storage, work area, or the like. An exception permits a single receptacle supplying a single appliance in a dedicated space to be installed without GFCI protection, figure 14-22 (page 229). There is also an exception that permits the same installation in a garage but not in a bathroom.

A duplex receptacle without GFCI protection is permitted when two appliances occupy the dedicated space. An example could be a deep freeze and a refrigerator installed side by side.

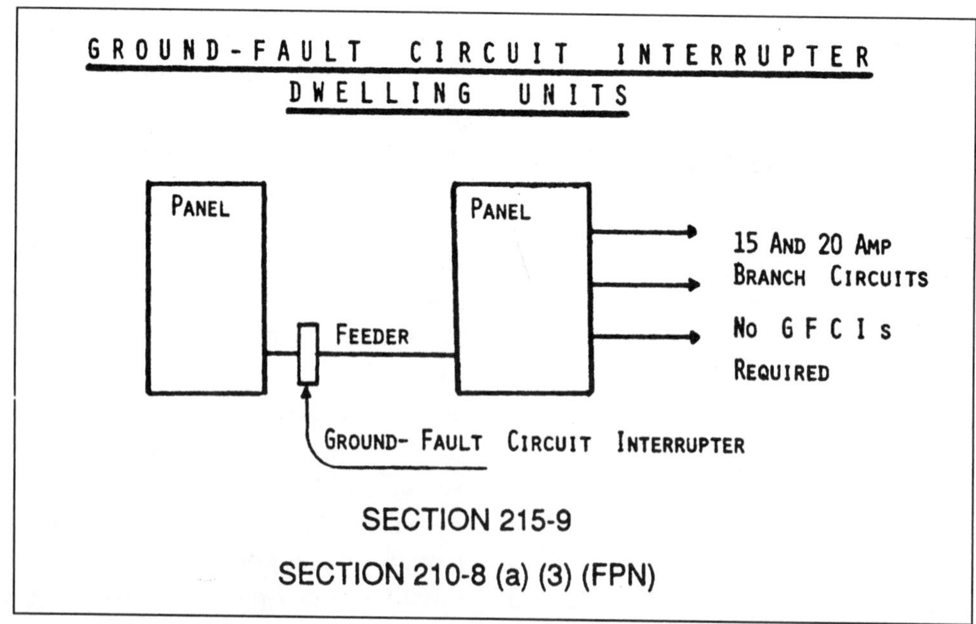

Fig. 14–20 Receptacle GFCI protection is not required when a feeder has GFCI protection.

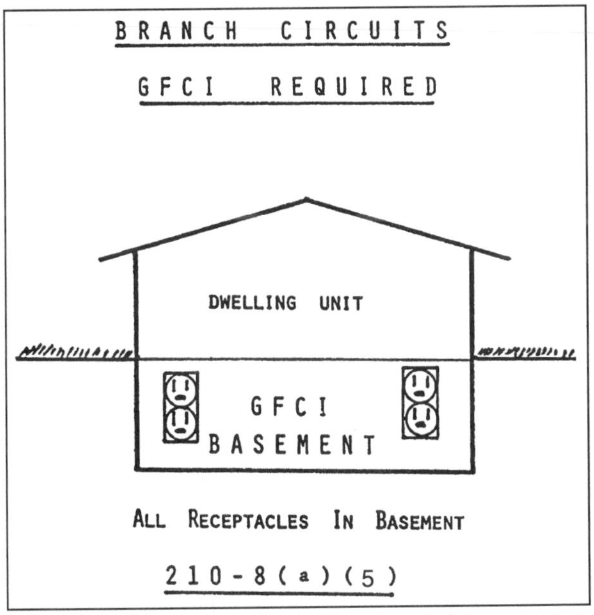

BRANCH CIRCUITS

GFCI REQUIRED

DWELLING UNIT

GFCI BASEMENT

ALL RECEPTACLES IN BASEMENT

210-8(a)(5)

Fig. 14–21 All receptacles in unfinished basement of a dwelling unit shall be GFCI protected.

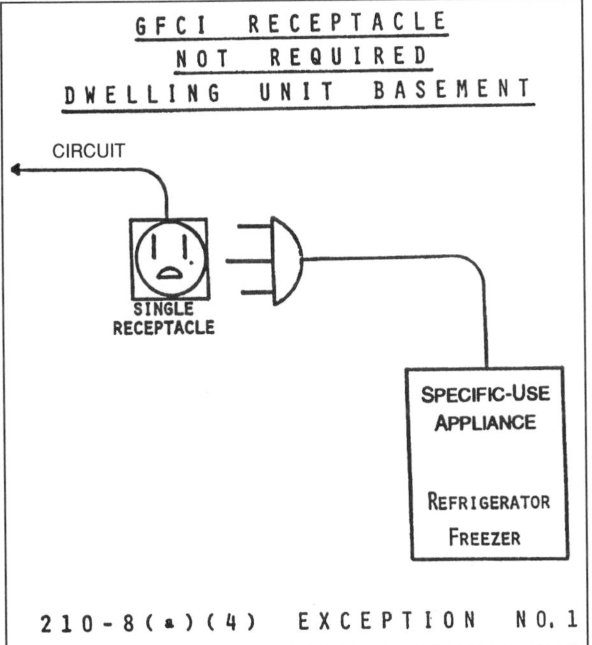

Fig. 14–22 No GFCI required in unfinished basement for specific appliance with dedicated space.

Fig. 14-23 illustrates *Section 210-8(a)(6)*, which requires GFCI protection on ALL receptacles serving the kitchen counter top surfaces in a swelling unit. The receptacle supplying a refrigerator in the kitchen area is not considered as a receptacle serving the kitchen counter top surface; therefore, it is not required to be GFCI protected.

Fig. 14-24 illustrates *Section 210-8(a)(7)*, which requires GFCI protection for a receptacle

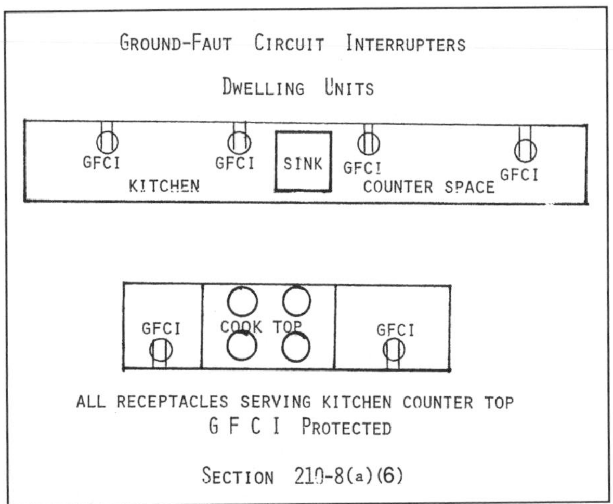

Fig. 14–23 GFCI protection required for all receptacles serving kitchen counter top.

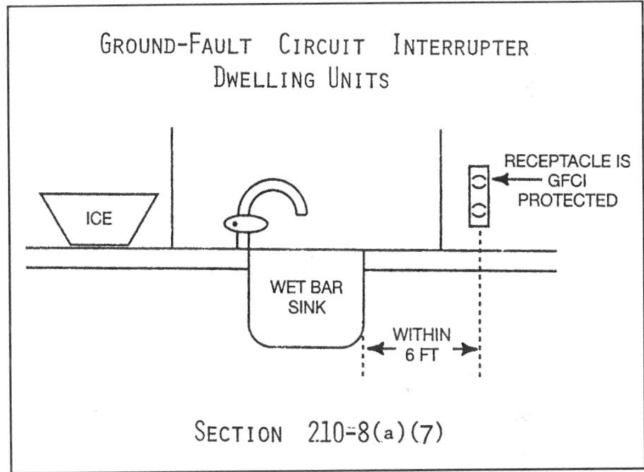

Fig. 14–24 Receptacle within 6 feet of dwelling unit wet bar sink, GFCI protected.

serving the countertop surface within 6 feet of a wet bar sink in a swelling unit. All receptacles by sinks are not required to be GFCI protected. When there is a countertop surface to be served by the receptacle, there is usually GFCI protection required.

Section 210-8(b)(1) requires receptacles installed in bathroom areas, motel and hotel to be GFCI protected. Figure 14-25 (page 230) illustrates the requirement for GFCI-protected receptacles in bathroom areas of motel and hotels. Often the tun or shower and commode are installed in what technically is one room, and the washbowl is installed in a separate room. The Code does not consider these two separate rooms but one "bath area," and all receptacles installed in this area shall be GFCI protected.

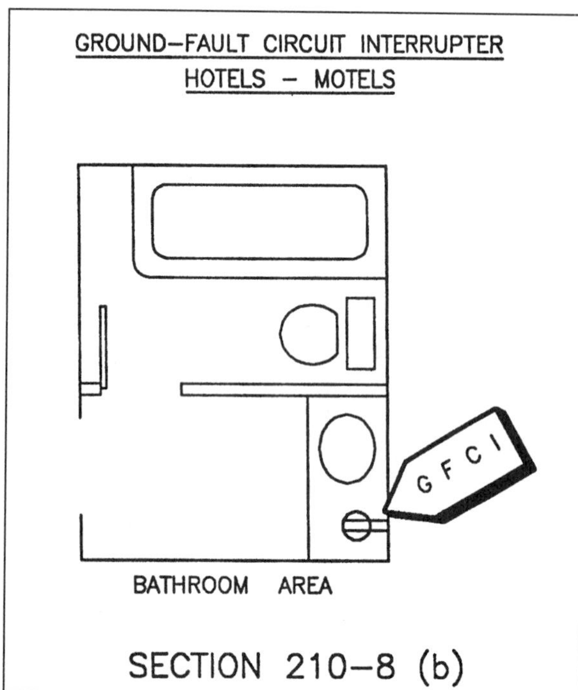

Fig. 14–25 GFCI-protected receptacles are required in the bathroom area of hotels and motels.

Figure 14-26 illustrates a second application of *Section 210-8(b)(1)* which requires all receptacles installed in bathrooms, in any location, to be GFCI protected. This includes any bathroom area meeting the definition of a bathroom. It includes public restrooms, commercial, industrial, dormitories, and all other types of installations. The Code does not require receptacles to be installed in these locations. But, if they are, they shall be GFCI protected. *Section 517-21* exempts hospital area where the toilet and washbowl are located in the immediate patient care area. When the bathroom in a hospital is a separate room from the patient care area, GFCI protection is required.

The Code requires one receptacle to be installed on a rooftop, within 25 feet of the equipment to be service, and *Section 210-8(b)(2)* requires it to be GFCI protected, figure 14-27. Should other than the required receptacle be installed on the rooftop, all rooftop receptacles are required to be GFCI protected. Rooftops are often wet or made of metal and do present an electrical hazard.

When a spa or hot tub is installed outdoors, *Section 680-40* Exception No. 2 permits a cord- and plug-connection (figure 14–28), provided:

1. the cord is not over fifteen feet in length.
2. the supply has GFCI protection.

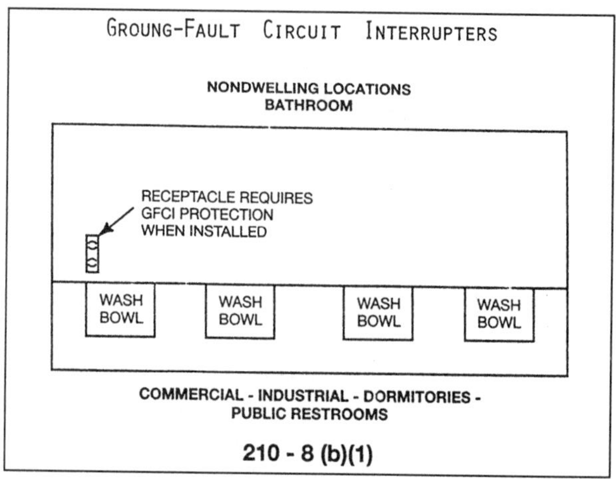

Fig. 14–26 Receptacles installed in all bathrooms are GFCI protection.

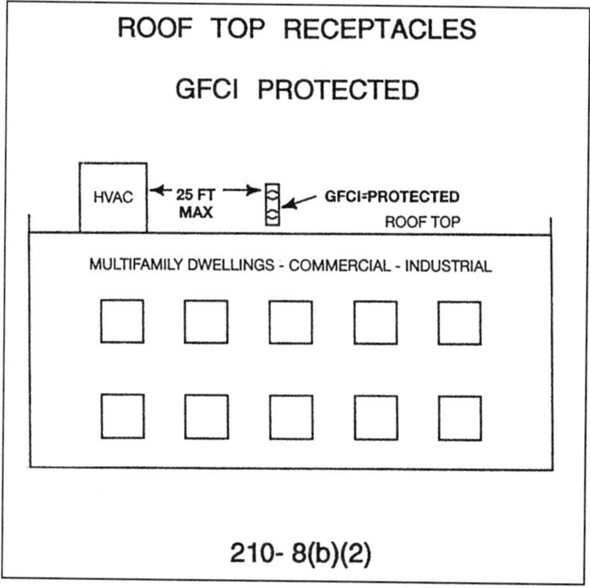

Fig. 14–27 Rooftop receptacles GFCI protected.

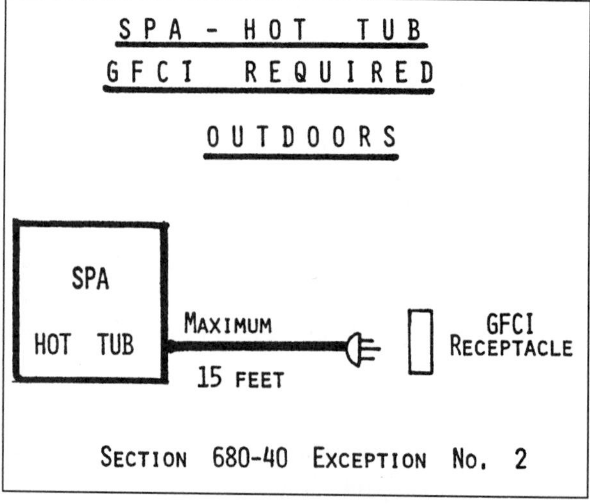

Fig. 14–28 Cord- and plug-connected spa or hot tub outdoors with GFCI protection.

This can be accomplished by the use of a GFCI circuit breaker or an individual GFCI-type receptacle installed for the hot tub or spa supply.

When a package unit spa or hot tub is installed indoors, and rated 20 amperes or less, *Section 680-41(a)(3)* requires the receptacle that provides the power for the spa to be GFCI protected (figure 14–29).

Section 680-41(a)(2) requires all receptacles installed within ten feet of the inside wall of an indoor spa or hot tub to have GFCI protection (figure 14–30).

A third type of connection for the spa or hot tub is the hardwired, or permanently installed, hot tub (figure 14–31). Because of the heaters used, these hot tubs often operate at 240 volts and over 20 amperes. When they are installed, *Section 680-42* requires the spa or hot tub and all its associated equipment to have GFCI protection. A packaged unit may come with built-in GFCI protection for the associated equipment. The associated equipment of a spa or hot tub includes blower, controls, heaters, lights, pumps, and all other wiring. When the manufacturer has incorporated the GFCI protection into the listed equipment and it has been so marked, additional protection is not required.

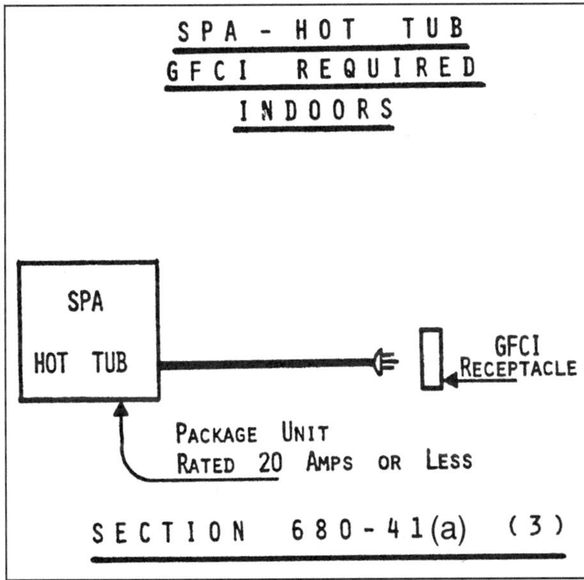

Fig. 14–29 Cord- and plug-connected spa or hot tub indoors with GFCI protection.

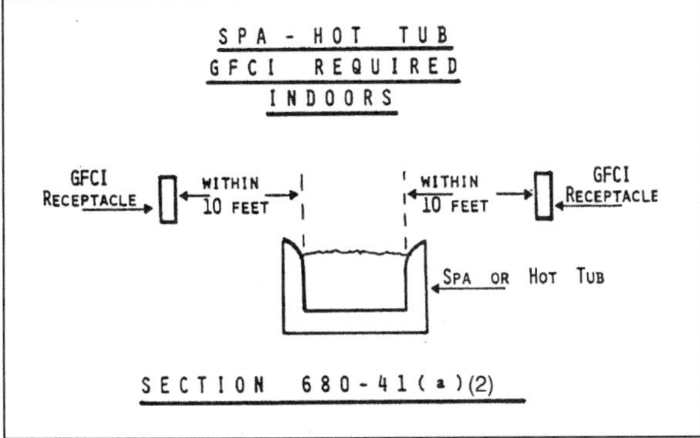

Fig. 14–30 Receptacles within 10 feet of the inside wall of a spa or hot tub shall have GFCI protection.

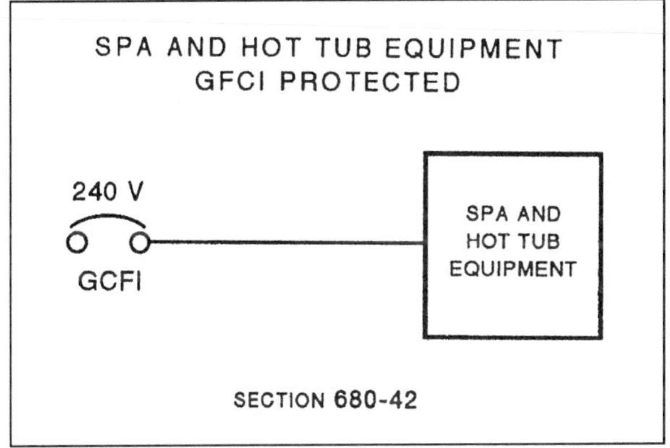

Fig. 14–31 240-volt GFCI for spa or hot tub and associated equipment.

The GFCI designed to be used on a single-phase, 240-volt circuit for personnel protection operates like the 125-volt GFCI. The two ungrounded conductors pass through a coil; when there it an unbalanced current flow between the two conductors, there will be induction in the monitor winding connected to the sensor. The sensor in turn will actuate the GFCI breaker and interrupt the circuit.

Ground-Fault Protection Equipment

GFPE, ground-fault protection equipment, is ground-fault protection against a fire hazard. It operates on the same principle as the GFCI, but it allows more current to pass before it operates, normally about 30 milliamperes. It may trip the circuit breaker, or it may just give an audible or visible alarm.

CAUTION: GFPE and GFCI are not interchangeable for the protection of people. Each has its responsibility and use.

Section 426-28 requires GFPE to be installed for the branch circuit protection of fixed outdoor snow-melting and deicing equipment (figure 14–32).

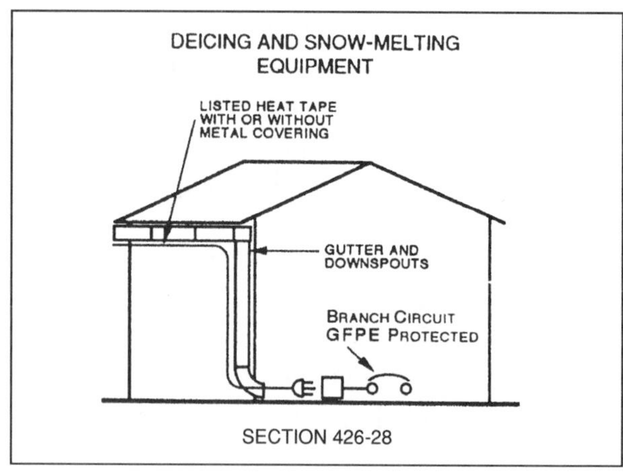

Fig. 14–32 GFPE used for protection when heating tape is used on piping.

GFCI Required for Installations Other Than Receptacles

The following is a list of installations other than receptacles required to have ground-fault circuit interrupter protection for personnel. Note that the requirements are located in articles throughout the Code. The list also illustrates the Code's thoroughness regarding electrical equipment located near or used in damp or wet locations.

517-20(a)	Health care facilities: receptacles and fixed equipment in wet locations
600-10(c)(2)	Portable electric sign
680-6(b)(2)	Lighting over swimming pool
680-26(b)	Electric motors and controllers for pool covers
680-31	Storable pools: all electrical equipment, including supply cord
680-41(b)(1)	Lighting and fans above spa or hot tub
680-42	Spa or hot tub and associated equipment
680-51(a)	Branch circuits supplying fountain equipment (except 15-volt or less)
680-62(a)	Therapeutic equipment in health care facilities: all therapeutic equipment except portable
680-70	Hydromassage bathtubs and associated equipment

FOLLOW UP

Topics for self-study, discussion, or questioning.

1. Define and discuss the separation of "ground-fault protection of equipment."
2. Discuss when ground-fault protection must be installed at the service.
3. Discuss when ground-fault protection must be installed on feeders.
4. Discuss the exceptions to the basic rule for the installation of ground-fault protection at the service.
5. Define a "ground-fault circuit interrupter" (GFCI).
6. Discuss the theory of operation of a GFCI circuit breaker.
7. Discuss the specific locations where receptacles must have GFCI protection.
8. Explain the replacement of a two-wire receptacle with a GFCI.
9. Discuss specific situations where GFCI protection is required, other than for receptacles.

CHAPTER 15

System and Circuit Grounding 1 kV and Over

OBJECTIVES

After completing this chapter, the student should be able to:

- explain why systems operating at 1 kV and over are required to be grounded.
- identify where neutral grounded systems are required for systems operating at 1 kV and over.
- explain the requirements for the grounded system required for portable electrical equipment operating at 1 kV and over.
- identify the various methods for grounding a system operating at 1 kV.
- identify the procedures for the installation of the equipment grounding conductor for equipment operating at 1 kV and over.

Chapter 7 of this text covered the requirements for alternating-current system and circuit grounding for systems under 1000 volts, which are the more common installations. This chapter will be devoted to those systems and circuits rated over 1 kV (1000 volts). Part M of *Article 250* gives special attention to the grounding of alternating-current systems and circuits rated 1 kV and over, such as a 4160-volt, three-phase, wye connected system with the center tap intentionally grounded (figure 15–1).

Why are systems of over 1000 volts grounded? The Fine Print Note to *Section 250–1* answers this question. Systems and circuits are solidly grounded for several reasons. These are:

1. To limit the voltage due to lightning
2. To limit the voltage due to line surges
3. To limit the voltage due to unintentional contact of the supply with higher voltage lines
4. To stabilize the voltage to ground during normal operation
5. To facilitate the operation of the overcurrent device in case of ground fault

These are the same reasons that lower voltage circuits are grounded.

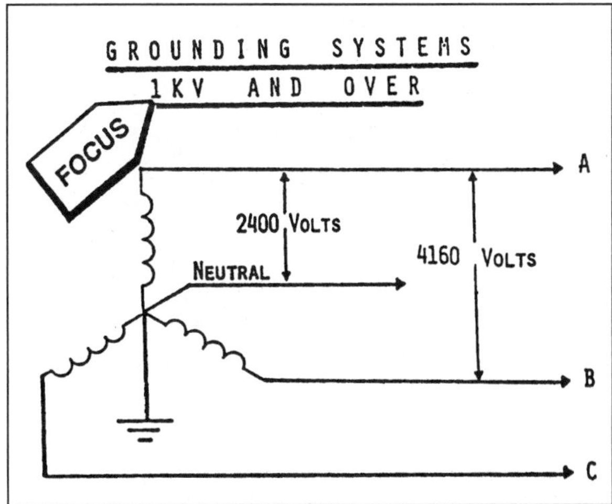

Fig. 15–1 Grounding systems 1 kV and over.

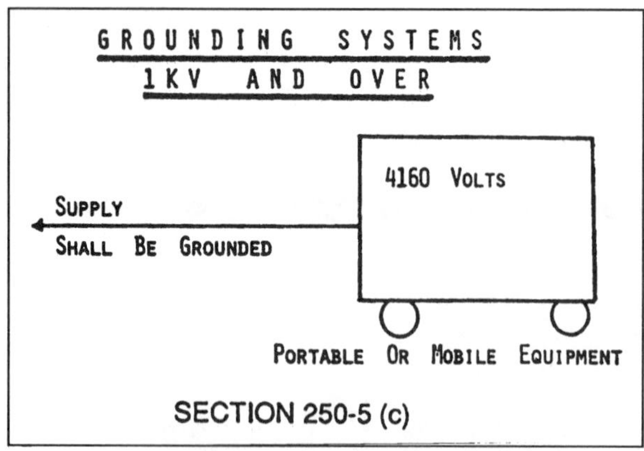

Fig. 15–2 Grounding high-voltage systems when they supply portable and mobile equipment.

NEUTRAL GROUNDED SYSTEMS

There are three systems used for grounded neutral systems 1000 volts and over, and each will be covered separately. They are:

1. Transformer-grounded neutral systems
2. Solidly grounded neutral systems
3. Impedance-grounded neutral systems

The key to understanding grounding for circuits 1 kV and over is in *Section 250-5(c)*. The only time the Code requires high-voltage systems to be grounded is when the system supplies portable or mobile equipment (figure 15–2). All other high-voltage systems are not required to be grounded but are permitted to be grounded. Figure 15–3 illustrates a 4160-volt motor in a stationary location that is not required to have a grounded supply. However, the supply is permitted to be grounded.

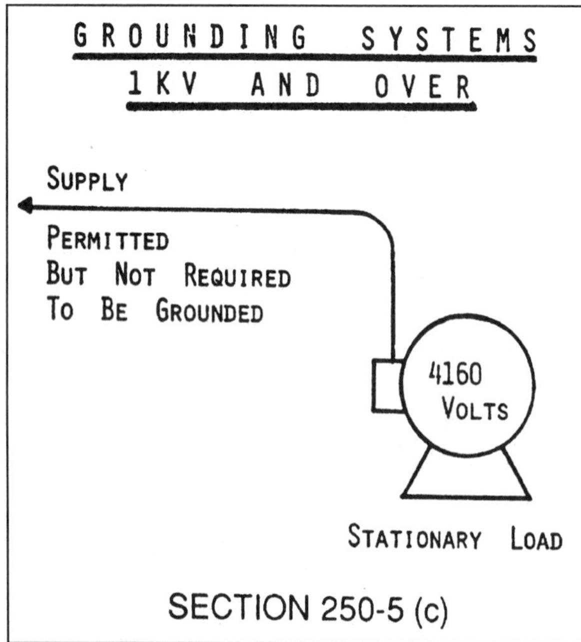

Fig. 15–3 Systems over 1 kV are permitted to be grounded.

NEUTRAL GROUNDED SYSTEMS REQUIRED AND PERMITTED

Section 250-5(c) makes three special points for grounding systems 1000 volts and over. These are:

1. AC systems of 1000 volts and over supplying mobile or portable equipment are required to be grounded.

Comment: The details for accomplishing this requirement are contained in *Section 250-154*.

2. AC systems of 1000 volts and over supplying other mobile or portable equipment are permitted to be grounded.

Comment: It is interesting to note that any other system operating at 1000 volts or over is permitted with or without a grounded neutral system when the system does not supply portable or mobile equipment.

3. When 1000-volts-and-over systems are installed with a grounded neutral, all applicable sections of *Article 250* apply.

Comment: The applicable provisions of *Article 250* cover such things as the materials and types of connections; these are repeated at the beginning of Part M. This part indicates that systems of over 1000 volts, when grounded, shall be installed in accordance with the applicable provisions of *Article 250*. For example, the grounding electrode conductor will be installed the same for either a system over 1000 volts or one under 1000 volts.

Portable or Mobile Equipment

The requirement for portable or mobile equipment operating at 1000 volts or over to be supplied by a neutral grounded system was given in *Section 250-5(c)* and is repeated in *Section 250-154*, along with how this shall be accomplished. *Section 250-154* gives more details for grounding high-voltage systems supplying portable or mobile equipment, other than substations installed on a temporary basis. The following lists the requirements:

1. It shall have its neutral grounded through an impedance.
2. When a delta connected system is used, a system neutral shall be derived.
3. The voltage developed by the flow of maximum ground fault current is limited to 100 volts between the portable or mobile equipment frame and ground.
4. Any high-voltage system component developing a ground fault shall be automatically de-energized by ground fault detection and relaying.
5. The grounding electrode shall be isolated from and separated in the ground by at least 20 feet from any other equipment grounding electrode.
6. No direct connection is permitted between buried pipe or fence electrodes.

Comment: This really narrows the supply system for portable or mobile equipment to two supply systems. These are:

1. An impedance neutral grounded system
2. A system with a neutral grounding transformer

Note the mandatory statement "to automatically de-energize." This does not permit the use of an audio or visual alarm and then manual operation of the system disconnecting means.

Grounding Transformers

Section 250-151 permits the use of a system neutral, derived from a grounding transformer, to ground high-voltage systems. Figure 15–4 illustrates the use of a wye connected transformer to establish a neutral grounded point. The secondary of a supply transformer is an ungrounded, delta connected system. It is connected directly to a grounding transformer, which establishes a neutral grounded system through the grounding transformer.

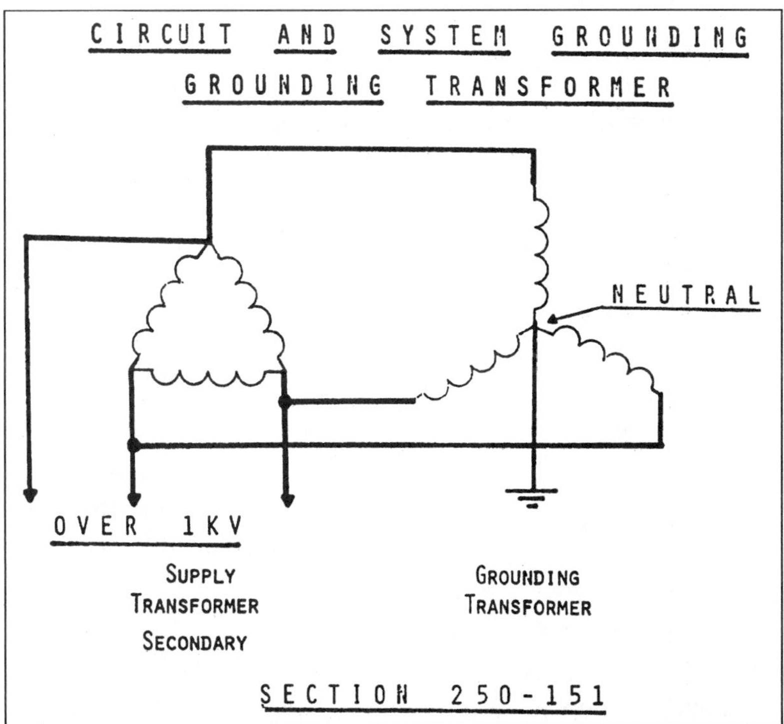

Fig. 15–4 Circuit and system grounding when using a wye connected grounding transformer.

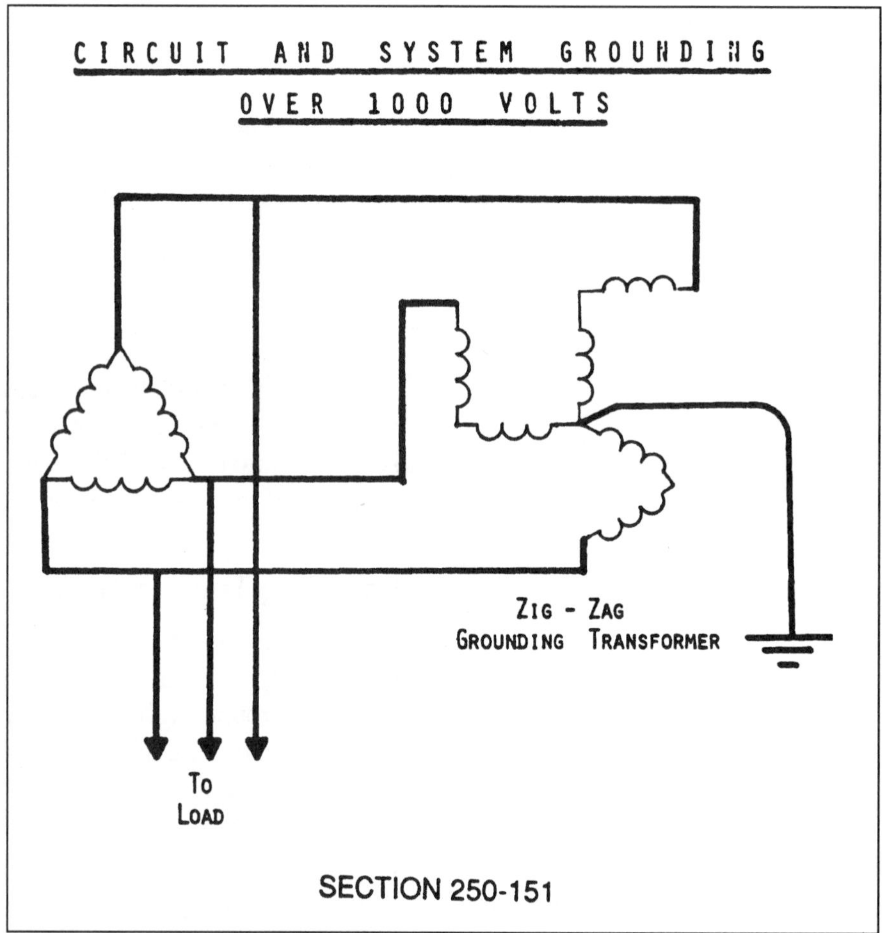

Fig. 15–5 Circuit and system grounding when using a zig-zag connected grounding transformer.

Figure 15–5 illustrates the use of a zig-zag transformer connection to establish the grounded neutral system. The three-phase, delta connected system utilizing a grounding transformer of either the wye or zig-zag connection is permitted for neutral grounded systems for portable or mobile equipment, as outlined by *Section 250-154*.

Solidly Grounded Systems

A solidly grounded system is illustrated in figure 15–6 (page 237), as permitted in *Section 250-152*, with a phase-to-phase voltage of 4160 volts and 2400 volts to ground or the neutral. The phase conductors are insulated for 5000 volts but the neutral is already at ground potential, so the neutral insulation is permitted to be only 600 volts.

Section 250-152 covers the installation of a solidly neutral grounded high-voltage system. It sets the following requirements for the neutral conductor.

1. The neutral shall have a minimum insulation level of 600 volts, with the following exceptions:

    a. as a service entrance conductor.
    b. as a portion of direct buried feeder.
    c. as overhead conductors outdoors.

Comment: The solidly grounded neutral is the same potential as ground. The purpose of using the 600-volt insulation is to have just enough insulation to keep the neutral from touching ground, such as when it is run in metal raceways, and to establish a ground path for circulating currents.

2. *Section 250-152(c)* permits the neutral grounding conductor to be a bare conductor when:

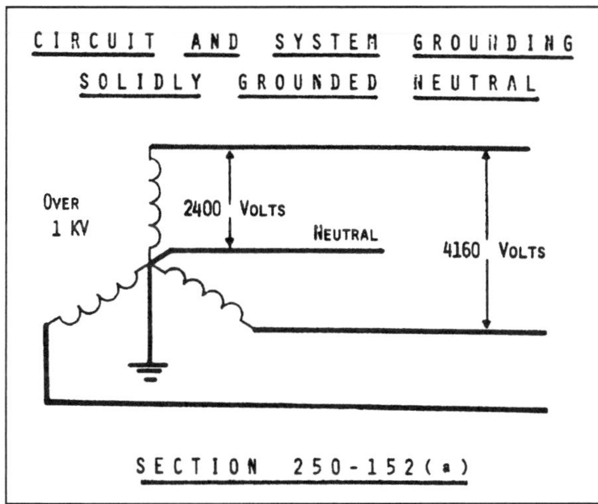

Fig. 15–6 Solidly grounded neutral system.

a. isolated from phase conductors
b. and protected from physical damage.

3. The solidly grounded neutral system is permitted to be grounded at more than one point for:

   a. services,
   b. direct buried portions of feeders employing a bare copper neutral,
   c. overhead portions of feeders installed outdoors.

Impedance-Grounded Systems

Impedance grounding means there is opposition to current flow (impedance) intentionally connected in series with the grounding electrode conductor and the system neutral. The impedance will intentionally limit the current flow to ground. A resistor or impedance coil is used and both are referred to as "impedance" because of the alternating current.

The purpose of impedance grounding is to limit the current flow to ground in case of a fault, thereby offering a measure of protection for equipment from ground faults. By limiting the current flow, the arc at the point of fault can be eliminated or limited. This is one of the reasons the neutral impedance-grounded system is required for use with portable or mobile equipment operating at 1000 volts or more.

Figure 15–7 illustrates an impedance-grounded neutral system, as permitted by *Section 250-153. Section 250-153(a)* requires the impedance for an impedance-grounded neutral system to be inserted in the grounding conductor between the grounding electrode of the supply system and the neutral point of the supply transformer or generator.

Comment: The term *grounding conductor* as used here refers to the grounding electrode conductor. The impedance must be connected in series with

- the neutral,
- the grounding electrode,
- the grounding electrode conductor.

Section 250-153(b) further requires the neutral of an impedance-grounded neutral system to be fully insulated with the same insulation as the phase conductors and identified.

Comment: The means of identification can be any of those listed in *Article 200* and covered in Chapter 8 of this text. Note that for an impedance neutral grounded system, the neutral originates at the transformer. The neutral only extends from the center point of the wye to

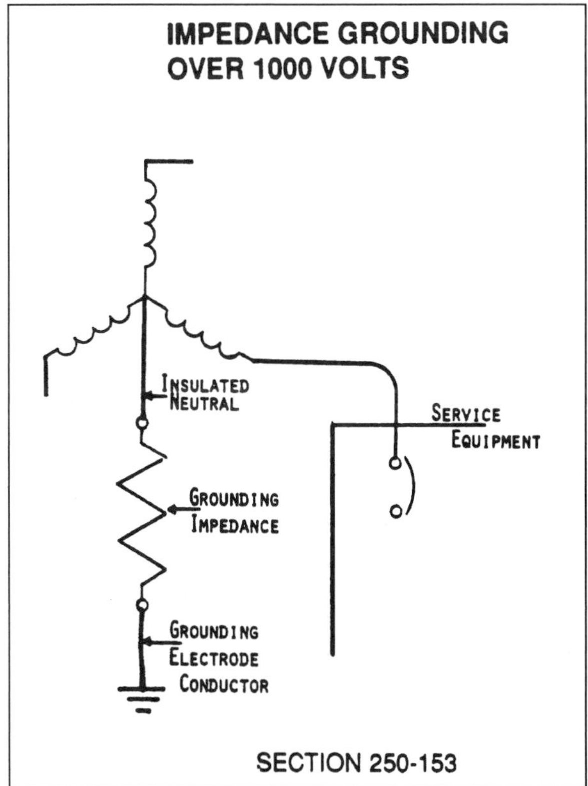

Fig. 15–7 Impedance-grounded neutral system.

the line side of the grounding resistor. The line side of the resistor is the neutral. The grounded side of the resistor is the grounding electrode conductor. Therefore, there is a voltage between the line side and the grounded side of the system neutral impedance, which also results in a voltage between the neutral and ground. The voltage from the neutral to ground will be the voltage drop across the impedance, which will vary with the impedance of the resistor and the current flowing through the impedance. However, the neutral conductor must be insulated the same as the phase conductors. In the case of a 4160-volt system using 5 kV insulation, the neutral conductor must have 5 kV insulation.

Section 250-153(c) prohibits connecting the neutral to ground, except through the grounding impedance.

Comment: The neutral is not used as a circuit conductor, which it is with a solidly grounded system.

Section 250-153(d) is directed at the equipment grounding conductor for high-voltage systems. The conductor is permitted to be bare. It is required to be connected to the ground bus and the grounding electrode conductor at the service-entrance equipment and extended to the system ground.

Comment: This is the same requirement made for grounding systems under 1000 volts. All the grounding conductors are brought to one point and the grounding electrode conductor connects them to the grounding electrode.

CAUTION: The neutral is NOT connected to the grounding electrode conductor. The conductor connected to the grounded side of the grounding impedance is connected to the grounding electrode conductor. The equipment grounding conductor is not connected to the neutral at the service or ahead of the grounding impedance, but to the grounding electrode conductor on the grounded side of the grounding impedance (figure 15–8) *(Section 250-153)*.

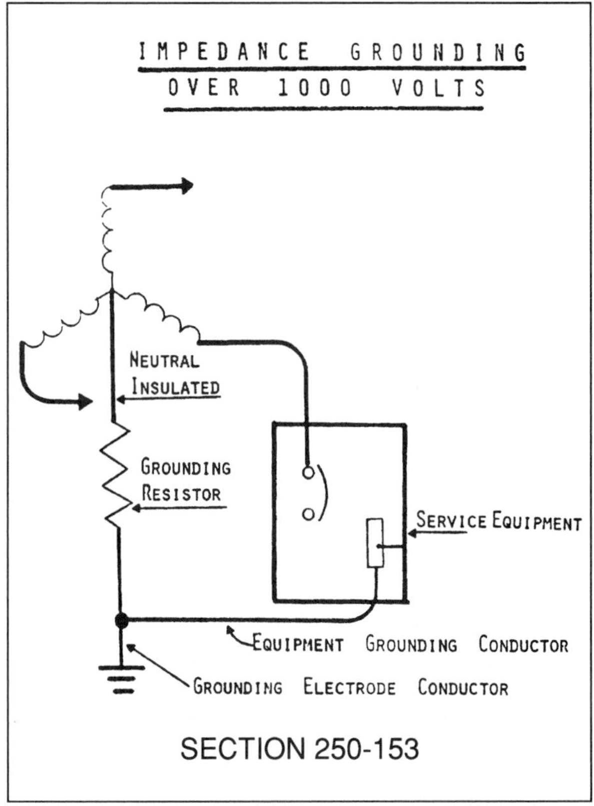

Fig. 15–8 Equipment grounding conductor connection in a neutral impedance-grounded system.

EQUIPMENT GROUNDING

The grounding of high-voltage equipment is extended to cover the housings and fencing containing high-voltage current-carrying equipment. *Section 250-155* requires noncurrent-carrying metal parts of high-voltage equipment to be grounded. This includes the following:

1. Fixed equipment
2. Portable equipment
3. Mobile equipment
4. Associated fences
5. Equipment housings
6. Equipment enclosures
7. Conductor enclosures
8. Supporting structures

The equipment grounding conductor, when not an integral part of a cable assembly, shall not be smaller than:

1. No. 6 copper
2. No. 4 aluminum

High-voltage equipment is not required to be grounded when it is isolated from ground and located so it prevents any person who can make contact with ground from contacting such metal parts when the equipment is energized. Such equipment is not required to be grounded when it is elevated and is used for pole-mounted distribution equipment.

Table 250-95 shows the equivalent equipment grounding conductor for a 200-amp circuit. Therefore, a 60-amp or 100-amp circuit will be required to have the minimum grounding conductor. Circuits rated at over 200 amps shall have their equipment grounding conductor sized according to *Table 250-95*.

Where there is a solidly grounded system, the equipment grounding conductor is connected the same as for systems under 1000 volts. Where there is an impedance-grounded system, caution must be taken in making the connection. The connection must be made to the grounding electrode conductor and not to the neutral conductor.

Section 250-154(d) protects against the loss of continuity of the equipment grounding conductor for high-voltage systems feeding portable or mobile equipment by requiring the equipment grounding conductor to be monitored for continuity. It shall be continuously monitored for continuity. Upon loss of continuity of the equipment grounding conductor, the high-voltage feeder is automatically de-energized.

This regulation illustrates the importance placed on the equipment grounding conductor by requiring the monitoring of the continuity of the equipment grounding conductor. The second thing this regulation indicates is that a system supplying portable or mobile equipment shall not be operated unless the equipment grounding conductor is in place and has continuity.

Grounding Shielded High-Voltage Cable

Figure 15–9 illustrates a shielded cable with the shield grounded to confine the voltage stresses to the insulation caused by high voltage, as required by *Section 310-6*. All high-voltage shielded cable operating at over 2000 volts shall have the insulation shield grounded with an effective grounding path.

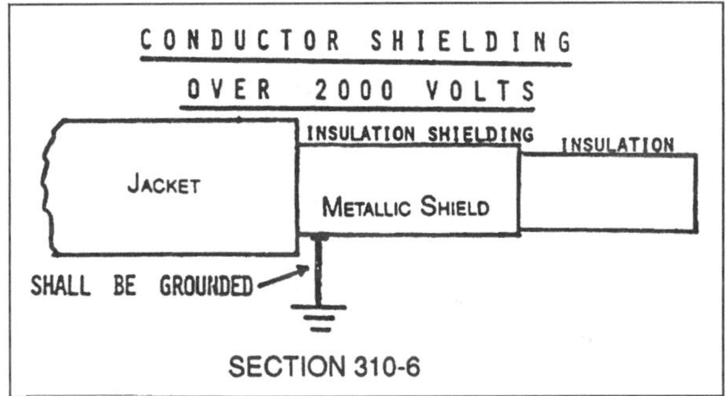

Fig. 15–9 Shielding over 2000 volts is required to be grounded.

FOLLOW UP

Topics for self-study, discussion, or questioning.

1. Discuss the reasons for grounding systems 1 kV and over.
2. Discuss the grounding of portable equipment operating at 1 kV and over.
3. Discuss regulations for a solidly grounded system operating at 1 kV and over.
4. Discuss the regulations for a transformer-grounded system operating at 1 kV and over.
5. Discuss the regulations for an impedance-grounded system operating at 1 kV and over.
6. Discuss the size and installation of the equipment grounding conductor for equipment operating at 1 kV and over.

CHAPTER 16

Separately Derived Systems

OBJECTIVES

After completing this chapter, the student should be able to:

- identify a separately derived system.
- compare the installation of a separately derived system, secured from a bank of transformers, to the installation of a service.
- identify when a standby system is or is not a separately derived system.
- identify where the grounding electrode conductor is permitted to be installed.
- identify where the main bonding jumper for a separately derived system is permitted to be installed.
- describe a five-wire, three-phase, wye connected grounded system.
- explain how the system is grounded when a portable generator is used as a separately derived system.
- explain how the system is grounded when a vehicle-mounted generator is used as a separately derived system.

A good way to look at a separately derived system is as another supply system, other than the utility company supply. The separately derived system might be a generator with a gas or diesel engine for the prime mover, an alternator converter, a motor generator set, or a transformer with no electrical connection between the primary and the secondary. Figure 16–1 (page 241) illustrates some of the various ways to create a separately derived system. The most common of the separately derived systems is the transformer. This chapter focuses on Code regulations for separately derived systems of less than 1000 volts.

DEFINITION OF *SEPARATELY DERIVED SYSTEM*

Figure 16–2 (page 241) illustrates a separately derived system, as covered in *Section 250-26*, with the secondary of the transformer connected wye and a grounded center tap for the neutral. The Code does not put it in so many words, but the secondary of the transformer can be treated almost as another service.

A gas engine-operated generator that is used for emergency or standby power upon failure of the normal or utility company system can be a separately derived system, provided the neutral is not common to both the normal and the standby supply. Figure 16–3 (page 241) illustrates a normal supply and a standby supply using an automatic transfer switch. Note that the

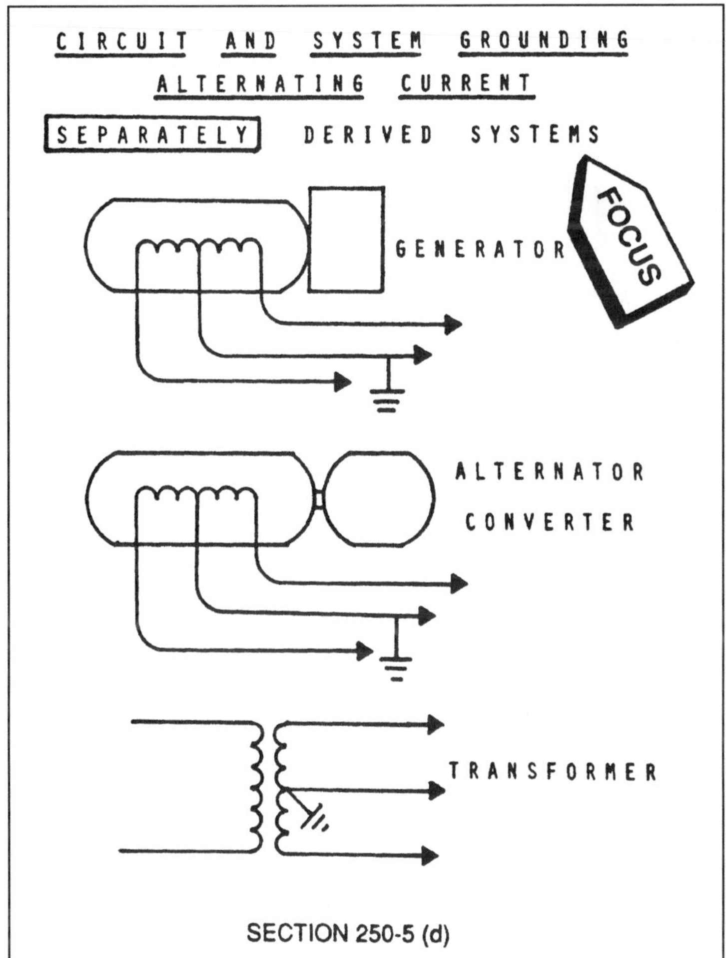

Fig. 16–1 Creating a separately derived system.

neutral is switched and is not a common conductor through the transfer switch. Therefore, the standby system is a separately derived system.

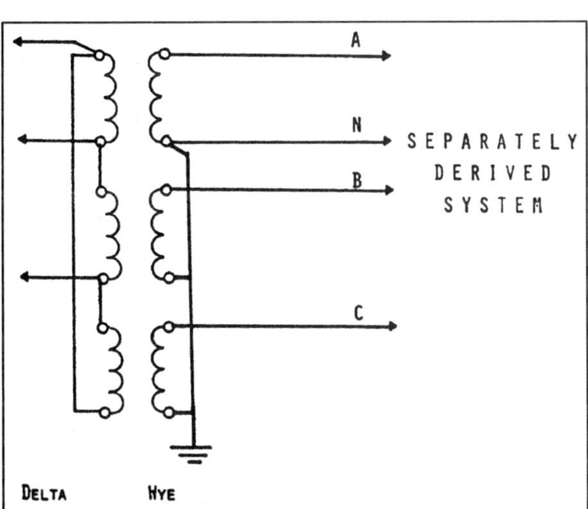

Fig. 16–2 A separately derived system with a transformer delta as the primary and a wye as the secondary.

Figure 16–4 (page 242) illustrates a normal system with a standby system and a transfer switch. The transfer switch does not break the neutral conductor. The neutral conductor is solidly connected to both the normal and the standby

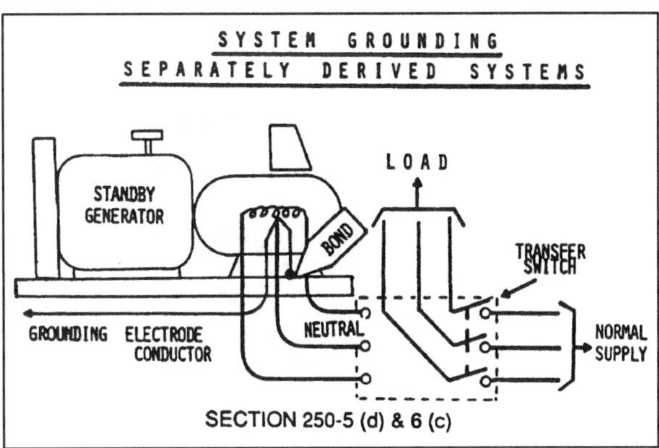

Fig. 16–3 A standby generator with a transfer switch switching the neutral.

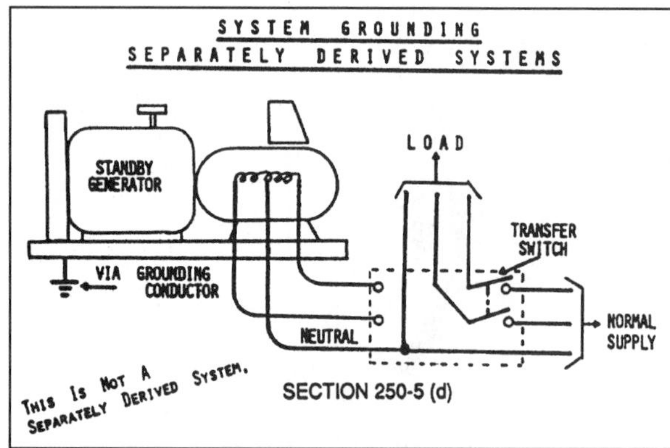

Fig. 16–4 A standby generator where the transfer switch does not switch neutral. It is not a separately derived system.

supplies. Therefore, the FPN No. 1 to *Section 250-5(d)* says that this is not a separately derived system because the neutral is common to both supplies.

Figure 16–5 illustrates a two-winding transformer with no electrical connection between the primary and secondary of the transformer. The neutral of the transformer's primary and the neutral of the transformer's secondary are completely separate. The 120/240-volt secondary of the transformer is a separately derived system.

There is no electrical connection built into a transformer between the primary and secondary of the transformer (other than autotransformers), and there are no connections made in the field between the conductors feeding the primary and the distribution conductors of the secondary. The transformer is the most common separately derived system the average electrician will install.

Figure 16–6 (page 243) illustrates an autotransformer, which has one conductor that is common to both the primary supply and the secondary supply. The 240-volt secondary of the transformer is not a separately derived system because one of the conductors is common to both the supply and the load.

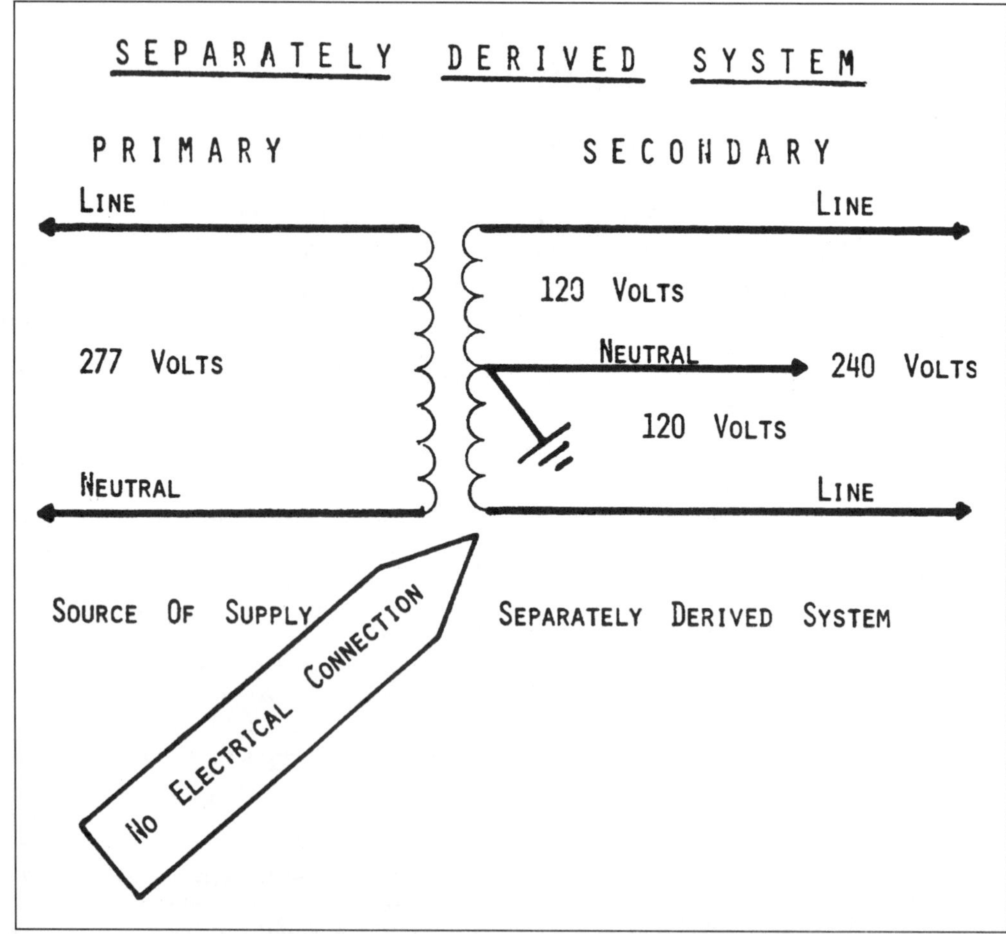

Fig. 16–5 A separately derived system with a single-phase transformer.

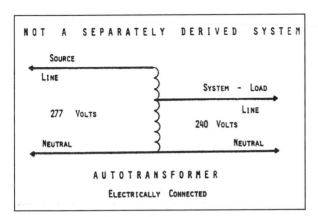

Fig. 16–6 An autotransformer is not a separately derived system.

Although a separately derived system is not considered a service and the Code does not describe it as such, it can be considered the same as a service for most practical purposes and, with very few exceptions, it can be treated as one. Compare the following points covered in *Section 250-26* with the requirements for grounding a service.

1. A main bonding jumper is required.
2. A grounding electrode is required.
3. A grounding electrode conductor is required.
4. All grounded conductors present at the source of supply shall be connected together.

MAIN BONDING JUMPER

Figure 16–7 illustrates a separately derived system feeding a panel without any overcurrent protection. The main bonding jumper is installed at the transformer, as permitted by *Section 250-26(a)*. The connection of the main bonding jumper, the grounded conductor (the neutral), the grounding electrode conductor, and the equipment grounding conductor is made at the transformer.

Figure 16–8 (page 244) illustrates a separately derived system feeding a panel, with the feeder terminating in an overcurrent protective

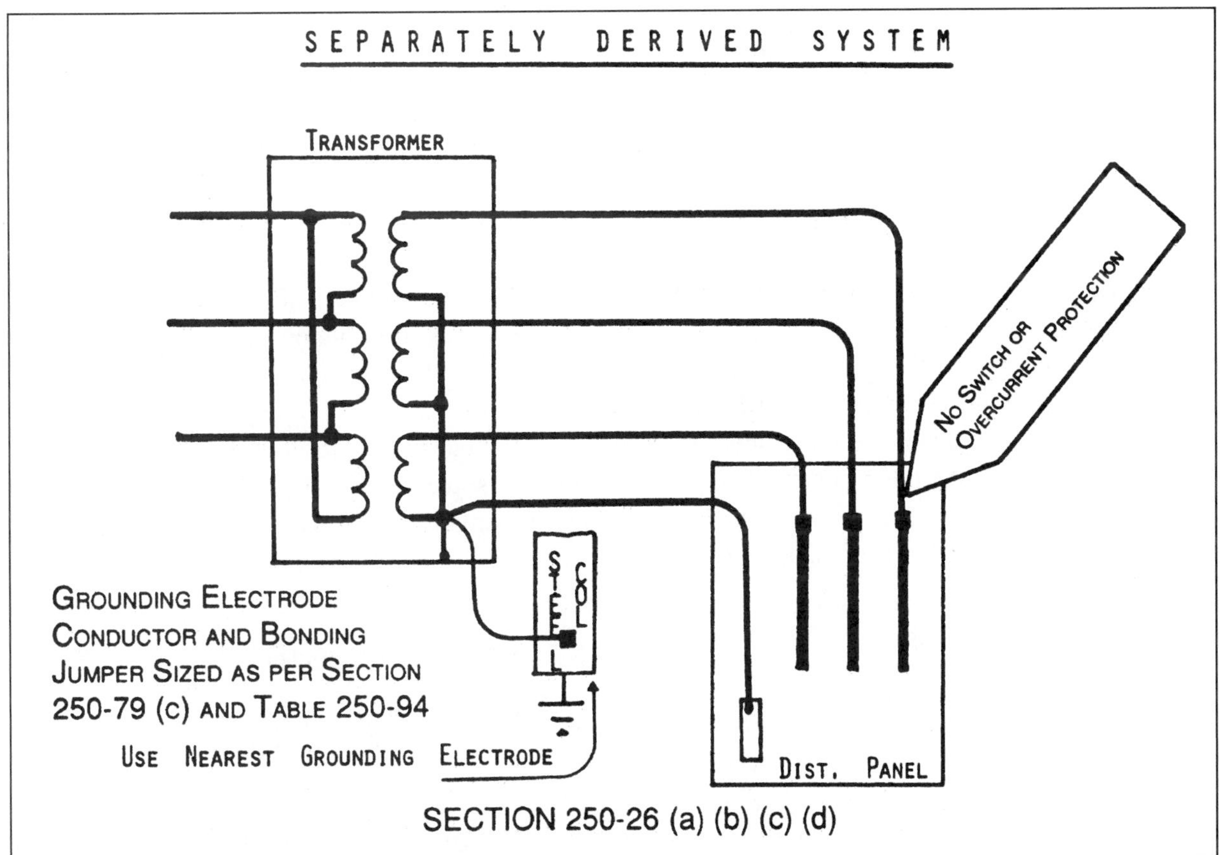

Fig. 16–7 A separately derived system with the main bonding jumper and grounding electrode conductor connections made at the transformer.

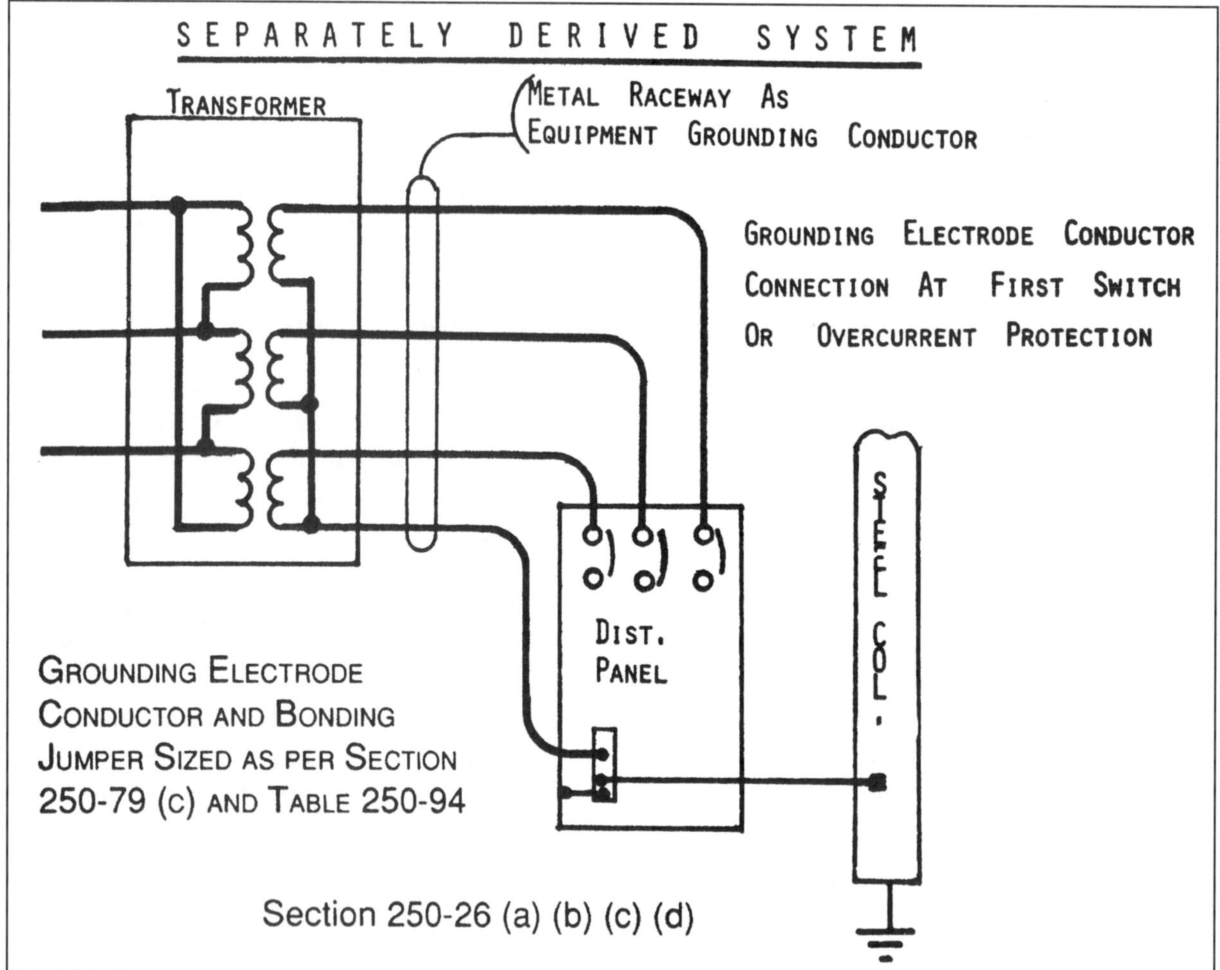

Fig. 16–8 A separately derived system with the main bonding jumper and grounding electrode conductor connections made at the first disconnecting means.

device. The main bonding jumper is permitted by *Section 250–26(a)* to be installed in the panel. The main bonding jumper, the grounding electrode conductor, the grounded conductor, and the equipment grounding conductor are all connected together at the panel. The main bonding jumper is sized according to *Section 250-79(d)* for the derived phase conductors, as discussed in Chapter 9 of this text.

GROUNDING ELECTRODE CONDUCTOR

The materials and installation of the grounding electrode conductor are the same as for a service installation. The size of the grounding electrode conductor is based on the size of the separately derived phase conductor and is taken from *Table 250-94*. There are two permitted locations for the connection of the grounding electrode conductor as illustrated in figures 16–7 and 16–8.

The use of the grounded conductor, the neutral, of a separately derived system for grounding equipment is explained and illustrated in Chapter 13 (figures 13–7 and 13–8, pages 213 and 214).

GROUNDING ELECTRODE

Section 250-26(c) covers the special requirements for the grounding electrode for a separately derived system. These are:

1. The grounding electrode shall be located as near as practical to the grounding conductor connection (the grounding target of the separately derived system).

2. Preferably it shall be located in the same area as the grounding conductor connection to the system.
3. The grounding electrodes are listed in this section in order of preference. They shall be
   a. nearest the effectively grounded building steel,
   b. nearest the effectively grounded water pipe,
   c. other electrodes as specified in *Sections 250-81* and *250-83* when the above electrodes are not available.

There are a few things here that are a bit different than the installation of the grounding electrode system at the service. These are:

1. The grounding electrode should be as near as possible to the separately derived system.
2. The structural steel and the metal water pipe are preferred over the use of other grounding electrodes listed in *Sections 250–81* and *250–83*.
3. The goal is to keep the grounding electrode conductor as short as possible.

The grandfather or saving clause is last; it appears in *Section 250-26(d)*. It says that if anything is not covered in this section for grounding separately derived systems, the grounding methods used shall comply with the requirements set down in other parts of the Code.

BONDING AT SEPARATELY DERIVED SYSTEMS

When other than the effectively grounded water pipe or building steel is used as the grounding electrode for a separately derived system, and there is metal water pipe in the area that may become energized the metal water piping in the area is required to be bonded to the grounded conductor of the separately derived system. (Figure 16–9)

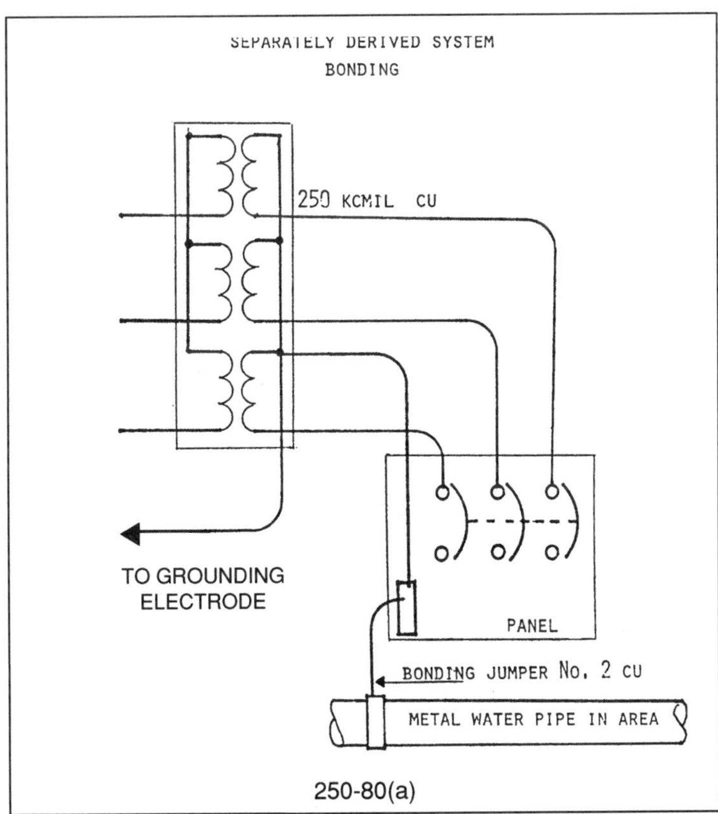

Fig. 16–9 Bonding metal water piping to separately derived systems.

Section 250-81 limits the use of the water pipe as the grounding electrode to the first 5 feet entering the building. When the building steel is used as the grounding electrode for a separately derived system, there can be a difference of potential between the two. Therefore, the metal water pipe is required to be bonded to the grounded conductor of the separately derived system.

The installation of the bonding jumper for the metal water pipe is the same as if it was a grounding electrode conductor. The bonding jumper is sized according to the size of the separately derived system conductors using *Table 250-94*. The installation is made according to *Section 250-92(a)*which is for the installation of the grounding electrode conductor. The point of connection is also required to be accessible.

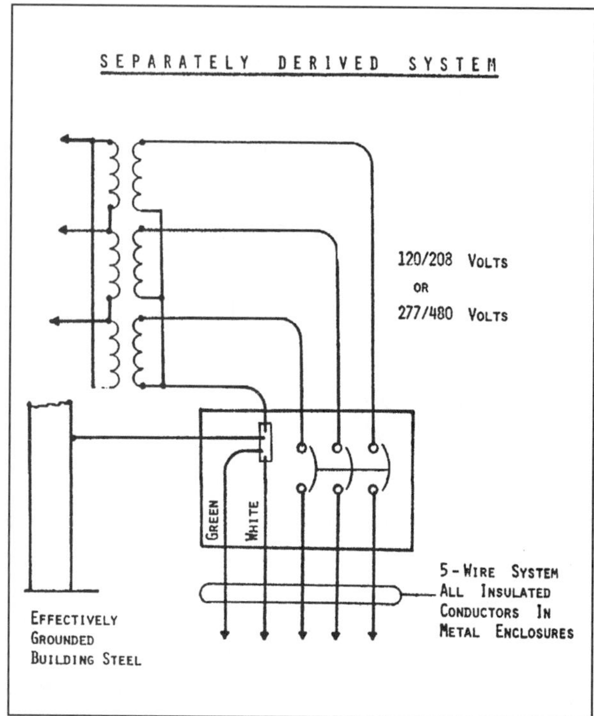

Fig. 16–10 A separately derived system furnishing a five-wire, wye connected system with an insulated equipment grounding conductor.

DEDICATED FIVE-WIRE SYSTEM

The terminology *five-wire system* is being heard more and more. The term indicates a grounded system with an insulated equipment grounding conductor carried throughout the system and the system installed in metal conduit. The metal conduit is not used as the equipment grounding conductor; a separate insulated conductor is installed in the conduit. Figure 16–10 illustrates the use of a separately derived system furnishing a five-wire system. Such a system is used in conjunction with computer and data processing equipment.

CAUTION: The metal conduit system enclosing the five-wire system with the equipment grounding conductor installed in it is installed just as if it were going to be used as the equipment grounding conductor. The metal conduit system must maintain continuity at all points of connection and is grounded at the source via the main bonding jumper. It is, therefore, also an equipment grounding conductor.

PORTABLE GENERATORS

Figure 16–11 (page 247) illustrates a generator for a separately derived system. The generator has a neutral conductor and is required to be bonded to the frame of the generator, according to *Section 250-6(c)*. Such a system could be installed in a remote area where there is no utility company distribution, or it could be used for temporary power.

According to *Section 250-6(a)*, the frame of a portable generator is permitted to be the grounding electrode (figure 16–11, page 247) when it is the supply system and provided all the following conditions are met:

1. The generator supplies only equipment mounted on the generator and/or cord- and plug-connected equipment through receptacles mounted on the generator, or both.

2. The noncurrent-carrying metal parts of equipment are bonded to the generator frame.

3. The equipment grounding conductor terminals of the receptacles are bonded to the generator frame.

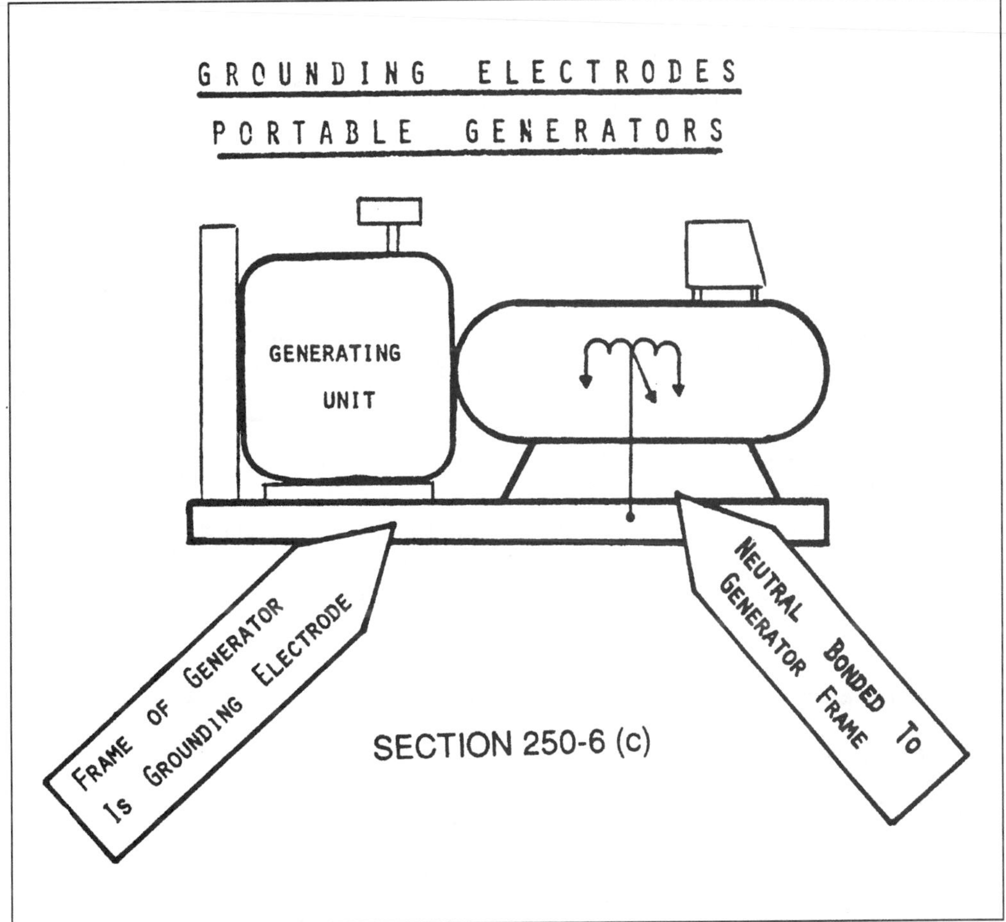

Fig. 16–11 A portable-generator frame is permitted to be used as a grounding electrode.

VEHICLE-MOUNTED GENERATORS

The frame of the vehicle on which a vehicle-mounted generator is mounted is permitted to be the grounding electrode (figure 16–12) when it is the supply system and all the following conditions are met:

1. The frame of the generator is bonded to the vehicle frame.
2. The generator supplies only equipment mounted on the generator.
3. The generator supplies cord- and plug-connected equipment through receptacles mounted on the vehicle or generator, or both.
4. The noncurrent-carrying parts of equipment are bonded to the generator frame.

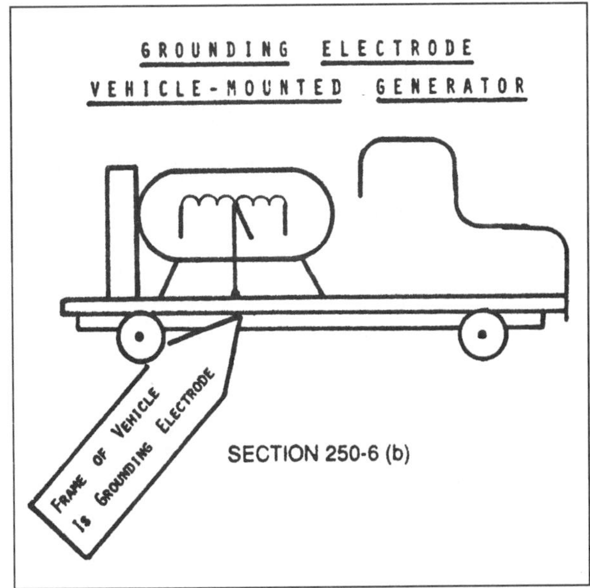

Fig. 16–12 The vehicle frame of a vehicle-mounted generator is permitted to be the grounding electrode.

5. The equipment grounding conductor terminals of the receptacles are bonded to the generator frame.
6. The system complies with all other provisions of *Article 250.*

Permission to use the frames of the portable generator and vehicle-mounted generator as the grounding electrode is an example where ground can be something other than earth. Figure 16–13 illustrates *Section 250–6(c),* where a neutral conductor is used in conjunction with a vehicle-mounted generator and is bonded to the vehicle frame.

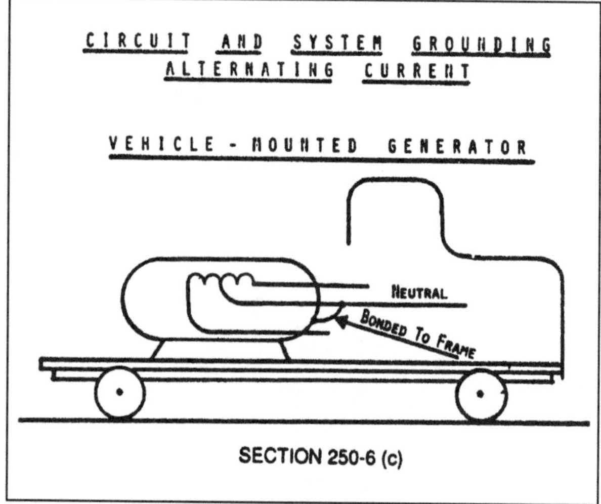

Fig. 16–13 A neutral conductor used with a vehicle-mounted generator. It is bonded to the generator frame.

FOLLOW UP

Topics for self-study, discussion, or questioning.

1. Discuss what a separately derived system is.
2. Discuss how to identify when a standby system is or is not a separately derived system.
3. Compare the installation of a bank of transformers for a separately derived system to the installation of a service.
4. Explain the requirements for the installation of the grounding electrode conductor for a separately derived system.
5. Explain the requirements for the installation of the main bonding jumper for a separately derived system.
6. Discuss the five-wire system.
7. Discuss the use of a portable generator as a separately derived system.
8. Discuss the use of a vehicle-mounted generator as a separately derived system.

CHAPTER 17

Two or More Buildings Supplied By One Service

OBJECTIVES

After completing this chapter, the student should be able to:

- compare the installation of the feeder to a second building to the service in the first building, when both buildings are supplied by the same service.
- explain when a grounding electrode is required to be installed at the second building.
- explain when a main bonding jumper is required to be installed at the second building.
- explain the equipment grounding for the second building when only one circuit is installed in the second building.
- explain the use of the equipment grounding conductor when carried to the second building.
- use *Table 250-95* to calculate the size of the grounding electrode conductor needed at the second building.
- use *Table 250-95* to calculate the size of the main bonding jumper needed at the second building.
- explain the requirements for a disconnecting means at the second building when the service is 600 volts or less.
- explain the requirements, when the service is over 600 volts and is permitted to be installed without a service disconnecting means.
- explain the special requirements, when the second building is an agricultural building.

This chapter focuses on installing a common electrical service for two or more buildings or structures on the same premises (figure 17–1, page 250). Although there could be more than two buildings and/or structures, this chapter uses two buildings for illustration purposes. The same regulations that apply to the second building also apply to a third, fourth, or any number of buildings or separate structures installed on the same premises and fed from one common service.

A pole or lighting standard may meet the definition of a structure. However, individual poles or groups of poles used as lighting standards are not considered separate structures where the disconnecting means is remotely located,

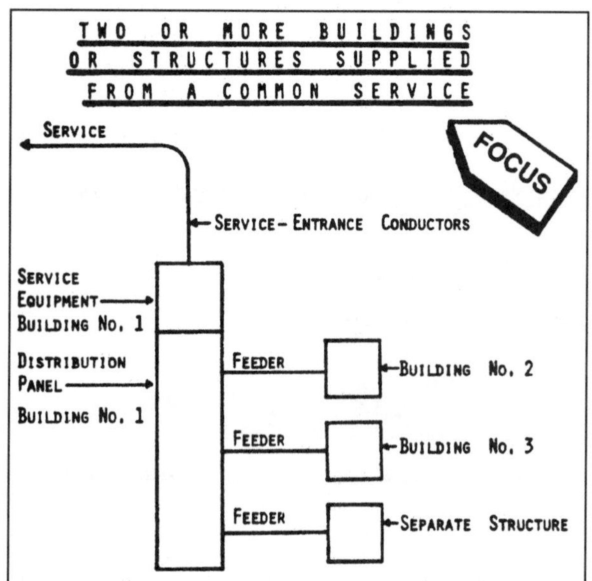

Fig. 17–1 Two or more buildings or structures supplied from a common service.

Section 225-8(b) Exception No. 3. Parking lot lighting or other area lighting may have a lighting fixture mounted on a pole and be controlled from a remote location and not be considered a separate structure.

When one service serves two buildings, there are some special Code regulations that apply to the grounded conductor (the neutral) and the equipment grounding conductor.

A helpful hint or a rule of thumb when two or more buildings or structures are supplied by one service is to think of it in the following terms, as illustrated in figure 17–2: Treat the conductors leaving the first building as a feeder and treat the same conductors, when they arrive at the second building as service-entrance conductors, as terminating in service equipment.

The Code does not contain this statement, but in a practical way this is what is taking place. When the feeder arrives at the second building and the system is a grounded system, it can be treated as a new service.

Part of the reason for thinking of a feeder arriving at the second building as a service stems from the regulations listed in previous editions

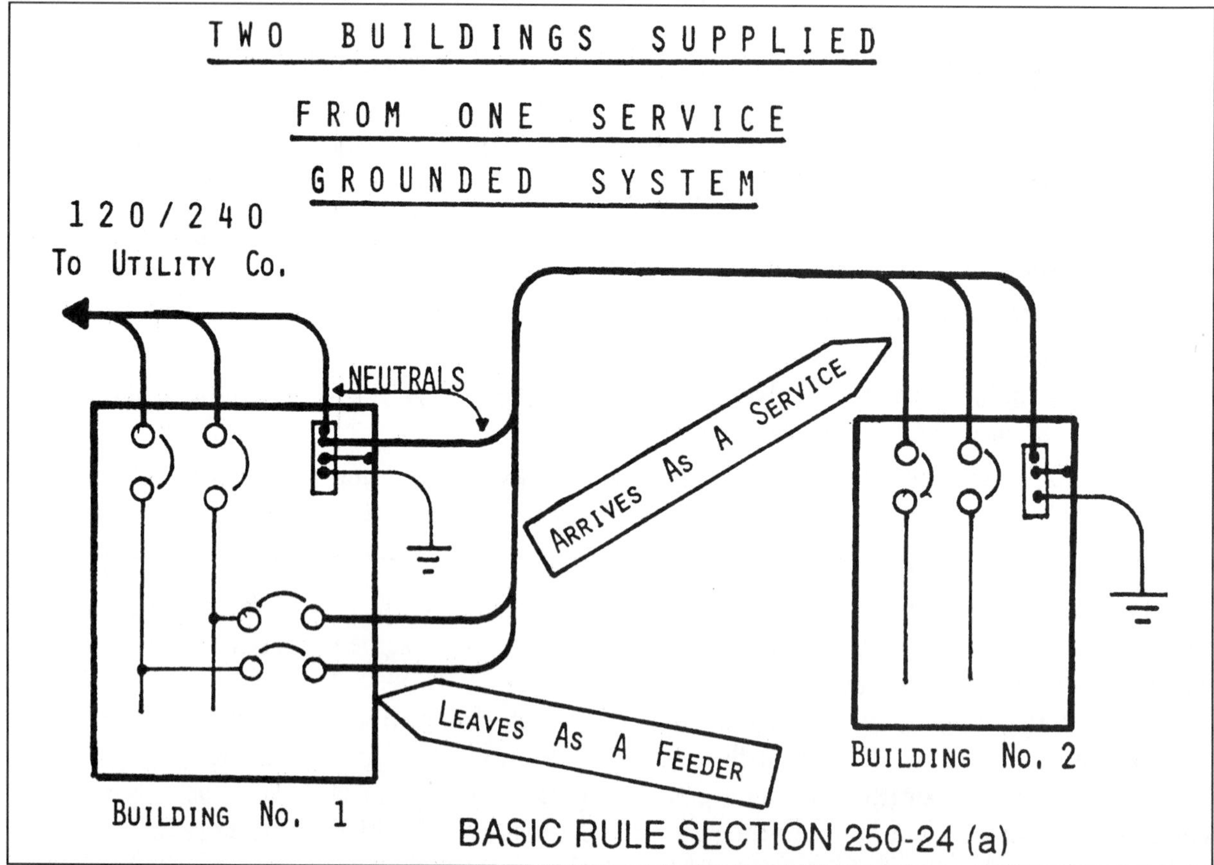

Fig. 17–2 Suggested rule of thumb and basic rule for two buildings supplied from one grounded service.

of the Code in *Article 230, Services*. The 1993 edition moved these requirements to *Article 225, Outside Branch Circuits and Feeders*. However, even with this move, *Section 225-8(b)* refers to *Section 230-70* of *Article 230, Services*. The location of the disconnect at the second building is the same as for a service and is spelled out in *Section 230-70*. *Section 225-8(c)* requires the disconnecting means at the second building to be listed as suitable for service equipment. This means the disconnecting means at the second building will have provisions in it for connecting the grounding electrode conductor and the main bonding jumper. However, there are some differences from a regular service, and some special situations to be taken into consideration when installing the grounding at the service disconnecting means for the second building.

GROUNDED AND UNGROUNDED SYSTEMS

The rules for two buildings supplied from one service are set down for both the grounded system in *Section 250-24(a)* (figure 17–2) and the ungrounded system in *Section 250-24(b)* (figure 17–3). The variation in the rules for grounded and ungrounded systems is small. Anything required for a grounded system is also required for an ungrounded system. Exceptions made for grounded systems are also made for ungrounded systems.

When two or more buildings or structures are supplied from one common service (a grounded system or an ungrounded system), the second building shall have a grounding electrode of its own established.

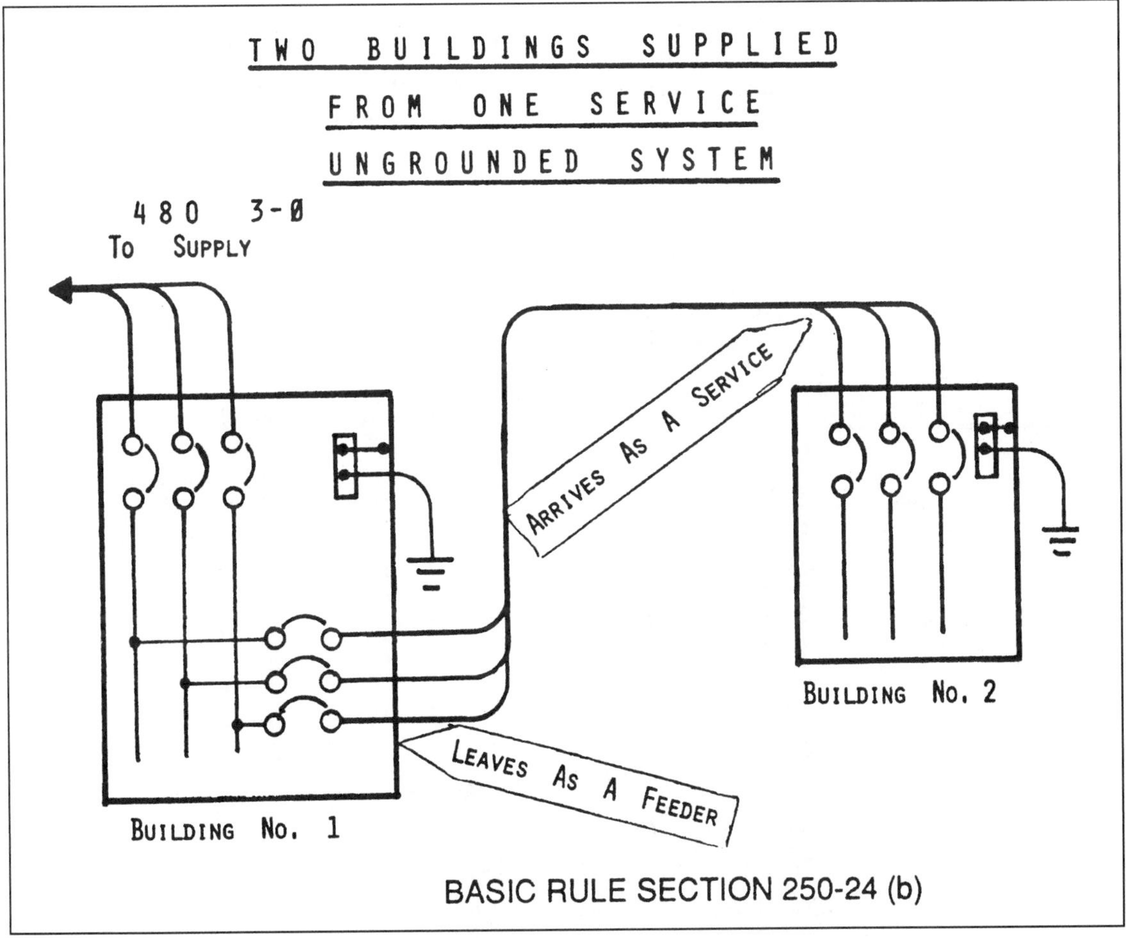

Fig. 17–3 Suggested rule of thumb and basic rule for two buildings supplied from one ungrounded service.

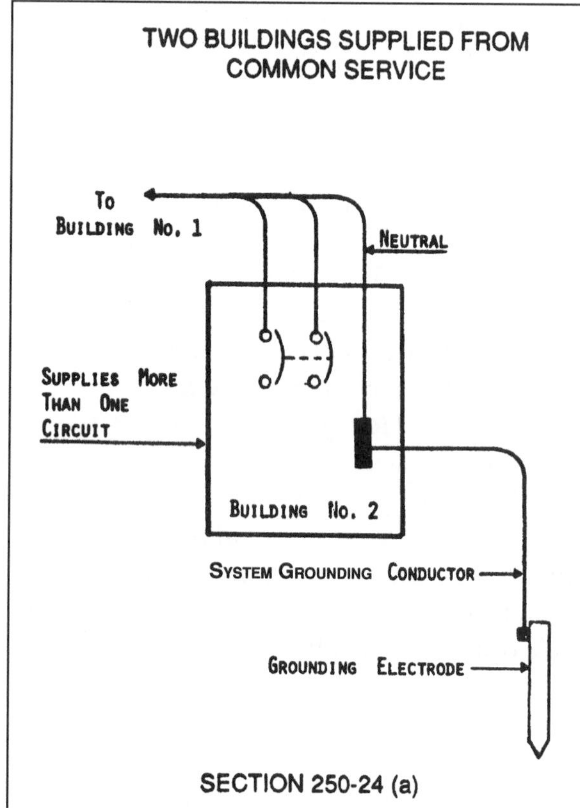

Fig. 17–4 Grounding electrode system established at a second building when two buildings are supplied from one service.

GROUNDING INSTALLATION AT SECOND BUILDING

Section 250-24(a) requires a grounding electrode to be installed at the second building when more than one building or structure is supplied from one common service. The section states the following:

1. The grounded system in each building or structure shall have a grounding electrode.
2. The electrode shall be installed in accordance with Part H of *Article 250.*
3. The grounding electrode shall be connected to the system grounded circuit conductor and the metal enclosure for the building disconnecting means.
4. The connection shall be on the supply side of the building disconnecting means.

Figure 17–4 illustrates a ground rod being used for the grounding electrode. Any grounding electrode permitted by Part H may be used.

Exception No. 1 of *Section 250-24(a)* permits installing a grounded conductor without the

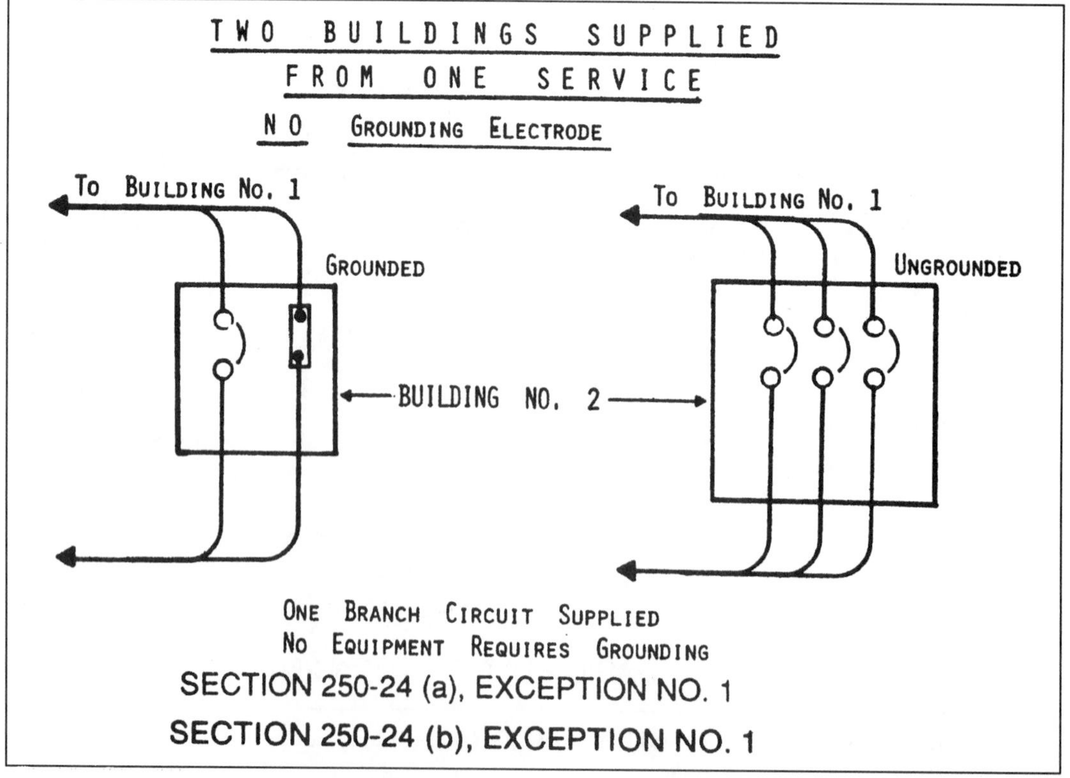

Fig. 17–5 Two buildings supplied from one service when only one branch circuit is supplied.

grounded conductor being connected to a grounding electrode conductor at the second building (figure 17–5, page 252). This can be accomplished when there is only one branch circuit to be served and there is no equipment required to be grounded.

Section 250-24(a), Exception No. 2, permits the installation of a grounded conductor to a second building without connecting the grounded conductor to a grounding electrode. This installation can be made provided an equipment grounding conductor is also installed from building number one and only one branch circuit is served in building number two. The following paragraphs cover five points required for the use of the exception. Note that all five points must be fulfilled in order for the exception to be used.

1. The equipment grounding conductor is installed with the phase conductors from the first building.

Reason: In case of a ground fault, the impedance of the ground fault path is reduced when the equipment grounding conductor and the circuit conductors are in the same raceway or cable enclosure.

2. The equipment grounding conductor is run to the second building to ground any non-current-carrying equipment, interior metal piping system, and building or structural metal frames.

Comment: This indicates the equipment grounding conductor (figure 17–6) is installed to perform its specific function—grounding non-current-carrying metal parts of metal enclosures. The equipment grounding conductor is also used to ground any metal framing that might be present at the second building or in case a steel structure could be used to ground the steel structure.

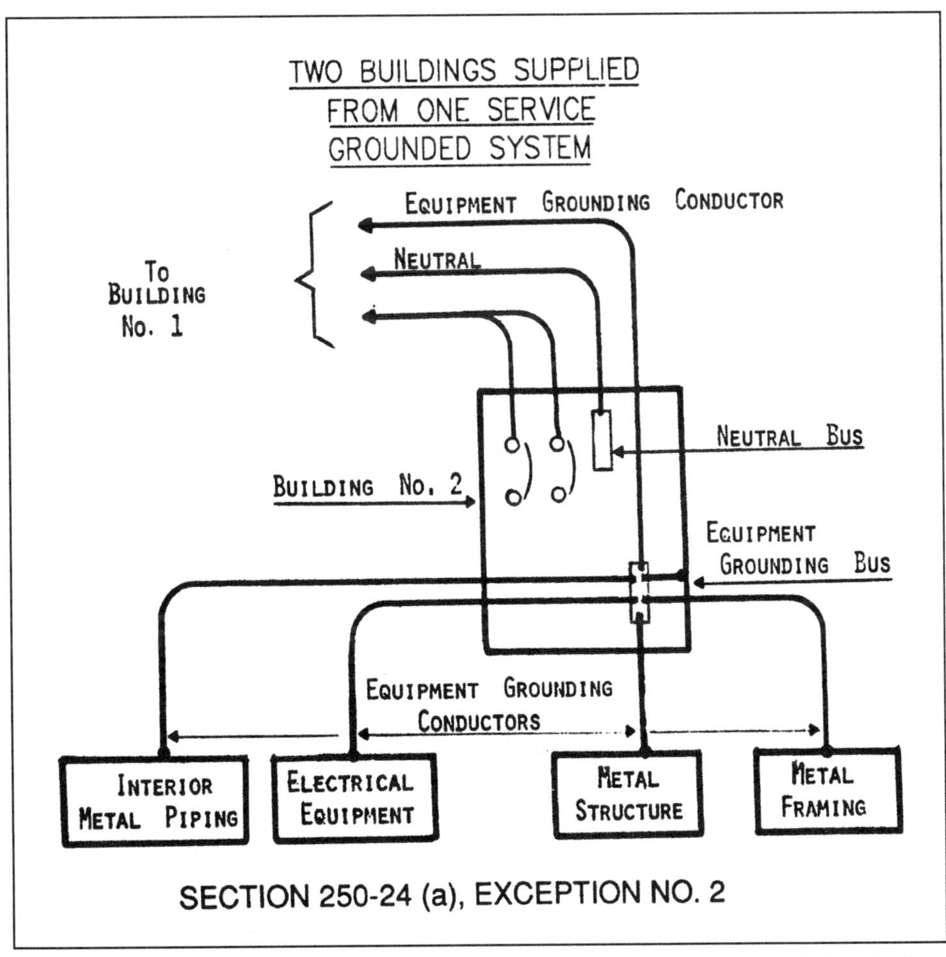

Fig. 17–6 An equipment grounding conductor is run to the second building for equipment grounding.

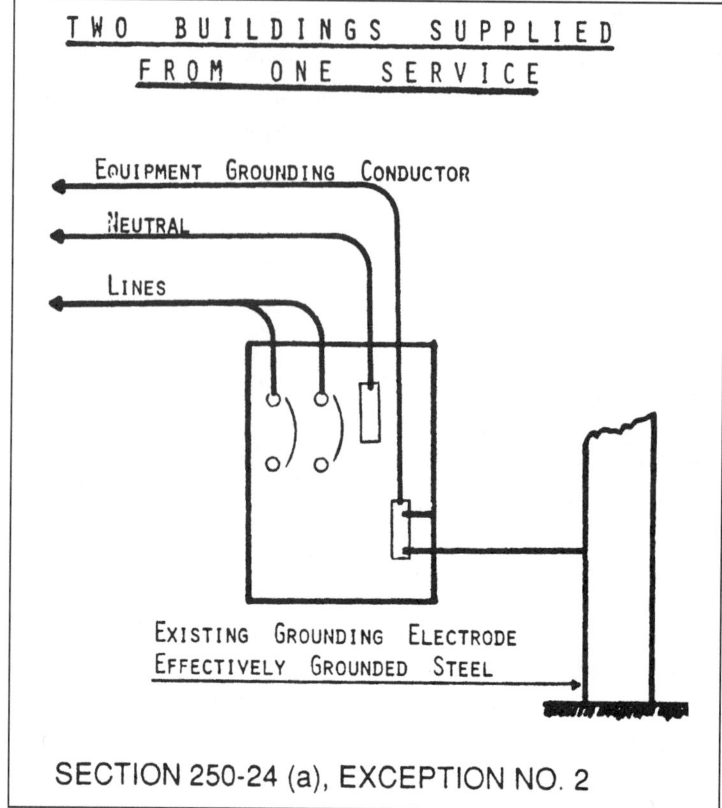

Fig. 17–7 An equipment grounding conductor is connected to effectively grounded building steel in the second building.

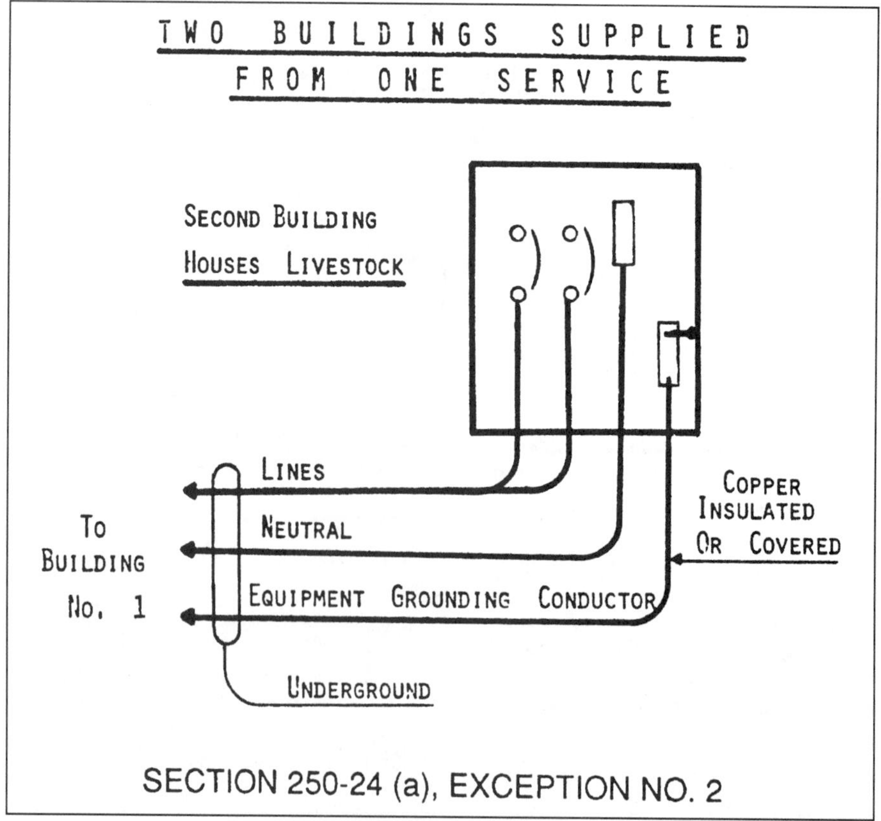

Fig. 17–8 Two buildings supplied from one service when the second building houses livestock.

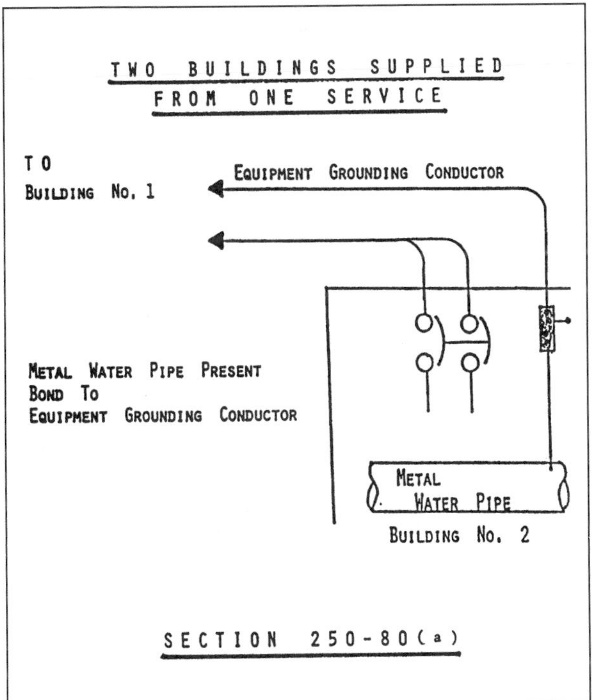

Fig. 17–9 An equipment grounding conductor is run to the second building and bonded to metal water piping.

3. There is no existing grounding electrode in the second building.

Comment: The existing grounding electrodes referred to here are what the Code lists in Part H as grounding electrodes, such as effectively grounded metal water piping or building steel (figure 17–7). If there is an existing grounding electrode, the installation will be in accordance with the applicable sections of *Article 250* for bonding and grounding.

4. There is only one branch circuit in the second building.

Comment: When there is more than one branch circuit in the second building, a grounding electrode system is required. Where there is no effectively grounded metal water piping or building steel, a made electrode shall be installed, such as ground rod or other made electrode.

5. Where livestock are housed in the second building, an equipment grounding conductor run underground to the disconnecting means in the second building shall be an insulated or covered copper conductor.

Reason: Livestock are very sensitive to any kind of voltage or current caused by leakage or circulating ground currents, and the insulated or covered equipment grounding conductor protects against circulating ground currents. The copper requirement recognizes the durability of copper over aluminum when installed underground (figure 17–8).

The installation of the equipment grounding conductor overhead is not mentioned in this section; therefore, it can be assumed that bare copper or aluminum is permitted.

Should the installation be made using the equipment grounding conductor, and a metal water pipe is present in the second building, as in figure 17–9, the metal water pipe shall be bonded to the equipment grounding conductor, according to *Section 250-80(a)*.

SIZING THE GROUNDED CONDUCTOR

The grounded conductor, neutral, is normally sized according to *Article 220*. When there is very little neutral load, the neutral is permitted to be smaller than the ungrounded conductors. When an installation is made to a second building and an equipment grounding conductor is not installed, Section *250-24(a)* requires the grounded conductor to be not smaller than the equipment grounding conductor required by *Table 250-95* (figure 17–10, page 256).

In figure 17–10, the feeder to the second building is protected with a 200-ampere circuit breaker. With no equipment grounding conductor installed to the second building, the minimum size of the grounded conductor is No. 6, *Table 250-95*.

SIZING THE SYSTEM GROUNDING CONDUCTOR AT THE SECOND BUILDING

The sizing of the system grounding conductor at the second building is covered in *Section 250-24(d)*. The supply conductor to the second building is technically a feeder. The supply feeder is protected by an overcurrent protection device in the

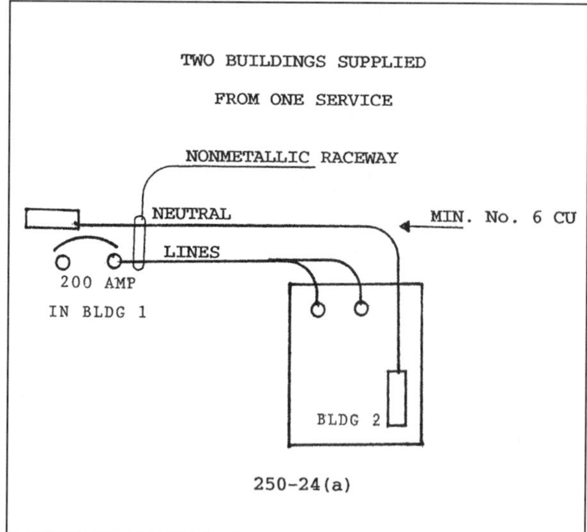

Fig. 17–10 Sizing the grounded conductor when no equipment grounding conductor is installed.

first building. Therefore, the system grounding conductor in the second building is an equipment grounding conductor and is sized as an equipment grounding conductor. The size of the system grounding conductor in the second building is based on the overcurrent protection device in the first building and is taken from *Table 250-95.*

The big differences are:

1. A service is not considered to have any overcurrent protection on the supply side of the service.
2. The only protection for the supply conductors of a service is the next utility company protection back on the utility company's line, which is not sized to protect the service-entrance phase conductors.
3. The supply to the second building is protected by an overcurrent protective device, which is sized according to the load in the second building and the supply conductors to the second building.
4. When the feeder to the second building is protected by an overcurrent device, the overcurrent device will limit the let through fault current the system grounding conductor might be subjected to.

NOTE: The system grounding conductor for the second building is not sized according to the size of the supply conductors entering the second building. However, it is never required to be larger than any phase conductor feeding the second building.

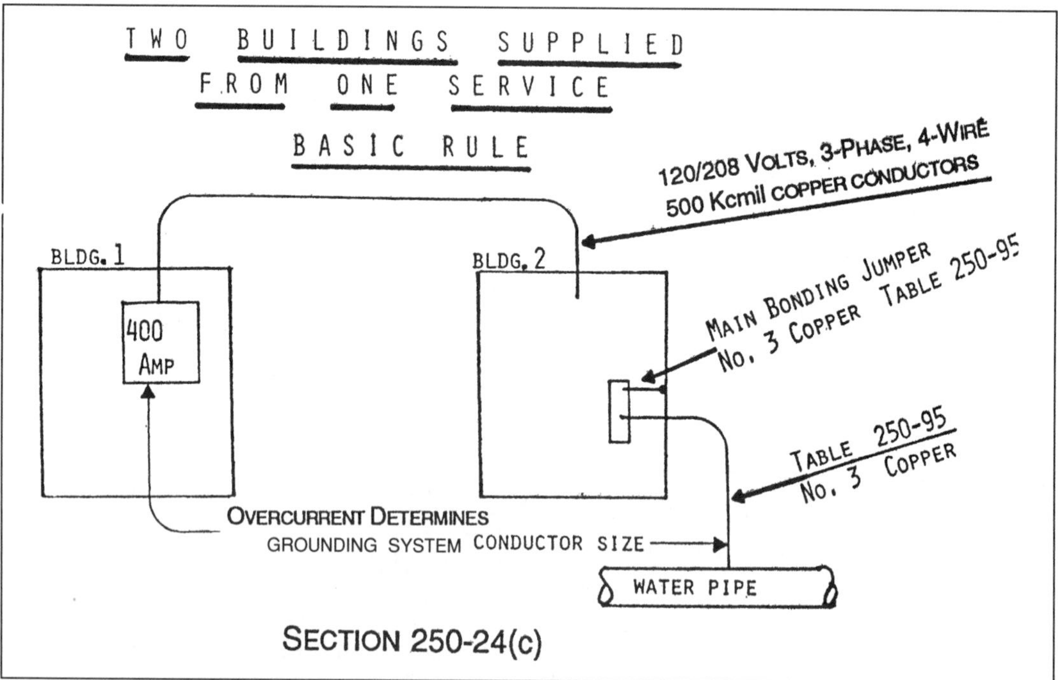

Fig. 17–11 The size of the system grounding conductor at the second building is based on the overcurrent protection for the feeder supplying the second building.

Rating or Setting of Automatic Overcurrent Device in Circuit Ahead of Equipment, Conduit, etc., Not Exceeding (Amperes)	Size	
	Copper Wire No.	Aluminum or Copper-Clad Aluminum Wire No.*
15	14	12
20	12	10
30	10	8
40	10	8
60	10	8
100	8	6
200	6	4
300	4	2
400	3	1
500	2	1/0
600	1	2/0
800	1/0	3/0
1000	2/0	4/0
1200	3/0	250 kcmil
1600	4/0	350 "
2000	250 kcmil	400 "
2500	350 "	600 "
3000	400 "	600 "
4000	500 "	800 "
5000	700 "	1200 "
6000	800 "	1200 "

Fig. 17–12 ***Table 250-95*** **for sizing the system grounding conductor at a second building with an existing grounding electrode.***

Figure 17–11 (page 256) illustrates the sizing of the grounding conductor for the second building, when 500 kcmil copper conductors are installed and are protected by a 400-amp circuit breaker in the first building and a metal water pipe or other existing grounding electrode is available in the second building. Technically, according to the definition of the grounding electrode conductor, the so-called grounding electrode conductor at the second building is not a grounding electrode conductor. It is not on the line side of the service. It is on the load side of the service and therefore is technically a grounding conductor and is identified as the "system grounding conductor."

Figure 17–12, using *Table 250-95*, indicates a 400-amp overcurrent protection device requires a No. 3 copper grounding electrode conductor at the second building.

Table 250-95 is also used to size the main bonding jumper at the second building. In this case it would be the same size as the grounding electrode conductor, as illustrated in figures 17–11 and 17–12.

When there is no existing grounding electrode in the second building and a made electrode such as a ground rod is installed, the grounding electrode conductor need not be larger than a No. 6 copper or No. 4 aluminum conductor, as illustrated in figure 17–13 (page 258). The reason, as discussed earlier in this text, is that the No. 6 copper or No. 4 aluminum conductor will carry all the fault current the made electrode can dissipate into the earth.

The regulations for the mechanical installation of strapping, terminating, and protecting of the grounding electrode conductor are the same for the second building as previously discussed in Chapter 6.

NO DISCONNECTING MEANS AT SECOND BUILDING

Section 225-8(b), under outside feeders, requires a disconnecting means for the supply at the second building. Exception No. 1 to this requirement permits the disconnecting means to be located remote from the second building when:

1. The installation is 600 volts or less.
2. It is a large-capacity multibuilding industrial installation.
3. All buildings are under one management.
4. Safe switching procedures can be established.
5. Safe switching procedures can be maintained.

Section 250-24(c) works in conjunction with this exception and puts some specifics to be met when such an installation is made, as illustrated in figure 17–14 (page 258).

When an installation 600 volts nominal or under is made to a second building and the disconnecting means is located in the first building, all of the following requirements must be fulfilled:

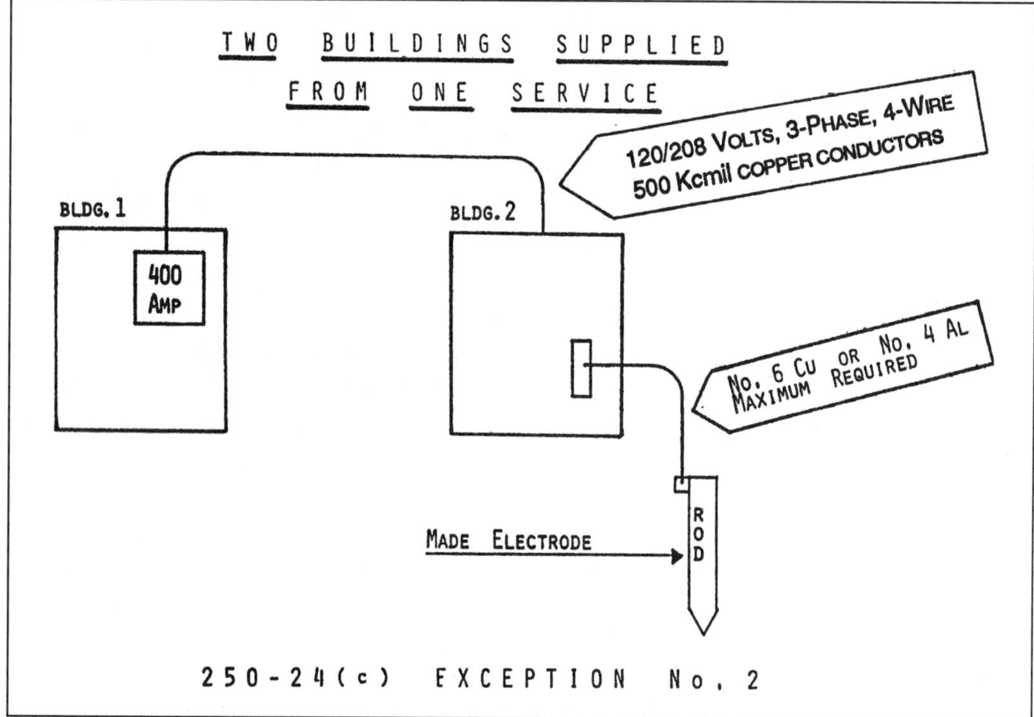

Fig. 17–13 Maximum size system grounding conductor required for a second building, when a made electrode is installed.

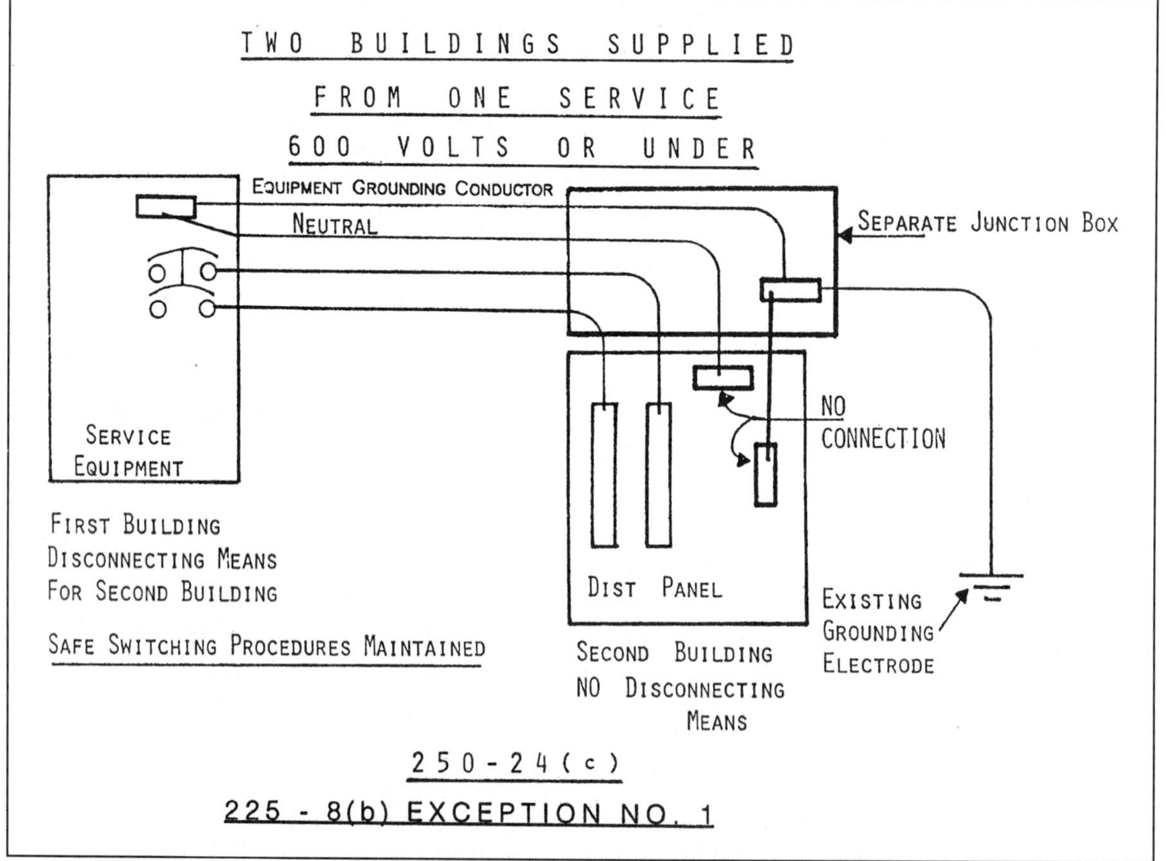

Fig. 17–14 Requirements when no disconnect is installed at the second building and the supply is 600 volts or less.

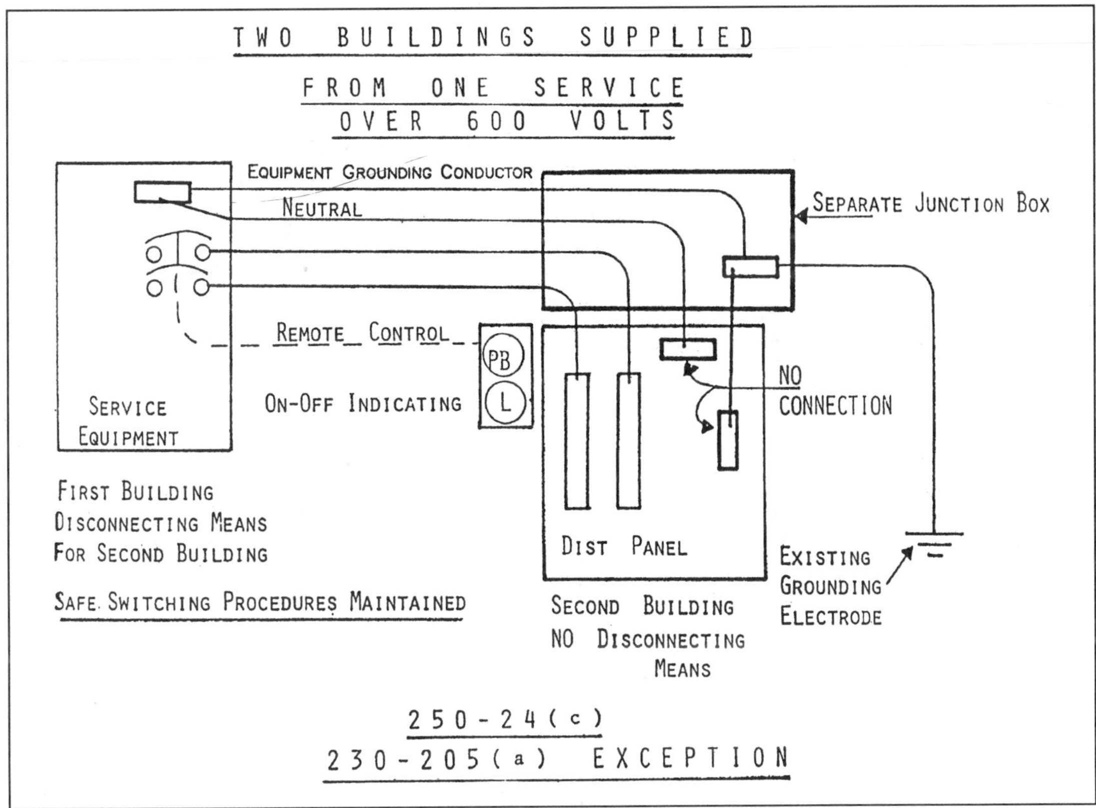

Fig. 17–15 Requirements when no disconnect is installed at the second building and the supply is over 600 volts.

1. The neutral must be carried to the second building.
2. The equipment grounding conductor must be carried to the second building with the circuit conductors.
3. There must be no connection made between the neutral and the equipment grounding conductor at the second building.
4. There must be no connection between the neutral and the grounding electrode conductor at the second building.
5. The equipment grounding conductor shall be connected to the grounding electrode conductor in a separate junction box, panelboard, or similar enclosure located immediately inside or outside the separate building or structure.
6. The equipment grounding conductor shall be connected to an existing grounding electrode via a grounding electrode conductor at the second building.
7. When there is no existing grounding electrode conductor, a made electrode shall be installed.
8. The grounding electrode conductor installed at the second building shall be installed to function as a grounding electrode conductor. Where necessary, enclosure bonding is required.

NOTE: The term "grounding electrode conductor" is used here to identify the conductor from the grounding electrode to the building disconnect switch. Technically, according to the definitions in *Article 100*, this is not a grounding electrode conductor, but rather a grounding conductor. The grounding electrode conductor is defined as terminating at the service, but technically this conductor does not terminate at the service. The safe thing to do is to make the installation just as if it were a grounding electrode conductor.

When an installation over 600 volts nominal (for example, 4160 volts) is made to a second

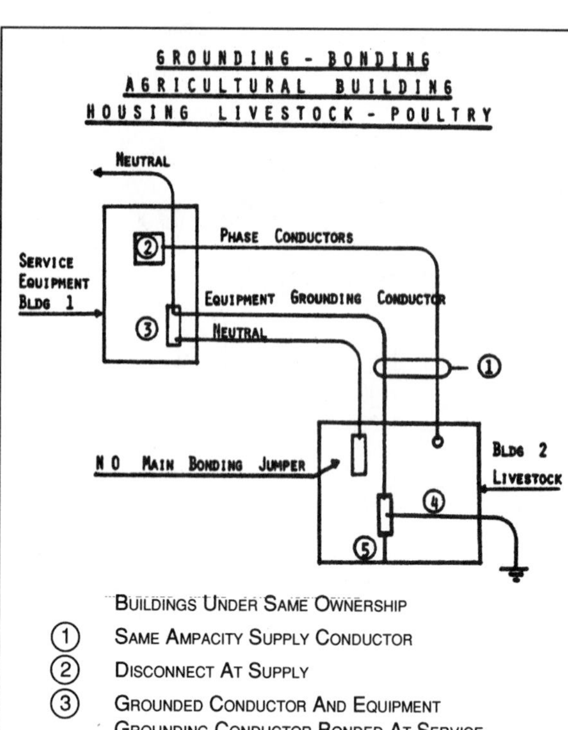

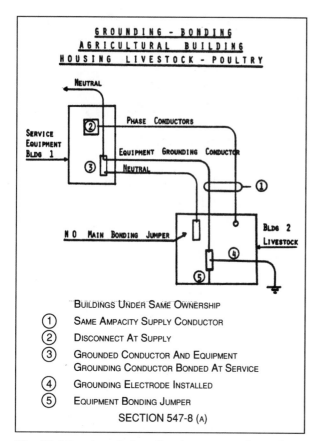

Fig. 17–16 A main bonding jumper can be omitted when a second building houses livestock and special requirements are met.

building and the disconnecting means is located in the first building, *Section 230-205(a)* requires a disconnecting means to be located at the second building. The exception to *Section 230-205(a)* permitting the location of the disconnecting means in the first building has a few different requirements, as illustrated in figure 17–15 (page 259).

1. All the buildings must be under single management.
2. Disconnecting means for second building must be capable of being electrically opened.
3. A readily accessible control device shall be located close to the service entrance of the second building for the operation of the electrically controlled disconnecting means.
4. Control device shall be permanently marked to identify its function.

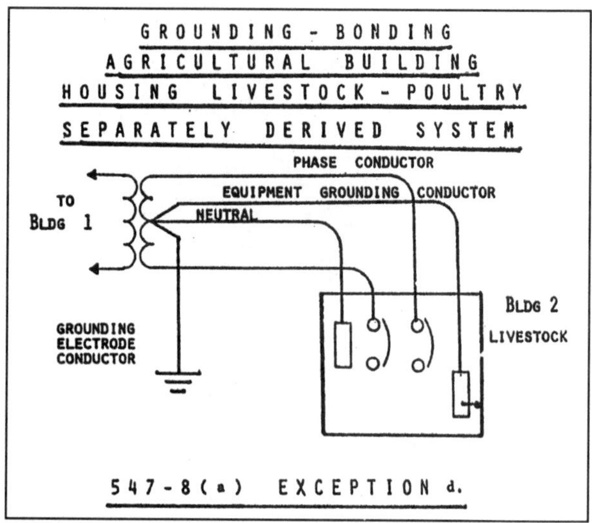

Fig. 17–17 Separately derived system in an agricultural building.

5. There shall be visual indication of the ON and OFF status of the remote disconnecting means.

Once again, *Section 250-24(c)* is applicable and all the requirements listed for 600 volts nominal or under will apply to over 600-volt nominal installations. This is a situation where the Code uses only one section to apply to installations of 600 volts and under as well as over 600 volts.

AGRICULTURAL BUILDING HOUSING LIVESTOCK

Agricultural buildings are covered in *Article 547*, which contains some specific regulations for grounding. Figure 17–16 illustrates an agricultural building being supplied by a feeder from building No. 1. Figure 17–17 illustrates an agricultural building being supplied by a separately derived system.

When a second building is used to house livestock and it is supplied by a grounded system, the main bonding jumper at the second building can be omitted, provided that all the following conditions are met (figure 17–15, page 259):

1. The supply to the second building arrives at a distribution panelboard.

2. All buildings and premises are under one ownership.
3. The equipment grounding conductor is the same ampacity as the circuit conductors.
4. The equipment grounding conductor is run with the circuit conductors.
5. A service disconnect is provided in or near the distribution panel in the second building.
6. The grounded circuit conductor (neutral) and the equipment grounding conductor are bonded at the service equipment or at the source of a separately derived system.
7. A grounding electrode is provided and connected to the equipment grounding conductor in the distribution panel at the second building.

Figure 17–17 illustrates the use of a separately derived system for the agricultural building in accord with *Section 547-8(a)*, part d of the Exception No. 1. The illustration shows the grounded conductor and the equipment grounding conductor bonded at the source of supply. Therefore, there is no main bonding jumper from the neutral bar to the enclosure.

FOLLOW UP

Topics for self-study, discussion, or questioning.

1. Compare the installation at a second building to the installation of a service.
2. Discuss the requirements in *Article 230, Services*, that apply to the installation of a service at a second building.
3. Discuss the installation to a second building when there is only one branch circuit in the second building.
4. Explain the sizing of the grounding electrode conductor at the second building.
5. Explain the sizing of the main bonding jumper at the second building.
6. Discuss the requirement for a disconnecting means at the second building when the service is 600 volts or less.
7. Discuss the requirements when an installation to the second building is over 600 volts and is permitted to be installed without a disconnecting means at the second building.
8. Discuss the special requirements for the installation of a service to a second building, when the second building is an agricultural building.

CHAPTER 18

Calculating Fault Currents and Grounding Conductor Withstand Rating

OBJECTIVES

After completing this chapter, the student should be able to:

- explain the relationship between grounding and overcurrent protection of equipment against the damaging effects of fault currents.
- identify some of the protective terminology used in conjunction with fuses and circuit breakers.
- explain the difference between "overload" protection and "overcurrent" protection.
- identify the markings used on fuses and circuit breakers.
- use the point-to-point method of calculating potential fault currents.
- discuss equipment grounding conductor "withstand" ratings and their ability to safely carry fault currents under any condition.

INTRODUCTION

Before starting this chapter, review Chapter 4, "Faults." Pay particular attention to the stresses faults place on equipment and wire.

When we talk about fault currents, many different terms are used; however, they all basically mean the same thing. Some of these terms are **Fault current**, **Available short-circuit current**, **available fault-current**, **potential fault current**, and **short-circuit current**.

Also for this chapter, think B I G. Think in terms of extremely large amounts of current, or a tremendous number of electrons all rushing to one point at the same time. Visualize, if you will, a wall of water coming down a stream, overflowing its banks, and destroying everything in its path. Now visualize fault current as an extremely large wall of electrons trying to flow in a conductor sized for comparatively few amperes, overflowing the conductor, and destroying all conductors and equipment in its path.

Damage

The main concern when installing an electrical system is to make sure that it is a safe installation *(Section 90-1(a))*. When a fault occurs, whether it be a line-to-line fault or a line-to-ground fault, the overcurrent protective device must clear the fault before extensive damage occurs *(Section 110-10)*. The overcurrent protective device itself must also have an adequate interrupting rating to safely clear a fault *(Section 110-9)*. Bonding and grounding must be capable of safely conducting **any** value of fault current to which it may be subjected *(Sections 250-1* (FPNs), *250-51, 250-71*, and *250-75)*. The sizing of grounding electrode conductors is done using *Table 250-94*. The sizing of equipment grounding conductors is done using *Table 250-95*.

Simply stated, there are two types of damaging effects on electrical equipment that are caused by faults: magnetic forces and thermal stresses.

Magnetic Forces. Magnetic forces vary as the square of the peak current. For example, if we compare the magnetic forces of a 10,000-ampere fault to those of a 20,000-ampere fault, we find that the magnetic forces of the 20,000-ampere fault are four times greater than those of the 10,000-ampere fault. Magnetic forces push and pull conductors against sharp metal corners, causing insulation failure and bent bus bars. They also push and pull bus bars from their insulating mountings and pull conductors out of their lugs.

Thermal Stresses. Thermal stress (thermal damage, due to heat) varies as the square of the RMS (the current read on an ammeter) multiplied by the time (measured in seconds). We can state that:

THERMAL STRESS (heat) = I^2t

This is referred to as *ampere-squared seconds*. Therefore, when selecting and applying overcurrent protective devices, the objective is to reduce the magnitude of the fault current by using current-limiting overcurrent devices and to reduce the length of time the fault current will flow by using overcurrent devices that can clear a fault quickly. Current-limiting fuses can clear a fault in less than one-quarter cycle; regular circuit breakers can clear a fault in approximately one cycle; current-limiting circuit breakers can clear a fault in approximately one-half cycle.

By applying the thermal stress formula above, you can see that the long opening time under fault conditions can cause a tremendous amount of heat buildup and magnetic stress in the equipment. Therefore, care needs to be exercised when utilizing circuit breakers with adjustable trip settings that allow opening times of as long as 30 seconds.

Stated in another way, overcurrent protection is a matter of

HOW MUCH CURRENT WILL FLOW?

AND HOW LONG WILL THE CURRENT FLOW?

The manufacturers of fuses and circuit breakers can supply time-current characteristics curves that clearly show:

HOW MUCH?

AND HOW LONG?

We can then match the equipment's "withstand" capability with the time-current characteristics of the overcurrent device.

PURPOSE OF GROUNDING

The main purposes of grounding are covered in *Section 250-1*. The intent is to provide a low-impedance path for the fault current to travel on until it reaches the circuit's or equipment's overcurrent protective device. Therefore, there is a close relationship between the equipment grounding conductors and the overcurrent protective device of the circuit. Should an equipment grounding conductor, a grounding electrode conductor, or a main bonding jumper be sized too small to safely carry ground fault currents, the conductor can easily burn off, leaving the equipment "hot." Result: a very dangerous situation. This is clearly a violation of the Code rules mentioned earlier in this chapter.

A review of the two terms *overload* and *overcurrent*, as defined in *Article 100*, under *Definition*, indicates the device used for protecting the circuit has two jobs:

1. To protect against overload
2. To protect against overcurrent

When there is protection only against overloads, a dangerous situation develops, which will be shown in this chapter.

Overcurrent

Any current that is above normal current is an overcurrent. This could be an overload, short circuit, or a ground fault. The current flow could be contained within its intended path, or it could flow outside of its intended path (thus the term "short circuit").

Overload. Any current that is above normal current that stays within its intended path is an overload current. An example of this would be an overloaded motor. The high current stays within the windings. If the motor is properly protected, it will be taken off the line before the motor winding insulation breaks down. If the overload is allowed to continue, it will turn into a short circuit or a ground fault.

An overload current is generally considered to be from one to six times the normal current level and is common for starting motors and transformer energizing current. The protective device must withstand these momentary inrush currents for a short period of time so as to eliminate nuisance tripping.

Another example of an overload is a situation where a 20-ampere circuit is asked to supply 22 or 23 amps. The overload protective device has no problem interrupting the overload current.

SHORT CIRCUITS AND GROUND FAULTS

A short circuit or ground fault is any current that is above or below normal current value and that flows outside of its intended path.

When a fault occurs line-to-line, or line-to-ground, the potential fault current can reach thousands of amperes. The overcurrent protective device must interrupt this high current quickly without destroying itself (*Section 110-9*), while at the same time protecting the conductors and equipment (*Section 110-10*).

When a fault current reaches a level beyond the capability of the protective device, the device itself may actually rupture and start a fire. Even if the overcurrent device is capable of safely interrupting the available fault current as required by *Section 110-9*, the downstream electrical components can be severely damaged if they do not have sufficient withstand capabilities as required by *Section 110-10*.

When a severe electrical fault has occurred and a fire is started, it is not uncommon to find in a follow-up inspection that part of the conductor has disintegrated. The conductor appears to have evaporated. It has burned off. This is particularly evident when the fault takes place at a connection point. Extremely high fault currents have the ability to completely destroy conductors and equipment.

When considering fault current, we must always consider the worst-case conditions, whether that be L–L–L, L–L, L–N, or L–G (see below):

L–L–L means a Line-to-Line-to-Line, bolted, three-phase fault

L–L means a Line-to-Line, single-phase fault

L–N means a Line-to-Neutral fault

L–G means a Line-to-Ground fault

PROTECTIVE-DEVICE TERMS

The following identification lettering is often found on fuses and circuit breakers:

1. AIC (Ampere Interrupting Capacity)

   This means the amount of current the device can interrupt without damaging or destroying the protective device in a time period of less than one cycle.

2. SCA (Short-Circuit Amperes)

   This means the amount of current the device is rated to interrupt under short-circuit or ground-fault, conditions in a period of time to protect the circuit and equipment against short-circuit or ground-fault currents.

3. IR (Interrupting Rating)

   The interrupting rating is the highest current at rated voltage that a device is intended to interrupt under standard test conditions.

See *Article 100, Definitions*, Interrupting Rating.

4. AR (Ampere Rating)

   The ampere rating is the normal current rating for the device.

5. CL (Current Limiting)

   When a fuse passes certain tests and meets the Underwriters Laboratories requirements for current limitations, it is labeled a "current limiting" device. The test is concerned with current and time. The term current limiting means that a fuse, when tested on a circuit capable of delivering a specific short-circuit current (RMS amperes symmetrical) at rated voltage, will start to melt within 90 electrical degrees and will clear the circuit within 180 electrical degrees, which is one-half cycle. However, the silver-link design of some current limiting fuses allows the fuse to clear the circuit in one-quarter cycle or less under fault-current conditions, as illustrated in figure 18–1.

Note in figure 18–1 that the current limiting device opens prior to the system's peak current capability for the first one-half cycle (see *Section 240-11*).

A protective device has two ratings. Figure 18–2 shows a typical Class L, time-delay, current limiting fuse. Note the fuse has a CURRENT INTERRUPTING rating of 200,000 amps and a NORMAL rating of 2000 amps. If there is no marking on a fuse, then its interrupting rating is 10,000 amperes RMS (*Section 240-60(c)*).

Note the markings on the circuit breaker in figure 18–3 indicating it has a NORMAL rating of 225 amps and an INTERRUPTING rating of

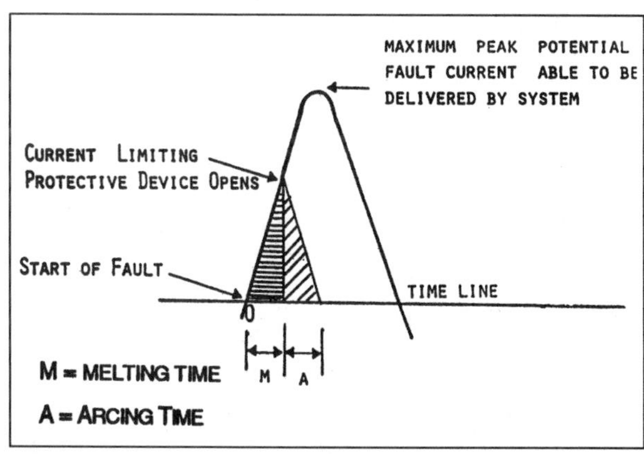

Fig. 18–1 Sine wave, with time element, for the operation of a current limiting protective device.

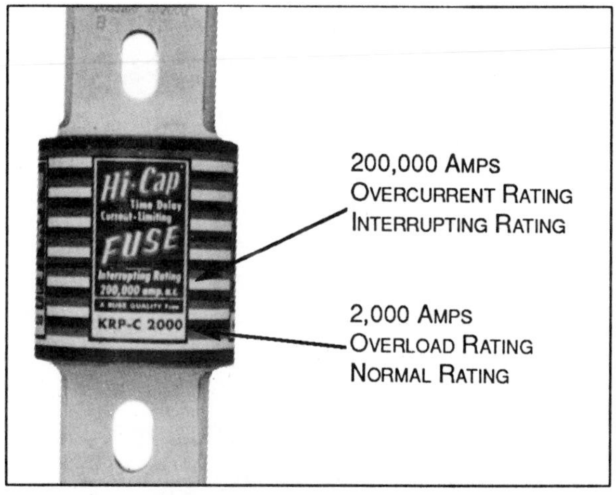

Fig. 18–2 Fuse with normal and interrupting ampacity ratings on label. Courtesy Bussmann Cooper Industries.

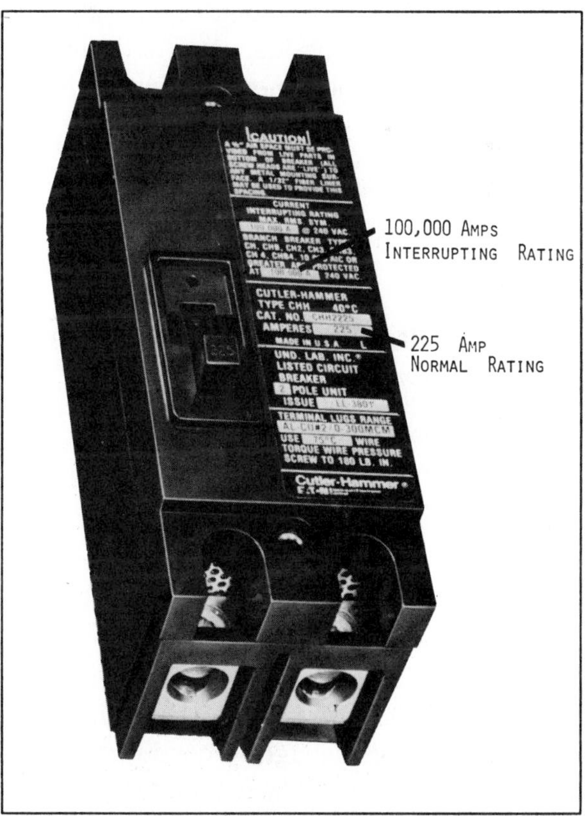

Fig. 18–3 Circuit breaker with normal current rating and maximum interrupting rating showing on the label. Courtesy Eaton Corporation, "Cutler-Hammer" Products.

100,000 amps. If there is no marking on a circuit breaker, then its interrupting rating is 5,000 amperes RMS (*Section 240-83(c)*).

IMPORTANT CODE SECTIONS

Section 110-3(b) requires that all electrical equipment must be installed per the instructions included in the listing or labeling of the equipment.

Section 110-9 requires that any and all electrical equipment intended to break current at fault level must have an interrupting rating sufficient for the system voltage and current available at the line terminals of the equipment. The fault current available at the line terminals of equipment will vary from point to point throughout the system.

Section 110-9 includes fuses, circuit breakers, motor controllers, disconnect switches, contactors, GFCI devices, and other similar equipment that is intended to break current.

Section 110-10 lists some of the things that must be taken into consideration for the protection of electrical components against fault currents.

1. Total impedance
2. Component's short-circuit "withstand" rating
3. Other characteristics such as:

    amount of voltage (pressure)
    amount of current
    type and size of conductor
    length of circuit

Section 230-65 requires the service equipment to be suitable for the short-circuit current available at its supply terminals.

Sections 250-70 and *250-75* both indicate that the equipment grounding and bonding jumpers shall be large enough to conduct the fault current that either may be exposed to.

Section 250-1, first FPN, indicates that systems and circuit conductors are solidly grounded to facilitate overcurrent device operation in case of ground faults. This is referring to the grounded conductor that is always required to be brought to the service, which under fault conditions becomes the equipment grounding conductor path to the protective device.

Section 250-1, second FPN, refers to conductive materials enclosing electrical conductors, or equipment forming part of such equipment, which are also grounded to facilitate overcurrent device operation in case of ground fault. These are the metal raceways and enclosures used as the equipment grounding conductor under fault conditions.

Section 250-51 demands that the grounding path be "effective," and that it have the capacity to conduct safely any fault current likely to be imposed on it.

Table 250-94 indicates grounding electrode conductor size based upon the cross-sectional area of the service-entrance conductors.

Table 250-95 shows the **minimum** sizes of equipment grounding conductors based upon the ampere rating of the overcurrent device protecting that circuit. Note the word *minimum*. A larger size equipment grounding conductor is permitted.

AVAILABLE FAULT CURRENT

Use figure 18–4 throughout the following discussion of fault current.

The **Point-to-Point** method of calculating fault current was used to arrive at the indicated available fault current in figure 18–4. The calculations for the values in figure 18–4 are on the last page of this chapter. For now, accept them and check later. Figure 18–4 illustrates several things:

1. The available fault current at the service is 16,292 amps.
2. The available fault current at the load is 5,824 amps.
3. The available fault current at the service is much greater than the available fault current at the load.

Reason: All conductors offer some opposition to the flow of current and there is a voltage drop

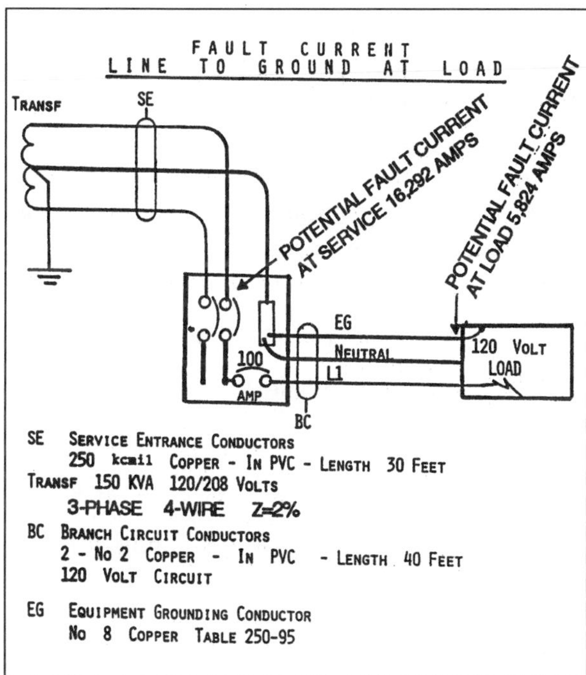

Fig. 18–4 Potential fault current for line to ground fault at load.

(loss of pressure) over the length of the conductor. A change in wire size, using copper instead of aluminum wire, using steel instead of aluminum conduit, or installation of the conductors in open air or PVC conduit will change the impedance of the circuit.

4. The No. 8 copper equipment grounding conductor run to the load will be expected to carry the available fault current until the overcurrent protective device operates and opens the circuit.
5. The figure indicates that the 100-amp overcurrent device in the panel must have an interrupting rating of 10,000 amperes (a standard rating) to safely interrupt the 5,824 amps of fault current. A protective device having an interrupting rating of 5,000 amperes would not be a safe selection.

Question: How long would the No. 8 copper conductor carry the 5,824 amperes of fault current before it was damaged?

There are a number of ways to determine this; some are very complicated, but there are a couple of easy-to-understand methods that will provide acceptable answers.

Method One

Actual tests conducted years ago established that a copper conductor can carry one ampere of current for 5 seconds for each 42.25 circular mils of cross-sectional area without being damaged. This was a bolted-joint test. Apply this theory to the No. 8 copper equipment grounding conductor.

Circular mil area of No. 8=16,510 circular mils

$$\frac{16{,}510 \text{ cmil}}{42.25 \text{ cmil}} = 391$$

This means 391 amps is the maximum amount of current that a No. 8 conductor can carry for five seconds without being damaged.

Method Two

An easier way to determine the short-time "withstand" rating of a conductor is to refer to charts that are published by the Insulated Cable Engineers Association. Using these charts, it is merely necessary to look at the value of available fault current, cross over to the time of opening of the overcurrent protective device, and then drop down to the bottom base line to select the minimum size conductor that is capable of withstanding that amount of fault current for that amount of time. Although the chart below covers insulated 75°C conductors, it is often used to determine the safe "withstand" rating of bare conductors. This is because in most cases a bare equipment grounding conductor is in the same raceway as the insulated circuit conductors. Then the grounding conductor is called upon to carry fault currents, and the heat generated is immediately transferred to the adjacent insulated conductors. The result is thermal damage to the insulated circuit conductors.

Tables are available that show the actual melting I^2t values for copper and aluminum conductors. This data is not shown here because if the conductor melts off, it is too late; the damage has been done. What we are working for is a safe installation.

Use the chart in figure 18–5 for the following illustrations.

Example 1: What is the minimum size copper equipment grounding conductor permitted where the available line-to-ground fault current is 20,000 amperes RMS symmetrical? The overcurrent protective device is rated as clearing the fault in two cycles.

20,000 amperes intersects two-cycle line at No. 2 AWG

Example 2: Using the same values from Example 1, determine the conductor size when the overcurrent protective device is rated as clearing the fault in one-quarter cycle.

20,000 amperes intersects 1/4-cycle line at No. 6 AWG

Example 3: A 60-ampere overcurrent device is used to protect a branch circuit load. The available fault current is 15,000 amperes. The overcurrent device is rated one cycle trip. Determine the correct size copper equipment grounding conductor.

Table 250-95 60 ampere No. 10 copper

Now compare this to the conductor withstand chart.

15,000 amps intersects two-cycle line between 2 and 4 for a No. 3 AWG

If the No. 10 were installed and the fault were to take place, the No. 10 would burn off under fault conditions, leaving the equipment "live."

The above illustrations clearly show that the issue of how much current will flow and how long the current will flow is very important when selecting conductors, whether they be branch circuit conductors or grounding conductors.

FACTORS AFFECTING AMOUNT OF FAULT CURRENT

It is necessary to consider many factors when calculating fault current; many of them are variables. Although the point-to-point method may not be the most accurate because of the variables, it is considered reasonably accurate, is less complicated, and will give a very good indication of what the fault current will be at a particular point in the system. There are other methods that can be used in calculating fault currents, such as computer software programs.

Some of the factors taken into consideration are:

1. the impedance of the supply transformer
2. the voltage available
3. the length of the conductors
4. the size of the conductors
5. the type of material the conductors are made of
6. the type of raceway the conductors are installed in
7. whether the fault is:
   a. all three phases together
   b. two phase conductors together
   c. one phase conductor to ground

TRANSFORMER SECONDARY CURRENT

Power transformers are rated in KVA. The following are the methods and equations for solving the secondary current of a transformer.

Three-Phase Transformer (either three- or four-wire)

I_s = Transformer Full Load Secondary Current

E_s = Transformer Secondary Voltage

$$I_s = \frac{KVA \times 1000}{1.73 \times E_s \text{ (line – to – line voltage)}}$$

Example: What is the secondary current of a 50-KVA, three-phase, 120/208-volt transformer?

$$I_s = \frac{KVA \times 1000}{1.73 \times E_s}$$

$$I_s = \frac{50 \times 1000}{1.73 \times 208} = 138.9 \text{ amps}$$

(round off to 139)

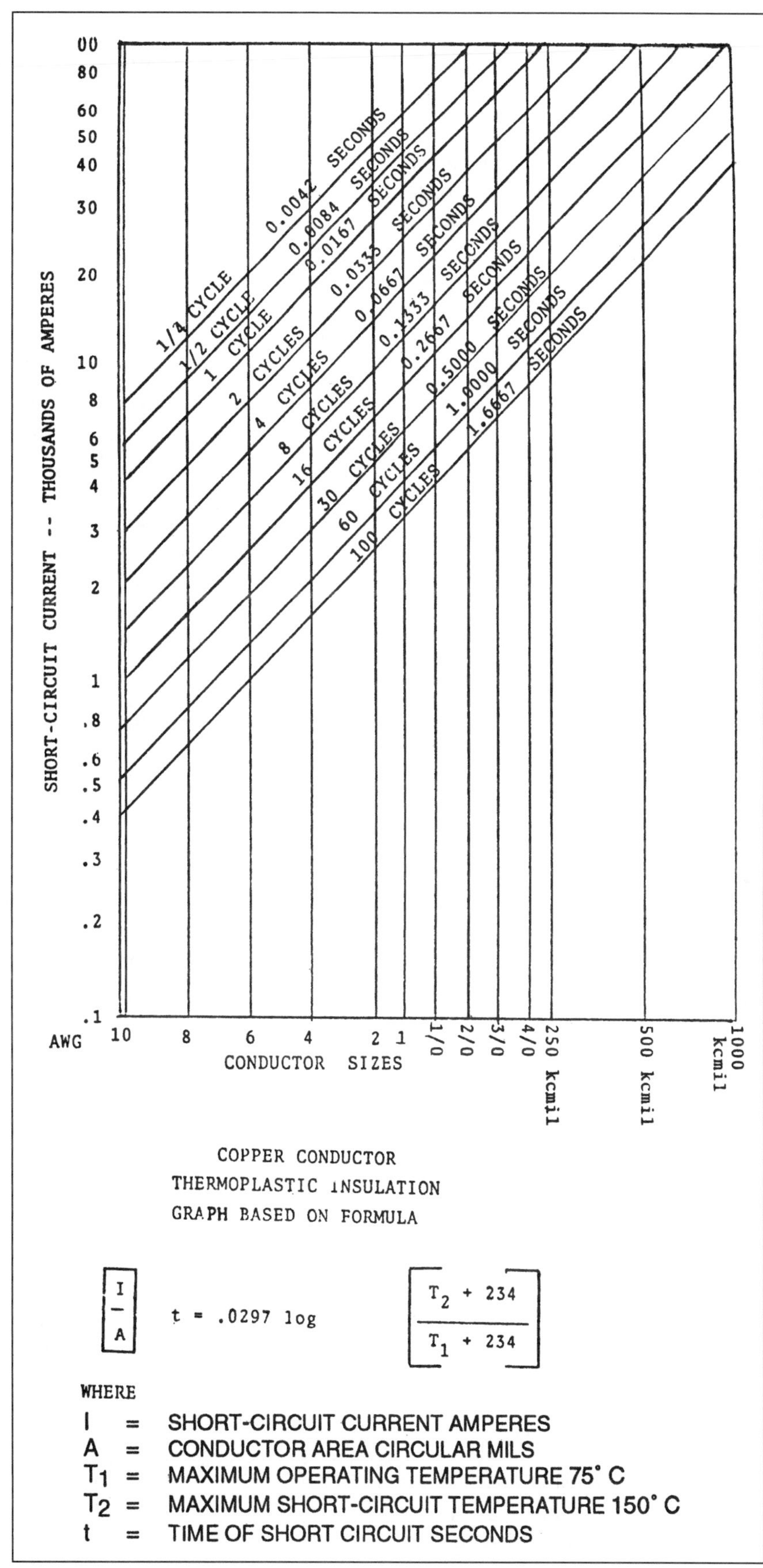

Fig. 18–5 Chart showing allowable short-circuit currents of insulated copper conductors. (Courtesy Bussmann Cooper Industries)

Single-Phase Transformer

$$I_s = \frac{KVA \times 1000}{E_s \text{ (line − to − line voltage)}}$$

Example: What is the secondary current of a 25-KVA, single-phase, 120/240-volt transformer?

$$I_s = \frac{KVA \times 1000}{E_s}$$

$$I_s = \frac{25 \times 1000}{240} = 104.1 \text{amps}$$

(round off to 104 amps)

TRANSFORMER IMPEDANCE

The impedance of a transformer is expressed in a percent (e.g., "2%"), and is found on the nameplate of the transformer.

Figure 18–6 illustrates how the impedance of a transformer is established.

For a 300-KVA, three-phase transformer with a primary voltage rating of 2400 volts and a secondary voltage rating of 240 volts, the impedance of the transformer would be derived in the following manner:

1. Calculate full-load current rating of the primary.

$$I_p = \frac{KVA \times 1000}{E_p \times 1.73}$$

$$I_p = \frac{300 \times 1000}{2400 \times 1.73} = 72.2 \text{ amps}$$

2. Calculate full-load current rating of the secondary.

$$I_s = \frac{KVA \times 1000}{1.73 \times E_s}$$

$$I_s = \frac{300 \times 1000}{1.73 \times 240} = 722 \text{ amps}$$

3. Connect an ammeter (A_s) directly to the secondary with no other load connected to the secondary. This is actually a short-circuit condition for the secondary of the transformer. There is no problem in short-circuiting the secondary of the transformer as long as the rated full load current of the secondary is not exceeded.
4. Connect an ammeter (A_p) and voltmeter (V_p) to the primary of the transformer.
5. Connect a variable voltage supply to the primary of the transformer.
6. Energize the transformer with a low voltage; gradually increase the primary voltage until the ammeter on the secondary of the transformer (A_s) reads 722 amps, the rated full load secondary current. The ammeter on the primary (A_p) reads 72.2 amps, the rated full load current of the primary.
7. Read the primary voltmeter (V_p). In this case, the primary voltmeter reads 48 volts.
8. The impedance is equal to the primary voltage applied divided by the rated primary voltage.

$$\%Z = \frac{E_p \text{ applied primary}}{E_p \text{ rating of primary}}$$

$$\%Z = \frac{48}{2400} = .02 \text{ or } 2\% \text{ impedance}$$

Thus, under a short-circuit condition of the transformer secondary, when only 2 percent of the total rated primary voltage is applied, full load secondary current is reached.

$$\frac{E_p \text{ rating}}{E_p \text{ applied}} = \frac{2400}{48} = 50$$

This means that when the full voltage is applied to the primary, 50 times as much current will be available at the secondary terminals under short-circuit conditions. When 100 percent of the rated primary voltage is applied, 50 times as much short-circuit current will be available at the transformer secondary terminals.

9. Secondary Short-Circuit Current

I_{sca} secondary = $I_s \times 50$

I_{sca} secondary = $722 \times 50 = 36{,}100$ amps

This leads to the equation

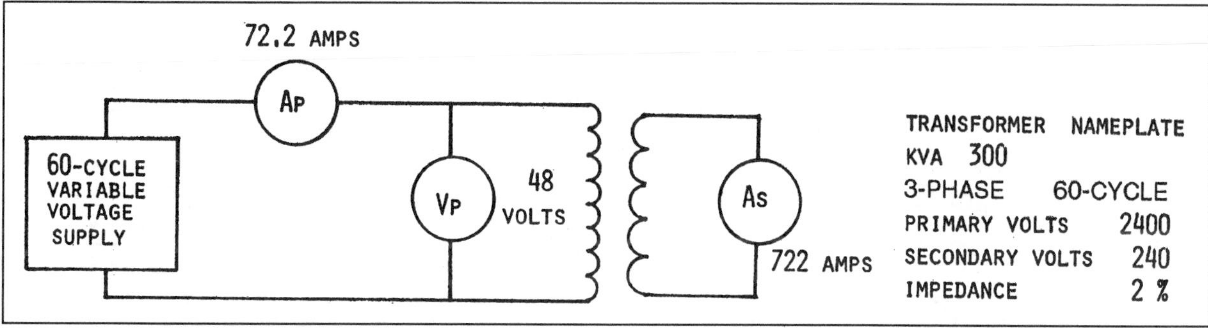

Fig. 18–6 Method of measuring the impedance of a transformer as used for calculating fault current.

$I_{sca} = I_s \times$ Multiplier (M)

Multiplier = 100 % divided by % impedance

$$\text{Multiplier} = \frac{100\%}{2\%} = 50$$

Note: Although impedance is expressed in a percent, and a percent is usually converted to a decimal fraction, in this case percent is being divided by percent and whole numbers are used.

The short-circuit current available at the secondary of a transformer is directly proportional to the impedance of the transformer, as illustrated in the following examples using the transformer in figure 18–6.

If the transformer had been marked 2% impedance:

$$\text{Multiplier} = \frac{100}{Z}$$

$$\text{Multiplier} = \frac{100}{2} = 50$$

$I_{sca} = I_s \times M$

$I_{sca} = 722$ amps $\times 50 = 36{,}100$ short-circuit amps

If the transformer had been marked 1% impedance:

$$\text{Multiplier} = \frac{100}{Z}$$

$$\text{Multiplier} = \frac{100}{1} = 100$$

$I_{sca} = I_s \times M$

$I_{sca} = 722$ amps $\times 100 = 72{,}200$ short-circuit amps

If the transformer had been marked 4% impedance:

$$\text{Multiplier} = \frac{100}{Z}$$

$$\text{Multiplier} = \frac{100}{4} = 25$$

$I_{sca} = I_s \times M$

$I_{sca} = 722$ amps $\times 25 = 18{,}050$ short-circuit amps

If the transformer had been marked 6% impedance:

$$\text{Multiplier} = \frac{100}{Z}$$

$$\text{Multiplier} = \frac{100}{6} = 16.67$$

$I_{sca} = I_s \times M$

$I_{sca} = 722$ amps $\times 16.67 = 12{,}036$ short-circuit amps

OTHER FACTORS AFFECTING FAULT-CURRENT VALUES

The voltage, number of phases, and the length of the circuit are all taken into consideration in the equation used for the point-to-point method of calculating.

The size of conductors or cable, the type of conductors, the material the conductors are made of, and the type of raceway the conductors are enclosed in are all variable factors. Combined into one table, they are represented in the point-to-point equation by "C" (see figure 18–7, page 272).

" C" Values for Conductors and Busway

Copper												
AWG or kcmil	Three Single Conductors						Three-Conductor Cable					
	Conduit						Conduit					
	Steel			Nonmagnetic			Steel			Nonmagnetic		
	600V	5KV	15KV	600V	5KV	15KV	600V	5KV	15KV	600V	5KV	15KV
14	389	389	389	389	389	389	389	389	389	389	389	389
12	617	617	617	617	617	617	617	617	617	617	617	617
10	981	981	981	981	981	981	981	981	981	981	981	981
8	1557	1551	1557	1558	1555	1558	1559	1557	1559	1559	1558	1559
6	2425	2406	2389	2430	2417	2406	2431	2424	2414	2433	2428	2420
4	3806	3750	3695	3825	3789	3752	3830	3811	3778	3837	3823	3798
3	4760	4760	4760	4802	4802	4802	4760	4790	4760	4802	4802	4802
2	5906	5736	5574	6044	5926	5809	5989	5929	5827	6087	6022	5957
1	7292	7029	6758	7493	7306	7108	7454	7364	7188	7579	7507	7364
1/0	8924	8543	7973	9317	9033	8590	9209	9086	8707	9472	9372	9052
2/0	10755	10061	9389	11423	10877	10318	11244	11045	10500	11703	11528	11052
3/0	12843	11804	11021	13923	13048	12360	13656	13333	12613	14410	14118	13461
4/0	15082	13605	12542	16673	15351	14347	16391	15890	14813	17482	17019	16012
250	16483	14924	13643	18593	17120	15865	18310	17850	16465	19779	19352	18001
300	18176	16292	14768	20867	18975	17408	20617	20051	18318	22524	21938	20163
350	19703	17385	15678	22736	20526	18672	19557	21914	19821	22736	24126	21982
400	20565	18235	16365	24296	21786	19731	24253	23371	21042	26915	26044	23517
500	22185	19172	17492	26706	23277	21329	26980	25449	23125	30028	28712	25916
600	22965	20567	47962	28033	25203	22097	28752	27974	24896	32236	31258	27766
750	24136	21386	18888	28303	25430	22690	31050	30024	26932	32404	31338	28303
1000	25278	22539	19923	31490	28083	24887	33864	32688	29320	37197	35748	31959
Aluminum												
14	236	236	236	236	236	236	236	236	236	236	236	236
12	375	375	375	375	375	375	375	375	375	375	375	375
10	598	598	598	598	598	598	598	598	598	598	598	598
8	951	950	951	951	950	951	951	951	951	951	951	951
6	1480	1476	1472	1481	1478	1476	1481	1480	1478	1482	1481	1479
4	2345	2332	2319	2350	2341	2333	2351	2347	2339	2353	2349	2344
3	2948	2948	2948	2958	2958	2958	2948	2956	2948	2958	2958	2958
2	3713	3669	3626	3729	3701	3672	3733	3719	3693	3739	3724	3709
1	4645	4574	4497	4678	4631	4580	4686	4663	4617	4699	4681	4646
1/0	5777	5669	5493	5838	5766	5645	5852	5820	5717	5875	5851	5771
2/0	7186	6968	6733	7301	7152	6986	7327	7271	7109	7372	7328	7201
3/0	8826	8466	8163	9110	8851	8627	9077	8980	8750	9242	9164	8977
4/0	10740	10167	9700	11174	10749	10386	11184	11021	10642	11408	11277	10968
250	12122	11460	10848	12862	12343	11847	12796	12636	12115	13236	13105	12661
300	13909	13009	12192	14922	14182	13491	14916	14698	13973	15494	15299	14658
350	15484	14280	13288	16812	15857	14954	15413	16490	15540	16812	17351	16500
400	16670	15355	14188	18505	17321	16233	18461	18063	16921	19587	19243	18154
500	18755	16827	15657	21390	19503	18314	21394	20606	19314	22987	22381	20978
600	20093	18427	16484	23451	21718	19635	23633	23195	21348	25750	25243	23294
750	21766	19685	17686	23491	21769	19976	26431	25789	23750	25682	25141	23491
1000	23477	21235	19005	28778	26109	23482	29864	29049	26608	32938	31919	29135

Fig. 18–7 Table for C values used in fault current equation. Use with calculations for figure 18–8. Courtesy Bussmann Cooper Industries.

POINT-TO-POINT CALCULATIONS

Use figure 18–8 in the following calculations for establishing the potential fault current at the various points marked throughout the distribution system (a point is established wherever there is a change in wire size). The point-to-point system will work its way from the secondary of the supply transformer to the equipment at the end of the branch circuit. A new point is established each time there is a change in wire size. I_{sca} will be used to indicate the potential fault current at the various locations throughout the system. These will be bolted L–L–L values.

Approximate L–L values are 87 percent of the L–L–L value.

Approximate L–G values are 50 percent of the L–L–L value.

The L–G or L–N value could be 25 to 125 percent of the L–L–L value.

Point 1 Transformer Secondary I_{sca}

$$I_{sca} \text{ secondary} = \frac{KVA \times 1000}{1.73 \times E_s \text{ line}}$$

$$I_{sca} \text{ secondary} = \frac{167 \times 1000}{1.73 \times 208} = 464 \text{ amps}$$

$$\text{Multiplier} = \frac{100}{Z} = \frac{100}{2} = 50$$

$$I_{sca} = I_s \times \text{Multiplier}$$

$$I_{sca} = 464 \text{ amps} \times 50 = 23{,}200 \text{ amps}$$

Point 2 I_{sca} at Service

$$f = \frac{1.73 \times L \times I_{sca} \text{ (at transformer)}}{C \times E \text{ line}}$$

f is for factors—the many factors to be considered.

L is the length of the circuit.

1.73 is used with L for the length of a 3-phase circuit.

C factor from Table (figure 18–7)
600 kcmil copper in steel 22,965

$$f = \frac{1.73 \times L \times I_{sca} \text{ (at transformer)}}{C \times E_{line}}$$

$$f = \frac{1.73 \times 25 \times 23{,}200}{22{,}965 \times 208} = .2101$$

(round off at fourth digit)

M will give the percentage of fault current at point 1 that will be available at point 2

$$M = \frac{1}{1+f} = \frac{1}{1+.2101} = \frac{1}{1.2101} = .8264$$

I_{sca} (at service) = I_{sca} (at transformer) × M

I_{sca} (at service) = 23,200 amps × .8264

I_{sca} = 19,172 amps

Point 3 I_{sca} at MCC (Motor Control Center)

C factor from Table (figure 18–7)
300 kcmil copper in steel 18,176

$$f = \frac{1.73 \times L \times I_{sca} \text{ (at service)}}{C \times E_{line}}$$

$$f = \frac{1.73 \times 50 \times 19{,}172}{18{,}176 \times 208} = .4387$$

$$M = \frac{1}{1+f} = \frac{1}{1+.4387} = \frac{1}{1.4387} = .6951$$

I_{sca} (at MCC) = I_{sca} (at service) × M

I_{sca} (at MCC) = 19,172 × .6951

I_{sca} (at MCC) = 13,326 amps

Point 4 I_{sca} at Motor

A motor, being an inductive piece of electrical equipment, will add to the potential fault current. A reasonable value to use for the motor's contribution to the potential fault current is four times the full-load current of the motor. Motor full-load currents are taken from tables in *Article 430*. In this case, this will be added to the I_{sca} available at the MCC.

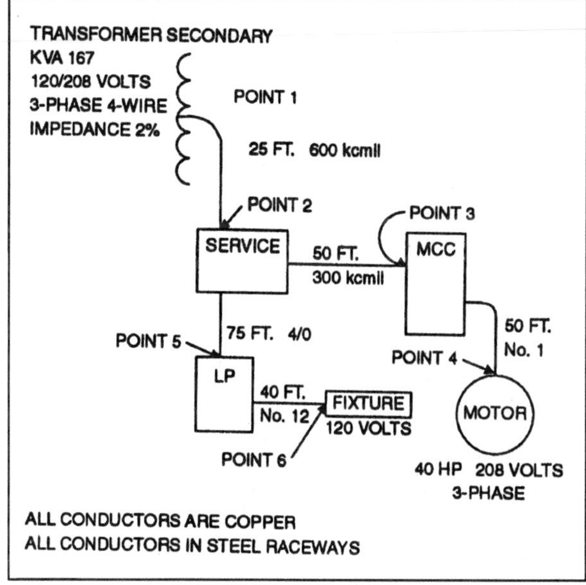

Fig. 18–8 Distribution system for calculating fault currents using point-to-point method.

Three different faults could occur at the motor; each will be looked at individually.

1. Three-phase fault calculated at 208 volts.
2. Phase-to-phase fault (single-phase fault) calculated at 208 volts.
3. Phase-to-ground fault calculated at 120 volts.

   Motor's contribution to fault:

   Motor FLI × 4

   40 HP, 208 volts = 114.4 amps (*Table 430-150*)

   I_{sca} (at motor) 114.4 × 4 = 458 amps

   C factor from Table (figure 18–7)
   No. 1 copper in steel 7,292

$$f = \frac{1.73 \times L \times I_{sca} \text{ (at MCC)}}{C \times E_{line}}$$

$$f = \frac{1.73 \times 50 \times 13{,}326}{7292 \times 208} = .76$$

$$M = \frac{1}{1+f} = \frac{1}{1+.76} = \frac{1}{1.76} = .5682$$

I_{sca} (at motor) = I_{sca} (at MCC) × M

I_{sca} (at motor) = 13,326 × .5682 = 7,572 amps

$I_{sca\ total}$ (at motor) = I_{sca} (at motor) + motor FLI × 4

$I_{sca\ total}$ (at motor) = 7,572 + 458 = 8,030 amps

The line-to-line bolted fault value at the motor is approximately 87 percent of the L–L–L bolted fault value.

Therefore: 8,030 × 87% = 6,986 amperes

The approximate line-to-ground fault value is 50 percent of the L–L–L bolted fault value.

Therefore: 8,030 × 50% = 4,015 amperes

These values are approximate, but accurate enough to determine interrupting ratings of fuses and circuit breakers, and to determine proper conductor sizes, when considering their withstand capabilities.

Summary of Point 4 Faults. The following is a comparison of the potential fault currents for the three types of faults that might occur at the motor.

Three phases bolted together	8,030 amperes
Line-to-line single-phase fault	6,986 amperes
Line-to-ground fault	4,015 amperes

A No. 1 THHN conductor is rated 150 amperes and will be subjected to a much higher current under any of the fault conditions. With the line-to-ground fault, the steel raceway or equipment grounding conductor will be required to conduct the 4,015 amperes until such time as the overcurrent protective device opens the circuit. This once again points up the importance of having all mechanical connections of a steel raceway installed with continuity maintained, just as if they were the circuit conductors.

Point 5 I_{sca} at Lighting Panel (LP)

C factor from Table (figure 18–7)
C factor No. 4/0 copper in steel 15,082

$$f = \frac{1.73 \times L \times I_{sca}\ (\text{at service})}{C \times E_{line}}$$

$$f = \frac{1.73 \times 75 \times 19{,}172}{15{,}082 \times 208} = .793$$

$$M = \frac{1}{1+f} = \frac{1}{1+.793} = \frac{1}{1.793} = .5577$$

I_{sca} (at LP) = I_{sca} (at service) × M

I_{sca} (at LP) = 19,172 × .5577 = 10,692 amps

Point 6 I_{sca} at Lighting Fixture—Line-to-Ground Fault

The approximate L–G fault current at the lighting fixture is 50 percent of the calculated L–L–L fault current. The line-to-ground and line-to-neutral fault currents are calculated the same way.

C factor from Table (figure 18–7)
No. 12 copper in steel 617

$$f = \frac{2 \times L \times I_{sca}\ (\text{at LP})}{C \times E_{L-N}}$$

$$f = \frac{2 \times 40 \times 10{,}692}{617 \times 120} = 9.9931$$

$$M = \frac{1}{1+f} = \frac{1}{1+9.9931} = \frac{1}{10.9931}$$

M = .091

I_{sca} (at fixture) = I_{sca} (at LP) × M

I_{sca} (at fixture) = 10,692 × .091 = 973 amps

CAUTION: Should an individual be working on the lighting fixture while in contact with ground and while it is hot, and accidentally touch a hot conductor, the potential amps available at 120 volts would be large.

The following is a comparison of the fault currents from the transformer to the lighting fixture.

I_{sca} at transformer (L–L–L)	23,200
I_{sca} at service (L–L–L)	19,172
I_{sca} at Lighting Panel (L–L–L)	10,692
I_{sca} at Lighting Fixture (L–G)	973

FAULT CURRENT AND PARALLEL CONDUCTORS

Figure 18–9 illustrates an installation of parallel conductors from the utility transformer to the service equipment.

Transformer Full Load Current

$$I_s = \frac{KVA \times 1000}{1.73 \times E_s \text{ Line}}$$

$$I_s = \frac{500 \times 1000}{1.73 \times 480}$$

$$I_s = 602 \text{ amps}$$

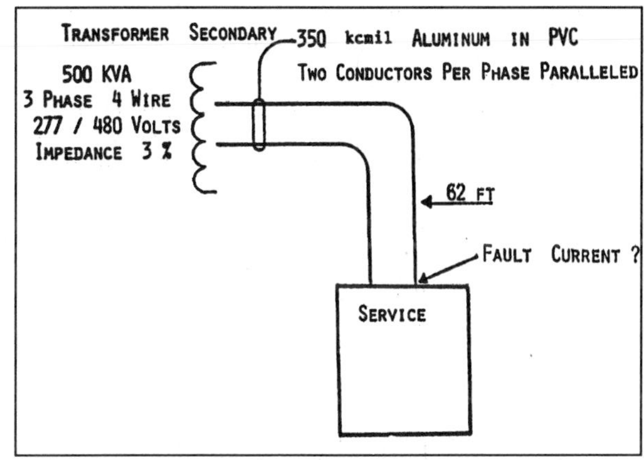

Fig. 18–9 Fault current when parallel conductors are installed.

I_{sca} (at Transformer)

$$\text{Multiplier} = \frac{100}{Z}$$

$$\text{Multiplier} = \frac{100}{3} = 33.33$$

$$I_{sca} = \text{(at Transformer)} = I_s \times \text{Multiplier}$$

$$I_{sca} = 602 \times 33.33 = 20{,}065 \text{ amps}$$

I_{sca} at Service

C factor from Table (figure 18–10, page 276) 350-kcmil aluminum in PVC 14,200

When the conductors are in parallel, the C table value is multiplied by the number of conductors in parallel.

C (for parallel conductors) = C × number conductors paralleled.

$$C = 22{,}736 \times 2 = 45{,}472$$

$$f = \frac{1.73 \times L \times I_{sca} \text{ (at transformer)}}{C \times E_{line}}$$

$$f = \frac{1.73 \times 62 \times 20{,}065}{45{,}472 \times 480} = .0986$$

$$M = \frac{1}{1+f} = \frac{1}{1+.0986} = \frac{1}{1.0986}$$

$$M = .9102$$

$$I_{sca} \text{ (at service)} = I_{sca} \text{ (at transformer)} \times M$$

$$I_{sca} \text{ (at service)} = 20{,}065 \times .9102$$

$$I_{sca} \text{ (at service)} = 18{,}263 \text{ amps}$$

This example uses parallel conductors as the service-entrance conductors. The same procedure is used for parallel feeder conductors.

COMBINING FUSE AND CIRCUIT BREAKER FOR PROTECTION

Fuses and circuit breakers are used together as a protection team in most installations (figure 18–11, page 276).

As illustrated in figure 18–11, we have a main current-limiting fuse ahead of the branch circuit breakers. Note that this is a **Series** connection. This arrangement is used when the available fault current exceeds the interrupting rating of the branch circuit breakers. For example, if the available fault current at the branch circuit breaker is 25,000 amperes and the interrupting rating of the branch circuit breaker is 10,000 amperes, then should a fault occur on one of the branch circuit breakers, the current-limiting fuse would "limit" the let-through fault current to the branch circuit breaker to a level that is within the capability of the branch circuit breaker.

In this example, the branch circuit breaker handles overloads and low-level fault currents that are within the interrupting rating of the breaker. It is only when the fault current begins to exceed the capability of the breaker that the current-limiting fuse comes into play.

The current-limiting fuse could be located in the breaker panel, or it could be located remotely in a main distribution panel, thereby

" C" Values for Conductors and Busway

Copper												
AWG	Three Single Conductors						Three-Conductor Cable					
or	Conduit						Conduit					
kcmil	Steel			Nonmagnetic			Steel			Nonmagnetic		
	600V	5KV	15KV	600V	5KV	15KV	600V	5KV	15KV	600V	5KV	15KV
14	389	389	389	389	389	389	389	389	389	389	389	389
12	617	617	617	617	617	617	617	617	617	617	617	617
10	981	981	981	981	981	981	981	981	981	981	981	981
8	1557	1551	1557	1558	1555	1558	1559	1557	1559	1559	1558	1559
6	2425	2406	2389	2430	2417	2406	2431	2424	2414	2433	2428	2420
4	3806	3750	3695	3825	3789	3752	3830	3811	3778	3837	3823	3798
3	4760	4760	4760	4802	4802	4802	4760	4790	4760	4802	4802	4802
2	5906	5736	5574	6044	5926	5809	5989	5929	5827	6087	6022	5957
1	7292	7029	6758	7493	7306	7108	7454	7364	7188	7579	7507	7364
1/0	8924	8543	7973	9317	9033	8590	9209	9086	8707	9472	9372	9052
2/0	10755	10061	9389	11423	10877	10318	11244	11045	10500	11703	11528	11052
3/0	12843	11804	11021	13923	13048	12360	13656	13333	12613	14410	14118	13461
4/0	15082	13605	12542	16673	15351	14347	16391	15890	14813	17482	17019	16012
250	16483	14924	13643	18593	17120	15865	18310	17850	16465	19779	19352	18001
300	18176	16292	14768	20867	18975	17408	20617	20051	18318	22524	21938	20163
350	19703	17385	15678	22736	20526	18672	19557	21914	19821	22736	24126	21982
400	20565	18235	16365	24296	21786	19731	24253	23371	21042	26915	26044	23517
500	22185	19172	17492	26706	23277	21329	26980	25449	23125	30028	28712	25916
600	22965	20567	47962	28033	25203	22097	28752	27974	24896	32236	31258	27766
750	24136	21386	18888	28303	25430	22690	31050	30024	26932	32404	31338	28303
1000	25278	22539	19923	31490	28083	24887	33864	32688	29320	37197	35748	31959
Aluminum												
14	236	236	236	236	236	236	236	236	236	236	236	236
12	375	375	375	375	375	375	375	375	375	375	375	375
10	598	598	598	598	598	598	598	598	598	598	598	598
8	951	950	951	951	950	951	951	951	951	951	951	951
6	1480	1476	1472	1481	1478	1476	1481	1480	1478	1482	1481	1479
4	2345	2332	2319	2350	2341	2333	2351	2347	2339	2353	2349	2344
3	2948	2948	2948	2958	2958	2958	2948	2956	2948	2958	2958	2958
2	3713	3669	3626	3729	3701	3672	3733	3719	3693	3739	3724	3709
1	4645	4574	4497	4678	4631	4580	4686	4663	4617	4699	4681	4646
1/0	5777	5669	5493	5838	5766	5645	5852	5820	5717	5875	5851	5771
2/0	7186	6968	6733	7301	7152	6986	7327	7271	7109	7372	7328	7201
3/0	8826	8466	8163	9110	8851	8627	9077	8980	8750	9242	9164	8977
4/0	10740	10167	9700	11174	10749	10386	11184	11021	10642	11408	11277	10968
250	12122	11460	10848	12862	12343	11847	12796	12636	12115	13236	13105	12661
300	13909	13009	12192	14922	14182	13491	14916	14698	13973	15494	15299	14658
350	15484	14280	13288	16812	15857	14954	15413	16490	15540	16812	17351	16500
400	16670	15355	14188	18505	17321	16233	18461	18063	16921	19587	19243	18154
500	18755	16827	15657	21390	19503	18314	21394	20606	19314	22987	22381	20978
600	20093	18427	16484	23451	21718	19635	23633	23195	21348	25750	25243	23294
750	21766	19685	17686	23491	21769	19976	26431	25789	23750	25682	25141	23491
1000	23477	21235	19005	28778	26109	23482	29864	29049	26608	32938	31919	29135

Fig. 18–10 Table for C values used in fault-current equation. Use with calculations for figure 18–9. Courtesy Bussmann Cooper Industries.

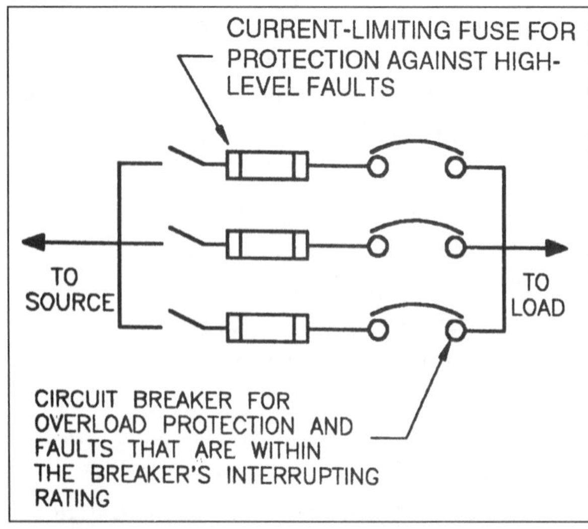

Fig. 18–11 Fuse and circuit breaker used together as a protecting team.

protecting the feeder to the panel in addition to providing the current-limiting feature required to protect the underrated circuit breaker against high-level faults.

SUMMARY

The potential fault current can be exceptionally high. Therefore, in case of a fault the overcurrent protective device must operate quickly in order to protect the conductors and equipment. When there is a ground fault, the equipment grounding path plays an important part in furnishing a low-impedance path to the overcurrent protective device.

FOLLOW UP

Topics for self-study, discussion, or questioning.

1. Discuss the relationship between the overcurrent protective device and grounding.
2. Explain how to calculate the full load current of the secondary of a transformer.
3. Discuss how the impedance of a transformer is arrived at.
4. Explain the use of the "C" table.
5. Identify the factors used in the equation

$$f = \frac{1.73 \times L \times I_{sca}}{C \times E}$$

6. Discuss when E stands for phase voltage and when it stands for line-to-neutral voltage in the above equation.
7. Discuss how the "C" table is used when parallel conductors are used.
8. Discuss the use of fuses and circuit breakers in series for protection.

The following are the calculations for the fault currents illustrated in figure 18–4.

I_s = Transformer full load Secondary current

$$I_s = \frac{KVA \times 1000}{1.73 \times E}$$

$$I_s = \frac{150 \times 1000}{1.73 \times 208} = 417 \text{ amps}$$

Point 1 I_{sca} at Transformer

$$\text{Multiplier} = \frac{100}{Z}$$

$$\text{Multiplier} = \frac{100}{2} = 50$$

I_{sca} at Transformer × Multiplier

417 × 50 = 20,850 amps potential fault current at transformer

20,850 amps potential fault current at transformer

Point 2 I_{sca} at Service

$$f = \frac{1.73 \times L \times I_{sca} \text{ (at transformer)}}{C \times E_{line}}$$

$$f = \frac{1.73 \times 30 \times 20{,}850}{18{,}593 \times 208} = .2798$$

$$M = \frac{1}{1+f} = \frac{1}{1+.2798} = \frac{1}{1.2798} = .7814$$

I_{sca} (at service) = I_{sca} (at transformer) × M

I_{sca} (at service) = 20,850 × .7814

I_{sca} (at service) = 16,292 amps potential fault current

Point 3 I_{sca} at Load

$$f = \frac{1.73 \times L \times I_{sca} \text{ (at service)}}{C \times E_{line}}$$

$$f = \frac{1.73 \times 40 \times 16{,}292}{6{,}044 \times 120} = 1.797$$

$$M = \frac{1}{1+f} = \frac{1}{1+1.797} = \frac{1}{2.797}$$

M = .3575

I_{sca} (at load) = I_{sca} (at service) × M

I_{sca} (at load) = 16,292 × .3575

I_{sca} (at load) = 5,824 amps potential fault current

APPENDIX

**Maximum length of Electrical Metallic Tubing that may safely be used as an equipment grounding circuit conductor.
Based on a ground-fault current of 400% of the overcurrent device rating.
Circuit 120 volts to ground: 40 volts drop at the point of fault.
Ambient Temperature 25°C**

EMT Size Inches	Conductors AWG No.	Overcurrent Device Rating Amps. 75° C*	Fault Clearing Current 400% O.C. Device Rating Amps.	Maximum Length of EMT Run in Ft.
1/2	3-#12	20	80	395
	4-#10	30	120	358
3/4	4-#10	30	120	404
	4-#8	50	200	332
1	4-#8	50	200	370
	3-#4	85	340	365
1 1/4	3-#2	115	460	391
1 1/2	3-#1	130	520	407
	3-#2/0	175	700	364
2	3-#3/0	200	800	390
	3-#4/0	230	920	367
2 1/2	3-250 kcm	255	1020	406
3	3-350 kcm	310	1240	404
	3-500 kcm	380	1520	370
	3-600 kcm	420	1680	353
4	3-900 kcm	520	2080	353
	3-1000 kcm	545	2180	347

*60° C for 20- and 30-ampere devices.

Based on 1994 Georgia Tech Model

Derived from software (SCA) and testing developed at Georgia Institute of Technology and sponsored by the NEMA producers of steel EMT, IMC and rigid conduit.

Maximum length of Intermediate Metal Conduit that may safely be used as an equipment grounding circuit conductor.
Based on a ground-fault current of 400% of the overcurrent device rating.
Circuit 120 volts to ground: 40 volts drop at the point of fault.
Ambient Temperature 25°C

IMC Size Inches	Conductors AWG No.	Overcurrent Device Rating Amps. 75° C*	Fault Clearing Current 400% O.C. Device Rating Amps.	Maximum Length of IMC Run in Ft.
1/2	3-#12	20	80	398
	4-#10	30	120	383
3/4	4-#10	30	120	399
	4-#8	50	200	350
1	4-#8	50	200	362
	3-#4	85	340	382
1 1/4	3-#2	115	460	392
1 1/2	3-#1	130	520	402
	3-#2/0	175	700	377
2	3-#3/0	200	800	389
	3-#4/0	230	920	375
2 1/2	3-250 kcm	255	1020	368
3	3-350 kcm	310	1240	367
	3-500 kcm	380	1520	338
	3-600 kcm	420	1680	325
4	3-900 kcm	520	2080	320
	3-1000 kcm	545	2180	314

*60° C for 20- and 30-ampere devices.

Based on 1994 Georgia Tech Model

Derived from software (SCA) and testing developed at Georgia Institute of Technology and sponsored by the NEMA producers of steel EMT, IMC and rigid conduit.

Maximum length of Galvanized Rigid Conduit that may safely be used as an equipment grounding circuit conductor. Based on a ground-fault current of 400% of the overcurrent device rating. Circuit 120 volts to ground: 40 volts drop at the point of fault. Ambient Temperature 25°C

GRC Size Inches	Conductors AWG No.	Overcurrent Device Rating Amps. 75° C*	Fault Clearing Current 400% O.C. Device Rating Amps.	Maximum Length of GRC Run in Ft.
1/2	3-#12	20	80	384
	4-#10	30	120	364
3/4	4-#10	30	120	386
	4-#8	50	200	334
1	4-#8	50	200	350
	3-#4	85	340	357
1 1/4	3-#2	115	460	365
1 1/2	3-#1	130	520	377
	3-#2/0	175	700	348
2	3-#3/0	200	800	363
	3-#4/0	230	920	347
2 1/2	3-250 kcm	255	1020	356
3	3-350 kcm	310	1240	355
	3-500 kcm	380	1520	327
	3-600 kcm	420	1680	314
4	3-900 kcm	520	2080	310
	3-1000 kcm	545	2180	304

*60° C for 20- and 30-ampere devices.

Based on 1994 Georgia Tech Model

Derived from software (SCA) and testing developed at Georgia Institute of Technology and sponsored by the NEMA producers of steel EMT, IMC and rigid conduit.

Maximum length of Equipment Grounding Conductor that may safely be used as an equipment grounding circuit conductor.
Based on a ground-fault current of 400% of the overcurrent device rating.
Circuit 120 volts to ground; 40 volts drop at the point of fault.
Ambient Temperature 25°C

Copper Equipment Grounding Conductor Size***	Copper Circuit Conductors	Maximum Lengthof Run (in ft.) using Copper Equipment Ground Conductor	Aluminum Equipment Grounding Conductor Size***	Aluminum Circuit Conductors	Maximum Length of Run (in ft.) using Aluminum Equipment Ground Conductor	For Copper & Aluminum: Overcurrent Device Rating Amps. 75° C**	For Copper & Aluminum: Fault Clearing Current 400% O.C. Device Rating Amps.
#14	#14	253	#12	#12	244	15	60
#12	#12	300	#10	#12	226	20	80
#10	#10	319	#8	#8	310	30	120
#10	#8	294	#8	#8	232	40	160
#10	#6	228	#8	#4	221	60	240
#8	#3	229	#6	#1	222	100	400
#6	#3/0	201	#4	250kcm	195	200	800
#4	350 kcm	210	#2	500kcm	204	300	1200
#3	600 kcm	195	#1	900kcm	192	400	1600
#2	2-#4/0	160	#1/0	2-400kcm	163	500	2000
#1	2-300kcm	160	#2/0	2-500kcm	161	600	2400
#1/0	3-300kcm	134	#3/0	3-400kcm	131	800	3200
#2/0	4-250kcm	114	#4/0	4-400kcm	115	1000	4000
#3/0	4-300kcm	106	250 kcm	4-500kcm	107	1200	4800
#4/0	4-600kcm	93	350 kcm	4-900kcm	97	1600	6400
250 kcm	5-600kcm	78	400 kcm	5-800kcm	79	2000	8000
350 kcm	6-600kcm	*	600 kcm	6-900kcm	*	2500	10000
400 kcm	8-500kcm	*	600 kcm	8-750kcm	*	3000	15000
500 kcm	8-1000kcm	*	800 kcm	8-1500kcm	*	4000	16000
700 kcm	10-1000kcm	*	1200 kcm	10-1500kcm	*	5000	20000
800 kcm	12-1000kcm	*	1200 kcm	12-1500kcm	*	6000	24000

*Calculations Necessary
**60°C for 20- and 30-ampere devices.
***Based on NEC Chapter 9 Table 8

Based on 1994 Georgia Tech Model

Derived from software (SCA) and testing developed at Georgia Institute of Technology and sponsored by the NEMA producers of steel EMT, IMC and rigid conduit.

Maximum Length Equipment Grounding Conductor, Copper, Aluminum, Steel EMT, IMC or GRC
Which May Be Safely Used As A Return Fault Path To Overcurrent Device
Based on 1994 Georgia Tech Modeling (Version 1.2)
Based on 40 Arc Voltage & 4IP at 25° C Ambient

Circuit Voltage To Ground	Overcurrent Device Rating Amperes (75° C)	400% (4IP) Overcurrent Device Rating Amperes	Circuit Conductor Size AWG-kcmil Copper or Aluminum	(1) Conduit Trade Size	(2) Equipment Grounding Conductor Size Copper or Aluminum	Length of EMT Run Computed Maximum (In Feet)	Length of IMC Run Computed Maximum (In Feet)	Length of GRC Run Computed Maximum (In Feet)	(2) Copper Grounding Conductor Max Run (In Feet)	(2) Aluminum Grounding Conductor Max Run (In Feet)	REQUIRED CONDUIT SIZE BASED ON NEC 310-16/250-95 & TABLES 1, 4 AND 5 OF CHAPTER 9					
											EMT	IMC	GRC	ENT	SCH 40 PVC	SCH80 PVC
120	30	120	10	**1/2**	—	358	383	384	—	—						
120	30	120	10	—	10	—	—	—	318	—	1/2	1/2	1/2	1/2	1/2	1/2
120	30	120	8 AL	—	8 AL	—	—	—	—	310	3/4	3/4	3/4	1	3/4	1
120	40	160	8	**3/4**	—	407	414	395	—	—						
120	40	160	8	—	10	—	—	—	294	—	3/4	3/4	3/4	3/4	3/4	1
120	40	160	8 AL	—	8 AL	—	—	—	—	232	3/4	3/4	3/4	1	3/4	1
120	60	240	6	(a) **1**	—	404	400	382	—	—						
120	60	240	6	—	10	—	—	—	228	—	1	3/4	1	1	1	1
120	60	240	4 AL	—	8 AL	—	—	—	—	221	1 1/4	1	1 1/4	1 1/4	1 1/4	1 1/4
120	100	400	3	**1 1/4**	—	402	397	373	—	—						
120	100	400	3	—	8	—	—	—	228	—	1 1/4	1 1/4	1 1/4	1 1/4	1 1/4	1 1/4
120	100	400	1 AL	—	6 AL	—	—	—	—	222	1 1/2	1 1/2	1 1/2	1 1/2	1 1/2	1 1/2
120	200	800	3/0	**2**	—	390	369	363	—	—						
120	200	800	3/0	—	6	—	—	—	201	—	2	2	2	*N/A	2	2 1/2
120	200	800	250 AL	—	4 AL	—	—	—	—	195	2 1/2	2 1/2	2 1/2	*N/A	2 1/2	3

(1) Applies only when steel conduit is used.
(2) Per NEC Table 250-95.
Applicable to non-metallic conduit runs.
(a) 3/4 IMC - maximum length of run - 399 feet
Note: Software computes all sizes, not just to 2".

*Conduit not available in necessary size

Derived from software (SCA) and testing developed at Georgia Institute of Technology and sponsored by the NEMA producers of steel EMT, IMC and rigid conduit.

Maximum Length Equipment Grounding Conductor, Copper, Aluminum, Steel EMT, IMC or GRC Which May Be Safely Used As A Return Fault Path To Overcurrent Device
Based on 1994 Georgia Tech Modeling (Version 1.2)
Based on 40 Arc Voltage & 4IP at 25° C Ambient

Circuit Voltage To Ground	Overcurrent Device Rating Amperes (75° C)	400% (4IP) Overcurrent Device Rating Amperes	Circuit Conductor Size AWG-kcmil Copper or Aluminum	(1) Conduit Trade Size	(2) Equipment Grounding Conductor Size Copper or Aluminum	Length of EMT Run Computed Maximum (In Feet)	Length of IMC Run Computed Maximum (In Feet)	Length of GRC Run Computed Maximum (In Feet)	(2) Copper Grounding Conductor Max Run (In Feet)	(2) Aluminum Grounding Conductor Max Run (In Feet)	REQUIRED CONDUIT SIZE BASED ON NEC 310-16/250-95 & TABLES 1, 4 AND 5 OF CHAPTER 9					
											EMT	IMC	GRC	ENT	SCH 40 PVC	SCH80 PVC
277	30	120	10	1/2	—	1061	1135	1080	—	—						
277	30	120	10	—	10	—	—	—	946	—	1/2	1/2	1/2	1/2	1/2	1/2
277	30	120	8 AL	—	8 AL	—	—	—	—	920	3/4	3/4	3/4	1	3/4	1
277	40	160	8	3/4	—	1208	1228	1170	—	—						
277	40	160	8	—	10	—	—	—	871	—	3/4	3/4	3/4	3/4	3/4	1
277	40	160	8 AL	—	8 AL	—	—	—	—	690	3/4	3/4	3/4	1	3/4	1
277	60	240	6	(a) 1	—	1197	1186	1131	—	—						
277	60	240	6	—	10	—	—	—	676	—	1	3/4	1	1	1	1
277	60	240	4 AL	—	8 AL	—	—	—	—	657	1 1/4	1	1 1/4	1 1/4	1 1/4	1 1/4
277	100	400	3	1 1/4	—	1192	1176	1107	—	—						
277	100	400	3	—	8	—	—	—	680	—	1 1/4	1 1/4	1 1/4	1 1/4	1 1/4	1 1/4
277	100	400	1 AL	—	6 AL	—	—	—	—	659	1 1/2	1 1/2	1 1/2	1 1/2	1 1/2	1 1/2
277	200	800	3/0	2	—	1157	1155	1077	—	—						
277	200	800	3/0	—	6	—	—	—	598	—	2	2	2	*N/A	2	2 1/2
277	200	800	250 AL	—	4 AL	—	—	—	—	578	2 1/2	2 1/2	2 1/2	*N/A	2 1/2	3

(1) Applies only when steel conduit is used.
(2) Per NEC Table 250-95.
Applicable to non-metallic conduit runs.
(a) 3/4 IMC - maximum length of run - 399 feet
Note: Software computes all sizes, nut just to 2".

*Conduit not available in necessary size

Derived from software (SCA) and testing developed at Georgia Institute of Technology and sponsored by the NEMA producers of steel EMT, IMC and rigid conduit.

INDEX

Note: Numbers followed by an *i* indicate illustrations.

A

AC. *See* Alternating current
Agricultural buildings
  equipment grounding conductor in, 151, 151*i*
  equipotential plane in, 183–84, 183*i*, 184*i*
  for livestock, 260–61, 260*i*
  single service for, 249–61
AIC. *See* Ampere interrupting capacity
Alternating current (AC)
  direct current vs., 17
  grounding electrode conductor
    sizing of, 68–78, 68*i*–78*i*
  Ohm's law and, 19–21, 19*i*–21*i*
Alternating-current system
  grounded conductor connection in, 95–96
  grounding of, 85–92, 85*i*–91*i*
Ampacity
  of ground path, 124
  of wire size, 17
Ampere interrupting capacity (AIC), 264
Ampere rating (AR), 265
Amps
  overcurrent protective devices and, 22, 22*i*
Appliances
  grounded conductors for, 212–14, 213*i*
  grounding of, 196–97, 196*i*–97*i*
AR. *See* Ampere rating
Article 100
  on bonding, 154, 154*i*
  on bonding jumper, 155
  on equipment bonding jumper, 155, 155*i*
  on equipment grounding conductor, 121, 122*i*
  on ground-fault protection of equipment, 217, 217*i*
  on main bonding jumper, 109, 109*i*
  of *National Electrical Code*®, 3, 4
  on overcurrent, 31
  on overload, 31
  on raceway, 132–33, 133*i*
  for voltage, 81–82
Article 200, 104
Article 220, 8
Article 230, 218–21, 218*i*–19*i*
Article 250
  on AC grounding electrode conductor, 69–78, 69*i*–78*i*
  on bonding, 4–5
  on bonding grounding electrodes, 54–55, 54*i*–55*i*
  on capacitance, 20–21
  on circuit grounding, 3
  on computers, 204–07
  on concrete-encased electrode, 50–51
  on DC grounding electrode conductor, 68–69, 68*i*–69*i*

Article 250 (continued)
on enclosure bonding, 65–66
on enclosure grounding, 4, 188–90
on equipment grounding, 4, 191–92
on ground-fault protection, 218–21
on grounding conductor connections, 5
on grounding conductors, 5
on grounding electrode system, 5
on grounding target, 12
on impedance grounding, 237–38, 237*i*–38*i*
on instrument transformers, 5
on lightning rods, 54–56, 55*i*–56*i*
on made electrodes, 51–52, 51*i*, 53*i*
on mobile equipment, 234–35
of *National Electrical Code*®, 1–12
on ≥1 kV circuits, 5
overview of, 3–5
Part B of, 71
Part D of, 188–89
Part E of, 192
Part H of, 40–41, 46, 47, 252–53
Part M of, 234
on plug-in equipment, 197
on relays, 5
scope of, 1*i*
on single service, 251–56, 251*i*–56*i*
on sizing grounded conductors, 98–102, 98*i*–101*i*
on system grounding, 3–4, 95
Article 517, 10, 21, 26
Article 760, 84

B

Basement
receptacles for, 229*i*
Bathrooms
receptacles for, 226*i*, 230*i*
Bonding
Article 250 on, 4–5
definition of, 4–5, 154, 154*i*
enclosure
equipment and, 153–85
for grounding electrode system, 178–81, 180*i*
intersystem, 178–81, 178*i*–79*i*
of lightning rods, 182–83, 182*i*–83*i*
at loose-fitting sections, 174, 174*i*
metal pipes and, 175–76, 175*i*
methods of, 159–62, 159*i*–62*i*
at nonservice equipment, 172–75
at prepunched knockouts, 173–74, 173–75*i*
receptacles for, 181–82, 181*i*–82*i*
at service equipment, 156–62, 157*i*–61*i*
for swimming pool, 184–85, 185*i*
Bonding jumper
definition of, 154

C

Cable
as equipment grounding conductor, 134–35, 134*i*
high-voltage, 239, 239*i*
Cable tray
as equipment grounding conductor, 138–40, 138*i*–39*i*
for service-entrance conductors, 157–58
Capacitance
Article 250 on, 21
Article 517 on, 21
Capacitors. *See* Condensers
CEMF. *See* Counter-electromotive force
Circuit
definition of, 123–24, 124*i*
parallel, 22–23, 22*i*–23*i*
series, 17–19, 17*i*–18*i*
fault with, 18, 18*i*
Circuit breakers. *See also* Protective devices
fuses with, 275–76, 276*i*
Circuit grounding, 80–92
Article 250 on, 3
Circuit grounding
conductors and, 103, 103*i*
reasons for, 9–10, 10*i*, 81*i*

CL. *See* Current limiting
Computers
  grounding of, 195*i*, 203–07, 204*i*–07*i*
Concrete-encased electrode, 50, 50*i*
Condensers
  definition of, 20–21
Conductivity
  of earth, 41–42, 42*i*
Conductor(s)
  body tissue vs., 25–26, 25*i*
  circuit
    direct-current system and, 128, 129*i*
    grounded, 209–14, 209*i*–14*i*
    raceway for, 129–31, 129*i*–31*i*
  equipment grounding, 4
  grounded. *See* Grounded conductor
  grounding. *See* Grounding conductor
    definition of, 8–9, 9*i*
  grounding electrode. *See* Grounding electrode conductor
  neutral. *See* Neutral conductor
Conduit
  flexible metal
    as grounding conductor, 135–38, 135*i*–37*i*
    in raceway, 172, 172*i*
Connector(s)
  zig-zag, 236, 236*i*
Continuity
  of ground path, 124–25
  for grounding conductor, 140–41
  of metal raceway, 140*i*
  splicing and, 124–25, 125*i*
Counter-electromotive force (CEMF), 19–20
Current flow, 14–15, 14*i*
Current limiting (CL), 265–66, 265*i*

D

DC. *See* Direct current
Deicing equipment
  receptacles for, 232*i*
Decks
  receptacles for, 227
Delta connection
  with grounded leg, 95, 95*i*
  with grounded phase, 88–89, 88*i*–89*i*
  with multiple disconnecting means, 97–98, 97*i*–98*i*
Direct current (DC)
  alternating current vs., 17
  grounding electrode conductor
    sizing of, 68–69, 68*i*–69*i*
  Ohm's law and, 16–17, 16*i*
Direct-current system
  circuit conductor in, 128, 129*i*
  grounded conductor connection in, 95
  grounding of, 83–85, 83*i*–85*i*

E

Earth
  conductivity of, 41–42, 42*i*
  electrode resistance of, 43–44, 44*i*
  electron flow to, 42–43
  as equipment grounding conductor, 140, 139*i*
  ground vs., 42
Electric shock
  grounding and, 27–29, 27*i*–29*i*
  severity of, 4–26, 25*i*
Electrical stress, 32, 32*i*
Electrical theory
  on grounding, 14–23
Electrode(s)
  building steel as, 49–50, 50*i*
  concrete-encased, 50–51, 50*i*
  cross section of, 45*i*
  definition of, 40
  ground ring, 51, 51*i*
  grounding, 40–47, 41*i*–47*i*
  made, 51–52, 51*i*
    spacing of, 53*i*
  water pipe as, 47–49, 48*i*–49*i*

Electrolytic ground rod, 52–54, 53*i*
Electromagnetic induction (EMI), 32
Electron creed, 15
Electrons
  properties of, 15–16
EMI. *See* Electromagnetic induction
Enclosure and raceway grounding, 188–91, 189*i*–91*i* *See also* System enclosures
  Article 250 on, 4, 188–91
  reason for, 187–88, 188*i*
Equipment
  ground-fault protection of, 216–21, 216*i*–21*i*
  grounding of, 191–95, 191*i*–95*i*
  guarding of, 192–93
  high-voltage, 238–39
  isolated, 192–93
    grounding receptacles for, 200–02, 201*i*–02*i*
  mobile, 234–35
  nonelectrical, 194–95, 195*i*
  nonresidential, 196, 197*i*
  office, 195*i*
  portable, 234–35
  protective, 264–66, 265*i*
  residential, 196, 196*i*
  snow-melting, 232*i*
Equipment bonding jumper
  connections for, 156
  definition of, 155, 155*i*
  lightning rods and, 182–83, 182*i*–83*i*
  load side
    sizing of, 176–78, 176*i*–79*i*
  materials for, 156
  supply side
    sizing of, 162–70, 162*i*–70*i*
Equipment grounding conductor, 5, 120–51*i*
  in agricultural buildings, 151, 151*i*
  Article 250 on, 4
  cable assemblies as, 134–35, 134*i*
  cable tray as, 138–40, 138*i*–39*i*
  connections for, 140–41, 140*i*
  continuity of, 141
  definition of, 121, 122*i*
  earth as, 140
  flexible metal raceways as, 135–36, 135*i*
  identification of, 126–28, 126*i*–27*i*
  installation of, 128–31, 129*i*–31*i*
  in junction box, 150–51, 151*i*
  raceway as, 131–40, 132*i*–39*i*
  service enclosure and, 128, 129*i*
  sizing of, 141–48, 142*i*–48*i*
  types of, 125, 125*i*
  wire for, 125
Equipotential plane, 183–84, 184*i*

F

Fault(s)
  calculation of, 266–70, 267*i*–69*i*
  damage from, 262–63
  definition of, 7
  ground. *See* Ground fault
  in grounded systems, 33–35, 33*i*–35*i*
  ionization and, 32–33, 33*i*
  phase-to-phase, 34*i*
  series circuit with, 18, 18*i*
  stress and, 32, 32*i*–35*i*
  types of, 31, 31*i*
  in ungrounded systems, 37–38, 37*i*–38*i*
Fault current
  calculation of, 266–68, 267*i*
  factors affecting, 268, 271, 272*i*
Fuses. *See also* Protective devices
  circuit breakers with, 275–76, 276*i*

G

Garages
  receptacles for, 226, 226*i*
Generators
  gasoline-operated, 240
  portable, 246, 247*i*
  vehicle-mounted, 247i–248i
GFCI. *See* Ground-fault circuit interrupter

Ground
accidental, 7
definition of, 6–7, 6*i*
earth vs., 42–43
Ufer, 50
Ground conductor
sizing of, 98–102, 98*i*–101*i*
Ground fault, 30, 30*i*
detectors of, 39, 39*i*
protection from, 216–32
short circuits and, 264
Ground-fault circuit interrupter (GFCI), 9–10
definition of, 221–23, 222*i*
receptacles with, 223–32, 224*i*–32*i*
Ground path
establishment of, 124–25, 124*i*–25*i*
Ground ring electrode, 51, 51*i*
Ground rod, 43–46, 43*i*–46*i*
electrolytic, 52–54, 53*i*
Grounded
definition of, 7, 7*i*
Grounded circuit conductors, 209–14, 209*i*–14*i*
Grounded conductor, 94–107
in AC system, 95–96
in DC system, 95
definition of, 8, 8*i*, 81, 81*i*, 94–95
identification of, 104–7, 104*i*–7*i*
installation of, 102–03, 102*i*–03*i*
for overcurrent protection, 107, 107*i*
to service enclosure, 96–97, 96*i*
Grounding
of ≥1 kV circuits, 5, 233–39, 233*i*–39*i*
Article 250 on. *See* Article 250
circuit. *See* Circuit grounding
of computers, 203–07, 204*i*–07*i*
definition of, 3, 8
of electrical equipment, 191–94, 192*i*–95*i*
enclosure. *See* Service enclosures
equipment. *See* Equipment grounding conductor
of high-voltage equipment, 238–39
methods of, 4
of nonelectrical equipment, 194–95, 195*i*
of office equipment, 195*i*
purpose of, 263–64
requirements for, 11–12, 11*i*–12*i*
safety and, 24–29
shock and, 27–29, 28*i*–29*i*
substitutes for, 2
system. *See* System grounding
theory of, 14–23
of towers, 202–203, 204*i*
Grounding conductor. *See* Equipment grounding conductor
Grounding electrode
grounding electrode conductor to, 66–68, 66*i*–67*i*
for separately derived system, 243–44, 243*i*–44*i*
Grounding electrode conductor, 5, 59–78
alternating current
sizing of, 68–78, 69*i*–78*i*
aluminum for, 62–63, 63*i*
Article 250 on, 66–68, 67*i*
connections to, 66–68, 66*i*
definition of, 60–61, 60*i*
direct current
sizing of, 68–69, 68*i*
enclosure bonding to, 65–66, 64*i*
installation of, 62–63, 62*i*
magnetic fields and, 63–65, 63*i*–65*i*
materials for, 61
raceway for, 62
for separately derived systems, 244
sizing of, 255–57, 255*i*–57*i*
splicing of, 61–62, 61*i*–62*i*
Grounding electrode system, 40–57
Article 250 on, 5
bonding at, 54–55, 54*i*–55*i*, 178–81, 180*i*
for multiple buildings, 252–56, 252*i*–56*i*
resistance and, 54–55, 54*i*–55*i*
responsibilities of, 41–43, 42*i*–43*i*
supplemental, 48–49, 49*i*–50*i*
types of, 51–52, 51*i*
Grounding receptacle, 181–82, 181*i*–82*i*
for isolated equipment, 200–02, 201*i*–03*i*
Grounding target, 12, 12*i*

H

High-impedance grounding, 91–92, 91*i*
High-voltage cable, 239, 239*i*
High-voltage equipment, 238–39
Hot tubs
  receptacles for, 230*i*–231*i*

I

Impedance
  definition of, 11, 21, 21*i*
  of ground path, 124
  of transformers, 270–71, 271*i*
Impedance grounding, 35–36, 36*i*, 237–38, 237*i*–238*i*
Induced currents, 20, 20*i*
Inductance, 19–20, 20*i*
Induction, 20
Instrument transformers
  Article 250 on, 5
Interrupting rating (IR), 264–65
Ionization, 32–33, 33*i*
IR. *See* Interrupting rating
Isolated system
  grounding of, 91*i*

J

Jumper
  bonding
    definition of, 154–55
    equipment. *See* Equipment bonding jumper
    main. *See* Main bonding jumper
Junction box
  equipment grounding conductor in, 148–51, 149*i*–51*i*

K

Kitchens
  receptacles for, 229*i*
Knockouts
  prepunched
    bonding at, 173, 173*i*

L

Lighting
  underwater, 125*i*
Lightning
  electron flow in, 42–43
Lightning rods
  bonding of, 182–83, 182*i*–83*i*
  grounding electrode for, 55–56, 55*i*–56*i*
Listed
  definition of, 68
Livestock
  buildings for, 260–61, 260*i*

M

Magnetic force
  damage from, 263
  stress from, 32, 32*i*
Main bonding jumper, 108–18
  connections with, 112
  definition of, 109–10, 109*i*
  location of, 110–11, 110*i*
  materials for, 111–12, 111*i*
  for separately derived system, 243–44, 243*i*–44*i*
  sizing of, 112–18, 113*i*–18*i*
Mechanical stress, 32, 32*i*
Metal enclosures. *See* Service enclosures
Multiple buildings
  single service for, 249–61
Multiple service disconnecting means, 97–98, 97*i*–98*i*

N

National Electrical Code® (*NEC®*)
Article 250 of, 1–12
National Fire Protection Association (NFPA), 1
NEC®. *See National Electrical Code®*
Neutral conductor, 82
for equipment grounding, 209–10, 210*i*
identification of, 104–07, 104*i*–06*i*
with vehicle-mounted generator, 248, 248*i*
Neutral grounded systems, 234–38, 234*i*–38*i*
Neutral system
solidly grounded, 236–37, 237*i*
NFPA. *See* National Fire Protection Association

O

Office equipment
grounding of, 195*i*
Ohm's law,16–17, 16*i*
body resistance and, 26
Overcurrent, 264
definition of, 31
Overcurrent protection
amps and, 21–22, 22*i*
grounded conductor for, 107, 107*i*
terms for, 264–66, 265*i*
Overload, 264
definition of, 31

P

Panelboard
grounding of, 197–200, 198*i*–200*i*
Parallel circuit, 22–23, 22*i*–23*i*
Pipes
bonding at, 174–75, 175*i*
Point-to-point calculations, 266–67, 267*i*
Portable generators, 246, 247*i*–48*i*
Potential difference
definition of, 26–27, 26*i*–27*i*
Power tools
grounding of, 196–97, 196*i*–97*i*
Protective devices
amps and, 21–22, 22*i*
grounded conductor for, 107, 107*i*
terms for, 264–66, 265*i*

R

Raceway
choking effect in, 64*i*
circuit conductors and, 128–31, 129*i*–31*i*
continuity of, 140*i*
definition of, 132, 133*i*
as equipment grounding conductor, 131–40, 132*i*–40*i*
flexible metal conduit for, 172, 172*i*
for grounding electrode conductor, 62–63
induction in, 63–64, 64*i*
for service-entrance conductors, 157–58, 157*i*–58*i*
Reactance
capacitive, 20–21, 20*i*
inductive, 19–20, 20*i*
Receptacle
grounding, 181–82, 181*i*–82*i*
isolated, 200–02, 201*i*–03*i*
Relays
Article 250 on, 5
Resistance
of grounding electrode, 54–55, 54*i*–55*i*
pure, 19, 19*i*

S

Safety
grounding for, 24–29
SCA. *See* Short-circuit amperes
Self-induction
definition of, 20
Separately derived systems, 240–47, 241*i*–47*i*

Series-parallel circuit, 23, 23*i*
Service
  cable for, 89–90, 89*i*–90*i*
  single
    multiple buildings and, 249–61
Service enclosure(s)
  equipment bonding with, 153–85
  equipment grounding conductor and, 128, 129*i*
  grounded conductor to, 96–97, 96*i*
  grounding electrode conductor from, 65–66, 65*i*
  grounding electrode conductor to, 171–72, 170*i*–71*i*
  grounding of, 4, 11–12, 11*i*, 188–90, 189*i*–91*i*
    reason for, 10–11, 10*i*
  grounding target at, 12, 12*i*
  multiple, 56–57, 56*i*–57*i*
  multiple disconnectors in, 97–98, 97*i*–98*i*
Service equipment
  bonding at, 156–62, 157*i*–63*i*
  pipes and, 175–76, 175*i*
Shock
  grounding and, 27–29, 27*i*–29*i*
  severity of, 24–26, 25*i*
Short
  direct, 30–31, 31*i*
Short-circuit amperes (SCA), 264
Short circuits. *See also* Fault(s)
  ground faults and, 264
Snow-melting equipment
  receptacles for, 232*i*
Spa
  receptacles for, 230*i*–231*i*
Splicing
  continuity and, 124–25, 125*i*
Static electricity
  definition of, 16
Steel
  building
    as electrode, 49–50, 50*i*
Stress
  faults and, 32, 32*i*
Swimming pool
  bonding grid for, 184–85, 185*i*
  lighting for, 125*i*
System
  definition of, 121–23, 122*i*
  five-wire, 246, 246i
  separately derived, 240–48, 241*i*–48*i*
    definition of, 240–43, 241*i*–43*i*
    grounding electrode conductor for, 244
    grounding electrode for, 244–45
    main bonding jumper for, 243–44, 243*i*–44*i*
System enclosures. *See* System enclosure(s)
System grounding, 80
  ≥1 kV circuits, 233–39, 233*i*–39*i*
  Article 250 on, 3
  conductors and, 103–04, 103*i*
  direct-current, 83–85, 83*i*–85*i*
  faults in, 33–35, 33*i*–36*i*
  isolated, 90, 91*i*
  reasons for, 9–10, 10*i*, 81*i*
System grounding connections
  Article 250 on, 3–4
  location of, 3–4

T

Thermal stress, 32, 32*i*
  damage from, 263
Tools
  power
    grounding of, 196–97, 196*i*–97*i*
Transformers
  grounding of, 235–36, 235*i*–36*i*
  impedance of, 270–71, 271*i*
  as secondary current, 268–70
  single-phase, 270
  three-phase, 268

U

Ufer ground, 50
Umbrella words, 5–6, 5*i*–6*i*

Underwater lighting, 125*i*
Ungrounded systems
faults in, 37–38, 37*i*–38*i*

V

Vehicle-mounted generators, 247, 247*i*
Voltage
definition of, 24
terminology for, 81–82, 82*i*

W

Water meter
grounding electrode system with, 47–48, 48*i*
Water pipe electrode, 47–49, 48*i*–49*i*
ground rod vs., 45, 45*i*
Water pipes
service bonding and, 175–76, 175*i*
Wire
sizing of, 17
Wiring
permanent, 193–94, 193*i*–95*i*

Z

Zig-zag connection
for transformer, 236, 236*i*